SECOND EDITION

In this book Professor Bullough has
pro___d a series of brief practical ___
___ more than ___
___

PRACTICAL INVERTEBRATE
ANATOMY

PRACTICAL INVERTEBRATE ANATOMY

by

W. S. BULLOUGH

Ph.D., D.Sc.(Leeds)

Professor of Zoology in the University of London

SECOND EDITION

LONDON
MACMILLAN & CO LTD
NEW YORK · ST MARTIN'S PRESS

© W. S. Bullough 1958

First Edition 1950
Reprinted 1951, 1954
Second Edition 1958
Reprinted 1960, 1964, 1966, 1968

MACMILLAN AND COMPANY LIMITED
Little Essex Street London WC 2
also Bombay Calcutta Madras Melbourne

THE MACMILLAN COMPANY OF CANADA LIMITED
70 Bond Street Toronto 2

ST MARTIN'S PRESS INC
175 Fifth Avenue New York NY 10010

PRINTED IN GREAT BRITAIN

PREFACE TO THE SECOND EDITION

In 1954 de Beer * wrote: " Few . . . zoologists could have thought it possible that, in the middle of the twentieth century, all text-books of zoology should require the drastic revision of the current theory of the origin and evolution of the Metazoa. Yet that and nothing less is the situation resulting from the researches which for half a century Jovan Hadzi has made into the structure and development of the lower animals. They have led him to put forward a theory that multinuclear Protozoa evolved into Turbellaria Acoela, which latter (not the Coelenterata) would be the most primitive Metazoa." Close examination of Hadzi's theory, which de Beer explained for the first time in English, indicates that it offers what is probably the most satisfactory explanation of the facts as they are now known, and consequently this second revised edition has been prepared. Recently Hadzi has written an extended explanation of his theory in English.†

In this second edition the platyhelminths are examined before the coelenterates, the turbellarians are considered in greater detail, and in particular a description is given of the acoelan genus *Convoluta*. Within the coelenterates, the actinozoans are treated first as the most primitive class, and the terms " diploblastic " and " triploblastic " have been abandoned.

The opportunity has also been taken to include two new chapters and to introduce much extra information which, during the years, has been offered by many helpful critics. In particular I am indebted to Dr. I. Griffiths for his generous help with the descriptions of the Turbellaria and the Nemertea.

W. S. Bullough

Birkbeck College,
University of London
December 1957

* de Beer, G. R. (1954), "The Evolution of the Metazoa", Chapter 2 of *Evolution as a Process*, edited by J. Huxley. London.
† Hadzi, J. (1963), *The Evolution of the Metazoa*. London.

PREFACE TO THE FIRST EDITION

THE main intention of this book is to provide brief and practical descriptions of the anatomy of those invertebrate animals which are commonly used as types in the study of zoology. Previously, such descriptions, if they existed at all, were widely scattered and not always easy either of discovery or of access. Furthermore, they were not always made from a practical point of view, or accompanied by figures which had any great practical value. To meet this situation, descriptions have been made of 122 commonly studied genera. These genera are primarily selected for their availability in the British Isles and in North America, but in most cases they, or closely related forms, also occur all over the world. In making the descriptions it was soon found that limits had to be imposed in order to keep the book to a reasonable size. Thus, it was decided to include only those features which can be demonstrated in whole specimens of adult animals, and, in particular, to exclude any consideration of prepared sections and of young or larval forms. In a few instances it has been found necessary to make exceptions, but in general this rule has been closely observed.

It is felt to be highly important that each genus studied should, as far as possible, be appreciated in its natural systematic, ecological, and functional setting. For this reason, the details of classification have been briefly inserted into the text, the description of each animal has been prefaced by a short account of its distribution and mode of life, and notes on the function and special significance of unusual organs or structures have been briefly interpolated. By these various means it is hoped that the anatomical details may assume a maximum significance and interest. In case further information should be required, references to more detailed descriptions are given wherever it has been possible to trace them, and at the ends of most of the chapters appendices are included which describe the methods of culture, where these are practical, of killing, fixing, and preserving, and of any special techniques which have proved valuable. The general appendix at the end of the book includes details of the composition of the fixatives, stains, and other solutions which are mentioned in the text.

The book is centred round, and originated with, its figures which have all been newly drawn from preparations or dissections. They were first made for the use of classes in McGill University, Montreal, when it became apparent how inadequate for practical purposes were most of the current textbook illustrations. The figures are all semi-diagrammatic, and it should be unnecessary to state that they are in no way intended as substitutes for the student's personal drawings of his own specimens. They are designed to save time and bewilderment, and not to replace personal investigation and effort.

Many debts of gratitude have been incurred during the writing of this manuscript, and the first of these, since they concerned the beginning of the book, are to Professor N. J. Berrill and the students in the Zoology Department at McGill University. Professor Berrill did all in his power to provide the necessary facilities for the work, most of which was completed in his department, and he also readily gave his special knowledge and critical attention to the chapters on the coelenterates and the chordates. The students, of whom Mr. P. A. Orkin may be specially mentioned, formed an eager and critical group with whose help the figures, descriptions, and techniques could be tested. Also at McGill University, constant encouragement and advice were received from Professor V. C. Wynne-Edwards, who made particular comments on the chapter dealing with the echinoderms, and from Professor T. W. M. Cameron, who provided much material for, and was repeatedly consulted about, the descriptions of parasitic protozoans, platyhelminthes, nematodes, acanthocephalans, and arachnids. Later, in the University of Sheffield, facilities for finishing the work were afforded by Professor L. E. S. Eastham. Also in England, much information has been gratefully received from Mr. T. Kerr on the platyhelminthes, Dr. T. B. Reynoldson on the annelids, Dr. F. Segrove on the myriapods, and Professor L. E. S. Eastham and Dr. H. Henson on the insects. Other help, which it is a pleasant duty to recall, came from Mrs. L. Terrill, who, as librarian in the Blacker Library of Zoology in McGill University, gave tireless assistance in the often difficult and tedious task of tracing important references; and from Mr. J. Hancock, who, as laboratory steward in the Sheffield Department of Zoology, has given unreservedly from his extensive knowledge of practical techniques. Finally, a special mention must be made of my wife who, in a hundred ways, has helped in the production of this book from its beginning to its end.

W. S. BULLOUGH

University of Sheffield
  December 1947

CONTENTS

ix

CONTENTS

CHAPTER VI. PHYLUM **NEMERTEA**

CHAPTER VII. PHYLUM **NEMATODA**

CHAPTER VIII. PHYLUM **ACANTHOCEPHALA**

CHAPTER IX. PHYLUM **ROTIFERA**

CHAPTER X. PHYLUM **ENDOPROCTA**

CHAPTER XI. PHYLUM **ECTOPROCTA**

CHAPTER XII. PHYLUM **BRACHIOPODA**

CHAPTER XIII. PHYLUM **CHAETOGNATHA**

CHAPTER XIV. PHYLUM **ANNELIDA**

CHAPTER XIX.   PHYLUM **ARTHROPODA** (*continued*)

CHAPTER XX.   PHYLUM **MOLLUSCA**

CONTENTS

CHAPTER I

PHYLUM **PROTOZOA**

Characteristics : Non-cellular organisms of small size which are usually motile in their main phase.

These animals possess such a uniquely simple structure that the phylum also ranks as a sub-kingdom, the other two animal sub-kingdoms being the Parazoa (sponges) and the Metazoa. They live freely in salt water, in fresh water, or in damp places on land, and many of them are parasitic. They are the simplest organisms recognised as being animals, and they are almost inseparable from the simplest plants. Many of the Mastigophora must in fact be regarded as simple plants, since they live holophytically and sometimes possess a cellulose cell wall. Such creatures may be regarded as the modern representatives of that common stock which gave rise to both the plants and the animals.

1.00. Class **Mastigophora (Flagellata)**

Characteristics : Protozoa which move by means of one or more long flagella; with a firm ectoplasmic pellicle, and therefore usually a definite body form (however, a few species may develop pseudopodia); no cilia; no macronucleus; often parasitic, but rarely intracellular.

In practice, the mastigophorans are often difficult to distinguish from the algae, on the one hand, and the rhizopods, on the other.

1.10. Subclass **Phytomastigina**

Characteristics : Mastigophora usually possessing chromoplasts and feeding holophytically (however, some, obviously closely related, have lost the chromoplasts and feed saprophytically or even holozoically); often with rigid cellulose capsules.

This subclass contains the primitive mastigophorans which cannot be separated from the algae.

1.11. Order **Euglenoidida**

Characteristics : Phytomastigina with a firm but flexible pellicle which limits movement to the type known as euglenoid; with a gullet swelling into

B   I

a reservoir into which opens a contractile vacuole ; with one or more flagella emerging from the gullet ; usually with numerous chloroplasts, but sometimes colourless ; and with paramylum (starch) granules.

Genus **Euglena**

I.   GENERAL ACCOUNT

a. The various species of this genus swarm in stagnant pools and ditches, especially those contaminated with dung, and they are often so abundant as to give the water a green, soup-like appearance.   Feeding is mainly holo-

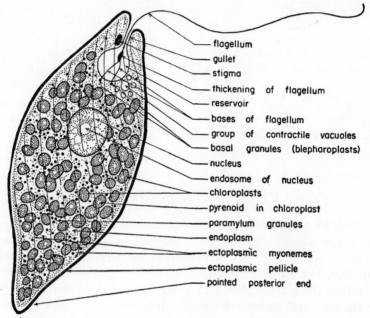

flagellum
gullet
stigma
thickening   of   flagellum
reservoir
bases   of   flagellum
group   of   contractile   vacuoles
basal   granules   (blepharoplasts)
nucleus
endosome   of   nucleus
chloroplasts
pyrenoid   in   chloroplast
paramylum   granules
endoplasm
ectoplasmic   myonemes
ectoplasmic   pellicle
pointed   posterior   end

FIG. 1.—*Euglena.*   A combination of the features visible in living and in stained preparations.

phytic, in the manner of a plant.   However, they thrive better if amino-acids are present in the water, and, in the absence of light, some species are able to live entirely as saprophytes.   They probably never feed holozoically. Reproduction is by longitudinal binary fission, and in adverse conditions, such as drought, the flagellum is withdrawn, the body becomes spherical, and a resistant cyst is secreted.   The animals may be cultured by the method given on p. 34.

2.   ANATOMY

a. Examine some living specimens through a low-power microscope. Notice that they are coloured green, that they twist spirally when swimming, and that their posterior ends are pointed. Watch the euglenoid **movements** of the body, during which waves of contraction and expansion pass along the length of the animal without, however, entirely destroying its fusiform shape.

b. Arrest the animals by the agar method (described on p. 35), and study the detailed structure of the body through a high-power microscope. At the blunt **anterior end** watch closely for the single, rapidly undulating flagellum (the undulations are considered to start at the base and to travel forward). The flagellum enters the narrow gullet, which at its base enlarges into the reservoir. By the base of the gullet is a group of red pigment granules forming the stigma (this is probably light sensitive), while posterior and lateral to the reservoir is a contractile vacuole (which discharges into the reservoir, a new one being formed immediately from a ring of smaller vacuoles). The anterior end of the body contains little, if any, green colouring matter.

c. In the **central and posterior regions** of the body notice the firm pellicle (toughened outer layer of ectoplasm), beneath which, in some species, extremely fine spirally arranged myonemes (contractile fibres) can be seen ; the numerous oval or elongated chloroplasts (containing chlorophyll), and within each a small refringent body, the pyrenoid (this, a protein granule, is the centre of starch formation) ; the refringent paramylum granules scattered throughout the granular endoplasm (according to the species these starch-like deposits are small or large discs or rods) ; and the nucleus with its central endosome.

d. In a permanent **stained preparation** (see method on p. 36) notice again the pyrenoid in the centre of each chloroplast, and the structure of the nucleus and the endosome. In good preparations, and with the use of an oil-immersion objective, the details of the base of the flagellum may be visible. On entering the reservoir the flagellum splits into two, and at the point of splitting it is swollen. Its two basal fibres pass into the endoplasm at the posterior end of the reservoir, each joining into a tiny basal granule, or blepharoplast (these granules are regarded as nuclear extensions which are concerned with the control of flagellum movement).

e. In a rich culture, or in a permanent preparation containing large numbers of individuals, look for stages of longitudinal **binary fission** (fission is first apparent at the anterior end).

3. CONCLUSION

a. Observing the specimens, review the characteristics of the phylum, of the class, of the subclass, and of the order.

b. Notice those features which may be considered animal-like and those which may be considered plant-like.

4. REFERENCE

MAINX, F. (1928). " Beiträge zur Morphologie und Physiologie der Eugleninen." *Archiv für Protistenkunde*, Vol. 60, p. 305.

1.12. Order **Dinoflagellida**

Characteristics : Phytomastigina with two flagella lying in grooves, one directed posteriorly and the other encircling the body ; either naked or encased in a shell, the theca, which is usually composed of cellulose ; with green, yellow, or brown chromoplasts.

The members of this order are mostly free living, pelagic, and marine, and many are phosphorescent. However, some live in brackish water, some in fresh water, and some are parasitic (particularly in the alimentary canals of copepods).

Genus **Ceratium**

I. GENERAL ACCOUNT

a. The species of *Ceratium* all live in salt water, and nearly all are pelagic in the open seas, where their long spines offer resistance to sinking. Since their

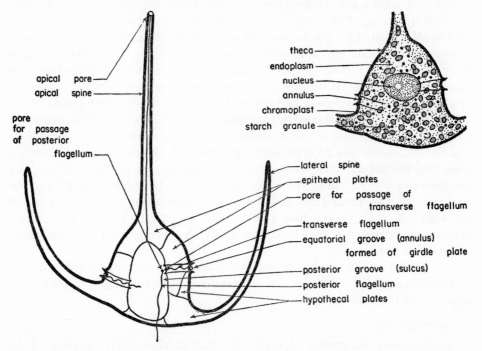

FIG. 2.—*Ceratium.* The external appearance and, on the right, a specimen seen in optical section.

two flagella are set at right angles to each other, they travel through the water with a jerky spiral movement. They live holophytically, like plants, by means of their chromoplasts, which contain chlorophyll, and because of this they occur only in the surface waters, where sunlight can penetrate. Asexual reproduction, which takes place mainly at night, is by oblique fission, each half developing those thecal plates which it lacks. Only rarely has spore formation been observed.

2. ANATOMY

a. Examine a permanent preparation of *Ceratium*. The theca enclosing the dorso-ventrally flattened body is drawn out into three hollow spines, and has a bizarre **anchor-shape**. The apical spine extends straight forwards and ends in a pore (function doubtful), while the two lateral spines curve outwards and forwards and end in closed points.

b. Examine the **external features** in detail through a high-power microscope. The deep equatorial groove, termed the annulus, almost completely encircles the body, and contains the transverse flagellum. A shallower, broader groove, termed the sulcus, runs posteriorly on one side of the body, and contains the trailing posterior flagellum. The points of emergence of the two flagella, through pores in the theca, are close together. The region anterior to the annulus is termed the epicone, while that posterior to the annulus is the hypo-cone. The plates covering the epicone are the epithecal plates, the groove of the annulus is formed of the girdle plate, and the hypocone is covered by hypothecal plates. The surfaces of these plates are often sculptured with tiny spines and pits.

c. Within the theca distinguish the prominent **nucleus** situated towards the centre of the mass of **endoplasm**. Also within the endoplasm are large numbers of small yellow-brown chromoplasts (containing chlorophyll) and of food-reserve granules (starch).

3. CONCLUSION

a. Observing the specimen, review the characteristics of the phylum, of the class, of the subclass, and of the order.

b. Notice those features which are particularly associated with the pelagic mode of life.

4. REFERENCE

LEBOUR, M. V. (1925). " The dinoflagellates of northern seas." Plymouth.

1.13. Order **Phytomonadida (Volvocina)**

Characteristics : Phytomastigina usually with two flagella, but with neither gullet nor grooves ; body usually enclosed in a rigid cellulose capsule ; usually holophytic with a single cup-shaped green chloroplast (a few are saprophytic and lack a chloroplast) ; starch deposits formed around one or more pyrenoids ; typically solitary, but often colonial.

Of all the Protozoa, the members of this order most resemble plants, and many live symbiotically with other animals. They are found in the sea, in fresh water, and in damp places on land.

Genus **Chlamydomonas**

I. GENERAL ACCOUNT

a. Living in shallow pools and ditches, these animals are often so abundant as to turn the water green and opaque.   The chlorophyll which they contain enables them to live holophytically, but their preference for water contaminated by manure indicates that they are also partly saprophytic.   Asexual reproduction is by means of repeated division into two, four, or eight.   The cellulose capsule of the parent then becomes mucilaginous, so that the young ones can burst through and escape.   In adverse conditions the capsule of the parent does not break down, and as many as thirty-two tiny individuals are formed

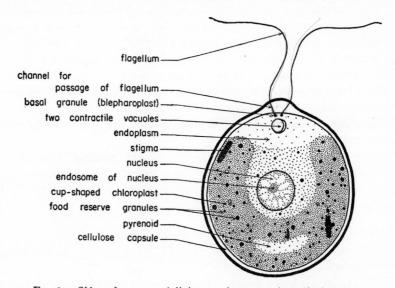

FIG. 3.—*Chlamydomonas.*   A living specimen seen in optical section.

within it.   This is the palmella stage, and the young escape only when conditions are again favourable.   Sexual reproduction is by isogametes formed by repeated division.   The fusion of two gametes produces a zygote which encysts and rests for a time as a zygospore.   Culture methods are described on p. 34.

2. ANATOMY

a. Through a microscope watch the rapid swimming **movements** of living *Chlamydomonas* (they travel with the flagella in front).   Notice the spherical or ovoid shape of the body, and the green colouration.

b. Prevent the movement by means of the agar method (described on p. 35), and, using the highest magnification available (preferably an oil immersion objective), examine the detailed structure of the **anterior region**.   Distinguish the clear capsule which encloses the body (it is a lifeless cellulose structure) ; the two flagella (each of which enters the body through a pore in the capsule and, on reaching the endoplasm, joins into a basal granule called a blepharo-plast) ; the two contractile vacuoles which are set on a line at right angles to that formed by the basal granules (these vacuoles discharge alternately into the crack between the body and the capsule, the water then diffusing out through the capsule) ; and the endoplasm which is clear and transparent in this part of the body.

c. The **posterior region** of the body is mainly occupied by a single cup-shaped chloroplast. Examine this in optical section. Notice laterally the red stigma (probably light sensitive) ; posteriorly the single refringent pyrenoid (a special-ised protein granule around which starch is formed) ; and centrally the spherical nucleus with its central endosome. Food-reserve granules (starch and occasion-ally oil droplets) may also be visible.

3. CONCLUSION

a. Observing the specimen, review the characteristics of the phylum, of the class, of the subclass, and of the order.

b. Distinguish those features which are animal-like and those which are plant-like.

4. REFERENCES

DILL, E. O. (1895). " Die Gattung *Chlamydomonas* und ihre nächsten Verwandten." *Jahrbuch für wissenschaftliche Botanik*, Vol. 28, p. 323.
SMITH, G. M. (1933). " The fresh-water algae of the United States." New York.

1.20. Subclass **Zoomastigina**

Characteristics : Mastigophora which lack chromoplasts, do not form starch reserves, and are holozoic or parasitic ; often more than two flagella ; parasitic forms often with parabasal bodies.

1.21. Order **Protomonadida**

Characteristics : Zoomastigina which rarely show amoeboid movement, and which possess only one or two flagella.

Genus **Trypanosoma**

1. GENERAL ACCOUNT

a. A parasitic flagellate, *Trypanosoma* alternates in its life cycle between vertebrates, where it occurs particularly in the blood, and invertebrates, where it occurs particularly in the alimentary canal. The alternate hosts of species infecting land vertebrates are biting insects, while those of aquatic vertebrates are often leeches. The species of *Trypanosoma* which occur in man cause sleeping sickness when they penetrate into the cerebrospinal fluid. Their alternate host is *Glossina*, the blood-sucking tsetse fly. *Trypanosoma* moves by means of its flagellum, which is directed forwards ; nutrition is by absorption of food substances digested by the host ; and reproduction takes place asexually by longitudinal binary fission.

2. ANATOMY

a. Examine a stained preparation of **infected blood** through a high-power microscope, and find the tiny trypanosomes among the red blood corpuscles. Their bodies are long, slender, and undulating, and each, at its anterior end, tapers to a whip-like flagellum.

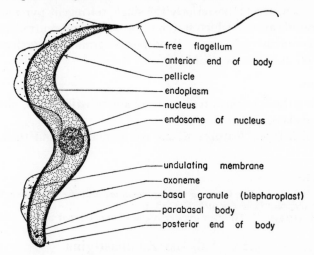

FIG. 4.—*Trypanosoma.*   A stained preparation from a blood smear.

b. Study the **body structure** more closely, using the highest magnification available (preferably an oil-immersion objective).   The body, flattened from side to side, is leaf-like, and when at rest, it is curved, one margin being convex and the other concave (in a smear the animals are not usually seen in a resting position).   A firm ectoplasmic pellicle encloses the endoplasm, which is usually featureless, but which sometimes contains numbers of " chromatoid granules " (significance unknown).   The disc-shaped nucleus is situated near the centre of the body and contains a prominent central endosome.

c. The single **flagellum**, projecting forwards, is composed of a central fibre, the axoneme, enclosed in a thin cytoplasmic sheath.   From the base of the flagellum the axoneme continues back along the convex side of the body, and forms the outer edge of a thin extension of the pellicle, known as the undulating membrane.   Near the posterior end of the body the axoneme passes into the endoplasm, and ends in a tiny dark staining basal granule, or blepharoplast. Immediately adjacent to the basal granule is another and larger granule, the parabasal body (these two granules may be concerned with the movements of the flagellum ; together they are known as the kinetoplast).

3. CONCLUSION

a. Observing the specimen, review the characteristics of the phylum, of the class, of the subclass, and of the order.

b. Notice the points of resemblance and of difference between *Trypanosoma* and *Euglena*.

4. REFERENCE

For further details of this, and of related genera, see :

WENYON, C. M. (1926). " Protozoology." London.

2.00. Class **Sarcodina (Rhizopoda)**

Characteristics : Protozoa which move by means of pseudopodia, although the gametes and young forms may move by means of flagella; no cilia; no macronucleus; rarely parasitic.

This class is closely related to, and is probably derived from, the Mastigophora.

2.01. Order **Lobosa (Amoebina)**

Characteristics : Sarcodina with neither shell nor supporting skeleton ; with relatively short and blunt (i.e. lobose) pseudopodia; ectoplasm not vacuolated.

Genus **Amoeba**

1. GENERAL ACCOUNT

a. Amoeba occurs commonly among decaying vegetable matter in ponds and slow-flowing streams, but many species are marine, and many live in the soil. The food varies with the species. In fresh-water forms it consists to some extent of smaller animals such as other protozoans, but particularly of bacteria and of small non-cellular plants such as diatoms. Reproduction is asexual, and is usually by binary fission. In difficult conditions, as when the water freezes or dries up, *Amoeba* can encyst and lie dormant for many months. It can be cultured by the method described on p. 34.

2. ANATOMY

a. The animal, which is a tiny whitish mass of protoplasm just visible to the naked eye, should first be examined alive. Pipette it, in a small drop of water, on to a glass slide, and watch its movements through a low-power microscope. Notice that its shape is constantly changing with the protrusion and retraction of **pseudopodia** (amoeboid movement), but that nevertheless anterior and posterior ends are clearly defined and permanent. Only the tips of the pseudopodia touch the ground, the main body of the animal being surrounded by water. Within the pseudopodia (which also serve for food capture) the protoplasm can be seen flowing in the direction of movement. Jar the slide, or touch the specimen with a fine needle point, and watch the rapid contraction reaction.

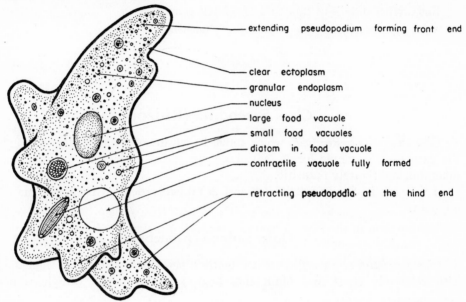

FIG. 5.—*Amoeba.* A living specimen seen in optical section.

b. Add a cover-glass, and examine the structure more closely through a high-power microscope. The protoplasm is divided into a clear outer film, the **ectoplasm** (which forms an elastic skin), and a granular inner mass, the **endoplasm** (which is more fluid). The larger endoplasmic granules are food particles in small vacuoles (into which digestive enzymes are secreted), while the smaller granules are food reserves (e.g. droplets of fat). Foreign bodies, such as tiny sand grains, may occasionally be present. Also visible, though not so distinctly, is the nucleus (the organisation centre of the animal). This spherical or plate-shaped body is more refractive than the endoplasm, lacks food vacuoles, and may be situated anywhere within the body.

c. Distinguish the **contractile vacuole**, which, when full of water, is a large clear spherical structure (occasionally there may be more than one). Watch the vacuole form, swell slowly, and burst outwards through the ectoplasm, after which another is formed, usually about the same place (this vacuole may be considered as a baling organ which removes the water leaking into the animal by osmosis; incidentally it must also help to eliminate carbon dioxide and nitrogenous waste).

d. In a stained preparation of *Amoeba* (see method on p. 36) the **nucleus** is easily visible as a spherical or flattened structure with dark-staining chromatin on its surface, a pale nuclear sap inside, and a small dark-staining central sphere, the endosome.

3. CONCLUSION

a. Observing the specimen, review the characteristics of the phylum, of the class, and of the order.

4. REFERENCES

DOFLEIN, F. (1916). " Lehrbuch der Protozoenkunde." Jena.
LEIDY, J. (1879). " Fresh-water rhizopods of North America." *Report of the United States Geological Survey*, Vol. 12.

Genus **Entamoeba**

1. GENERAL ACCOUNT

a. This is one of the few parasitic genera of the Sarcodina, and its species, which are small in size, are mostly found in the alimentary canals of vertebrates. In man, *E. gingivalis* (Gros) lives harmlessly in the mouth, feeding on the bacteria around the bases of the teeth; *E. coli* (Grassi), also harmless, feeds on the bacteria in the large intestine; while *E. histolytica* Schaudinn is pathogenic, causing dysentery by feeding on the tissues and red blood corpuscles, particularly in the large intestine. Reproduction is asexual, and is usually by binary fission.

2. ANATOMY

a. Using a high-power microscope, examine a stained preparation of one of the species of *Entamoeba* found in man. Notice the extremely small size and simple **structure**. The outer ectoplasm is very thin; the endoplasm contains numbers of food granules in the process of digestion (the granules are usually bacteria, but in *E. histolytica* the remains of host cells and of red blood corpuscles may be recognised); and the nucleus is relatively large. This last structure appears in optical section as a ring of darkly staining chromatin enclosing a non-staining nuclear sap towards the centre of which is a dark endosome. There is no contractile vacuole.

b. Scrape some white material from between the bases of the molar teeth, tease it out on a slide in a drop of 0·7% aqueous sodium chloride solution, and add a cover-glass. Through a high-power microscope examine the preparation for **living** *E. gingivalis* (it is estimated that about 50% of the population are infected). On the slide there should be some relatively large dead cells from

the lining of the mouth ; enormous numbers of tiny bacteria of various kinds
(they are so small that they are at the limit of visibility and show Brownian
movement) ; and, between these two extremes of size, considerable numbers
of spherical or ovoid leucocytes. The *Entamoeba* have a diameter about
twice that of the leucocytes, and they move, often very slowly, by throwing
out short blunt pseudopodia. Usually only one, or at the most two, pseudopodia are developed at a time, and since they are formed of ectoplasm alone,
they are transparent. Notice the granular endoplasm (the larger granules

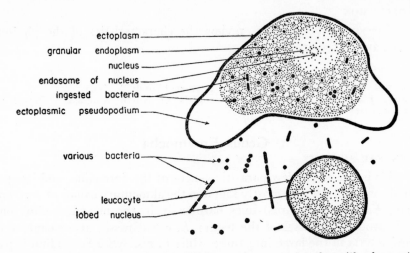

FIG. 6.—*Entamoeba gingivalis* (Gros).   A living specimen seen together with a leucocyte
and some of the bacteria which are also present in the mouth.

are ingested bacteria) ; the more highly refractive and less granular nucleus ;
and the lack of a contractile vacuole.

3.   CONCLUSION

    a. Observing the specimens, review the characteristics of the phylum, of
the class, and of the order.

    b. Notice the points of difference between the parasitic *Entamoeba* and the
free living *Amoeba*.

4.   REFERENCE

    For further details of the structure of *Entamoeba* and of related genera
see :

    WENYON, C. M. (1926). " Protozoology." London.

2.02. Order **Heliozoa**

Characteristics : Sarcodina without shells, but sometimes with a siliceous
skeleton ; many pseudopodia which, having the form of stiffened radiating

filaments, are termed axopodia; body spherical; ectoplasm highly vacuolated.

The members of this fresh-water order are mostly free floating forms, but some are anchored by thin stalks. Other species, parasitic in algae, are sometimes included here.

Genus **Actinosphaerium** (sun animalcule)

(The smaller *Actinophrys* is similar, but it has only one nucleus.)

I. GENERAL ACCOUNT

a. This relatively large protozoan occurs in ponds, floating among the aquatic plants. Its slow movement is a rolling action apparently induced by

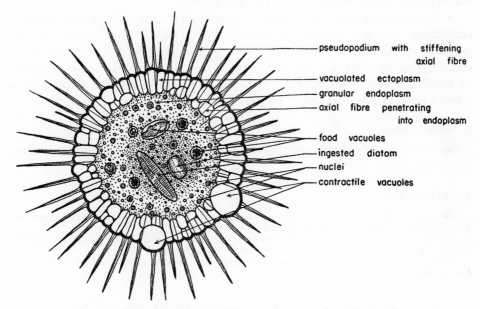

pseudopodium with stiffening
axial fibre
vacuolated ectoplasm
granular endoplasm
axial fibre penetrating
into endoplasm
food vacuoles
ingested diatom
nuclei
contractile vacuoles

FIG. 7.—*Actinosphaerium.* A living specimen seen in optical section.

the contraction and expansion (not bending) of those pseudopodia which are in contact with a solid object. The stiff pseudopodia are also used for anchoring, their tips then becoming viscid. *Actinosphaerium* feeds on such small animals and plants as amoebae, rotifers, and diatoms, which, when they touch the spinous pseudopodia, stick and are paralysed, perhaps by some toxic secretion. The axial fibres of the pseudopodia are then absorbed so that bending may occur and the food may be engulfed into a food vacuole. Reproduction is by binary fission of the cytoplasm (the nuclei do not divide and the process is termed plasmotomy), or by a form of self-conjugation called autogamy. For a method of culture see p. 34.

2. ANATOMY

a. Through a low-power microscope watch the **movements** of a living specimen. Notice the stiff, ray-like pseudopodia and the central spherical body of frothy protoplasm. By focusing through the animal, notice that the clear vacuoles which give the frothy appearance are confined to an outer layer of thickened ectoplasm, sometimes termed the cortex (the vacuoles increase the animal's buoyancy).

b. Gently add a cover-glass. With the high power of the microscope examine the **ectoplasm** more closely, and find within it the large contractile vacuole (there may be more than one). Also examine a pseudopodium to see the fine axial fibre passing down its centre and piercing the vacuolated ectoplasm to end in the outer zone of the endoplasm.

c. By focusing into the animal, examine the structure of the granular **endoplasm**, which is sometimes termed the medulla. The largest granules may be recognisable as engulfed rotifers or diatoms, but the contents of the smaller food vacuoles may be partly digested. Many nuclei should be visible as small refractive bodies, but these are more easily seen in a permanent stained preparation (method of preparation on p. 36).

3. CONCLUSION

a. Observing the specimen, review the characteristics of the phylum, of the class, and of the order.

4. REFERENCES

BRONN, H. G. (1880–82). Volume 1 and part 1 of "Klassen und Ordnungen des Thier-Reichs. Protozoa. Sarkodina und Sporozoa." Leipzig and Heidelberg.
BĚLAŘ, K. (1923). "Untersuchungen an *Actinophrys sol* Ehrenberg. I. Die Morphologie des Formwechsels." *Archiv für Protistenkunde,* Vol. 46, p. 1.
LEIDY, J. (1879). "Fresh-water rhizopods of North America." *Report of the United States Geological Survey,* Vol. 12.

2.03. Order **Foraminifera**

Characteristics : Sarcodina usually possessing shells which are calcareous, but which are occasionally chitinous, siliceous, or gelatinous with embedded foreign bodies; usually with long, thin, anastomosing pseudopodia (reticulopodia); vacuolated ectoplasm in pelagic species; often di- or even tri-morphic.

This definition applies to such fresh-water forms as *Arcella* and *Difflugia*, which are sometimes included in the order Lobosa. However, most living foraminiferans are marine, and the members of the genus *Globigerina* are so numerous that their empty shells form the ooze which covers enormous areas of the floor of the deep sea, particularly in the Atlantic, Indian, and Southern Oceans.

Genus **Polystomella**

1. GENERAL ACCOUNT

a. A marine genus, *Polystomella*, is common from the sea-shore to depths of about 300 fathoms, and from the coasts of Greenland southwards across the equator. It also occurs in brackish waters. It moves sluggishly, particularly among the seaweeds, and feeds on such smaller organisms as diatoms which are caught by the pseudopodia. It is dimorphic, the microspheric form giving

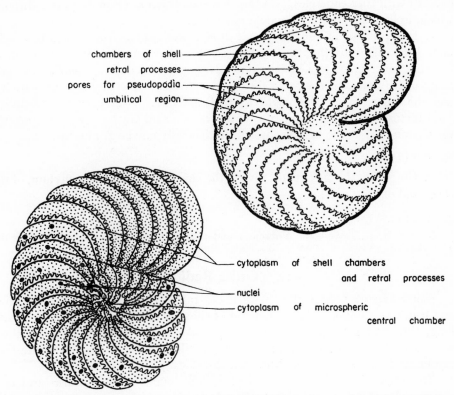

chambers of shell
retral processes
pores for pseudopodia
umbilical region

cytoplasm of shell chambers
and retral processes
nuclei
cytoplasm of microspheric
central chamber

FIG. 8.—*Polystomella.* The shell (above), and a microspheric form decalcified and stained to show the many nuclei.

rise to the macrospheric form by multiple fission. In its turn the macrospheric form produces flagellated gametes which, after fusing in pairs, develop into the microspheric form.

2. ANATOMY

a. Examine the **shell** of *Polystomella*. It is biconvex, and is composed of a series of chambers of increasing size, arranged in a coil. The cavity of the last and largest chamber is separated from the exterior by a perforated septum (internally the chambers are also separated from each other by perforated septa through which protoplasmic continuity is maintained). Since the chambers of the last turn of the spiral overlap those previously formed, and since, in addition, the shell is greatly thickened in the central umbilical region, the smallest and oldest chambers are totally obscured. From the posterior edges of each chamber retral processes emerge to overlap the sides of the previously formed chamber (these processes are hollow and blind ending).

b. Through a high-power microscope notice that the **surface of the shell** is covered with tiny tubercles, and that between them are minute pores (through which, in life, the fine pseudopodia emerged).

c. In a permanent stained preparation of individuals from which the shells have been dissolved (for the method see p. 37) distinguish the cytoplasm of the tiny inner chambers which were previously obscured. Identify the two forms of *Polystomella*, the one, called microspheric, with a tiny central chamber, and the other, called macrospheric, with a relatively large central chamber. The **microspheric form** has large numbers of small nuclei scattered through the chambers, but the **macrospheric form** has only one large nucleus.

3.   CONCLUSION

a. Observing the specimens, review the characteristics of the phylum, of the class, and of the order.

4.   REFERENCE

BRONN, H. G. (1880–82). Volume 1 and part 1 of " Klassen und Ordnungen des Thier-Reichs. Protozoa. Sarkodina und Sporozoa." Leipzig and Heidelberg.

2.04.   Order **Radiolaria**

Characteristics : Sarcodina with a central capsule of chitin-like material, and usually an outer spicular skeleton of silica or of strontium sulphate ; with long, thin, radiating pseudopodia (filopodia) usually without an axial fibre ; ectoplasm highly vacuolated ; no contractile vacuole ; usually containing symbiotic zooxanthellae (modified dinoflagellates).

The group is exclusively marine, and is found in both warm and cold waters. Its members are commonly pelagic close to the surface, but they also occur to great depths. Huge areas of the floors of the deeper oceans, and particularly of the Pacific Ocean, are covered by an ooze (radiolarian ooze) which is mainly formed of their siliceous skeletons.

Genus **Sphaerozoum**

I.   GENERAL ACCOUNT

a. Sphaerozoum is a specialised genus, in that it is colonial, but this habit has not greatly altered the fundamental structure of the units of the colony, nor their mode of life. It is cosmopolitan and common among the plankton, especially in warmer seas, and it feeds on smaller animals and plants caught by the pseudopodia. Reproduction is either asexual by binary fission which results in increased colony size, or sexual by spores which unite in pairs to form the first individuals of new colonies.

2. ANATOMY

a. If possible examine a whole **colony**. It is a spherical or ellipsoid gelatinous mass which in its outer layer contains large numbers of individuals. The centre of the mass is occupied by one or more large vacuoles, which increase the buoyancy.

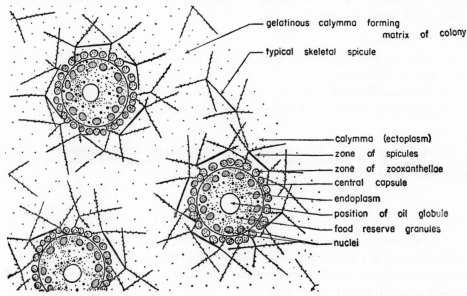

gelatinous calymma forming matrix of colony

typical skeletal spicule

calymma (ectoplasm)
zone of spicules
zone of zooxanthelloe
central capsule
endoplasm
position of oil globule
food reserve granules
nuclei

FIG. 9.—*Sphaerozoum.* Part of the surface of a colony with the individuals seen in optical section.

b. Through a microscope examine a preparation of a piece of colony wall. Notice that the many **individuals** embedded in it are apparently separated from one another by a structureless jelly known as the calymma (this jelly actually represents thickened ectoplasm; in solitary radiolarians it contains large numbers of vacuoles, but in *Sphaerozoum* the vacuoles are fewer and larger and are confined to the centre of the colony). Each individual is composed of a central spherical mass of granular endoplasm enclosed in a capsule; of a zone of spicules, the skeleton, external to the capsule; and of the calymma, or ectoplasm, in which the spicules are embedded, and from which, at the colony surface, fine pseudopodia arise (digestion takes place in the calymma). In addition, close against the outer surface of each central capsule are large numbers of zooxanthellae (these contain chlorophyll and live holophytically and symbiotically).

c

c. Although they may vary considerably, the siliceous **spicules** in the common species of *Sphaerozoum* are fundamentally composed of a bar, at each end of which are attached three spines, each embossed along its length with tiny spines. The bar is placed tangentially to the central capsule.

d. The **central capsule** is a thin-walled sphere (made of a chitin-like substance) pierced by numerous tiny pores, but its detailed structure is usually obscured by the zone of zooxanthellae. Within the capsule the endoplasm contains food reserves (including tiny crystals of protein material, and a large centrally placed oil globule which assists buoyancy, but which disappears in a permanent preparation). Forming a zone just inside the capsule are large numbers of spherical nuclei.

3. CONCLUSION

a. Observing the specimen, review the characteristics of the phylum, of the class, and of the order.

b. Distinguish those features which are associated with the colonial mode of life, and those which are associated with the pelagic habit.

4. REFERENCE

BRANDT, K. (1885). " Die koloniebildenden Radiolarian (Sphaerozoëen) des Golfes von Neapel und der angrenzenden Meeresabschnitte." *Fauna und Flora des Golfes von Neapel*, Vol. 13.

3.00. Class **Sporozoa**

Characteristics : Protozoa which lack locomotory structures or are amoeboid (although gametes and young forms may develop flagella) ; no cilia ; no macro-nucleus ; large numbers of spores produced after conjugation ; parasitic and usually intracellular at some stage.

3.10. Subclass **Telosporidia**

Characteristics : Sporozoa in which the trophozoite has only one nucleus ; spore cases, when formed, are simple and contain several sporozoites.

3.11. Order **Gregarinida**

Characteristics : Telosporidia in which the trophozoites become extra-cellular ; no asexual reproduction ; gametocytes identical ; sporozoites in cysts.

Parasitic in the alimentary canals, body cavities, and tissues of the inverte-brates, these forms are found particularly in the annelids, the arthropods, and the ascidians.

Genus **Monocystis**

I. GENERAL ACCOUNT

a. Several species of the genus, some attaining the length of about ¼ inch, are commonly found in the seminal vesicles of earthworms. The trophozoites, as they are called when in the feeding stage, lie inside groups of developing spermatozoa and absorb the nutrient fluid which fills the seminal vesicles. When fully grown they are termed gametocytes, and they fuse in pairs. Each pair secretes a thin-walled cyst, and then undergoes multiple fission to form gametes, which unite in pairs to form zygotes. Each zygote secretes a small

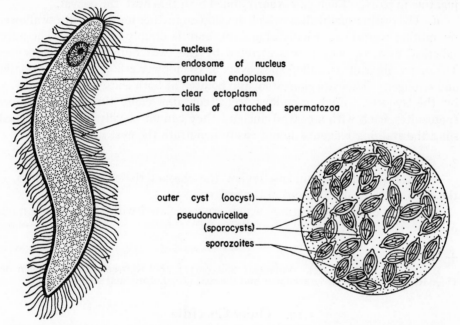

nucleus
endosome of nucleus
granular endoplasm
clear ectoplasm
tails of attached spermatozoa

outer cyst (oocyst)
pseudonavicellae (sporocysts)
sporozoites

FIG. 10.—*Monocystis.* A trophozoite and an oocyst containing sporocysts and sporozoites.

cyst, the pseudonavicella, within which it divides to produce eight sporozoites. The pseudonavicellae either escape via the vasa deferentia or, swallowed with the worm, they pass unchanged through the alimentary canal of a bird. Reaching the soil and being eaten by another worm, the cysts are dissolved by the digestive enzymes, and the released sporozoites penetrate the tissues, reach the testes, and burrow into the sperm mother cells. These cells continue their development, producing spermatids and spermatozoa which remain attached to the parasite until both they and it are fully developed.

2. ANATOMY

a. Extract a seminal vesicle from a large sexually mature earthworm, and stain a smear of its contents by the method described on p. 37. Through a microscope notice the masses of developing spermatozoa, and search for the glassy cysts, which are usually present in large numbers, and the trophozoites, which are much less common.

b. Each **trophozoite** is cigar-shaped, with a thin outer layer of firm, clear ectoplasm, and an inner mass of finely granular endoplasm. When almost fully grown it appears to be strongly ciliated, due to the large numbers of attached spermatozoa. Notice that the endoplasm contains no prominent structures except the single nucleus with its dark staining endosome.

c. Occasionally full-grown parasites, then called **gametocytes,** are seen conjugating in pairs. Each pair is surrounded by a thin cyst, the oocyst.

d. The resting **sporozoites** (which develop no further until they are swallowed by another worm) are usually abundant, and lie doubly encysted. The outer spherical cyst, or oocyst, was secreted by the two conjugating gametocytes. The many inner cysts, called sporocysts or pseudonavicellae, are much smaller and stronger. They are elongated, and pointed at both ends, and were secreted by the zygotes. Each pseudonavicella contains eight tiny banana-shaped sporozoites, each with a central nucleus (they cannot usually be distinguished, since the staining reagents do not easily penetrate the cyst walls).

3. CONCLUSION

a. Observing the specimens, review the characteristics of the phylum, of the class, of the subclass, and of the order.

b. Distinguish those features which are associated with the parasitic mode of life.

4. REFERENCE

BRONN, H. G. (1880–82). Volume 1 and part 1 of " Klassen und Ordnungen des Thier-Reichs. Protozoa. Sarkodina und Sporozoa." Leipzig and Heidelberg.

3.12. Order **Coccidia**

Characteristics : Telosporidia with trophozoites intracellular; asexual reproduction by multiple fission; male and female gametes different; zygote non-motile; sporozoites in cysts.

The members of this order are usually parasitic in the lining epithelia of the alimentary canals of such animals as platyhelminthes, annelids, arthropods, molluscs, and vertebrates.

Genus **Eimeria**

I. GENERAL ACCOUNT

a. The species of this genus are mostly parasitic in the alimentary canals of vertebrates, but some are found in invertebrates. *E. stiedae* (Lindemann) may be taken as typical. It occurs commonly in young rabbits, causing coccidiosis by attacking the lining cells of the bile ducts. The feeding stage, the trophozoite, undergoes multiple fission when fully grown, and produces large numbers of merozoites, which infect new cells and become trophozoites. After a few generations formed in this way, some merozoites develop into male and female gametocytes, which form male and female gametes respectively. After fertilisation the zygote encysts, escapes with the faeces, and then divides and forms four smaller cysts. These small cysts each contain two sporozoites, which infect a new host when they are eaten.

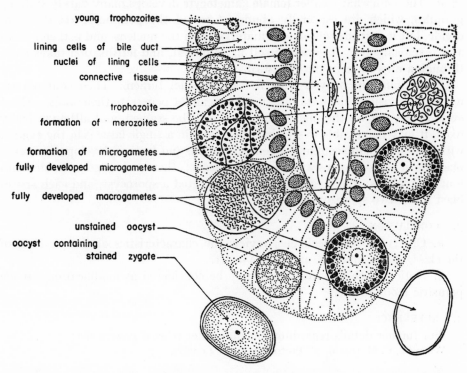

young trophozoites
lining cells of bile duct
nuclei of lining cells
connective tissue
trophozoite
formation of merozoites
formation of microgametes
fully developed microgametes
fully developed macrogametes
unstained oocyst
oocyst containing stained zygote

FIG. 11.—*Eimeria.* The various stages seen in a stained preparation of a section of the bile duct of an infected rabbit.

2. ANATOMY

a. Examine a permanent stained preparation of a section of an **infected bile duct.** Notice that large numbers of glassy cysts lie free in the duct cavity, while the trophozoites and other stages are numerous inside the cells of the lining epithelium.

b. The growing **trophozoites,** small and large, are embedded in the outer ends of the columnar lining cells. Each is a simple spherical body, inside which the only visible features are the granular endoplasm and the relatively small nucleus. In the largest trophozoites a darkly staining granule, the endosome, can be seen towards the centre of the nucleus. Search for trophozoites undergoing multiple fission.   The many small **merozoites** formed in this way (the actual number is very variable) escape into the duct cavity to infect more cells.

c. Some merozoites develop into gametocytes.   The **male gametocyte** is the largest stage of *Eimeria*.   Its nucleus divides to produce the nuclei of enormous numbers of tiny microgametes, while the endoplasm develops large vacuoles, in the walls of which the microgametes come to lie.

d. The somewhat smaller **female gametocyte** develops many darkly staining granules, which are especially abundant round the periphery.   It does not divide, but it extrudes chromatin material from the nucleus, and is then known as a macrogamete.   It encases itself in an oocyst, and fertilisation takes place through a micropyle in the cyst wall.

e. Examine the **oocysts** lying free in the duct lumen.   Their contents are not usually visible, since staining reagents cannot penetrate their walls.   However, a few, cut by the microtome knife, will be stained, and although badly fixed, it may be possible to see that they contain a single large cell, the zygote, with granular endoplasm and a central nucleus (no further development takes place until the oocyst escapes with the faeces; then each zygote divides into four sporoblasts, round each of which is secreted a sporocyst, and each sporoblast forms two sporozoites).

3.   CONCLUSION

a. Observing the specimens, review the characteristics of the phylum, of the class, of the subclass, and of the order.

b. Notice those features which may be considered as modifications to the parasitic mode of life.

4.   REFERENCE

For further details regarding this and other related genera see:
WENYON, C. M. (1926).   " Protozoology."   London.

3.13.   Order **Haemosporida**

Characteristics : Telosporidia with trophozoites intracellular in vertebrate blood cells;   asexual reproduction by multiple fission;   male and female gametes different;   zygote motile;   sporozoites naked.

These parasites are carried to new vertebrate hosts by blood-sucking invertebrates within which the zygotes are formed and the sporozoites produced.

Genus **Plasmodium**

1.   GENERAL ACCOUNT

a. Three species of *Plasmodium* which infect man are well known.   These are *P. vivax* Grassi and Feletti, which causes benign tertian malaria, *P. falci-*

parum Welch, which causes malignant tertian malaria, and *P. malariae* (Laveran), which causes quartan malaria. Their trophozoite stages grow by absorbing the contents of the red blood corpuscles in which they live. When fully grown they either divide by repeated binary fission (merogony) to form merozoites which infect more corpuscles, or they develop into gametocytes which lie quiescent inside the remains of the corpuscles and develop no further unless swallowed by an *Anopheles* mosquito. Inside the stomach of the mosquito the micro- and macro-gametes are formed. The union of a micro- with a macro-gamete produces a zygote which bores into, and encysts inside, the stomach wall, and there divides into sporozoites. The sporozoites escape into the mosquito's blood stream, and pass to the salivary glands to be injected with the saliva into the blood of another man. They then develop inside the liver cells for eight days before reappearing in the blood. These three species of *Plasmodium* are not known in any other vertebrate, except possibly the anthropoid apes.

2. ANATOMY

(The following descriptions refer to *P. malariae*, but the main differences in appearance of *P. vivax* and *P. falciparum* are indicated.)

a. In stained smears of infected human blood, search for the various forms of *Plasmodium* (preferably using a microscope with an oil-immersion objective). The trophozoites lie inside the red blood corpuscles, and usually all of them are in about the same stage of growth. Sometimes (particularly in heavy infections of *P. falciparum*) more than one trophozoite may occur within a single corpuscle. The **youngest trophozoites** usually appear as rings due to the development of a large vacuole within them, and the consequent displacement of the nucleus to one side. Sometimes, however, one may appear as a narrow band stretched across the diameter of the corpuscle.

b. Examine several blood-smears to find the various **trophozoite stages.** During growth the endoplasm becomes more prominent, and in it darkly pigmented granules are laid down (the pigment is largely melanin and is formed from haemoglobin). Older trophozoites lose the ring appearance, and may be ovoid, elongated, or of an irregular shape (the shape is particularly irregular in *P. vivax*, which develops long pseudopodia). When fully grown, they almost fill the corpuscle (*P. falciparum* only half fills the corpuscle).

c. Search for stages in the formation of the **merozoites.** These are produced by the repeated binary fission (merogony) of the trophozoite nucleus into from six to ten small nuclei (in *P. vivax* there are typically sixteen, and in *P. falciparum* from eight to twenty-four). The endoplasm then divides, some surrounding each nucleus, while the pigment granules, grouped together, are left aside within the residual endoplasm. The merozoites, then fully formed, are ready to escape and infect new red blood corpuscles (the corpuscle breaks

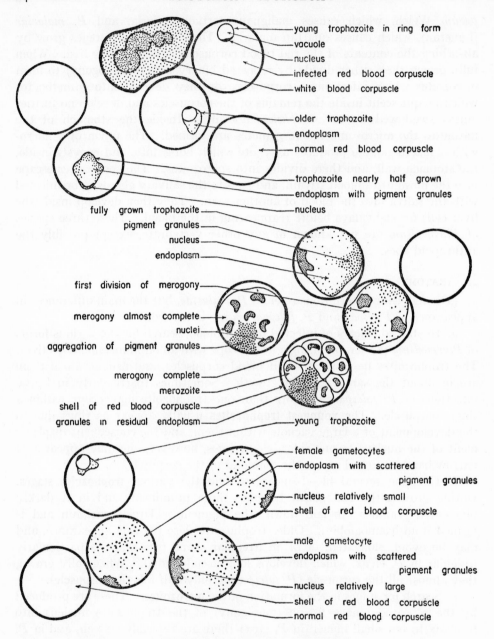

young trophozoite in ring form
vacuole
nucleus
infected red blood corpuscle
white blood corpuscle

older trophozoite
endoplasm
normal red blood corpuscle

trophozoite nearly half grown
endoplasm with pigment granules

fully grown trophozoite
pigment granules
nucleus
endoplasm
nucleus

first division of merogony

merogony almost complete
nuclei
aggregation of pigment granules

merogony complete
merozoite
shell of red blood corpuscle
granules in residual endoplasm
young trophozoite

female gametocytes
endoplasm with scattered
pigment granules
nucleus relatively small
shell of red blood corpuscle

male gametocyte
endoplasm with scattered
pigment granules
nucleus relatively large
shell of red blood corpuscle
normal red blood corpuscle

FIG. 12.—*Plasmodium malariae* (Laveran).

Above are trophozoites in early stages of growth, but, except in cases of double infection, such differing stages are not to be found in the same smear.

In the centre is a fully grown trophozoite, stages of merogony, and merozoites. Again, except in cases of double infection, such differing stages are not to be found in the same smear.

Below are the male and female gametocytes, which are usually present in any smear.

down to release them, and at the same time it liberates toxic substances, which cause fever in the host).

d. Some merozoites (infecting corpuscles which then stick in the blood-vessels of the bone marrow or in the spleen) develop into **gametocytes.** Fully grown gametocytes are usually to be found in large numbers in any smear (the corpuscles in which they lie having freed themselves and passed to the peripheral circulation). Each gametocyte (which develops no further until swallowed by a mosquito) remains inside the empty corpuscle, which it fills entirely. It has a single nucleus, and its endoplasm contains irregularly scattered pigment granules (in *P. falciparum* the gametocytes are crescentic). The male gameto-cyte may be distinguished from the female by its larger nucleus, and by the fact that, after Leishman's stain, its endoplasm appears lighter blue (these same differences occur in the other two species).

3. CONCLUSION

a. Observing the specimens and the drawings made, review the char-acteristics of the phylum, of the class, of the subclass, and of the order.

b. Distinguish those features which are associated with the parasitic mode of life.

4. REFERENCE

For further details and for a description of the stages within the mosquito, see :

WENYON, C. M. (1926). " Protozoology." London.

4.00.   Class **Infusoria (Ciliophora)**

Characteristics : Protozoa which move by means of cilia, at least at some stage of development; which possess a definite body form; and which are occasionally parasitic, but rarely intracellular.

4.10.   Subclass **Protociliata**

Characteristics : Infusoria with two or more nuclei which are alike; no oral groove; no contractile vacuole; no conjugation; intestinal parasites, mainly of Amphibia.

4.11.   Order **Opalinata**

Characteristics : Protociliata with more than two nuclei.

Genus **Opalina**

I. GENERAL ACCOUNT

a. This is a parasitic genus which is common in the rectum of frogs and toads. There it feeds by absorbing through its whole surface the food already digested by its host. Reproduction is normally by oblique or transverse binary fission, but in spring, when the frogs return to the water to breed, unusually rapid fission results in the production of large numbers of small individuals which encyst. These cysts pass out with the faeces, and later, if swallowed by a tadpole, each hatches to release a gametocyte which divides to produce either micro- or macro-gametes. The zygote, formed by the fusion of a micro- with a macro-gamete, contains only a single nucleus, but its growth is accompanied by rapid nuclear division so that, when the adult size is reached, the animal is again multinucleate.

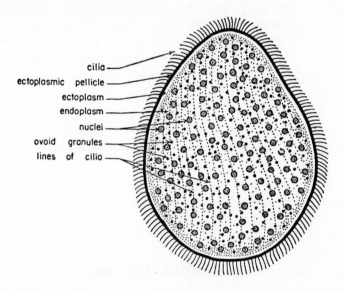

FIG. 13.—*Opalina*. A specimen from the rectum of a frog showing a combination of the features visible in living and in stained preparations.

2. ANATOMY

a. Living specimens of *Opalina* (readily obtained by the method described on p. 35) should be mounted on a microscope slide in a drop of 0·7% aqueous solution of sodium chloride. Distinguish the ciliates, which may be as large as 1 mm. in diameter, and watch their **movements**. Other genera, particularly *Nyctotherus* (see p. 30) and *Balantidium*, which belong to the subclass Euciliata, may also be present in the drop, but *Opalina* can be readily distinguished by its large size, and by its lack of an oral groove and of a contractile vacuole.

b. If necessary, arrest the movements of the animals by the agar method (described for parasites on p. 36). Notice the flattened and roughly oval shape of the leaf-like body. Through a high-power microscope watch the rapid action of the innumerable equal **cilia** which completely cover the body, and notice that these cilia are arranged in close-set parallel rows.

c. Distinguish the clear **ectoplasmic layer**, which is differentiated into a thin outer pellicle and a thicker inner layer (within the latter there lie longitudinal contractile fibres, the myonemes).

d. The **endoplasm** contains large numbers of small, spherical, and evenly distributed nuclei. These are more readily seen in a permanent stained preparation (method of preparation on p. 36). Also present are many smaller ovoid granules (the significance of which is unknown, although, since they stain like chromatin and are apparently of nuclear origin, they are sometimes considered to be homologous with the macro-nuclei of the euciliates).

3. CONCLUSION

a. Observing the specimens, review the characteristics of the phylum, of the class, of the subclass, and of the order.

b. Notice those simplifications of body structure which may be considered as related to the parasitic mode of life.

4. REFERENCES

METCALF, M. M. (1923). " The opalinid ciliate infusorians." *Smithsonian Institution of the United States National Museum*, bulletin 120.
WENYON, C. M. (1926). " Protozoology." London.

4.20. Subclass **Euciliata**

Characteristics : Infusoria with a micro- (or generative) and a macro- (or somatic) nucleus ; usually with an oral groove and contractile vacuoles ; and with the habit of conjugation.

4.21. Order **Holotrichida**

Characteristics : Euciliata with cilia of approximately equal length, usually covering the whole body surface.

Genus **Paramecium** (slipper animalcule)

1. GENERAL ACCOUNT

a. The members of this genus are among the commonest of the protozoans. They occur abundantly in water containing decaying vegetable matter, their food consisting mainly of the bacteria associated with the decay. One species, *P. bursaria* Ehr., contains symbiotic zoochlorellae, and if starved it can live for long periods on the food substances formed by the chlorophyll. *Paramecium* commonly multiplies by transverse binary fission, but this process cannot be continued indefinitely without the stimulus afforded by conjugation. This fusion results in the formation of new individuals, many of which are abnormal, weak, and destined to die, but many of which have an increased vigour which gives them and their descendants a new lease of life. A method of culture is described on p. 35.

2. ANATOMY

a. Examine living specimens of *Paramecium*. Notice their rigid, elongated **shape**, and the flickering actions of the cilia which cover them and which cause their spiralling forward movement. Notice further that the anterior end is blunter than the posterior end, and that on one side, termed ventral, there is a groove which leads inwards to the mouth.

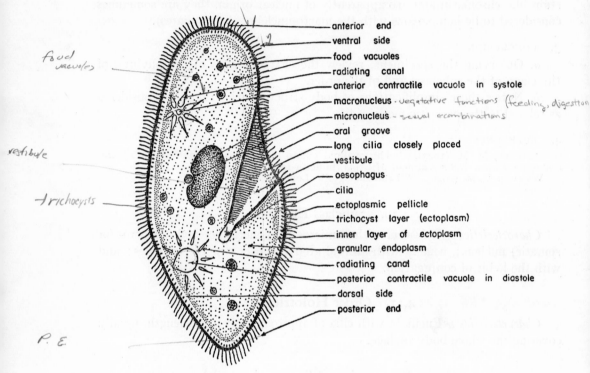

food
vacuoles

vestibule

trichocysts

P. E.

anterior end
ventral side
food vacuoles
radiating canal
anterior contractile vacuole in systole
macronucleus - vegetative functions (feeding, digestion
micronucleus - sexual recombinations
oral groove
long cilia closely placed
vestibule
oesophagus
cilia
ectoplasmic pellicle
trichocyst layer (ectoplasm)
inner layer of ectoplasm
granular endoplasm
radiating canal
posterior contractile vacuole in diastole
dorsal side
posterior end

FIG. 14.—*Paramecium*. A combination of the features visible in living and in stained preparations.

b. Arrest the movements of the specimens by the agar method described on p. 35. Then through a high-power microscope examine the clear elastic **ectoplasm**, and distinguish as many as possible of the four layers into which it can be subdivided. The outermost layer is the thin, but tough, pellicle. Focus on to the upper surface of the animal to see the rows of depressions in the pellicle, and notice that a cilium arises from each depression. The layer beneath the pellicle is also thin, and it contains the myonemes (fine contractile fibres which are visible in favourable circumstances as longitudinal striations). The next layer is relatively thick, and is most obvious at the sides of an animal seen in optical section. It contains large numbers of highly refractive, carrot-shaped trichocysts (each of which is a tiny cavity containing a viscid solution which can be squirted out through a pore in the pellicle to form a long thread : this is apparently a defence mechanism). The innermost layer of the ecto-plasm, also relatively thick, is spongy, and contains dorsally the two contractile vacuoles and their systems of radiating canals (at their extremities these canals may extend into the endoplasm).

c. Watch the action of the two **contractile vacuoles** (which remove the water leaking into the animal by osmosis), and notice how each is fed by its system of radiating canals and how, when full, it empties itself by bursting outwards (because of the proximity of the mouth, through which water enters rapidly, the posterior vacuole usually pulsates more rapidly than the anterior).

d. Examine the structure of the **oral groove**, which, entering the ventral side of the animal, passes back obliquely from left to right. Its outer and larger chamber, the vestibule, is lined by ectoplasm, lacks cilia on its ventral and right sides, but is densely lined by long cilia on its dorsal and left sides (this denseness is due to there being two cilia in each depression of the pellicle, and has given rise to the erroneous idea that the cilia are fused to form an undulating membrane). The small inner chamber, or oesophagus, of the oral groove lacks cilia, and is merely a cleft in the endoplasm.

e. The fluid **endoplasm** contains large numbers of tiny food-reserve granules, groups of undigested food particles enclosed in food vacuoles (containing digestive enzymes), and the large refractive nucleus.

f. Watch the process of digestion in animals previously fed with milk stained with Congo red (see method on p. 36). The ingested fat globules turn first blue (due to acid secretion into the food vacuole) and then through shades of purple to red (due to alkaline secretion).

g. Run a small drop of 1% acetic acid into the side of a drop of *Paramecium* culture. Before they die many of the irritated animals shoot out their **tri-chocysts**, which are narrower than the cilia and several times as long.

h. Examine permanent stained preparations of *Paramecium* (for a method of making these, see p. 36), and find again as many of the above-mentioned features as possible. In particular, examine the double nature of the **nucleus**. The tiny micronucleus (concerned with reproduction) is situated alongside, or is partly embedded in, the large macronucleus (concerned with somatic functions).

i. In permanent preparations containing large numbers of these protozoans, search for individuals undergoing transverse **binary fission**, and for others fusing in pairs during **conjugation**.

3. CONCLUSION

a. Observing the specimens, review the characteristics of the phylum, of the class, of the subclass, and of the order.

4.   REFERENCES

BRONN, H. G. (1887–89).   Volume 1 and part 3 of " Klassen und Ordnungen des Thier-Reichs.   Protozoa.   Infusoria."   Leipzig.

KENT, W. S. (1880–81).   "A manual of the Infusoria."   London.

4.22.   Order **Heterotrichida**

Characteristics : Euciliata with the cilia usually covering the whole body surface, and with an adoral row of membranelles.

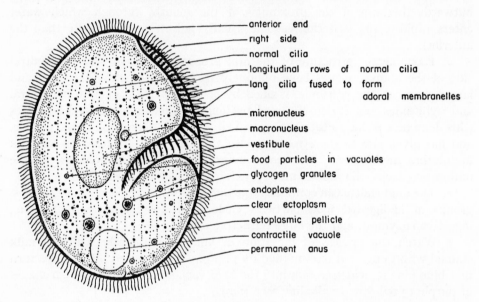

anterior   end
right   side
normal   cilia
longitudinal   rows   of   normal   cilia
long   cilia   fused   to   form
                     adoral   membranelles
micronucleus
macronucleus
vestibule
food   particles   in   vacuoles
glycogen   granules
endoplasm
clear   ectoplasm
ectoplasmic   pellicle
contractile   vacuole
permanent   anus

FIG. 15.—*Nyctotherus*.   A specimen from the rectum of a frog showing a combination of the features visible in living and in stained preparations.

Genus **Nyctotherus**

I.   GENERAL ACCOUNT

a. Species of *Nyctotherus* have been found, often commonly, in the alimentary canals of mammals, of fish, and of such arthropods as cockroaches, crickets, and myriopods, but the most readily obtainable species is *N. cordiformis* (Ehr.), which is almost universally present in the rectum of frogs.   This species is not pathogenic, and although possibly, like *Opalina*, it may absorb some already digested food, it also feeds on solid particles in the manner of a free living ciliate. In spring some individuals encyst, and pass out into the water, where they are later eaten by young tadpoles.   In the tadpole rectum small forms emerge to live and multiply by binary fission.   When the tadpole metamorphoses, these small forms conjugate in pairs and give rise to the larger forms seen in the adult frog.

2. BODY FEATURES

a. Living specimens (obtained as described on p. 35) should be mounted beneath a cover-glass in a small drop of 0·7% aqueous solution of sodium chloride. Other genera may be present in the preparation, but *Nyctotherus* can easily be distinguished from the larger protociliate *Opalina* by the presence of an oral groove, and from the heterotrich *Balantidium* by the fact that this groove is lateral and not sub-terminal. Notice that the **body** is bean-shaped, being flattened dorso-ventrally and having a notch, the entrance to the vestibule, in the middle of the right side. Watch the flickering movement of the complete covering of uniform cilia which are arranged in longitudinal rows. If necessary, arrest the movements of the animals by the agar method (described for parasites on p. 36).

b. Examine the structure of the **oral groove**, within which a row of prominent adoral membranelles leads from the anterior end of the body, down the right side, and into the vestibule (each membranelle is a plate-like structure formed by the fusion of a short, transverse row of long cilia). The membranelles line the anterior wall of the vestibule, but the posterior wall is not ciliated. The posterior end of the vestibule opens into the endoplasm.

c. Distinguish the clear layer of **ectoplasm** with its thin outer pellicle (there are no trichocysts). At the posterior end look closely for the inturned ectoplasm which lines the small, but permanent, anal aperture, and watch the action of the closely adjacent contractile vacuole.

d. Within the **endoplasm** are numerous granules. The fewer larger ones are food particles (within food vacuoles), while the large numbers of tiny particles are granules of glycogen (animal starch). Notice also the large refractive nucleus.

e. Review the body features again in stained and permanently mounted specimens (method of preparation on p. 36), and in particular distinguish the tiny generative or **micronucleus** from the larger somatic or **macronucleus**.

3. CONCLUSION

a. Observing the specimens, review the characteristics of the phylum, of the class, of the subclass, and of the order.

b. Compare the structure of *Nyctotherus* with that of *Opalina* and *Paramecium*.

4. REFERENCE

The structure of *Nyctotherus* and of the associated heterotrich *Balantidium* are described in detail by:

WENYON, C. M. (1926). " Protozoology." London.

4.23. Order **Peritrichida**

Characteristics : Euciliata, usually sedentary, with the adoral cilia arranged in a counter-clockwise spiral, and with an undulating membrane; no other cilia present except an aboral ring temporarily developed when swimming free, or permanently present in the few free-living species; macronucleus elongated and curved.

Genus **Vorticella** (bell animalcule)

I. GENERAL ACCOUNT

a. This is an extremely common genus, whose members are usually found anchored by their long stalks to weeds, stones, or to the bodies of such animals

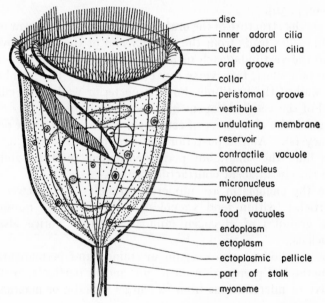

disc
inner adoral cilia
outer adoral cilia
oral groove
collar
peristomal groove
vestibule
undulating membrane
reservoir
contractile vacuole
macronucleus
micronucleus
myonemes
food vacuoles
endoplasm
ectoplasm
ectoplasmic pellicle
part of stalk
myoneme

FIG. 16.—*Vorticella.* A combination of the features visible in living and in stained preparations.

as aquatic worms, fishes, and amphibians.   Feeding largely on the bacteria of decay, they occur most abundantly in still water containing rotting organic material, plant, animal, or sewage. Asexual reproduction is by binary fission, one of the new individuals retaining the stalk and the other swimming away to grow a new stalk.   Periodically conjugation takes place, and in adverse conditions, such as starvation, the animals encyst.   Culture methods are described on p. 35.

2. ANATOMY

a. Examine living specimens of *Vorticella* under a microscope, and notice that each is made up of a bell-shaped **body**, to the base of which is attached a long stalk. The rim of the bell bears large numbers of cilia which lead to the mouth. When the animal is irritated the stalk contracts into a tight spiral and the cilia are folded out of sight.

b. The free end of the body, surrounded by the adoral cilia, is termed the disc. It is slightly convex, and on one side of it the vestibule opens. The cilia are based in a groove, the **peristome**, which lies between the sides of the disc and the prominent rim, or collar, which forms the edge of the bell (it is this collar which, on contraction, closes over the cilia). There are two rows of adoral cilia, the inner one standing straight up and the outer one curving outwards. The two rows are twisted into a spiral which, starting internally on the disc, makes about one and a half anti-clockwise turns before entering the vestibule and being abruptly replaced by the undulating membrane (formed of fused cilia). At its base the vestibule opens into a small chamber, the oesophagus, which is merely a cleft in the endoplasm.

c. The clear **ectoplasm** which lines the vestibule, covers the body, and is especially thick on the base of the body and on the stalk, bears no cilia except those already described, and contains no trichocysts. It consists of an elastic outer pellicle and a thicker inner layer in which run myonemes (contractile fibres). Notice that these myonemes, after running parallel to each other down the sides of the bell, converge as they approach the stalk. Within the stalk they join to form a single relatively thick myoneme, which lies in an open spiral (the contraction of this myoneme causes the spiral shortening of the stalk).

d. The single **contractile vacuole** lies close to the side of the vestibule. Periodically it discharges into a reservoir which has a permanent opening into the vestibule (undigested food is also passed into the vestibule through a temporary opening in the ectoplasm).

e. The granular **endoplasm**, not present in the stalk, contains food particles lying in food vacuoles, and a long, curved, refractive macronucleus.

f. In a rich culture stages of **binary fission** should be common. Notice that the newly formed individuals, when about to swim free, develop an aboral ring of cilia.

g. Re-examine the structure of *Vorticella* as seen in a permanent stained preparation (for a method of making such a preparation see p. 36), and in particular notice the tiny **micronucleus** lying close alongside the long **macronucleus**.

3. CONCLUSION

a. Observing the specimens, review the characteristics of the phylum, of the class, of the subclass, and of the order.

b. Identify those features which are associated with the sedentary mode of life.

D

4. REFERENCES

BRONN, H. G. (1887–89). Volume 1 and part 3 of " Klassen und Ordnungen des Thier-Reichs. Protozoa. Infusoria." Leipzig.

KENT, W. S. (1880–81). "A manual of the Infusoria." London.

APPENDIX TO THE PROTOZOA

I. CULTURE METHODS

a. Amoeba. This species is obtained most easily from the surface of the mud and rotten leaves at the bottom of ponds and slow streams, or from among *Sphagnum* moss. Small species of *Amoeba* may also be obtained from almost any type of soil. Set up several shallow dishes each containing about 100 c.c. of tap-water (not more than an inch deep), and to each add three or four grains of uncooked rice or wheat. Inoculate the dishes with small amounts of mud, or small pieces of *Sphagnum*, adding at the same time a few c.c. of pond-water. Cover the dishes with glass plates, disturb them as little as possible, and keep them away from direct sunlight and at a temperature of between 15° C. and 25° C. Within one or two weeks amoebae should be present in considerable numbers.

If it is then desired to maintain a purer culture, the amoebae must be separated and placed in an infusion made as follows. To each 100 c.c. of distilled water, add three or four grains of rice or wheat, or five or six hay-stems (each 1 inch long), boil for about ten minutes, and allow to stand for a few days before using. In such an infusion the amoebae feed on smaller organisms, like the flagellate *Chilomonas*, which are introduced with them. Larger organisms, such as rotifers and crustaceans, must be excluded. About every two months it is necessary to make a subculture.

b. Actinosphaerium. Considerable searching in small permanent ponds may be necessary before these animals are found floating among the pond-weeds. They may be cultured in shallow dishes, each containing about 100 c.c. of pond-water and three or four grains of rice or wheat. Larger organisms must be eliminated.

c. Euglena and Chlamydomonas. These may be collected from the stagnant green pools found commonly around farmyards and other places where there is considerable manuring of the ground. Suitable culture solutions can be made by adding to each 100 c.c. of tap or distilled water either three or four grains of rice or wheat, or five or six hay-stems (each about 1 inch long), or 1 c.c. of day-old pasteurised milk containing no cream, or a pinch of cow or horse manure. In any case, boil the mixture for about ten minutes, and let it stand for two or three days in tall bottles (such as milk-bottles) with cotton-wool pads as stoppers. After inoculation with *Euglena* or *Chlamydomonas*, stand the bottles in a light window. It may take from two to eight weeks before a soupy green culture is obtained. When the green colour begins to fade it is time to set up subcultures.

d. Paramecium. This, and related genera, occur abundantly in ditches and ponds where there is much decaying vegetable matter. A suitable culture solution is made by boiling (for about ten minutes) some three or four grains of rice or wheat, or five or six hay-stems (each about 1 inch long), in 100 c.c. of tap-water. Let the mixture cool in shallow dishes, cover with glass plates, and allow to stand for three or four days until a rich culture of bacteria has developed. Then add the paramecia, after which one or two weeks may pass before the culture is fully developed.

e. Vorticella may be cultured in the same way as *Amoeba*. It is found in large numbers, attached to plants, in ponds where there is much decaying organic material. The settling tanks of sewage works are an excellent source of supply.

2.   METHOD OF OBTAINING *OPALINA* AND *NYCTOTHERUS*

a. Open the rectum of a frog freshly killed by pithing or decapitation, and using a 0·7% aqueous solution of sodium chloride, wash out the contents into a small dish. Together with many other parasites, these ciliates will be found to be present in the majority of frogs examined.

3.   METHOD OF ARRESTING FAST-MOVING PROTOZOANS

a. Fresh-water protozoans. Of the several methods known for hindering the movements of active mastigophorans and infusorians so that they can be examined under a high-power microscope, the most effective appears to be the following. Place a *small* drop of the culture solution on to a glass slide, and check that the required species are present (avoid including sand grains or other large pieces of detritus, as they will hold up the cover-glass and prevent the use of high-power objectives). Place an equal-sized drop of a melted solution of agar in water (a 1% solution kept liquid at about 40° C. in a water-bath or oven) on a cover-glass, immediately invert the cover-glass, centre the drop of agar solution directly over the drop of culture solution, and let the cover-glass fall. As the two drops merge, and the temperature falls rapidly to below 30° C., the mixture sets solid. The agar jelly formed in this way contains large numbers of tiny water-spaces, most of which are considerably smaller than the field of a high-power microscope, and in these the protozoans are confined. Large species are often held so tightly that they are unable to move at all, but smaller ones can swim around in a small circle (if required, animals can be held more tightly by increasing the size of the agar drop relative to the water drop, or by using a 1·5% solution of agar). The animals continue living in these conditions for at least half an hour, and often for many hours, and the cover-glass is sufficiently firmly fixed for an oil-immersion objective to be used.   However, care must be taken that the cover-glass is not pressed upon or otherwise moved, as this will break the jelly reticulum.

b. Marine and parasitic protozoans.   In the case of marine protozoans, the agar solution must be made up in sea-water, and in the case of parasitic protozoans, such as *Opalina* and *Nyctotherus*, it must be made up in a o·7% aqueous solution of sodium chloride.

4.   METHOD OF DEMONSTRATING DIGESTION IN *PARAMECIUM*

a. For studying food vacuoles and digestion, mix, in a small test tube, equal quantities of a rich culture of *Paramecium* (if necessary concentrate the culture with a centrifuge) and of milk stained with a few grains of Congo red. An hour or two later the process of digestion is strikingly demonstrated.   The ingested red fat globules turn first blue (due to acid secretion into the food vacuole) and then through shades of purple to red (due to alkaline secretion).

5.   FIXATION METHODS

a. Free-living protozoans.   All the free-living protozoans described above may be fixed as follows.   Take up the animals in a fine pipette, together with as small a drop of water as possible (if necessary, gently centrifuge some of the culture solution to concentrate the individuals).   Allow the pipette to stand for about a minute (this is particularly necessary in the case of amoebae which may have withdrawn their pseudopodia).   Then rapidly mix the water-drop with a few c.c. of Schaudinn's fixative, and leave for about fifteen minutes. Gently centrifuge to concentrate the protozoans, the majority of which can then be pipetted, together with a very small amount of the fixative, into a few c.c. of 70% alcohol.   After a few minutes transfer to 90% alcohol and then to absolute alcohol, centrifuging gently before each change.   Smear slides thinly with albumen cement, and after again centrifuging the alcohol and drawing up the protozoans into a fine pipette, let a small drop of the liquid fall from a height of about 1 inch on to each slide (due to the fall and to the immediate coagulation of the albumen, the protozoans stick securely).   The slides must be placed immediately into absolute alcohol.

b. Sedentary protozoans.   The simplest method for *Vorticella* is to place an open rack of glass slides into the pond or culture in which the animals abound. After a few days, when large numbers have become attached, flood the slides suddenly with a fixative such as Schaudinn's fluid, leave for about fifteen minutes, and transfer to 70% alcohol.

c. Protozoans parasitic in the alimentary canal.   In the case of *Opalina* and *Nyctotherus*, take up a small part of the rectal contents of a frog, smear it thinly on a slide, and observe that the parasites are present.   Leave the smear in the air for a minute or so until its edges begin to dry, and then place the slide in Schaudinn's fixative.   After about fifteen minutes transfer it to 70% alcohol.

d. Monocystis. In a dry dish dissect open a large, sexually mature earthworm, and cut out one of the seminal vesicles. Make a thin smear of the vesicle contents by dabbing its cut end on to a slide which has previously been moistened with the breath. Immediately place the slide into fixative (either Schaudinn's fluid, Bouin's alcoholic fluid, or simply 90% alcohol), and leave it there for about fifteen minutes before transferring to 70% alcohol.

6. STAINING METHODS

a. Naked protozoans. The slides with the protozoans attached should first be taken through 90%, 70%, 50%, and 30% alcohols (about two minutes in each) to water. They may then be placed directly into a haematoxylin solution (suggested solutions are Delafield's, Ehrlich's, or Mayer's), and left there until the nuclei, but not the cytoplasm, are well stained (the actual time, perhaps from five to twenty minutes, varies according to the activity of the solution). Wash off the excess stain in water, and turn the rest of the stain blue by leaving the slides for a minute or two in slightly alkaline tap-water (if necessary, alkaline water can be made by adding one drop of concentrated ammonia to about 250 c.c. of water). Counterstain in eosin, which turns the cytoplasm red. Again wash off the excess stain in tap-water, and then transfer the slides through 30%, 50%, 70%, 90%, and absolute alcohols (two minutes in each) to xylol. Place a small drop of Canada balsam on to the preparation, and add a cover-glass.

If the animals become over-stained in haematoxylin, remove the excess in a 1% solution of hydrochloric acid in 70% alcohol, after which it is necessary to turn the stain blue again in alkaline 70% alcohol. It is impossible to overstain in eosin.

b. Polystomella. First dissolve away the shell in weak acid. If the animals are preserved in 70% alcohol, they may be transferred (with a pipette) into a 1% solution of hydrochloric acid in 70% alcohol, or if they are in formalin, they may be placed directly into a 1% aqueous solution of hydrochloric acid. When decalcification is complete wash the specimens (in 70% alcohol or in water, as the case may be) to remove the acid. If in 70% alcohol, they are then most easily stained in borax carmine. Over-stain for half an hour or more, extract the excess stain in acid 70% alcohol (watch through a microscope and pour off the acid when just sufficient stain remains), and then transfer through 90% alcohol and absolute alcohol to xylol (two or three minutes in each). If in water, the animals may be stained in a solution of haematoxylin as described above for other protozoans, and then transferred (by pipette) through 30%, 50%, 70%, 90%, and absolute alcohols to xylol (two or three minutes in each). Finally mount them on a slide in a drop of Canada balsam, and add a cover-glass.

CHAPTER II

PHYLUM **PORIFERA**

Characteristics : Multicellular, sessile animals with a single body cavity, the paragaster, wholly or partly lined with choanocytes; body-wall pierced by many tiny pores (inhalent) and by one or more large oscula (exhalent); and usually with a skeleton of calcareous or siliceous spicules or of horny fibres.

These animals, the sponges, also form the sub-kingdom Parazoa, which is distinguished from the sub-kingdom Protozoa by the fact that its members are multicellular, and from the sub-kingdom Metazoa by the fact that their principal opening is exhalent, that they lack a co-ordinating nervous system, that they possess choanocytes, and that their less specialised cells do not form tissues. They probably originated as aggregations of mastigophoran protozoans, which would account for their lack of co-ordination, integration, and individuality. They are mainly marine and are found everywhere from the sea-shore down to the ocean abysses.

1.00.   Class **Calcarea**

Characteristics: Skeleton composed of calcareous spicules.

This relatively small and sharply defined group contains the simplest of the sponges.   All of them are small in size, and all live in shallow seas.

1.01.   Order **Heterocoela**

Characteristics : Choanocytes confined to flagellated chambers which are thimble-shaped extensions of the paragaster.

Genus **Sycon**

I. GENERAL ACCOUNT

a. This is a common solitary sponge which occurs in shallow water from the low-tide mark down to a depth of about 60 fathoms.   It is found attached to rocks or wooden piles, and is presumed to feed on minute plants, animals, or particles of organic matter which are drawn in by the action of the flagella.   It reproduces asexually by budding from its base, so forming groups of individuals, and sexually by producing both eggs and spermatozoa and acting as a cross-fertilising hermaphrodite.   Early development takes place inside the parent, and the ciliated larva, or amphiblastula, escapes through the osculum to swim for a short time, settle, and grow.

2.   ANATOMY

a. Examine one of these sponges, and notice its tall vase-**shape**. Basally it has a small hold-fast (which was fixed to the substratum by a sticky secre-

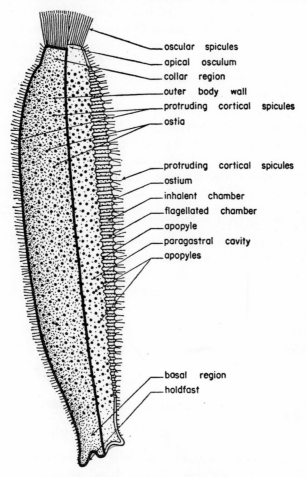

oscular   spicules
apical   osculum
collar   region
outer   body   wall
protruding   cortical   spicules
ostia

protruding   cortical   spicules
ostium
inhalent   chamber
flagellated   chamber
apopyle
paragastral   cavity
apopyles

basal   region
holdfast

FIG. 17.—*Sycon.*   Details of the surface are shown on the left, but on the right the colony has been cut open to show the internal structure.

tion) and apically there is the single large osculum (exhalent opening).   Through a lens examine the body-wall to see the tiny openings, or ostia, which lead into inhalent canals (thimble-shaped intuckings of the body-wall).   A collar region, immediately below the osculum, is not pierced by inhalent canals, and these canals are also absent from the basal region.

b. From the body-surface there protrude large numbers of **spicules**.   There is a prominent fringe of large spicules around the osculum (to discourage the entry of other animals), and the shorter cortical spicules partly conceal (and protect) the ostia.

c. With a sharp razor, cut the specimen in two from osculum to base.   The large central cavity is the **paragaster**, and its wall contains numerous pores, the apopyles (through which water enters the paragaster).   Examine the cut wall through a lens or binocular microscope to see that the outer ostia lead into straight, radially directed, blind ending, inhalent canals, and that between these canals are similar blind ending flagellated chambers (lined with choano-cytes), which open inwards through the apopyles (the cavities of the inhalent canals are in communication with those of the flagellated chambers through large numbers of microscopic pores, the prosopyles).

d. Compress part of the **body-wall**, including the collar region, beneath a cover-glass.   Through a microscope notice that the larger spicules (those which protrude) are monaxonic, while the smaller ones (those which lie within the wall) are triaxonic.   The triaxonic spicules are matted together to form a network (through the interstices of which pass the inhalent canals and flagel-lated chambers).   The sponge cells are also visible (but it is usually difficult to distinguish the different types).

e. Examine **isolated spicules** obtained by boiling part of the animal in a solution of potassium hydroxide (see details of method on p. 46).   To prove their calcareous nature, run a drop of dilute hydrochloric acid beneath the cover-glass and watch them dissolve with the production of bubbles of carbon dioxide.

3.   CONCLUSION

a. Observing the specimen, review the characteristics of the phylum, of the class, and of the order.

4.   REFERENCE

DELAGE, Y., and HÉROUARD, E. (1899).   Volume 2 and part 1 of " Traité de zoologie concrète."   Paris.

2.00.   Class **Demospongiae**

Characteristics : Porifera with a skeleton of siliceous spicules, of horny fibres, or of both ; spicules never six-rayed and usually of two kinds, macro-scleres and microscleres.

Most sponges, exhibiting the most diverse forms, belong to this dominant and widely distributed class.

2.01.   Order **Monaxonida**

Characteristics : Demospongiae with the macroscleric spicules monaxonic ; and with or without horny fibres.

Genus **Ephydatia**

(*Spongilla* is similar, and may be used as an alternative.)

1. GENERAL ACCOUNT

a. Only one family of the Porifera, the Spongillidae, occurs in fresh water, but this family contains some fifteen genera, and is cosmopolitan.

b. The common genus *Ephydatia* is found in clear water in streams, rivers, ponds, and lakes (to a depth of more than 300 fathoms). The animals spread over rocks or invest twigs, plants, or reed stems, and each as it grows develops into a flat plate or produces long, finger-like outgrowths. Although each must be considered as a colony, the individuals composing it are so closely merged as to be inseparable. Those species which grow in bright light have a greenish tinge, due to intracellular symbiotic zoochlorellae. For food, *Ephydatia* strains from the water tiny organic particles, unicellular plants, and animals such as infusorian protozoans. It reproduces sexually, and the resulting ciliated larvae escape via the oscula. In autumn, or at the approach of the dry season, it forms asexually the winter buds, or gemmules, which can withstand freezing, drying, and putrefaction. In better conditions the buds escape from their cases, crawl to a suitable position, and grow.

2. ANATOMY

a. The **shape** of *Ephydatia* is highly variable, and depends largely on the form of the object which supports it. The surface is pierced by several relatively large oscula (exhalent apertures), by large numbers of tiny pores (inhalent apertures), and (for protection) by the outer ends of numerous spicules which give it a rough hairy appearance.

b. If the specimen is large, it is possible to see much of its **internal structure** after cutting it in two with a razor so that the cut passes through one or more oscula. Examine the cut surface through a lens or binocular microscope. The inhalent pores open through a thin membrane, termed the dermis, into a narrow hypodermal cavity which extends beneath the whole surface of the colony. The dermis is supported over the cavity by the protruding spicules. Branching inhalent canals lead inwards from the hypodermal cavity to end blindly near the base of the colony, and between them lie the branching flagellated chambers (connexion between the inhalent canals and the flagellated chambers is through microscopic pores, or prosopyles). At the base of the colony the flagellated chambers open into large exhalent canals (branches of the paragaster). These canals converge to enter the base of one of the main paragastral cavities, a wide, chimney-like tube which passes straight up to open through an osculum (this is the rhagon type of canal system).

c. Shred part of the specimen on a slide, and compress it beneath a coverglass. Notice that the **spicules** are all monaxonic, but that some, the macroscleres, are large and (according to species) either smooth or spiny, while others, the microscleres, are small and usually spiny (the macroscleres protrude from the body, support the dermal layer, form a network beneath the surface, and

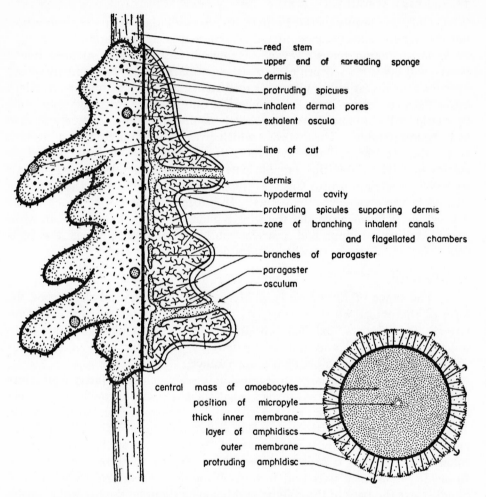

reed   stem
upper   end   of   spreading   sponge
dermis
protruding   spicules
inhalent   dermal   pores
exhalent   oscula

line   of   cut

dermis
hypodermal   cavity
protruding   spicules   supporting   dermis
zone   of   branching   inhalent   canals
                                    and   flagellated   chambers
branches   of   paragaster
paragaster
osculum

central   mass   of   amoebocytes
position   of   micropyle
thick   inner   membrane
layer   of   amphidiscs
outer   membrane
protruding   amphidisc

FIG. 18.—*Ephydatia.*   A colony growing on a reed stem and partly cut open to show the internal structure.   On the right is a gemmule.

are cemented together by thin layers of horny spongin; the microscleres lie freely in the body substance).

d. Distinguish as many as possible of the **cell types.**   Scleroblasts are to be seen closely applied to the sides of the spicules (which they secrete); large amoebocytes are common, and within them are refractive food-reserve granules, brown pigment granules, and often green symbiotic zoochlorellae; small pinacocytes (epithelial-like cells) are also common ; but the tiny choanocytes are difficult to identify.

e. Also present in specimens collected in autumn are the **gemmules** (asexual buds). Each consists of a central mass of amoebocytes (full of granular food reserves) surrounded by a capsule composed of three layers. The inner layer is a thick, hard membrane (secreted by external amoebocytes) ; the middle layer contains radially arranged spicules (secreted and carried into position by sclero-blast cells) ; and the outer layer is a thin membrane (secreted by the same amoebocytes which formed the inner layer). The spicules, called amphidiscs, are straight rods with thorny sides, and they bear a ring of hooks at each end (in *Spongilla* they are not amphidiscs, but are typical monaxons). The inner rings of hooks are buried in the inner layer, and some of the amphidiscs are especially long, and protrude right through the outer layer. On one side of the capsule is a small circular micropyle (a point of weakness through which the amoebocytes ultimately emerge).

f. Boil part of the specimen in a solution of potassium hydroxide, and make a preparation of **isolated spicules** (details of method on p. 46). Add dilute hydrochloric acid, and notice that it does not affect them, since they are not calcareous.

3. CONCLUSION

a. Observing the specimen, review the characteristics of the phylum, of the class, and of the order.

b. Compare the structure of *Ephydatia* with that of *Sycon*.

4. REFERENCE

DELAGE, Y., and HÉROUARD, E. (1899). Volume 2 and part 1 of " Traité de zoologie concrète." Paris.

2.02. Order **Keratosa**

Characteristics : Demospongiae without spicules, but with horny fibres.

Genus **Euspongia (Spongia)**

I. GENERAL ACCOUNT

a. The species of this genus are common from depths of about 1 to 100 fathoms on rocky sea-bottoms in tropical and subtropical seas, and particularly along the coasts of Australia and the West Indies and in the Indian and Mediterranean Seas. Many species grow to a large size, and are collected for domestic use. They are fixed to the substratum by a secretion of spongin, the horny substance of which the skeletal fibres are formed. Minute food particles of less than about 0·025 mm. diameter are sieved from the sea-water, but the actual nature of these particles is largely unknown.

b. These sponges are considered to be colonies, but the individuals composing them are almost unrecognisable.   Reproduction is sexual and the sexes are separate, but male colonies are rare.   Gametes are produced throughout the year, and internal fertilisation results in the formation of ciliated larvae which swim free to settle and develop into new colonies.   It is believed that a *Euspongia* colony may live for fifty years.   It has no enemies, but its internal cavities serve as homes for large numbers of commensal animals, particularly annelids and crustaceans.

2.   ANATOMY

a. The **shape** of the various species of *Euspongia* is very variable, but commonly a sponge is roughly spherical.   The largest oscula (up to 10 mm.

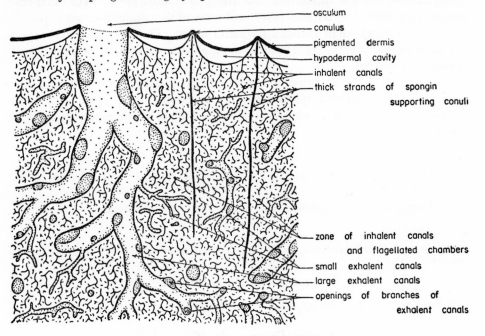

FIG. 19.—*Euspongia*.   Part of a colony cut open to show the internal structure.

diameter) are on the upper surface, while the more numerous smaller ones (of about 1 to 2 mm. diameter) are scattered over the whole surface (in a dried specimen only the largest oscula may be distinguishable).   However, some species are low and encrusting, some are branched, and some are cup-shaped, with the largest oscula within the cup.

b. Examine the surface layer, the **dermis**, of a piece of sponge preserved in alcohol.   It is dully pigmented brown or black, and it bears large numbers of small projections, the conuli.   Ridges often radiate from, and link together, the conuli, and between these elevations the dermis is smooth (and is pierced by inhalent pores of about 0·025 mm. diameter).

c. On the cut surface of a preserved specimen, examine through a lens the **internal structure**. The dark dermis, which is in sharp contrast to the yellow or orange interior, is a thin membrane roofing an extensive hypodermal cavity (reduced in some species to a series of large branching canals). From the floor of the hypodermal cavity rise projections which support the dermis and form the conuli (each is stiffened by one main and many branching subsidiary spongin fibres). Branching inhalent canals (of about 0·1 mm. diameter) lead downwards through the floor of the hypodermal cavity (and finally open into spherical flagellated chambers of about 0·04 mm. diameter). The exhalent canals are much larger and fewer, and form a branching paragastral cavity. Close to the surface they may attain a diameter of about 10 mm. before opening through the oscula.

d. The **skeleton** is composed entirely of a spongin network, easily visible in dried specimens. The thickest fibres are radially directed, and end in the conuli.

3. CONCLUSION

a. Observing the specimens, review the characteristics of the phylum, of the class, and of the order.

b. Compare the structure of *Euspongia* with that of *Ephydatia*.

4. REFERENCES

DELAGE, Y., and HÉROUARD, E. (1899). Volume 2 and part 1 of " Traité de zoologie concrète." Paris.
LENDENFELD, R. von (1889). " A monograph of the horny sponges." The Royal Society, London.

APPENDIX TO THE PORIFERA

1. CULTURE METHODS

a. Small marine sponges, such as *Sycon*, may survive in an aquarium for about a week, and even longer if the tank is large and fitted with running water.

b. The fresh-water sponges *Ephydatia* and *Spongilla*, which are most easily found when they attain their largest size in late summer and autumn, may also live for a week or two if placed in a large aquarium together with their supports. The gemmules can then easily be extracted and stimulated to grow by putting them in a dish of aquarium or pond-water and keeping them in the dark at a temperature of about 20° C. The floor of the dish should be lined with glass slides or other convenient objects to which the young sponges can attach themselves. After about ten days, growth should have started, and the slides can be transferred to a balanced aquarium. They may survive and grow for many weeks or even months, but it is very difficult to rear them to a large size.

2. FIXATION METHODS

a. Both marine and fresh-water sponges can be fixed in 90% or absolute alcohol, and stored, after twenty-four hours, in fresh 70% or 90% alcohol. Formalin or other watery solutions should not be used, or maceration will follow.

3. SPICULE EXTRACTION

a. Boil a fragment of sponge in a strong aqueous solution of potassium hydroxide, and when the cells have dissolved, let the spicules settle. Pour off as much of the liquid as possible, add water, and again let the spicules settle. Repeat this washing process, and then pipette some of the spicules on to a slide and add a cover-glass.

CHAPTER III

PHYLUM **PLATYHELMINTHES**

Characteristics : Bilaterally symmetrical, unsegmented animals which are flattened dorso-ventrally; with the alimentary canal embedded in a solid parenchyma of mesodermal cells and opening only through the mouth; usually with a protonephridial (flame-cell) excretory system; and usually hermaphrodite.

According to Hadzi's theory, this is the most primitive metazoan phylum, the original members of which were formed by the cellularisation of some multinucleate ciliate protozoan. It is suggested that the original metazoans closely resembled the modern acoelans. These usually possess a cellularised epidermis which is ciliated and contains sagittocysts comparable to the ciliate trichocysts. Internally is an imperfectly cellularised parenchyma in which mesoderm and endoderm are not clearly differentiated. An ectodermal pharynx, similar to a ciliate pharynx, leads into a series of irregular spaces within the parenchyma. Some of the syncytial parenchymatous cell masses are concerned with a phagocytic type of digestion, and some produce the gametes. The complex habit of cross-fertilising hermaphroditism is readily explicable if it is regarded as being inherited from the ciliate habit of conjugation. This is the most plausible theory so far advanced to account for the origin of the Metazoa.

The Platyhelminthes are typically free-living in the sea, in fresh water, and in damp places on land, but many of them are ecto- or endoparasites and are consequently considerably modified both in structure and life history.

1.00. Class **Turbellaria**

Characteristics : Platyhelminthes which are almost all free-living; which occasionally have suckers but never form proglottids; with epidermis ciliated and containing sagittocysts or rhabdites; with a ventrally directed mouth opening into an ectodermal pharynx, and with the alimentary canal, when present, never bifid.

1.01. Order **Acoela**

Characteristics : Marine Turbellaria which usually possess an ectodermal pharynx but which lack an intestine; with a syncytial parenchyma not clearly

47

differentiated into mesoderm and endoderm; with no protonephridial system; and with no oviducts, vitelline glands, or clearly delimited gonads.

Genus **Convoluta**

I. GENERAL ACCOUNT

a. Of this widespread genus the best-known species are *C. roscoffensis* (Graff.) and *C. paradoxa*, Oersted. Both contain symbiotic unicellular algae, the former being consequently green and the latter brown. *C. roscoffensis* lives gregariously on sandy shores, being especially well known on the coast of Brittany. *C. paradoxa* is a solitary animal living on the fronds of seaweeds between tide marks. As it glides slowly along it feeds on unicellular organisms by means of the solid syncytial gut which may be partly extruded like a pseudopodium through the mouth. It also commonly attaches itself to the substratum by its adhesive tail, and then it can catch larger organisms, such as crustacean larvae, by means of an abundant sticky mucus produced by sub-epidermal glands. It sometimes even swims freely to chase and catch its prey. *Convoluta* is a cross-fertilising hermaphrodite, and development is direct.

2. ANATOMY

a. If living specimens are available watch through a microscope the smooth gliding **movements** caused by the epidermal cilia.

b. In a stained preparation (method of fixation and staining for Protozoa on p. 36) notice the shape of the dorso-ventrally flattened **body** with its down-turned edges. Distinguish the epidermal cilia.

c. The anterior **sense organs** include a single large otocyst containing a calcareous otolith (this balance organ lies close above the cerebral ganglion), a frontal organ (probably chemoreceptive; small in *C. paradoxa* but large in *C. roscoffensis*), and laterally a pair of orange eye-spots (in *C. roscoffensis* numerous other eye-spots also occur in the region anterior to the otocyst).

d. The mouth opens antero-ventrally (it is capable of wide distension and it leads through a thin-walled **pharynx** into irregular spaces within the syncytial parenchyma; this parenchyma may sometime be seen protruding through the mouth). Notice the absence of any regular alimentary canal and the way in which food particles (in process of digestion) are irregularly scattered throughout the parenchyma.

e. Only if the specimen is sexually mature will the hermaphrodite reproductive system be visible. The **male reproductive system** consists of numerous small groups of spermatogonia and spermatocytes (which are not enclosed in any connective tissue walls and which lie loosely scattered in the parenchyma towards the posterior end; there are no ducts and, when formed, the spermatozoa escape along clefts in the parenchyma), and a single well-developed penis which may be protruded through the male pore (there are no true seminal vesicles, but before entering the penis the spermatozoa may lodge in larger spaces within the parenchyma).

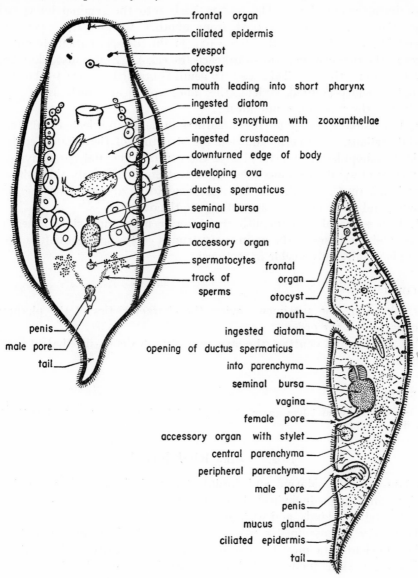

frontal organ
ciliated epidermis
eyespot
otocyst
mouth leading into short pharynx
ingested diatom
central syncytium with zooxanthellae
ingested crustacean
downturned edge of body
developing ova
ductus spermaticus
seminal bursa
vagina
accessory organ
spermatocytes
track of sperms

penis
male pore
tail

frontal organ
otocyst
mouth
ingested diatom
opening of ductus spermaticus into parenchyma
seminal bursa
vagina
female pore
accessory organ with stylet
central parenchyma
peripheral parenchyma
male pore
penis
mucus gland
ciliated epidermis
tail

FIG. 20.—*Convoluta paradoxa.*   A ventral view of a whole mount, and, on the right, a sagittal section.

f. The **female reproductive system** consists of lateral rows of isolated oogonia and oocytes (which lie freely in cavities within the parenchyma, and which are fertilised internally and are said to be laid either through the mouth or through

E

a rupture in the body wall). Midventrally is the single female pore which opens into a narrow vagina (the sole function of this duct is to receive spermatozoa during copulation). The vagina leads into the seminal bursa (which stores the spermatozoa received from another worm; this spermatozoa ultimately passes forwards through a narrow ductus spermaticus to enter the spaces of the parenchyma and so to reach the eggs). Notice also, close behind the female pore, the so-called accessory genital organ (this opens to the exterior through a sharp-pointed stylet; the inner spherical vesicle is apparently glandular; the function is unknown).

g. If possible examine all these features in detail in selected transverse or sagittal **sections.** Notice in addition the structure of the ciliated epidermis, the large subepidermal mucus glands, the central syncytial parenchyma, and the masses of symbiotic unicellular algae scattered irregularly throughout the parenchyma (in *C. roscoffensis* the algae tend to be absent along the lines of the inner and outer nerve cords posterior to the otocyst).

h. If possible also distinguish the anterior **nerve ring** close beneath the otocyst and the bases of the main nerve trunks emerging from it (the nervous system is usually only visible in sections).

3. CONCLUSION

a. Observing the specimen, review the characteristics of the phylum, of the class, and of the order.

b. Compare and contrast the structure of *Convoluta* with that of a ciliate protozoan.

4. REFERENCE

KUKENTHAL, W. and KRUMBACH, T. (1928–33) Volume 2, Part 1 of " Handbuch der Zoologie." Leipzig.

1.02. Order **Rhabdocoela**

Characteristics : Marine and fresh-water Turbellaria with a simple sac-like intestine; a protonephridial system; gonads few and compact, with or without vitelline glands, and with oviducts.

This order has assumed a new interest since Hadzi's suggestion that the phylum Coelenterata may be descended from some early rhabdocoel, which in adopting a sessile mode of life became fixed by its aboral end.

Genus **Mesostoma**

(There are many other common fresh-water and littoral genera which may be used as alternatives.)

I. GENERAL ACCOUNT

a. The genus is cosmopolitan, its members living among the weeds and débris at the bottoms of ponds, and one of the largest rhabdocoels known is *M. ehrenbergii* Focke. *Mesostoma* is carnivorous, catching smaller animals and also feeding on fresh carrion.   During the summer it produces thin-shelled self-fertilised eggs which are retained within the body and develop into

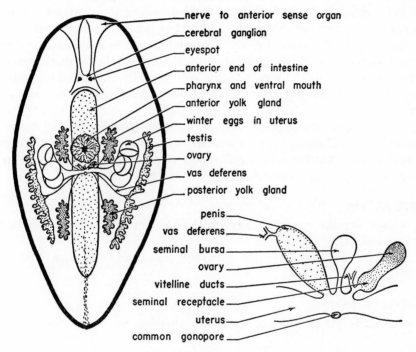

nerve to anterior sense organ
cerebral ganglion
eyespot
anterior end of intestine
pharynx and ventral mouth
anterior yolk gland
winter eggs in uterus
testis
ovary
vas deferens
posterior yolk gland

penis
vas deferens
seminal bursa
ovary
vitelline ducts
seminal receptacle
uterus
common gonopore

FIG. 21.—*Mesostoma*.   A ventral view of a whole mount, and, on the right, details of the region of the gonopore.

young worms.   These apparently escape by body rupture.   In autumn thick-shelled cross-fertilised eggs are produced which do not hatch until the spring.

2. ANATOMY

a. If living specimens are available watch the smooth gliding **movements** brought about by the epidermal cilia.

b. In a stained preparation (methods of staining on p. 76) distinguish the **alimentary canal**.   The ventral mouth opens upwards through the thick-walled muscular pharynx into the long unbranched intestine.   The whole system is set in the solid mass of the mesenchyme cells.

c. Anterior to the intestine distinguish the large **cerebral ganglion** above which are two prominent eye-spots. From the ganglion two large nerves extend forwards and spread out to innervate the highly sensitive anterior end (probably a tactile and chemoreceptive area). Two large nerve cords also extend posteriorly to the body, but their course is usually obscured by the reproductive system.

d. Identify the organs of the **female reproductive system.** The ovary is a small body close to the mid-ventral line just behind the pharynx. Left and right are the two arms of the thin-walled uterus, which in summer may contain thin-shelled eggs or developing embryos and in autumn thick-shelled hemispherical winter eggs. There are two pairs of yolk glands, the one anterior and the other posterior to the region of the ovary. The vitelline ducts converge to open by a common duct close to the seminal receptacle at the base of the ovary.

e. In the **male reproductive system** the two laterally placed testes are prominent. Close behind the pharynx the two vasa deferentia join to enter the muscular penis. During cross-fertilisation foreign sperm is received in the seminal bursa which lies between the penis and the ovary.

3. CONCLUSION

a. Observing the specimen, review the characteristics of the phylum, of the class, and of the order.

b. Compare and contrast the structure of *Mesostoma* with that of an anthozoan polyp.

4. REFERENCES

For descriptions and diagrams of the anatomy of other common genera see:

VON GRAFF, L. (1904–8). " Rhabdocoelida " in volume 4 and part 1c of " Bronn's Klassen und Ordnungen des Tier-Reichs." Leipzig.
KUKENTHAL, W., and KRUMBACH, T. (1928–33). Volume 2 and part 1 of " Handbuch der Zoologie." Berlin and Leipzig.

1.03. Order **Polycladida**

Characteristics: Typically marine Turbellaria with an intestine ending in many blind diverticula; gonads numerous and scattered; no vitelline glands; male and female openings separate or combined; and often with a planktonic larva (" Müller's larva ").

It has been suggested that the ctenophores were derived by neoteny from the polyclad larva. The details of the methods of cleavage and organogenesis are very similar in both groups, and like the " Müller's larva ", the ctenophores are pelagic, octoradial, and swim by means of ctenes.

Genus **Leptoplana**

(*Notoplana* is a similar alternative)

I. GENERAL ACCOUNT

a. Leptoplana is a common littoral genus, being found on rocky shores under shells and stones in places which are always wet. It moves either by creeping, a gliding movement due partly to the epidermal cilia and partly to

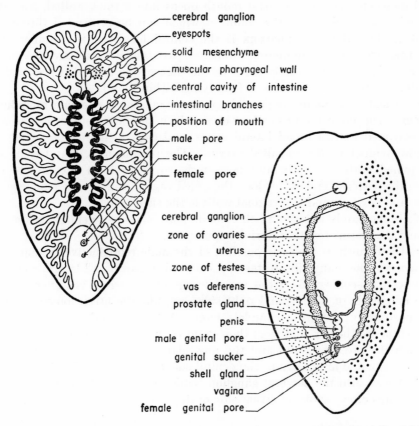

cerebral ganglion
eyespots
solid mesenchyme
muscular pharyngeal wall
central cavity of intestine
intestinal branches
position of mouth
male pore
sucker
female pore

cerebral ganglion
zone of ovaries
uterus
zone of testes
vas deferens
prostate gland
penis
male genital pore
genital sucker
shell gland
vagina
female genital pore

FIG. 22.—*Leptoplana.* Ventral views showing the alimentary canal and, on the right, the hermaphrodite reproductive system. For clarity, most of the left half of the male system and the right half of the female system are omitted.

the body muscles, or by swimming, a more rapid movement brought about by the undulations of the sides of the body (in the same way as a skate swims). It feeds nocturnally, especially on small polychaet worms. These it envelops and digestion begins externally by means of enzymes which are poured out of the extruded pharynx. The eggs are laid in spring and summer attached in

batches to stones and weeds. Although the young are pelagic, there is no
" Müller's larva " and development is direct.

2. ANATOMY

a. If living specimens are available watch the creeping and swimming
movements.

b. In a permanent preparation (see methods on p. 76) identify as much as
possible of the much-branched **alimentary canal**, which lies embedded in the
solid mesenchyme. The ventral mouth opens into a thick-walled, irregularly
shaped, central pharynx (the whole of which can be protruded through the
mouth). Dorsal to the pharynx is the central longitudinal chamber of the
intestine, from which numerous branches pass outwards to divide and subdivide until they end blindly close to the edge of the animal (these branches
are difficult to see unless there is food lying within them).

c. Identify as many as possible of the organs of the **female reproductive
system.** The large numbers of ovaries (which produce both eggs and yolk)
are scattered in two broad lateral zones, and each ovary is connected by a
narrow oviduct to the so-called uterus. The prominent left and right uteri
are joined both anteriorly and posteriorly so as to form a complete loop.
From the posterior end of this loop the coiled vagina leads to the female genital
pore, and close around the vaginal walls is the shell gland.

d. Immediately anterior to the female pore is a small **genital sucker** (used
to hold the worms together during copulation).

e. Distinguish as much as possible of the **male reproductive system.** Like
the ovaries, the many tiny testes are scattered in two broad lateral zones, and
each testis is connected to the vas deferens by a narrow vas efferens. The
vasa deferentia of the left and right sides are, like the uteri, joined anteriorly
and posteriorly to form a complete loop. Anteriorly and medially the vasa
deferentia are thicker, and from their point of junction a duct leads posteriorly
through the prostate gland and the muscular penis to the male genital pore,
which is situated anteriorly to the genital sucker.

f. Notice also the **cerebral ganglion** lying anterior to the uterine loop and
with groups of eye-spots on either side of it.

3. CONCLUSION

a. Observing the specimen, review the characteristics of the phylum, of
the class, and of the order.

1.04. Order **Tricladida**

Characteristics : Marine, fresh-water, and terrestrial Turbellaria which
possess an intestine with three main branches, one forward and two backward ;

two ovaries and many vitelline glands; two or more testes; one common genital opening; and no planktonic larva.

The triclads are the commonest turbellarians and they have also invaded the land. These terricolous forms, often brightly coloured, occur particularly in damp forests.

Genus **Dendrocoelum**

(*Dendrocoelum* is Eurasian; a similar alternative in North America is the genus *Procotyla*.)

I. GENERAL ACCOUNT

a. Unlike most turbellarians, *Dendrocoelum* has little pigment. It is usually less abundant than the well-known *Planaria*, but it and related genera are found all over the world in fresh-water streams and ponds. It feeds on small worms, crustaceans, and snails, which are entangled in a sticky secretion of the ventral surface, and which are broken up by the pumping action of the protrusible pharynx helped by extruded digestive enzymes. Compared with *Planaria, Dendrocoelum* has only poor powers of regeneration after injury or mechanical fragmentation. Methods of collecting and culturing are described on p. 76.

2. ANATOMY

a. In a living specimen (the black *Planaria* can be used for external features if necessary), notice that the **body** is flattened dorso-ventrally, that the head is broad, due to the development of two lateral lobes, and that the tail is pointed. Watch the method of locomotion. The animals glide rapidly (by means of the epidermal cilia) with the head, and especially the head lobes, lifted just clear of the ground.

b. On the dorsal side of the head are two black, cup-shaped **eyes** directed forwards and outwards; mid-ventrally the **pharynx** can be seen through the skin, with the mouth opening at its posterior end (the pharynx can protrude through the mouth to a considerable distance); and the small **genital opening** may be visible between the mouth and the tail.

c. In a preparation of *Dendrocoelum* (method of staining on p. 76) it is usually only possible to distinguish the **alimentary canal** by its contents (method of feeding with coloured material on p. 77). The postero-ventral mouth opens forwards into a cavity, the pharynx pouch (an invagination of the ectoderm), in which lies the large muscular pharynx. The long, narrow cavity of the pharynx extends forwards to the middle of the body, and there joins the intestine, which consists of three main branches, one anterior and two posterior. Each of these branches itself gives rise to many smaller branches, all of which

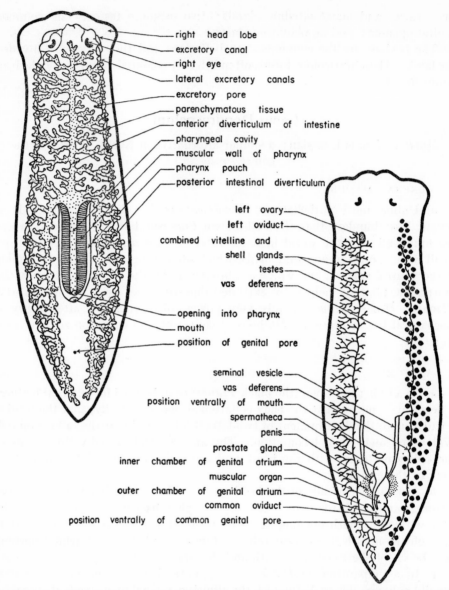

right   head   lobe
excretory   canal
right   eye
lateral   excretory   canals
excretory   pore
parenchymatous   tissue
anterior   diverticulum   of   intestine
pharyngeal   cavity
muscular   wall   of   pharynx
pharynx   pouch
posterior   intestinal   diverticulum

left   ovary
left   oviduct
combined   vitelline   and
shell   glands
testes
vas   deferens

opening   into   pharynx
mouth
position   of   genital   pore

seminal   vesicle
vas   deferens
position   ventrally   of   mouth
spermatheca
penis
prostate   gland
inner   chamber   of   genital   atrium
muscular   organ
outer   chamber   of   genital   atrium
common   oviduct
position   ventrally   of   common   genital   pore

Fig. 23.—*Dendrocoelum.*   A ventral view showing the alimentary canal and excretory system, and, on the right, a dorsal view showing the hermaphrodite reproductive system.   For clarity, most of the left half of the male system and most of the right half of the female system are omitted.

end blindly, and the whole system is embedded in the solid parenchymatous tissue.

d. In well-stained specimens the main vessels of the **excretory system** may occasionally be visible as anastomosing strands passing along the two sides of the animal (they are the longitudinal collecting ducts of the flame-cell system). Anteriorly they join in the region in front of the eyes, but posteriorly they remain separate. At intervals along their lengths short branches lead upwards to the four pairs of dorsal excretory pores (but these are not easily seen).

e. Also visible in well-stained specimens are the organs of the hermaphrodite reproductive system. The single common genital pore opens into the **genital atrium**, which is common to both male and female systems, and which is divided into inner and outer chambers.

f. In the **female reproductive system** the two small ovaries are at the anterior end of the body, just behind the head. From each a long, narrow oviduct passes back to a point behind the common genital pore, and receives on both sides the ducts from numerous glands (which are combined vitelline and shell glands). Posteriorly the two oviducts turn inwards to join and form the common oviduct, which opens into the inner chamber of the genital atrium (here fertilisation takes place and the shells harden).

g. In the **male reproductive system** the numerous small spherical testes lie in a broad zone along the borders of the animal among the vitelline glands. Spermatozoa escape through fine vasa efferentia, which join into one or other of the two longitudinal vasa deferentia (neither of these systems of vasa is easily visible). Each vas deferens opens through a short, inward-directed duct into a seminal vesicle (where the spermatozoa are stored), and the two seminal vesicles themselves open into the anterior end of the thick-walled, pear-shaped penis. Surrounding the penis is a zone of mixed glandular tissue and muscle-fibres, which is called either the prostate gland or the penis bulb. The penis opens into the inner chamber of the genital atrium (but during copulation it passes right through the outer chamber and protrudes from the common genital pore).

h. Spermatozoa introduced from another animal (copulation is reciprocal) are deposited in the **spermatheca**, an organ which is connected by a long duct with the outer chamber of the genital atrium (later the spermatozoa pass up the oviducts and lodge close to the ovaries). Near the base of this duct lies the so-called muscular organ (of doubtful function and not present in *Procotyla*).

i. The only other visible organ is the **brain**, which is situated ventrally in the middle line just behind the eyes. It is connected with the eyes by the two optic nerves, and posteriorly it gives rise to two long lateral nerves (which are not easily seen).

4. CONCLUSION

a. Observing the specimen, review the characteristics of the phylum, of the class, and of the order.

b. Contrast the reproductive system of *Dendrocoelum* with that of *Planocera*.

5. REFERENCES

IIJIMA, I. (1884). " Untersuchungen über den Bau und die Entwicklungsgeschichte der Süsswasser-Dendrocoelen (Tricladen)." *Zeitschrift für wissenschaftliche Zoologie*, Vol. 40, p. 359.

WILHELMI, J. (1909). " Tricladen." *Fauna und Flora des Golfes von Neapel*, Vol. 32.

1.05. Order Temnocephalida

Characteristics: Fresh-water Turbellaria which are ectocommensal, especially on crustaceans; anteriorly with from 2 to 12 tentacles and posteriorly usually with 1, or sometimes 2, suckers; epidermis syncytial, almost devoid of cilia, and covered with a cuticle; with two testes, each of which may be from 2- to 6-lobed, one ovary, and two vitelline glands; and with one common genital opening.

The temnocephalids are tropical and subtropical animals, and they are commonly regarded as a link between the turbellarians and the trematodes. From time to time they have been placed in each of these classes, but recent opinion suggests that they may be most closely related to the rhabdocoels. They are not parasitic and they catch small animals and diatoms from the flow of water caused by their host's movements.

Genus Temnocephala

1. GENERAL ACCOUNT

a. Members of the Temnocephalida are especially common in New Zealand, Australia, and South America, although they also occur in other tropical and subtropical areas. *Temnocephala* attaches itself to its host by its posterior sucker, and, using its anterior tentacles, it can change its position by looping movements. It does not, however, commonly change its host, which is usually a fresh-water crustacean. Food consists of diatoms, rotifers, and other small organisms which are swallowed whole. *Temnocephala* is a cross-fertilising hermaphrodite and development is direct.

2. ANATOMY

a. In a stained preparation (methods of staining on p. 76) notice the **body form**, with five anterior tentacles (tactile), an antero-ventral mouth, and a postero-ventral sucker (for adhesion to the host).

b. Distinguish the **alimentary canal**. The mouth opens through a thick-walled muscular pharynx into a simple lobulated intestine.

c. Lateral to the anterior end of the pharynx are the two dorsal pores of the **excretory system**. Each pore leads into an excretory ampulla (contractile) into which drain the main collecting ducts of the flame-cell system. The excretory ducts which serve the tentacles and the anterior end of the body are also usually visible.

d. In the **male reproductive system** the four testis lobes lie lateral and posterior to the intestine. From each side a vas deferens runs inwards to enter the single seminal vesicle from which a duct passes through the prostate gland into the penis. During copulation the penis can be protruded through the common genital atrium and the common genital pore.

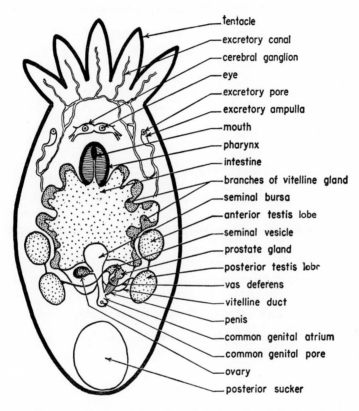

tentacle
excretory canal
cerebral ganglion
eye
excretory pore
excretory ampulla
mouth
pharynx
intestine
branches of vitelline gland
seminal bursa
anterior testis lobe
seminal vesicle
prostate gland
posterior testis lobe
vas deferens
vitelline duct
penis
common genital atrium
common genital pore
ovary
posterior sucker

FIG. 24.—*Temnocephala.* A ventral view of a whole mount.

e. In the **female reproductive system** there is only one ovary, which is connected with the common genital atrium by a single oviduct. Into the oviduct there also open the two vitelline ducts, which lead forwards to the pair of anastomosing yolk glands lying lateral and dorsal to the intestine. At its anterior end the oviduct swells to form the large seminal bursa (which stores sperm received during copulation and also digests any excess of genital products).

f. Anterior to the pharynx distinguish the two lobes of the **cerebral ganglion** and dorsal to them the two simple eyes.

3. CONCLUSION

  a. Observing the specimen, review the characteristics of the phylum, of the class, and of the order.

  b. Compare and contrast the structure of *Temnocephala* with that of the rhabdocoel *Mesostoma.*

2.00. Class **Trematoda**

Characteristics : Parasitic Platyhelminthes which possess suckers, but never form proglottids; epidermis not ciliated, without rhabdites, and covered by a thick cuticle; alimentary canal bifid and mouth anterior.

  The trematodes, or flukes, are ecto- or endo-parasites of the vertebrates. Species occur on the skin, in the mouth and gills (or lungs), in the alimentary canal and digestive glands, in the urinary bladder, and in the blood.

2.10. Subclass **Heterocotylea (Monogenea)**

Characteristics : Trematodes which are almost all ectoparasitic in only one host; with a large posterior sucker stiffened by chitin and often subdivided; two anterior excretory pores; male and female genital pores usually separate; and one or two vaginae.

  The majority of these animals occur on the gills of fish, but some are also found in amphibians and aquatic reptiles.

2.11. Order **Polyopisthocotylea**

Characteristics : Heterocotyleans with the posterior sucker subdivided; with two vaginae; and with a genito-intestinal canal.

Genus **Polystomum**

I. GENERAL ACCOUNT

  a. It is unfortunate that this, the most readily obtainable and almost cosmopolitan genus of the Heterocotylea, is in several respects atypical. The unusual features are that it is endoparasitic in the urinary bladders of frogs, toads, and turtles, that it has a common genital pore, and that cross-fertilisation is usual instead of exceptional.

  b. The eggs are laid in spring, and pass out from the bladder with the urine. The ciliated larvae, which hatch from them, infect tadpoles by attaching themselves to the external gills. Thence they usually travel down the alimentary canal to the bladder, and grow for three years before reaching sexual maturity, but a few remain in the gills, develop rapidly to sexual maturity, fertilise themselves, shed their eggs, and die when the tadpole metamorphoses. For food,

Polystomum breaks the delicate lining epithelia of the gills or the bladder and sucks the blood from the capillaries.

2. EXTERNAL ANATOMY

a. Extract the living *Polystomum* from the bladder of a frog or toad (it is stated that from 5% to 10% of these animals are infected, but there are doubtless great local variations). Watch the sluggish **movements** when one is placed in a dish of a 0·7% aqueous solution of sodium chloride.

b. The **body** is flattened dorso-ventrally, and the posterior end is marked by a disc bearing six large suckers. Antero-ventrally is the mouth, and just behind it is the opening of the common genital pore. Antero-laterally is a pair of prominent bulges on which are the many pore-like openings of the vaginae. Through the skin the main ramifications of the alimentary canal can be distinguished.

c. Flatten the specimen beneath a cover-glass, and through a low-power microscope examine the **posterior disc**. At its posterior end are two large chitinous hooks with curved points and bifurcated bases. Anteriorly and posteriorly on the disc, and in the centre of each sucker, are many smaller chitinous hooks. Each sucker is supported by radiating cuticular bars.

3. INTERNAL ANATOMY

a. Examine a permanent stained preparation of *Polystomum* (for method of preparation see p. 76), and distinguish the course of the **alimentary canal**. The mouth opens into a small muscular pharynx, which leads into the intestine (where digestion takes place). The intestine forks into two main trunks, which pass back laterally and give rise to many short branches. Most of these short branches end blindly, but a few cross the body and anastomose with those of the other side. Posteriorly, the two main trunks unite, and send a single median branch into the sucker region. Anteriorly, a median intestinal process extends forwards beneath the pharynx to open into the mouth (it is possible that the undigested waste is normally voided by this route).

b. The greater part of the **excretory system** is obscured by other organs. However, the terminal portions of the lateral excretory canals are often visible where they pass the bulging vaginal openings (the flame cells pass their excretory products into these lateral canals). Anterior to the vaginal opening, each canal narrows suddenly and joins into an excretory vesicle which opens ventrally through an excretory pore.

c. The single genital pore leads into a small **genital atrium** which is common to both male and female reproductive systems.

d. In the **female reproductive system** the single ovary is prominent on the left side behind the genital pore. It opens backwards into the junction of three ducts: the genito-intestinal canal (function unknown), which passes left to enter the intestine, the median vitelline duct, which bifurcates left and right to form the transverse vitelline ducts, and the oviduct, which turns forwards on the right side. Follow the course of the vitelline ducts. Each transverse duct, on approaching the edge of the body, divides to form an anterior and a posterior vitelline duct, and these branch to reach the vitelline glands (which secrete yolk). Anteriorly the left and right glands are widely separate, but posteriorly they unite across the dorsal side of the body, penetrate between the branches of the intestine, and extend into the posterior disc. The two vaginae arise from the two anterior vitelline ducts, and after swelling greatly, open through the lateral bulges already seen. The vaginal openings are complex, and consist of large numbers of tiny pores, each surrounded by a swollen ring (during copulation spermatozoa from another individual are passed into one or other of these sieve-like openings; thus spermatozoa as well as yolk droplets pass along the transverse and median vitelline ducts to the oviduct, where fertilisation occurs). The oviduct leads forwards into the shell gland (where the fertilised eggs receive shells), and so to the base of the wide and convoluted uterus, which opens forwards into the genital atrium.

e. In the **male reproductive system** the testes extend across the ventral side of the body beneath the vitelline glands, but they do not penetrate into the sucker region. The spermatozoa escape along a single vas deferens, which, passing forwards up the centre of the body to a point anterior to the genital pore, turns back and swells into a small penis. On either side of the penis is diffuse glandular tissue, the so-called prostate gland. The penis opens backwards into the genital atrium.

f. The nervous system, the centre of which is a circumoral ring, is not easily seen, but two pairs of small dark **eye-spots** (persisting from the free-swimming larval stage) may be visible on the dorsal side just behind the level of the mouth.

4. CONCLUSION

a. Observing the specimen, review the characteristics of the phylum, of the class, of the subclass, and of the order.

b. Distinguish those features which may be considered as specialisations to the peculiar mode of life.

5. REFERENCES

ZELLER, E. (1872). " Untersuchungen über die Entwicklung und den Bau des *Polystomum integerrimum* Rud." *Zeitschrift für wissenschaftliche Zoologie*, Vol. 22, p. 1.

ZELLER, E. (1876). " Weiterer Beitrag zur Kenntniss der Polystomen." *Zeitschrift für wissenschaftliche Zoologie*, Vol. 27, p. 238.

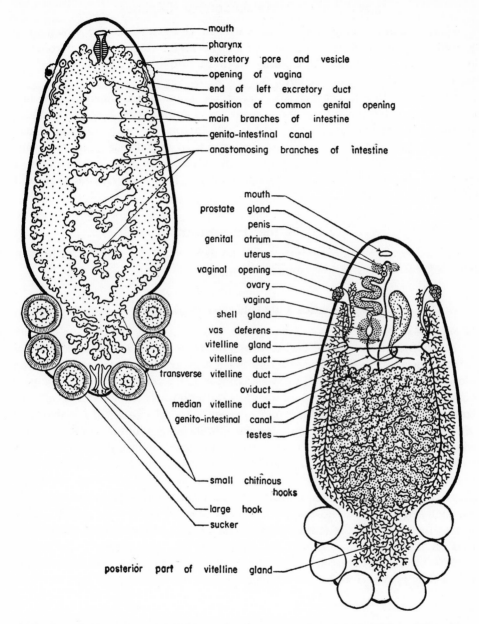

mouth
pharynx
excretory pore and vesicle
opening of vagina
end of left excretory duct
position of common genital opening
main branches of intestine
genito-intestinal canal
anastomosing branches of intestine

mouth
prostate gland
penis
genital atrium
uterus
vaginal opening
ovary
vagina
shell gland
vas deferens
vitelline gland
vitelline duct
transverse vitelline duct
oviduct
median vitelline duct
genito-intestinal canal
testes

small chitinous hooks
large hook
sucker

posterior part of vitelline gland

FIG. 25.—*Polystomum.* A ventral view showing the suckers and hooks, the alimentary canal, and part of the excretory system, and, on the right, a ventral view showing the hermaphrodite reproductive system.

2.20.   Subclass **Malacocotylea (Digenea)**

Characteristics: Trematodes which are all endoparasitic and which as a general rule have two hosts, a mollusc for the larval stages and a vertebrate for the adult; sucker not stiffened by chitin and often anterior; one posterior excretory pore; a common genital pore; and no vagina.

Exceptions to the general rule that these animals are digenetic are not uncommon.   Thus, on the one hand, a species of *Aspidogaster* becomes sexually mature in the mollusc *Anodonta* and has only the one host, while on the other, the genus *Pneumonaeces*, common in the lungs of frogs and toads, has two other hosts, a snail and a dragon-fly larva.   An extreme condition is shown by a species of *Alaria* which has four hosts, a snail, a frog, a small mammal, and finally a cat or weasel.

2.21.   Order **Prosostomata**

Characteristics: Malacocotylea with the mouth anterior; and usually with two suckers, one of which surrounds the mouth.

Genus **Fasciola** (liver fluke)

I.   GENERAL ACCOUNT

a. The adult liver fluke occurs throughout the world in the bile ducts of cattle, especially sheep.   It feeds on duct and liver cells, and perhaps also on blood and bile, and causes the disease known as " liver rot ".   The eggs pass out with the faeces of the host, and if they fall into water, they hatch as ciliated larvae, or miracidia, which bore their way into the soft tissues of a water snail of the genus *Lymnaea*.   There each miracidium changes into a sporocyst larva, which, by parthenogenetic ova, produces redia larvae within itself.   The redia larvae usually migrate to the digestive glands, and there, especially in cold weather (below 10° C.), several generations of redia are produced partheno-genetically.   At higher temperatures the redia produce cercaria larvae, again parthenogenetically.   These leave the snail and encyst on the ground, on a blade of grass, or in the surface film of the water.   If eaten by a sheep, they feed on the intestinal cells as they bore into the body cavity.   They then migrate to the liver, into which they bore by feeding on the liver cells, and in which they grow before finally settling into the bile ducts.

2.   EXTERNAL ANATOMY

a. Dissect open the **bile ducts** of a piece of " flukey liver " (obtainable from slaughter houses), and find the living animals.   Extract them, wash them clean in a 0·7% aqueous solution of sodium chloride, and watch their ineffective movements.

b. Notice that each fluke is flattened dorso-ventrally, and has a leaf-like

shape. The anterior end is marked by a conical projection, on the tip of which the mouth can be seen surrounded by the oral sucker. The second sucker is

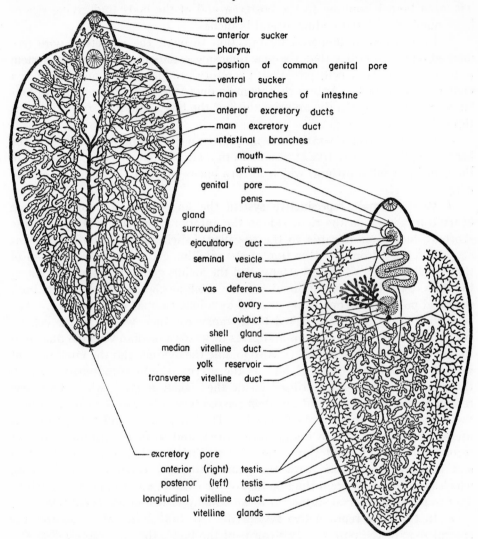

mouth
anterior sucker
pharynx
position of common genital pore
ventral sucker
main branches of intestine
anterior excretory ducts
main excretory duct
intestinal branches

mouth
atrium
genital pore
penis

gland surrounding
ejaculatory duct
seminal vesicle
uterus
vas deferens
ovary
oviduct
shell gland
median vitelline duct
yolk reservoir
transverse vitelline duct

excretory pore
anterior (right) testis
posterior (left) testis
longitudinal vitelline duct
vitelline glands

FIG. 26.—*Fasciola.* A ventral view of the alimentary canal and excretory system, and, on the right, a ventral view of the hermaphrodite reproductive system.

ventral, and between it and the mouth is the tiny common genital pore. At the posterior tip of the body is the single excretory pore.

3. INTERNAL ANATOMY

   a. In a permanent stained preparation of a liver fluke (see method on p. 76) distinguish the ramifications of the **alimentary canal.** The mouth opens

F

through the anterior sucker into a small muscular pharynx (which sucks in the food). This leads into the intestine which branches immediately right and left, each branch running to the posterior end of the body and giving rise to large numbers of blind-ending lateral branches.

b. In a specimen prepared by injection through the excretory pore (see method on p. 77) notice that the anastomosing canals of the **excretory system** (into which the flame cells pass their excretory products) open medially into a main excretory duct. Anteriorly this main duct is formed by the union of four large ducts which drain the anterior third of the body, and posteriorly it opens through the excretory pore.

c. In the stained preparation the most prominent body organs are those of the hermaphrodite reproductive system. Both male and female systems open into the common **genital atrium**, which in turn opens through the common genital pore.

d. In the **female reproductive system** the finger-like lobes of the single ovary can be seen on the right side in the anterior third of the body, and the short oviduct leads inwards to the so-called " shell gland " (the egg shell is actually formed from the secretion of the vitelline glands and the function of the " shell gland ", which is better called the Mehlis gland, is obscure). Along the sides of the body lie two broad zones of vitelline glands (which secrete both shell and yolk), each zone being drained by a longitudinal vitelline duct. The two longitudinal ducts are linked by a transverse duct, which, in the centre, swells to form the yolk reservoir and gives forwards a median vitelline duct into the centre of the " shell gland ". Also joining the oviduct and the vitelline duct in the centre of the " shell gland " is the uterus (spermatozoa enter through the uterus; the ova are fertilised inside the " shell gland ", where they also receive yolk and a shell, and are then passed forwards into the uterus, where the shells become tanned and hardened). The long, coiled, and very prominent uterus leads forwards into the genital atrium, and so to the genital pore. A second opening to the exterior is the Laurer–Stieda canal (of unknown function and possibly homologous with the genito-intestinal canal of *Polystomum*), which rises vertically from the junction of the oviduct and the median vitelline duct to pierce the dorsal surface (it is not usually visible in whole mounts).

e. In the **male reproductive system** the two branching testes occupy the central zone of the posterior two-thirds of the body, the one (morphologically the left) being anterior to the other. Two long vasa deferentia pass forwards to the region of the ventral sucker, where they join into the single seminal vesicle (which stores the spermatozoa). A narrow ejaculatory duct joins the anterior end of the seminal vesicle to the base of the muscular penis, and around the duct is a diffuse accessory gland (the so-called prostate gland). The penis, when retracted, lies inside a sheathing penis sac, and opens into the tiny genital atrium.

f. The **nervous system** is not usually visible, but it mainly consists of a circumoral ring and two lateral nerve-trunks.

4. CONCLUSION

a. Observing the specimens, review the characteristics of the phylum, of the class, of the subclass, and of the order.

b. Also review those features which are characteristic of endoparasites in the alimentary canal.

5. REFERENCES

SOMMER, F. (1880). "Die Anatomie des Leberegels *Distomum hepaticum* L." *Zeitschrift für wissenschaftliche Zoologie*, Vol. 34, p. 539.

THOMAS, A. P. (1883). "The life history of the liver-fluke (*Fasciola hepatica*)." *Quarterly Journal of Microscopical Science*, Vol. 23, p. 99.

Genus **Schistosoma** (**Bilharzia**)

1. GENERAL ACCOUNT

a. The species of *Schistosoma*, which are parasitic as adults in mammals, are remarkable in many respects. Living inside the blood-vessels, they are long and thin, and since their numbers are usually large within the one host, cross-fertilisation is the rule, and the sexes are separate.

b. *S. mansoni* Sambon, which is a human parasite in Africa, the West Indies, and South America, may be taken as typical. It is found in the hepatic portal and intestinal veins, and the eggs, laid in the intestinal capillaries, each contain a miracidium larva. The larva has histolytic glands, the secretion of which, passing through the shell, digests the tissue in front of the egg, and so opens a way into the intestine. Escaping with the faeces and reaching water, the miracidium hatches and bores its way into a water-snail of the genus *Planorbis*. Inside the snail it develops into a sporocyst larva, which, by parthenogenesis, produces a generation of daughter sporocysts. These, again by parthenogenesis, produce a generation of cercariae, which leave the snail, swim free, and penetrate the skin of a man when he is drinking, wading, or bathing. They bore through the skin with great rapidity to reach the capillaries, and so pass to the liver, where they pair.

c. *S. haematobium* Cobb, also a parasite of man, is similar except that the habitat is the blood-vessels of the bladder, and that the eggs escape with the urine.

2. EXTERNAL ANATOMY

a. Through a microscope examine a preparation of *Schistosoma*. In both sexes the anterior end of the **body** is marked by the mouth surrounded by the oral sucker, and the ventral surface by a second sucker close to the anterior end. A tiny excretory pore (through which the products of the flame-cells escape) may also be visible ventrally at the posterior end.

b. Distinguish the **sexes**. The male is shorter, and has a deep ventral gynaecophoral groove (in which the female is permanently held).

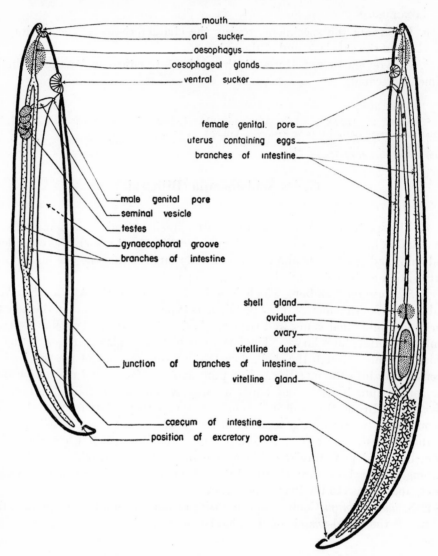

mouth

oral sucker

oesophagus

oesophageal glands

ventral sucker

female genital pore

uterus containing eggs

branches of intestine

male genital pore

seminal vesicle

testes

gynaecophoral groove

branches of intestine

shell gland

oviduct

ovary

vitelline duct

junction of branches of intestine

vitelline gland

caecum of intestine

position of excretory pore

FIG. 27.—*Schistosoma* (*Bilharzia*). Male and female specimens.

3. INTERNAL ANATOMY

a. In both sexes trace the course of the **alimentary canal**. The mouth, passing through the oral sucker, leads into a narrow oesophagus around which are clustered the oesophageal glands. The intestine arises from the posterior end of the oesophagus and bifurcates immediately left and right. Posteriorly, the intestinal branches again unite to form a long, blind-ending caecum.

b. The **male reproductive system** is simple. The group of close-set testes is conspicuous antero-dorsally, and from the anterior end of the group the sperm duct, which is swollen into a seminal vesicle (for the storage of spermatozoa), passes ventrally to open into the anterior end of the gynaecophoral groove.

c. In the **female reproductive system** the ovary is prominent just in front of the posterior junction of the intestinal branches. From it an oviduct emerges posteriorly, and turns forwards to enter the shell-gland, which lies immediately anterior to the ovary. Also entering the shell-gland is the single vitelline duct. Posterior to the ovary this duct divides into two long vitelline ducts which drain the two zones of vitelline glands lying alongside the caecum. From the shell-gland (inside which the eggs are fertilised and receive yolk and shells) a long, thin uterus, usually containing several eggs, runs forwards between the two intestinal branches to open through the female genital pore just behind the ventral sucker.

4. CONCLUSION

a. Observing the specimens, review the characteristics of the phylum, of the class, of the subclass, and of the order.

b. Contrast *Schistosoma* with the more typical *Fasciola*.

5. REFERENCES

FRITZSCH, G. (1888). " Zur Anatomie der *Bilharzia haemotobia* Cobb." *Archiv für mikroskopische Anatomie*, Vol. 31, p. 192.

HEGNER, R., ROOT, F. M., and AUGUSTINE, D. L. (1929). "Animal parasitology." New York.

KHALIL, M. (1924). "On the morphology of *Schistosoma bovis.*" *Journal of Helminthology*, Vol. 2, p. 81.

3.00.   Class **Cestoda**

Characteristics : Endoparasitic Platyhelminthes which lack an alimentary canal.

These are the most highly specialised of the parasitic flatworms, and, with an odd exception (*Archigetes* in the aquatic oligochaet *Tubifex*), they are found as adults in the alimentary canal of the vertebrates, where they absorb the already digested food.

3.10.   Subclass **Merozoa**

Characteristics : Cestodes with a well-developed head, or scolex, which usually bears suckers and hooks; and with a long body formed of a series of asexual buds, called proglottids.

The Merozoa are the tape-worms, and their long bodies are in strong contrast to the short ones of the Monozoa, the other subclass of the Cestoda. These latter are all small parasites of fish, and except for their lack of an alimentary canal, they resemble the Trematoda.

3.11.   Order **Pseudophyllidea**

Characteristics: Scolex usually without hooks, and with only two groove-like suckers, which may be reduced or even absent; no well-marked neck.

The adults of most of these animals occur either in fish or in fish-eating species.

Genus **Diphyllobothrium (Dibothriocephalus)**

1. GENERAL ACCOUNT

a. This genus has a world-wide distribution, the commonest species being *D. latum* Bremser, the broad or fish tape-worm, which is found in such fish-eating mammals as seals and porpoises, cats and dogs, and man.   It fixes itself to the intestine wall by the suckers on the scolex, and absorbs the digested food of its host.   From the back of the scolex a continuous ribbon of proglottids is budded off.   Each proglottid is self-fertilising, and as soon as they are formed the eggs are shed into the intestine to pass out with the faeces.   The posterior proglottids shrink, die, and are detached.   The worm may reach a length of 30 feet, and have 3000 to 4000 proglottids.

b. If the eggs reach water, ciliated onchosphere larvae hatch, swim free, and may be swallowed by copepods (*Cyclops* or *Diaptomus*) when they develop into procercoid larvae.   When an infected copepod is eaten by a fish, the larva bores its way into the muscles or the body-cavity, and grows into a plerocercoid larva about an inch long.   This develops into the adult when the fish is eaten raw by some mammal.

2. EXTERNAL ANATOMY

a. In a preserved specimen of *Diphyllobothrium* identify the tiny **scolex** at the anterior end of the long ribbon of **proglottids.** Notice that the pro-glottids are flattened, the anterior ones being immature and difficult to distinguish, while the others are mature and distinct.   Unless the worm has been broken, those at the extreme posterior end are empty and shrunken.

b. Through a microscope distinguish on the scolex the two groove-like suckers, or **bothria**, which are in line with the flattened sides of the proglottids. Notice that the scolex lacks hooks.

3. INTERNAL ANATOMY

a. In a stained preparation of the anterior end of the worm (method of staining on p. 76), examine the zone, immediately behind the scolex, where

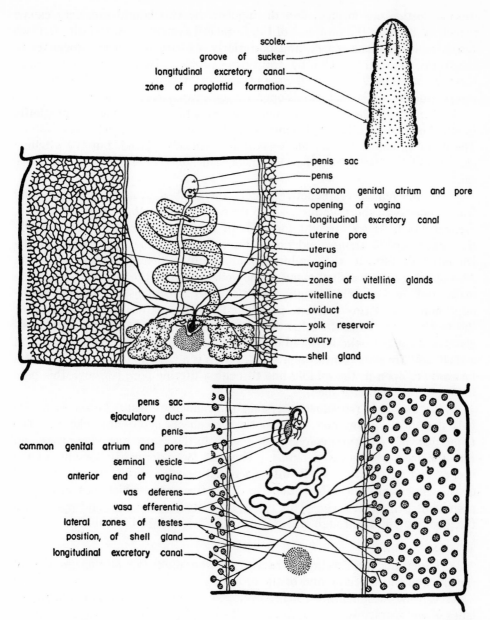

scolex
groove of sucker
longitudinal excretory canal
zone of proglottid formation

penis sac
penis
common genital atrium and pore
opening of vagina
longitudinal excretory canal
uterine pore
uterus
vagina
zones of vitelline glands
vitelline ducts
oviduct
yolk reservoir
ovary
shell gland

penis sac
ejaculatory duct
penis
common genital atrium and pore
seminal vesicle
anterior end of vagina
vas deferens
vasa efferentia
lateral zones of testes
position, of shell gland
longitudinal excretory canal

Fig. 28.—*Diphyllobothrium (Dibothriocephalus)*. A scolex as seen from either the dorsal or the ventral side, a mature proglottid showing the female reproductive system (the male system being omitted), and a mature proglottid showing the male reproductive system (the female system being omitted).

the proglottids are formed, and distinguish the two lateral **excretory canals** (which drain away the products of the flame-cell system). Anteriorly, the two canals join inside the scolex, and posteriorly, as they pass from proglottid to proglottid, they are linked by transverse canals. These transverse canals, however, are not found in all proglottids. At the posterior end of the last proglottid the two lateral canals open through two excretory pores.

b. Almost all the organs visible in a preparation of a **mature proglottid** (method of staining on p. 76) belong to the hermaphrodite reproductive system. The main organs of the female system are centrally placed, but the vitelline glands and the testes together fill the broad zones lateral to the excretory canals.

c. In the **female reproductive system** the bilobed ovary is posterior, and from it emerges a short oviduct. Into the oviduct opens the base of the vagina, a canal which passes straight forwards in the centre line to open anteriorly through a genital atrium and pore (this pore marks the ventral side of the animal). Posteriorly, the combined oviduct and vagina enter the shell-gland. Also opening into the shell-gland is the yolk reservoir, the swollen base of the main vitelline duct, which, right and left, gives anastomosing branches to the large numbers of tiny vitelline glands. These glands lie mainly in two flat sheets, one ventral and the other dorsal. The third duct to open into the shell-gland is the uterus (the fertilised eggs entering the shell-gland receive yolk and a shell, and are passed into the uterus). This is a capacious tube which twists forwards to open in the middle line through a uterine pore (through this pore the eggs are constantly shed).

d. In the **male reproductive system** the numerous testes lie on each side in a flat sheet sandwiched between the two sheets of vitelline glands. The numerous vasa efferentia converge to a point in the centre line where they join into the base of the vas deferens. This vas loops forwards dorsally to the uterus, and anteriorly it swells into a seminal vesicle. From the anterior end of the vesicle an ejaculatory duct leads to the penis, which lies inside the prominent penis sac. The penis itself is directed backwards, and opens into the genital atrium (through which it can be inserted into the vagina).

4. CONCLUSION

a. Observing the specimens, review the characteristics of the phylum, of the class, of the subclass, and of the order.

b. Review those features, here developed to extreme, which are characteristics of endoparasites.

5. REFERENCES

SOMMER, F., and LANDOIS, L. (1872). " Ueber den Bau der geschlechtsreifen Glieder von *Bothriocephalus latus* Bremser." *Zeitschrift für wissenschaftliche Zoologie*, Vol. 22, p. 40.

BAYLIS, H. A. (1929). "A manual of helminthology." London.

3.12. Order **Cyclophyllidea**

Characteristics : Scolex with four cup-shaped suckers, and usually with a crown of hooks set on a rostellum; neck well marked.

Genus **Taenia**

I. GENERAL ACCOUNT

a. Species of this genus occur commonly in cats and dogs, and to a lesser extent in man. The human species are *T. saginata* Goeze and *T. solium* L., the latter being the rarer.

b. Taenia grows by absorbing the already digested food of its host, and produces asexually large numbers of buds, or proglottids. Each proglottid is self-fertilising, but since there is no external uterine pore, the eggs cannot escape. The posterior proglottids, mere bags of eggs, are detached in small groups to pass out with the faeces. When swallowed by a suitable host (the ox for *T. saginata* and the pig for *T. solium*), each egg releases an onchosphere larva, which penetrates into the blood-stream and is carried to a striated muscle. There it develops into a cysticercus larva, or bladder worm, with an inverted scolex. When swallowed by man, the scolex everts and fixes itself into the intestine wall.

2. EXTERNAL ANATOMY

a. In a preserved specimen of *Taenia* distinguish the tiny anterior head, or **scolex**, which is the more prominent because of the narrower neck behind it.

b. Examine the long, flattened ribbon which hangs from the neck, and notice that while the younger **proglottids** are shorter than they are broad, the older ones are much longer. On one edge of each mature proglottid is a small protuberance, through which opens the common genital pore. Notice that these protuberances are irregularly situated on either side.

c. Through a microscope examine the scolex. Identify the four **suckers**, two of which are in line with each of the flat sides of the proglottids, and the anterior elevation, or rostellum, the edges of which bear two rows of outward-pointing hooks (the rostellum and its hooks are lacking in *T. saginata*).

3. INTERNAL ANATOMY

a. In a stained preparation of the anterior end of the worm (method of staining on p. 76) the two lateral **excretory canals** (which drain the flame-cell system) are visible in the narrow neck where the proglottids are budded off. These two canals join into a ring canal within the scolex, and they are also linked by a transverse duct at the posterior end of each proglottid. Examine a stained preparation of a sexually mature proglottid (method of staining on p. 76) to see the transverse duct.

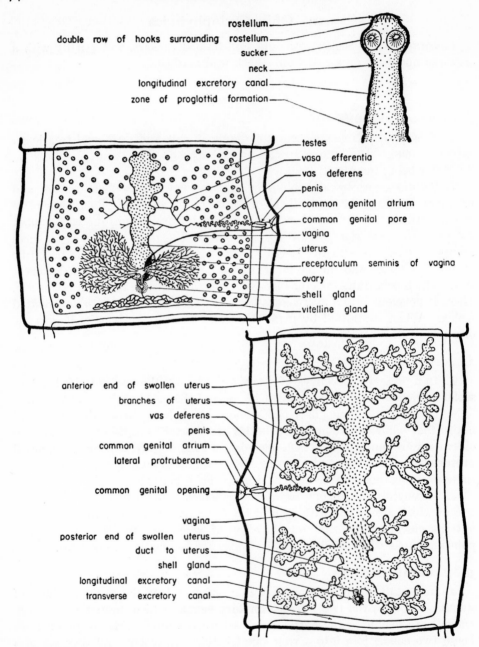

rostellum

double row of hooks surrounding rostellum

sucker

neck

longitudinal excretory canal

zone of proglottid formation

testes

vasa efferentia

vas deferens

penis

common genital atrium

common genital pore

vagina

uterus

receptaculum seminis of vagina

ovary

shell gland

vitelline gland

anterior end of swollen uterus

branches of uterus

vas deferens

penis

common genital atrium

lateral protruberance

common genital opening

vagina

posterior end of swollen uterus

duct to uterus

shell gland

longitudinal excretory canal

transverse excretory canal

FIG. 29.—*Taenia*. A scolex as seen from either the dorsal or the ventral side, a mature proglottid showing the hermaphrodite reproductive system, and an older proglottid showing the uterus distended with fertilised eggs.

b. The only other structures visible in a sexually mature proglottid belong to the hermaphrodite reproductive system.   In the **female reproductive system** the bilobed ovary is posterior.   The single median oviduct, passing back into the shell-gland, receives a duct from the receptaculum seminis (in which spermatozoa are stored).   This chamber is the swollen posterior end of the vagina, a long, thin canal which runs forwards and outwards to enter the common genital atrium.   Also opening into the shell-gland is a single vitelline duct from the posterior vitelline gland (fertilised eggs entering the shell-gland receive yolk and a shell, and are then passed forward into the uterus).   A narrow duct leaves the shell-gland to reach the base of the wide uterus, which, in a young proglottid, is an unbranched tube passing forwards up the centre line and ending blindly.   In older proglottids, the uterus, receiving more and more eggs, branches sideways, while the ovary and the vitelline gland shrink and finally disappear (the lack of an external uterine pore prevents the eggs from escaping until the proglottid bursts, when it is shed with the faeces).

c. The **male reproductive system** is most easily seen in a young proglottid. The small spherical testes form two broad lateral zones which merge anteriorly, but are widely separated posteriorly.   From each testis a filamentous vas efferens (not usually visible) leads towards the centre of the proglottid to join into the single vas deferens.   This highly convoluted duct passes outwards to enter the penis, which in turn opens into the common genital atrium (self-fertilisation is effected when the penis is turned through the atrium into the vagina).   In older proglottids, which are full of fertilised eggs, the testes shrink and disappear.

4. CONCLUSION

a. Observing the specimens, review the characteristics of the phylum, of the class, of the subclass, and of the order.

b. Also review those features, shared with *Diphyllobothrium*, which are characteristic of endoparasites.

5. REFERENCES

SOMMER, F. (1874).   " Ueber den Bau und die Entwickelung der Geschlechtsorgane von *Taenia mediocanellata* (Kuchenmeister) und *Taenia solium* (Linné)."   *Zeitschrift für wissenschaftliche Zoologie*, Vol. 24, p. 449.
CAMERON, T. W. M. (1940).   " The parasites of man in temperate climates."   Toronto.

APPENDIX TO THE PLATYHELMINTHES

I. CULTURE METHODS

a. Only the Turbellaria are easily cultured.   The following methods are given for fresh-water forms, but they may apply equally to the marine polyclad *Planocera* if small living marine worms and crustacea are available for food.

b. The pigmented triclad *Planaria* can be collected from beneath stones in rapid streams, or trapped in slower streams and ponds by using a jar baited with a freshly dead earthworm or small crustacean, or with a piece of raw beef. In aquaria the animals survive for a long time without food, and they live and breed indefinitely if fed with such living oligochaets as *Enchytraeus* or *Tubifex* (culture methods on p. 206) or with any small, freshly dead animals. However, in giving dead food there is danger of fouling the water, and planarians survive only in clean water.

c. In contrast, *Dendrocoelum* is not easily trapped, and is also more difficult to keep. It is best obtained by searching under stones, or by collecting large masses of pond-weeds, allowing them to stand just covered with water in a tub, and catching the animals when they come to the surface for oxygen. In an aquarium they can survive for a long time without food, but if a culture is required, they must be fed on living prey such as the cladoceran *Daphnia* (culture method on p. 331) or small amphipods and isopods.

2. FIXATION METHOD

a. For all common Platyhelminthes the same fixing and staining methods can be used. Place the live flatworm on a slide, and remove the excess water or saline solution. Then gently but firmly compress the worm by placing another slide on top (in the case of a small worm, or of the anterior end of a tape-worm, a piece of broken slide, or even a cover-glass, is heavy enough). Prevent the covering slide from lifting or slipping by binding it with cotton thread, or by the use of clips (bent paper clips will do). Immerse the whole in Bouin's fluid and leave for several hours (overnight for preference). Wash off the excess Bouin's fluid in 70% alcohol, and gently separate the two slides, when the worm usually sticks to one of them. Store the slide with the worm, or the worm alone, in 70% alcohol.

3. STAINING METHODS

a. Two simple stains give good results with the Platyhelminthes. Of these, the easier to use is borax carmine, into which the specimens may be transferred directly from 70% alcohol. Leave in the stain for an hour or two, or overnight, or until the specimens are heavily over-stained. Then, watching carefully through a low-power microscope, wash out the excess stain in a 1% solution of hydrochloric acid in 70% alcohol. When the internal organs show clearly, wash the specimens in normal 70% alcohol, and transfer through 90% alcohol, absolute alcohol, a mixture (half and half) of absolute alcohol and xylol, and xylol (the time in each liquid depends on the thickness of the worm; for a large liver fluke thirty minutes may advisable). When mounting in Canada balsam it is often necessary to support the edges of the cover-glass with small pieces of glass (with a diamond, cut a glass slide transversely into narrow strips).

b. The alternative stain is a haematoxylin solution, such as Delafield's or Mayer's. In this case transfer the worms to the stain via 50% alcohol, 30% alcohol, and water (the time in each depends on the thickness of the worm; twenty minutes may be taken as average). Again over-stain heavily, preferably overnight, wash in water or in 30% alcohol, and take the specimens through 50% alcohol to 70% alcohol. Extract the excess stain as before in acid 70% alcohol, stop the extraction in normal 70% alcohol when the organs are clearly visible, and turn the stain blue in a 1% solution of strong ammonia in 70% alcohol. Transfer to xylol as already described, and mount in Canada balsam.

c. To demonstrate the form of the intestine in such platyhelminthes as *Dendrocoelum* it is necessary to feed with coloured materials. First starve the worms for several days and then feed with a blood clot or with fresh liver which has been broken up in a thick paste of carmine or of powdered carbon. Leave the worms to feed undisturbed for several hours before they are fixed and mounted as described above.

4. INJECTION METHOD FOR EXCRETORY SYSTEM OF *FASCIOLA*

a. Make a suspension of Prussian blue in water, and by means of a fine hypodermic needle, or a fine glass capillary, force it into the excretory pore of a living *Fasciola*. Kill the animal by binding it between two slides and immersing it in 90% alcohol. After several hours detach it from the slides, and transfer it through absolute alcohol, a mixture (half-and-half) of absolute alcohol and xylol, to xylol (thirty minutes in each), and mount it in Canada balsam.

CHAPTER IV

PHYLUM **COELENTERATA** _Cnidaria_

Characteristics : Solitary or colonial, sedentary or free living animals which are fundamentally bilaterally symmetrical but which have become partially or wholly radially symmetrical; ectoderm and endoderm separated by a structureless mesogloea containing parenchymatous cells which are apparently mesodermal; nematocysts present; a single body cavity, the enteron, opening only through the mouth, and often subdivided by mesenteries or elaborated into a system of canals; nervous system a network; and often possessing both hydroid and medusoid forms.

Long considered to be " diploblastic " and the most primitive phylum of the sub-kingdom Metazoa, the modern tendency is to regard the coelenterates as being derived from some early bilaterally symmetrical turbellarian, perhaps one of the Rhabdocoela, which possessed an ectodermal pharynx, a lobed gut, and tentacles containing diverticula of the gut and bearing sagittocysts. On this view the modern coelenterate form is the result of simplification accompanying the adoption of a sessile mode of life. This has led to the development of radial symmetry, the multiplication of tentacles, the conversion of sagittocysts into nematocysts, the partial reduction of the mesoderm, and ultimately the development of the distributive medusoid form.

The coelenterates form a large and highly successful phylum which includes the anemones and corals, a multitude of tiny hydroids and medusoids, and the larger jelly-fish.

1.00. Class **Actinozoa (Anthozoa)**

Characteristics : Solitary or colonial coelenterates which are primitive in possessing a bilaterally symmetrical stomodaeum and in lacking a medusoid form; enteron subdivided by at least eight mesenteries which bear the gonads.

The actinozoans form a large and exclusively marine class. They are almost all sedentary animals, the best known being the anemones and the corals, but some burrow in sand, and one family is pelagic.

1.10. Subclass **Alcyonaria**

Characteristics : Colonial Actinozoa with eight pinnate tentacles; with one ciliated groove, or sulcus, in the stomodaeum; with eight complete mesenteries, each with a retractor muscle on its sulcal side; and with a spicular skeleton in the mesogloea.

1.11. Order **Alcyonacea**

Characteristics : Oral ends of polyps distinct, but bases fused to form a fleshy mass through which the enteron cavities of some polyps extend to the colony base; skeleton not axial, and composed of isolated calcareous spicules.

Genus **Alcyonium** (dead man's fingers)

1. GENERAL ACCOUNT

a. The genus *Alcyonium* is widely distributed, and even cosmopolitan, but it occurs particularly in the temperate and colder seas, where its range extends from the extreme low-tide mark to depths of about 100 fathoms. By asexual budding the colonies grow on rocks, stones, and shells, and the polyps catch and swallow almost any kind of small organism. The sexes of the colonies are separate, and in late autumn and in winter the ova and spermatozoa are shed into the sea, where fertilisation occurs. Each fertilised egg, containing much yolk, develops into a ciliated planula larva which, after swimming for a time, settles and grows into the first polyp of a new colony.

2. ANATOMY

a. The **colony** consists of a lobed and fleshy mass, called the coenenchyme, from which the oral ends of the polyps, called the anthocodiae, project (for protection the anthocodiae can be completely retracted inside the coenenchyme). The thickness of the base of the colony and the height reached depend largely on the type of object on which it is growing. In older colonies there is usually a basal stalk lacking anthocodiae altogether, and always the anthocodiae are more numerous distally.

b. Examine an **anthocodia** through a lens. It is crowned by an oral disc ringed by eight tentacles, each of which bears two lateral rows of pointed pinnules (both tentacles and pinnules contain extensions of the enteron, and their nematocysts are extremely small). Within the tentacle ring is the peristomial membrane, in the centre of which is the slit-like mouth (into that end of the slit directed towards the colony base there opens a ciliated groove, the sulcus, which carries water with oxygen into the enteron).

c. Detach an expanded anthocodia, and examine it through a low-power microscope (details are best seen in a permanent preparation stained by the method given on p. 117). Notice that the body-wall is composed of three layers, the ectoderm, mesogloea, and endoderm, and through the wall distinguish details of the **gastrovascular system.** Identify the stomodaeum (ectoderm lined) which projects downwards from the mouth ; the eight mesenteries which alternate with the tentacle bases, and which join the wall of the stomodaeum to the body-wall ; the eight enteron pouches which lie between these mesenteries, and which extend up into the tentacles ; and the eight rows of long pointed spicules which lie in the mesogloea of the enteron pouches. In the region below the base of the stomodaeum, identify again the eight mesenteries with their edges, now free, thickened into prominent, twisting,

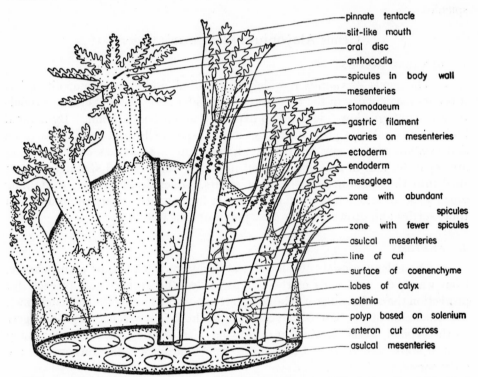

FIG. 30.—*Alcyonium*. On the left the surface of the colony is visible, but on the right and at the base the colony has been cut to show the internal features. On the right the structures visible through the transparent walls of the polyps are also shown.

septal filaments (the filaments of six mesenteries are endodermal and secrete digestive enzymes ; those of the other two, which are on the side away from the sulcus, are ectodermal and heavily flagellated, and they direct the respiratory water current up towards the mouth). All except the two asulcal mesenteries end at the base of the anthocodia.

  d. In the anthocodiae of the colonies taken in autumn or winter many small **gonads** (situated in the endoderm) can be seen attached to the bases of all except the two asulcal mesenteries. In a female colony the ovaries each contain a single spherical ovum, within which yolk droplets can be seen. In a male colony the testes are also seen as small spherical swellings, and they often appear to be hollow.

e. The **coenenchyme** has a ridged surface, and round the base of each anthocodia it projects upwards to form eight small lobes, together called the calyx (when the anthocodia is retracted these lobes close over the hole). In some specimens the coenenchyme may be almost transparent, but the internal structure is best seen by cutting the colony from tip to base. The enteron cavity of each polyp extends inwards and downwards sheathed in a tube of endoderm (the ectoderm does not penetrate, but covers the surface of the coenenchyme), and these endodermal tubes have thin cross connections, the solenia (which are either hollow or solid, and from which new buds arise). Notice the extreme length of each polyp which either extends to the colony base or originates on a solenium.

f. The solidity of the coenenchyme is due to the **spicular mesogloea**. With a sharp razor, cut as thin a transverse section as possible, and examine it through a low-power microscope. There is a densely crowded outer layer of short and irregularly shaped spicules (they are of calcium carbonate, and are in process of formation by the ectodermal cells), while internally there are fewer but longer spicules (these are fully formed, and are similar to those in the sides of the anthocodiae; they may be extracted by the method given for sponges on p. 46). Notice also that within each enteron cavity the two asulcal mesenteries are visible (they extend right to the base of each polyp).

3. CONCLUSION

a. Observing the specimen, review the characteristics of the phylum, of the class, of the subclass, and of the order.

4. REFERENCES

DELAGE, Y., and HÉROUARD, E. (1901). Volume 2 and part 2 of " Traité de zoologie concrète." Paris.

HICKSON, S. J. (1901). *"Alcyonium."* Memoirs of the Liverpool Marine Biology Committee, Vol. 5.

1.12. Order **Gorgonacea**

Characteristics : Alcyonaria with short polyps not extending to the colony base; and with an axial skeleton of calcareous spicules, of spongy horny material, or of both.

A few members of this order form low encrustations, but the great majority develop into tall, plant-like colonies. These latter are the seafans, and they sometimes reach a height of about 10 feet. The great majority are tropical or subtropical, and they occur from shallow water to depths of more than 2000 fathoms.

G

Genus **Gorgonia**

1. GENERAL ACCOUNT

a. The genus *Gorgonia* is widespread in tropical and subtropical seas. The branching colonies, based on rocks, occur most commonly in shallow water, but they are also known from depths of more than 100 fathoms. By asexual budding they grow to heights of several feet. The polyps catch and swallow almost any passing small organism, and for protection they can retract within the coenenchyme. The sexes of the colonies are separate, and in subtropical regions the ova and spermatozoa ripen in spring. Usually the gametes are shed into the sea, but at least one species is ovoviviparous. Each zygote grows into a planula larva which settles to form the first polyp of a new colony.

2. ANATOMY

a. The **colony** forms a tree-like growth, but its branches are in one plane, and in some species they anastomose. The base is enlarged as a holdfast, and from the branches protrude the oral ends, or anthocodiae, of the polyps.

b. Each **anthocodia** ends in an oral disc which is ringed by eight pinnate tentacles. The tentacle bases are packed with long spicules. The membrane inside the tentacle ring is the peristome, and in its centre is the slit-like mouth (into that end of the slit pointing to the colony base there opens the sulcus, a ciliated groove for respiratory water intake). Through the body-wall below the spicule zone can be seen the eight mesenteries, and possibly also the stomodaeum which extends to the base of the anthocodia. Round the base of the anthocodia the coenenchyme projects up into the eight lobes of the calyx (which close over the anthocodia when it is retracted).

c. Examine a small piece of a branch which has been split longitudinally, and distinguish the structure of the **inner part of a polyp**. It consists of an endodermal sac embedded in the common mesogloea of the colony (the ectoderm of the anthocodia continues on to the surface of the coenenchyme). Through the endoderm wall notice the mesenteries, with their free edges twisted and thickened into filaments (six filaments secrete digestive enzymes, but the others, the asulcar pair, are strongly ciliated, and pass the respiratory water current outwards).

d. Within the mesogloea is a network of branching **solenia** (narrow extensions of the enteron cavities which carry water with oxygen and digested food throughout the colony; from their endodermal walls new polyps arise). Towards the centre of the coenenchyme the solenia are especially well developed to form a ring of large longitudinal canals. Within this ring is the axial skeleton, which has a hard cortex and a softer and paler medulla (it does not contain spicules, but is formed of horny gorgonin lightly impregnated with calcium carbonate; it is secreted by an investing epithelium of unknown derivation).

e. The mesogloea is stiffened by large numbers of calcareous **spicules** which can be seen through a lens (they can be extracted by the method given for sponges on p. 46). They are of two main types. Small, irregularly shaped

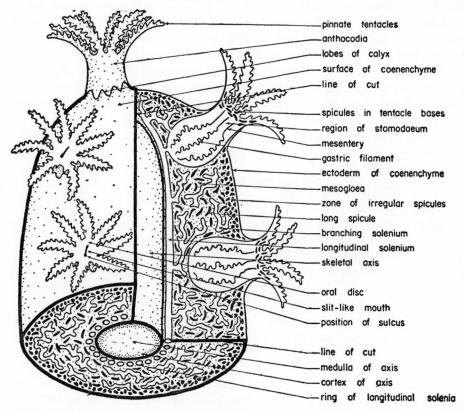

pinnate tentacles
anthocodia
lobes of calyx
surface of coenenchyme
line of cut

spicules in tentacle bases
region of stomodaeum
mesentery
gastric filament
ectoderm of coenenchyme
mesogloea
zone of irregular spicules
long spicule
branching solenium
longitudinal solenium
skeletal axis

oral disc
slit-like mouth
position of sulcus

line of cut
medulla of axis
cortex of axis
ring of longitudinal solenia

FIG. 31.—*Gorgonia.* The apex of one of the branches of a colony. On the left the surface of the branch is shown, but on the right and at the base the branch has been cut to show the internal features. On the right the structures visible through the transparent walls of the polyps are also shown.

spicules are densely packed in a narrow zone just beneath the surface of the coenenchyme, while larger and longer spicules occur more sparsely in the deeper layers.

3. CONCLUSION

a. Observing the specimen, review the characteristics of the phylum, of the class, of the subclass, and of the order.

b. Compare the structures, and particularly the skeletons, of *Gorgonia* and *Alcyonium.*

4. REFERENCE

For the structure of *Gorgonia, Corallium,* and other related genera see:

DELAGE, Y., and HÉROUARD, E. (1901).   Volume 2 and part 2 of " Traité de zoologie concrète."   Paris.

1.13.   Order **Pennatulacea**

Characteristics : Alcyonaria with the main colony stem formed of one long axial polyp ; with both gastrozooids and siphonozooids on the sides of the axial polyp ; and with a skeleton of isolated calcareous spicules.

These animals are the sea pansies and sea pens, and they are usually strongly pigmented and phosphorescent.   They occur as far north as Newfoundland and the North Sea, but are commonest in tropical and subtropical waters. Unlike the other Alcyonaria, they live on sandy or muddy bottoms, and by peristaltic contractions of the peduncle, they can move their position, and even burrow out of sight.

Genus **Pennatula** (sea pen)

1. GENERAL ACCOUNT

a. The genus has a world-wide distribution, and the colonies are found in great numbers on muddy and sandy bottoms in depths of from 20 to below 600 fathoms.   The gastrozooids sieve the passing water for the tiny organisms which serve as food, while the siphonozooids drive a respiratory current through the colony.   The sexes of the colonies are separate, and the gonads are developed in the gastrozooids.   The gametes are shed into the sea, and from each zygote a ciliated planula larva develops.   This settles to the bottom, and elongates greatly as it develops into the axial gastrozooid of a new colony.

2. ANATOMY

a. The **colony** is feather-shaped and bilaterally symmetrical.   It has a central axis divided into a basal peduncle (capable of peristaltic contractions) with an end bulb (to grip the sand), and a distal rachis bearing lateral branches called leaves.   That side of the rachis across which the bases of the two rows of leaves almost touch is termed the metarachidial, or dorsal, side, while that side on which they are widely separated is the prorachidial, or ventral, side.

b. The peduncle and rachis together make up the huge **axial polyp** (which contains an unbranched horny skeletal rod, an enteron completely subdivided by four mesenteries, and mesogloea within which are solenia and long calcareous spicules).   The base of the polyp is blind ending, while in young specimens its distal end protrudes as an anthocodia which has a mouth and a ring of eight pinnate tentacles.   With increasing age, however, both mouth and tentacles degenerate.

c. The fleshy **leaves**, formed from gastrozooids (feeding polyps) with their bases fused together in one plane, are inserted diagonally into the sides of the rachis. On each leaf the free ends of the gastrozooids, the anthocodiae, all face upwards, the oldest being distal and the youngest proximal (new buds arise from the rachis). The oral disc of an anthocodia consists of a peristomial

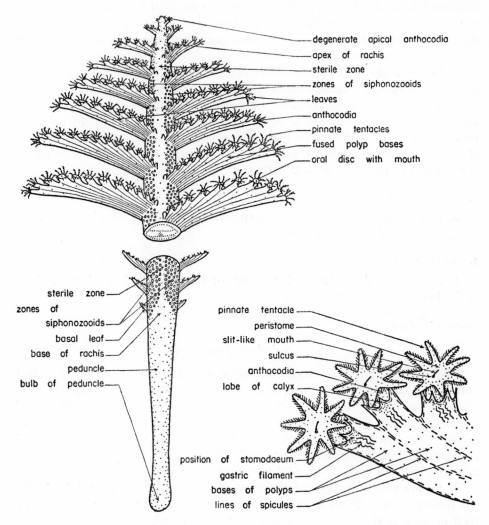

degenerate apical anthocodia
apex of rachis
sterile zone
zones of siphonozooids
leaves
anthocodia
pinnate tentacles
fused polyp bases
oral disc with mouth

sterile zone
zones of
siphonozooids
basal leaf
base of rachis
peduncle
bulb of peduncle

pinnate tentacle
peristome
slit-like mouth
sulcus
anthocodia
lobe of calyx

position of stomodaeum
gastric filament
bases of polyps
lines of spicules

Fig. 32.—*Pennatula*. Above is the distal end of a colony as seen from the metarachidial side, while below is the basal end as seen from the prorachidial side. On the right is the tip of one of the leaves to show the structure of the anthocodiae.

membrane surrounded by a ring of eight pinnate tentacles and with the slit-like mouth in its centre (the sulcal end of the mouth is directed towards the colony base). The base of each anthocodia is surrounded by the eight spinous lobes of the calyx (below which the anthocodia can be retracted for protection).

d. The **internal structure of the leaf** can be seen by holding the colony in front of a light. Within each anthocodia there is an opaque stomodaeum, and below it the twisting gastric filaments are visible in the free edges of the mesenteries. Only the two asulcal mesenteries (ciliated for water passage outwards) extend below the anthocodia. The bases of the gastrozooids (endodermal tubes embedded in a common mesogloea) are separated from each other by prominent rows of long, calcareous spicules.

e. Between the bases of the leaves and extending on to the prorachidial side are two zones of **siphonozooids** (polyps modified for creating a respiratory water current within the solenial tubes). These appear as warty papillae and lack tentacles (they have a highly developed ciliated sulcus, their mesenteries are reduced, and they do not develop gonads). Between the two zones of siphonozooids on both the pro- and meta-rachidial sides are the so-called sterile bands, which do not bear polyps.

3. CONCLUSION

a. Observing the specimen, review the characteristics of the phylum, of the class, of the subclass, and of the order.

4. REFERENCE

For the external and internal structure of *Pennatula* and of other members of the Pennatulacea see :

DELAGE, Y., and HÉROUARD, E. (1901). Volume 2 and part 2 of " Traité de zoologie concrète." Paris.

1.20. Subclass **Zoantharia**

Characteristics : Solitary or colonial Actinozoa with tentacles rarely branched and usually six, a multiple of six, or indefinite in number; commonly with two ciliated stomodaeal grooves, the sulcus and the sulculus; usually with six pairs of primary mesenteries, and often with secondary, tertiary, and even more pairs of mesenteries; with retractor muscle bands facing each other on each pair of mesenteries, but facing away from each other on the two pairs of directive mesenteries; and with skeleton, if present, not spicular.

There are wide variations of structure within this subclass, which is clearly not homogeneous. Some genera are so aberrant that no final agreement on their position in the classification has yet been reached.

1.21. Order **Actiniaria**

Characteristics : Solitary Zoantharia which lack a skeleton and usually possess a basal disc.

In this order are the familiar sea anemones, which occur the world over from between tide-marks to depths of more than 3000 fathoms.

Genus **Actinia** (beadlet anemone)

(A similar alternative genus is *Anemonia*. Also commonly used for dissection are *Taelia*, which is peculiar in having tentacles and mesenteries in multiples of five; *Metridium* (*Actinoloba*), which shows great individual variation in the number and arrangement of the mesenteries; and *Peachia*, in which only the primary mesenteries are fully developed.)

I. GENERAL ACCOUNT

a. The brightly pigmented genus *Actinia* is common in both northern and southern hemispheres. The European and North African species *A. equina* (*mesembryanthemum*) L. occurs in great abundance on rocky shores between the tide-marks. It resists the strongest wave action by the tight grip of the basal disc, which extends into every irregularity of the rock surface, and is further fixed by a cement-like secretion. Food consists of any animals, such as worms and crustaceans, which can be caught by the tentacles and swallowed. Apparently asexual reproduction does not occur. The sexes are separate, and breeding takes place particularly during spring and summer. Spermatozoa escape through the mouths of the males to fertilise the ova, which are retained inside the females until they develop into small anemones. Such viviparity is not general among anemones, even those of the genus *Actinia*, and usually there is a free-swimming planula larva. Individuals of *A. equina* have been known to live for nearly seventy years in aquaria. A culture method is described on p. 116, and a method of killing and preserving on p. 117.

2. EXTERNAL ANATOMY

a. Examine a well-expanded specimen. The **body** is divided into a basal disc (adhesive), a cylindrical column which usually appears wider than it is high, and an oral disc which bears the tentacles and has the mouth in its centre.

b. The **column of the body** is differentiated into a basal, thick-walled scapus and an upper, thin-walled capitulum. The lower edge of the scapus is only vaguely marked off from the basal disc, but its upper edge is sharply defined by a prominent fold, the parapet (in *Metridium* the scapus is pierced by tiny pores, the cinclides). Round the edge of the parapet are twenty-four bright blue tubercles called acrorhagi (covered with nematocysts, and possibly protective). Behind the parapet is a groove, the fosse, the inner side of which is formed by the capitulum.

c. The **tentacles** are neither haphazard nor innumerable, and it may be possible to distinguish the six cycles which, beginning internally, contain six, twelve, twenty-four, forty-eight, and ninety-six tentacles respectively. Break off one of the tentacles, and notice that it contains an extension of the enteron cavity which opens to the exterior through a terminal pore (during sudden contraction the water in the upper part of the enteron cavity can escape through these pores).

d. Between the tentacles and the mouth is a smooth membrane, the peris‧ tome. The **mouth** is elongated in the sagittal plane, and the symmetry is therefore bilateral. Through the mouth the stomodaeum (ectoderm lined) can be seen, and down its two corners pass two deep grooves, the sulcus and the sulculus (they are not distinguishable from each other, and both are strongly ciliated to pass a respiratory current inwards ; in *Peachia* there is only the sulcus, while in *Metridium* either one or two sulcal grooves are common, and individuals with from three to ten have been described).

3.   INTERNAL ANATOMY

a. Cut the specimen in two across the middle of the scapus. Through a lens the **body-wall** and the stomodaeal wall can be seen to contain three layers : the ectoderm, mesogloea (containing parenchymatous cells), and endoderm. The enteron cavity is subdivided by mesenteries, which are folds of the endo- dermal layer of the body-wall and contain mesogloea. Complete mesenteries join the body-wall to the stomodaeum, while incomplete mesenteries do not reach the stomodaeum.

b. There are six pairs of complete **primary mesenteries**, and two of them, the directives, are attached to the stomodaeum at the sulcal and asulcal ends. Of the other four pairs, two are attached to each of the flat sides of the stomo- daeum. Any two similar mesenteries which are situated opposite each other across the stomodaeum are called a couple, and therefore each pair of directive mesenteries is also a couple. On one side of each mesentery is a retractor muscle (endodermal). On each pair of directive mesenteries these muscle- bands face away from each other, but on each of the other pairs they are face to face. The section of enteron cavity enclosed by a pair of mesenteries is called endocoel, while the cavity between any two pairs is exocoel (the tentacles are based directly above these intermesenterial spaces).

c. The six pairs of **secondary mesenteries** (which appear second in develop- ment) arise in the exocoels between the pairs of primary mesenteries, and usually they too are complete. Each of these pairs also encloses an endocoel into which the retractor muscles bulge.

d. The **other mesenteries** are always incomplete. The tertiary mesenteries arise in twelve pairs in the twelve exocoels between the primary and secondary pairs of mesenteries ; the twenty-four pairs of smaller quaternary mesenteries arise later in the twenty-four exocoels thus formed ; and the forty-eight pairs of quinary mesenteries, often mere ridges, develop last of all in the forty- eight exocoels. In all cases the space enclosed by a pair is an endocoel, and into it the muscle-bands protrude (in the smaller mesenteries these bands are too small to be seen).

e. Cut each half of the specimen into two, the line of cut passing from mouth to basal disc in a plane at right angles to that of the stomodaeum. Notice that

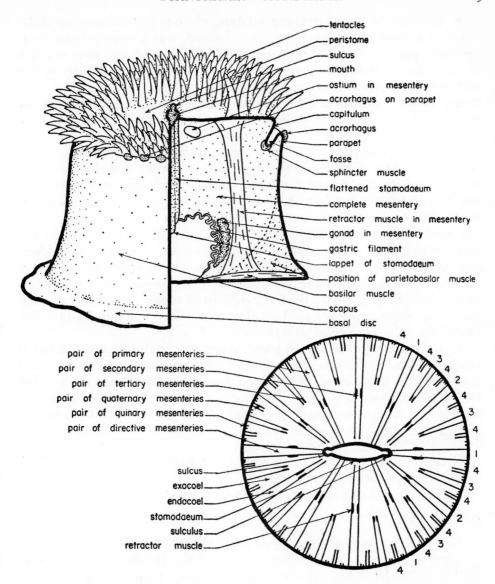

tentacles
peristome
sulcus
mouth
ostium in mesentery
acrorhagus on parapet
capitulum
acrorhagus
parapet
fosse
sphincter muscle
flattened stomodaeum
complete mesentery
retractor muscle in mesentery
gonad in mesentery
gastric filament
lappet of stomodaeum
position of parietobasilar muscle
basilar muscle
scapus
basal disc

pair of primary mesenteries
pair of secondary mesenteries
pair of tertiary mesenteries
pair of quaternary mesenteries
pair of quinary mesenteries
pair of directive mesenteries

sulcus
exocoel
endocoel
stomodaeum
sulculus
retractor muscle

FIG. 33.—*Actinia*. The body surface is visible on the left and the internal structure on the right. Below is a transverse section in the stomodaeal region to show the arrangement of the mesenteries, and on the right the primary, secondary, tertiary, and quaternary pairs of mesenteries are indicated by numbers.

the **stomodaeum** extends almost to the base of the enteron cavity, and that its two lower corners, with the sulcus and sulculus, project downwards as lappets. At the oral end the enteron cavity is continuous from pocket to pocket through ostia in the complete mesenteries.

f. Examine the endodermal **musculature**, which is best seen on one of the complete mesenteries. A retractor muscle-band, which usually lacks clear-cut edges, passes down the centre of one side of the mesentery from oral disc to basal disc; a triangular parietobasilar muscle sheet runs obliquely on the other side of the mesentery from the scapus wall to the basal disc; and a narrow basilar muscle runs along both sides of the mesentery base. A sphincter muscle circles the upper end of the body in the lower wall of the fosse, and can be seen on the cut surface.

g. On the free edges of all the mesenteries are the **gastric filaments.** These are swellings of the mesentery edges which start at the junction of the complete mesenteries with the stomodaeum or of the incomplete mesenteries with the oral disc, and which end just above the mesentery bases. At their two ends the filaments are relatively straight, but in the region between they are highly convoluted. Detach part of the upper end of an incomplete mesentery and mount it on a slide. Notice that the filament is made up of three long ridges, two being lateral (and strongly ciliated for water circulation) and the other forming the edge proper (and containing both nematocysts and cells which secrete digestive enzymes). In the straight basal region of the filaments only the central ridge is present (and in *Metridium* this is continued into a free thread, the acontium, of doubtful function).

h. The **gonads** (sexes are separate) appear as swollen and folded bands in all the larger mesenteries except the directives, which are sterile. They develop only in that part of the mesentery below the stomodaeum and between the gastric filament and the retractor muscle. In females taken in summer and autumn young anemones may be found developing in the enteron cavity.

4. CONCLUSION

a. Observing the specimen, review the characteristics of the phylum, of the class, of the subclass, and of the order.

b. Compare and contrast the structure of *Actinia* with that of *Hydra*.

5. REFERENCE

For the structure of *Actinia* and of many other genera see:

STEPHENSON, T. A. (1928–35). Volumes 1 and 2 of " The British sea anemones." The Ray Society, London.

1.22.   Order **Madreporaria**

Characteristics : Solitary or colonial Zoantharia with a calcareous exoskeleton.

These are the true, or stony, corals, and most of them form large colonies. Although they occur as far north as the Norwegian fjords in Europe and Cape Cod in America, it is in the tropics and subtropics that they flourish to form coral reefs and islands.

Genus **Astrangia**

1. GENERAL ACCOUNT

a. The genus *Astrangia* belongs to the largest family of the madreporites, the Astraeidae, and it is widespread in the Atlantic, Pacific, and Indian Oceans. The northern coral, *A. danae* Agassiz, is found in quiet, shallow water along the American coast from Florida to Cape Cod, and forms small colonies based on stones and shells. The food is stated to consist of such organisms as diatoms, various larvae, and small crustaceans. Although intracellular symbiotic zooxanthellae are generally found in shallow-water corals, they are absent from *Astrangia*. Asexual reproduction takes place by budding from the coenosarc, and results in increased colony size. After sexual reproduction the eggs are retained in the enteron until they develop into ciliated planula larvae. They then emerge, swim free, settle, and grow into the first polyps of new colonies.

2. ANATOMY

a. A **colony** of *Astrangia* consists of a group of small, transparent polyps growing on a calcareous base. In young colonies this base, which is called the corallum, is a thin disc, but in older colonies it may reach a thickness of more than an inch. New polyps bud from the zone round the colony edge.

b. Each **polyp** is based in a calcareous cup, the corallite (into which it is not fully retractible). In a young polyp the corallite is shallow, but in an old one it is deep. Through a lens or binocular microscope examine a fully expanded polyp. It has a glass-like transparency, due mainly to its poorly developed musculature. The body is divided into a basal region of varying length which is hidden inside the corallite (which it secretes), a featureless cylindrical column, and an oral disc which is surrounded by a ring of tentacles and pierced by the oval mouth.

c. There are usually twenty-four **tentacles** (one above each of the twenty-four intermesenterial spaces) arranged in three cycles. The inner cycle is formed of six large primary tentacles, the middle of six large secondary tentacles, and the outer of twelve smaller tertiary tentacles. Occasionally in older polyps a few extra short tentacles may develop as a fourth, but always incomplete, cycle. Each tentacle contains an extension of the enteron, has its surface studded with little wart-like swellings (bearing nematocysts), and terminates in a knob (also bearing nematocysts).

d. Visible through the transparent wall of the column are the **mesenteries** and the stomodaeum which leads into the enteron. There are six pairs of primary mesenteries (which are complete), six pairs of secondary mesenteries (which are incomplete), and occasionally in old polyps there may be a few pairs of tertiary mesenteries. The gastric filaments on the free edges of the mesenteries may also be visible (these filaments consist of a single ciliated ridge containing cells which secrete digestive enzymes).

e. Notice that the upper end of the basal region of the body bears a flange, the **extrathecal zone**, which overflows the edge of the corallite. This is continuous with the thin sheet of living tissue, the coenosarc, which covers (and

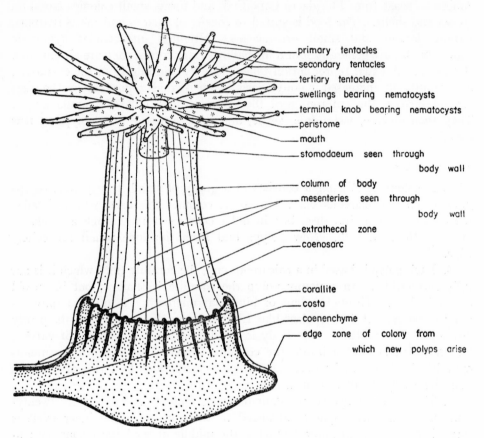

primary tentacles
secondary tentacles
tertiary tentacles
swellings bearing nematocysts
terminal knob bearing nematocysts
peristome
mouth
stomodaeum seen through
body wall
column of body
mesenteries seen through
body wall
extrathecal zone
coenosarc
corallite
costa
coenenchyme
edge zone of colony from
which new polyps arise

FIG. 34.—*Astrangia.* A single polyp on the edge of a colony.

secretes) the coenenchyme, which is the calcareous deposit filling the spaces between the corallites (through the coenosarc the enteron cavities of all the polyps are in communication).

f. Notice that the edges of the **corallite** are ribbed, and that these ribs alternate with the mesenteries. Examine a colony from which the polyps have been removed (by boiling in a strong aqueous solution of potassium hydroxide). The wall of the corallite is called the theca, and its base the basal plate. The ribs, already seen, continue inwards towards the centre of the cup as a series of septa which are sometimes called sclerosepta and which have irregular upper edges. Usually twelve of the septa reach the centre, and are therefore complete (of these six are primary septa laid down beneath the endocoels of the six pairs of primary mesenteries, and six are secondary septa beneath the endocoels of the six pairs of secondary mesenteries). In the spaces between the complete septa are twelve incomplete septa (beneath the twelve exocoels), and in very large corallites a few extra incomplete septa (a partial

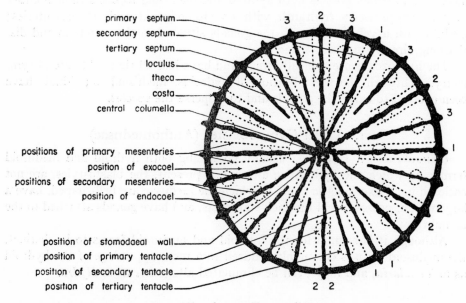

FIG. 35.—*Astrangia*. A corallite as seen from above. The relative positions of the stomodaeum, mesenteries, and tentacles of the polyp are indicated by dotted lines. The numbers above the figure refer to the primary, secondary, and tertiary septa of the corallite, while those below refer to the primary and secondary mesenteries of the polyp.

quaternary cycle) may be present on one side. In the centre of the cup is an irregular pillar, the columella, into which the complete septa join. The depressions between the septa are the loculi. On the outer surface of the corallite is a series of ridges, the costae, one opposite the end of each septum.

3. CONCLUSION

a. Observing the specimens, review the characteristics of the phylum, of the class, of the subclass, and of the order.

b. As far as possible compare the structure of *Astrangia* with that of *Actinia*.

4. REFERENCE

For the structures of many madreporarian genera see:

DELAGE, Y., and HÉROUARD, E. (1901). Volume 2 and part 2 of "Traité de zoologie concrète." Paris.

2.00.   Order Hydrozoa (Hydromedusae)

Characteristics : Solitary or colonial coelenterates which are radially symmetrical and which possess both hydroid and medusoid forms, although either may be suppressed; hydranth with no stomodaeum and no mesenteries; medusa with a velum, and with the gonads situated in the ectoderm and discharging directly into the water.

The hydrozoans are typically small and have lost all signs of bilateral symmetry. Through the specialisation of hydroids, medusoid individuals have been evolved to carry the gonads and to disperse the species.

2.01.   Order Gymnoblastea (Anthomedusae)

Characteristics : Hydrozoa usually possessing both hydroid and medusoid forms; in which the hydranths, and, when present, the blastostyles, are not enclosed in an exoskeleton; and in which the medusae are bell-shaped, have a large velum, possess ocelli but lack statocysts, and have gonads attached to the manubrium.

Although it is normal for the hydroid and medusoid forms to be distinct, the medusoid form is commonly reduced to a mere appendage of the hydroid as in *Tubularia*, and may even be eliminated altogether as in *Hydra*.

Genus Bougainvillea

1. GENERAL ACCOUNT

a. The family Bougainvilliidae is marine, and is widely distributed throughout the world. Its hydroid colonies are found attached to rocks, shells, and seaweeds from the lowest tide mark to depths of more than 50 fathoms. The colonies increase in size by asexual budding, and the many hydranth individuals feed by catching diatoms, various larvae, and tiny crustaceans. The medusae, formed by budding, detach themselves and swim free. They bear the gonads, the sexes are separate, and the gametes are shed into the sea, where fertilisation takes place. The zygote develops into a ciliated planula larva which, after two or three days, settles to the bottom and grows into the first hydranth of a new colony.

2. ANATOMY

a. Examine first a whole **colony** of *Bougainvillea*. It consists of a branching stem system, the hydrocaulus, rising from a filamentous rooting system, the hydrorhiza, which is closely applied to some supporting object.   Mount part of the colony on a slide, add a cover-glass, and through a low-power microscope notice its main features.   The hydrocaulus is thickest near its base, and its branches, especially the smaller ones, are usually alternate.

b. If necessary, stain the specimen by the method given on p. 117.   Each **stem** of the colony is a hollow tube composed of four layers.   The innermost layer is the endoderm, which is visible in optical section; then comes the thin and almost invisible mesogloea (a structureless, jelly-like substance of unknown chemical constitution which contains the cells of the reduced mesoderm); next there is the ectoderm; and the outermost layer is the thin, transparent exo-skeleton (composed of chitin secreted by the ectoderm).   The cavity of the stem is enteron (and is continuous throughout the colony), the endoderm, mesogloea, and ectoderm are together termed the coenosarc, and the exoskeleton is the perisarc.   Notice that the perisarc bears shallow annulations at the base of each branch (to permit bending).

c. Each branch ends in a naked polyp, or **hydranth**, the mouth of which is on the tip of a raised hypostome.   Round the base of the hypostome is a ring of about twelve tentacles, the points of insertion of which are alternately elevated or depressed.   The body of the polyp contains a capacious enteron (in which digestion takes place, and from which some food in fluid form is passed into the enteron of the coenosarc).   Through a high-power microscope distinguish the ectoderm and endoderm, and if possible the mesogloea.   Notice that the tentacles are solid, their cavities being obliterated by unusually large endodermal cells the walls of which give a septate appearance to the core of the tentacle.   The tentacle surface is papillated.   Each papilla contains a battery of nematocysts (stinging mechanisms each lying within a cnidoblast cell), and protruding from its surface are many cnidocils (the triggers of the nematocysts).

d. The **buds** of the colony are of two kinds, and they appear as outgrowths from the coenosarc, particularly in the region just beneath a hydranth.   The first type appears as a long, narrow, blind-ending tube.   Its base secretes an extension of the perisarc, and as development proceeds, its naked tip becomes a new hydranth.   Examine a series of stages of hydranth formation.   The second type of bud is a pear-shaped structure set on a short stalk, or peduncle, and it develops into a medusa.   The early stages appear as hollow evaginations completely invested in perisarc.   As development proceeds, four blunt out-growths appear which contain the radial canals (branches of the enteron), the outgrowths fuse sideways, and their cavities join distally to form a ring canal. Finally the complete medusa is ready to burst the perisarc and swim free. Find a series of stages of medusa formation.

e. In a preparation of **young medusae** notice the deep bell-shape of the umbrella.   The convex upper surface is the exumbrella, and the concave lower surface the subumbrella. From the centre of the subumbrella hangs the manubrium with, on its free end, the mouth surrounded by four oral tentacles (which are richly supplied with nematocysts). The enteron passes upwards to the base of the manubrium, and there divides into the four radial canals, which, in line with the oral tentacles, pass outwards and downwards to the edge of the

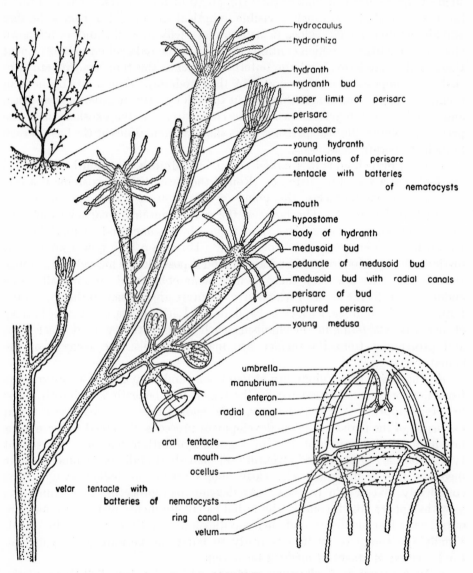

hydrocaulus
hydrorhiza
hydranth
hydranth bud
upper limit of perisarc
perisarc
coenosarc
young hydranth
annulations of perisarc
tentacle with batteries
    of nematocysts
mouth
hypostome
body of hydranth
medusoid bud
peduncle of medusoid bud
medusoid bud with radial canals
perisarc of bud
ruptured perisarc
young medusa

umbrella
manubrium
enteron
radial canal
oral tentacle
mouth
ocellus
velar tentacle with
batteries of nematocysts
ring canal
velum

FIG. 36.—*Bougainvillea*. A whole colony to show the method of branching (upper left), part of the hydrocaulus, and an immature medusa (lower right).

umbrella. There each canal swells as it joins into the ring canal. The edge of the umbrella is inturned to form the velum (a swimming organ containing circular muscle fibres), and beneath the end of each radial canal hang two velar tentacles (bearing batteries of nematocysts). If older medusae are available, notice the greater number of tentacles, and the four gonads on the sides of the manubrium in line with the radial canals.

3. CONCLUSION

a. Observing the specimens, review the characteristics of the phylum, of the class, and of the order.

b. Compare the structure of the hydranth with that of the medusa.

4. REFERENCE

For details of the structure of this and of other members of the Gymnoblastea (Anthomedusae) see :

ALLMAN, G. J. (1871–72). "A monograph of the gymnoblastic or tubularian hydroids." The Ray Society, London.

Genus **Hydra**

1. GENERAL ACCOUNT

a. This is an aberrant genus which is cosmopolitan and common in freshwater ponds and slow streams. It is peculiar in that the medusoid stage is entirely eliminated, and that the hydroid stage, which does not form colonies, reproduces sexually as well as asexually. Consequently a distinct order, the Hydrida, has been created to hold it, but it can equally be considered as a member of the Gymnoblastea which has become specialised for life in fresh water (such specialisation usually involves the elimination of the free-swimming distributive phases which are common features of the life-cycles of sedentary marine animals).

b. The species of *Hydra* feed mostly on small crustaceans, such as *Daphnia* and *Cyclops*, and the endoderm cells of one species, *H. viridis* L., contain symbiotic zoochlorellae. *Hydra* commonly reproduces by asexual budding, but particularly in summer and autumn, each individual may develop testes and ovaries. The zygotes, encased in thick shells, can withstand the drought of summer or the ice of winter. *Hydra* is easily cultured by the method given on p. 116.

2. ANATOMY

a. Place a living *Hydra* in a drop of water on a slide, and watch its **movements**. When left undisturbed for a few moments it expands greatly so that its long body and crown of tentacles are easily visible. Watch the writhing

H

movements of the tentacles.   Disturb the animal and watch the rapid shrinkage of both body and tentacles.

b. Lower a small cover-glass on to the drop of water, which should be large enough to take part of the weight.   When the animal is again extended examine it through a microscope.   The naked **body** is hollow, and its cavity is the enteron (where digestion begins ; it is completed intracellularly).   Within the ring of tentacles the mouth (which can be enormously dilated) opens into the enteron through the oral cone, or hypostome.   At the other end the body narrows, and terminates in the basal disc (the cells of which secrete a sticky mucus for adhesion, and sometimes also secrete gas which, caught as a bubble in the mucus, can lift *Hydra* to the surface).

c. Examine the structure of the **body-wall**.   In optical section it can be seen to consist of an outer layer of ectoderm, a very thin sheet of mesogloea (a structureless jelly with enclosed cells), and an inner layer of endoderm (which in *H. fusca* L. is brown, and in *H. viridis* L. is green, due to symbiotic zoo-chlorellae).

d. Examine the **tentacles** in detail (they are capable of enormous extension to many times the length of the body).   There are usually from six to eight of them, and each contains an extension of the enteron.   Through a high-power microscope they can be seen to have the same wall structure as the body, except that they are thickly covered with tubercles.   Each tubercle contains a battery of nematocysts (stinging mechanisms), which are visible as clear oval capsules. Each nematocyst is enclosed in a cell, the cnidoblast, the outer end of which protrudes from the surface of the ectoderm as a fine trigger, the cnidocil (when this is irritated, the nematocyst everts itself explosively as a long, thin thread which, acting like a hypodermic needle, injects a paralysing fluid).

e. Add a small drop of 1% acetic acid to the side of the preparation.   As it diffuses beneath the cover-glass the animal contracts.   Watch the tentacles through a high-power microscope to see the discharge of the **nematocysts** from the irritated cnidoblasts.   Four kinds of nematocysts can now be distinguished. The largest has a long, straight thread, and on its thickened base it bears three large and many small backward-pointing barbs ; the second, also large, tends to coil, and bears many minute spirally arranged barbs ; the third is small and has a straight thread lacking any barbs ; and the fourth is also small and without barbs, but has a tightly coiled thread (of these the first and the fourth are used only for food capture ; the second for defence ; and the third for gripping the substratum during locomotion).

f. Observe individuals bearing **buds**.   Notice that these are usually based about a third of the way up the body of the parent.   They are formed as hollow outgrowths of the body-wall, and before they are detached their free ends develop tentacles and a mouth.

g. In other individuals (particularly common in summer and autumn)

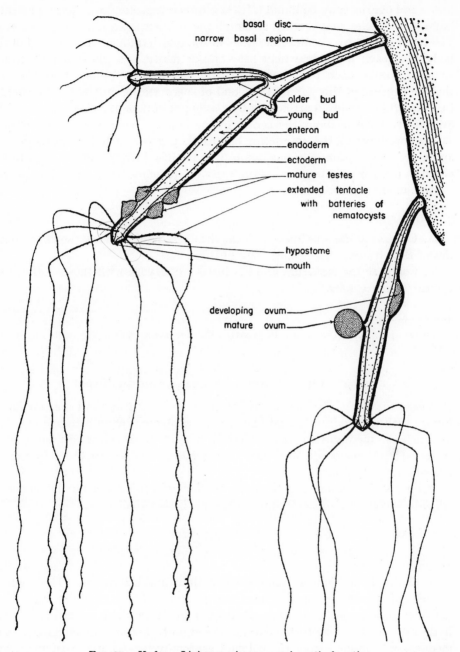

Fig. 37.—*Hydra*. Living specimens seen in optical section.

testes and ovaries may be found (*Hydra viridis* is a protandrous hermaphrodite, but other species may be either simultaneous hermaphrodites or dioecious). The **testes** are seen as conical swellings in the ectoderm near the oral end of the body, and each individual may bear one or many, according to the species. In most species each testis, when mature, has a tiny papilla at its free end (by the rupture of this papilla the cloud of spermatozoa bursts into the water; this can often be caused artificially by gentle pressure on the cover-glass). The **ovaries** are formed about the centre of the body. When young they appear as low swellings in the ectoderm, but as they grow each becomes spherical and is seen to contain only one ovum (it is fertilised while still attached to the parent; it then secretes a resistant capsule, detaches itself, and sinks to the bottom of the pond).

3.   CONCLUSION

a. Observing the specimens and the drawings made, review the characteristics of the phylum, of the class, and of the order.

b. Compare the structure and life-history of *Hydra* with those of the more typical *Bougainvillea*.

4.   REFERENCE

DELAGE, Y., and HÉROUARD, E. (1901).   Volume 2 and part 2 of " Traité de zoologie concrète."   Paris.

2.02.   Order **Calyptoblastea** (**Leptomedusae**)

Characteristics : Hydrozoa usually possessing both hydroid and medusoid forms; with the hydranths and blastostyles protected by an exoskeleton; and in which the medusae are saucer-shaped, have a small velum, usually possess statocysts but no ocelli, and have the gonads attached to the subumbrella beneath the radial canals.

As in the Gymnoblastea, there is a tendency in this order for the medusoid stage to become a degenerate appendage of the hydroid stage.

Genus **Obelia**

I.   GENERAL ACCOUNT

a. Obelia is a common and cosmopolitan marine genus. The hydroid colonies of the various species, attached to seaweeds, shells, rocks, etc., occur between tide-marks and down to depths of more than 50 fathoms. The hydranths feed by capturing larvae and minute animals of all kinds. The medusae are budded from the colonies especially in spring and summer, and they swim freely in the surface waters. The sexes are separate, and fertilisation is external. The zygote develops into an elongated, ciliated, planula larva which, after swimming for a short time, settles to the bottom, fixes itself by one end, and grows into the first hydranth of a new hydroid colony.

2. ANATOMY

a. Examine a whole **colony** attached, perhaps, to a frond of seaweed. The upright-branching stems form the hydrocaulus, and they spring from a fila-mentous rooting system, the hydrorhiza. Through a lens examine the hydro-caulus and notice its cymose system of branching.

b. If necessary, make a stained preparation of part of the hydrocaulus (method on p. 117). Each **stem** of the colony is a tube, and its cavity is the enteron (through which digested food is distributed in solution). The wall of the tube is formed internally by the endoderm (visible in optical section), medially by the mesogloea (a very thin layer of structureless jelly with enclosed cells), and externally by the ectoderm. These three layers together are the coenosarc, and surrounding them is the chitinous exoskeleton, the perisarc (secreted by the ectoderm). At the base of each branch and at intervals along the main stem the perisarc is annulated (to allow bending).

c. Each branch of the hydrocaulus terminates in a **hydranth** (a feeding individual) protected by a cup-shaped exoskeleton, the hydrotheca, which is continuous with the perisarc and which near its base bears an inward-directed flange, the basal plate. At the free end of the hydranth is a ring of about twenty-four tentacles inserted round the base of a prominent hypostome through the tip of which opens the mouth (capable of enormous distension). In optical section, it can be seen that the body of the hydranth contains an enteron cavity (in which digestion begins, and which is continuous with the enteron of the coenosarc) and that its wall consists of a thick inner endoderm, thin mesogloea, and outer ectoderm. Examine stages in the formation of new hydranths.

d. The enteron does not extend into the **tentacles**, each of which is filled by a single row of large endodermal cells. The walls separating these cells give the tentacle core a septate appearance. The tentacle surface bears large numbers of hair-like projections arranged in circular bands set at regular intervals. Each projection is a cnidocil (the trigger-like outer end of a cnido-blast cell which contains the stinging nematocyst).

e. In the older parts of the colony, blastostyles grow from the bases of the hydranth-bearing branches. Each **blastostyle** is a hollow extension of the coenosarc (and is regarded as a modified hydranth which lacks tentacles and a mouth and which buds medusae from its surface). It is enclosed in a flask-shaped extension of the perisarc termed the gonotheca. The column of the blastostyle is thin, but at its top it swells to form a disc (which secretes the gonotheca and which plugs its opening). Along the sides of the blastostyle are the medusoid buds, the youngest basal and the oldest distal, and these are

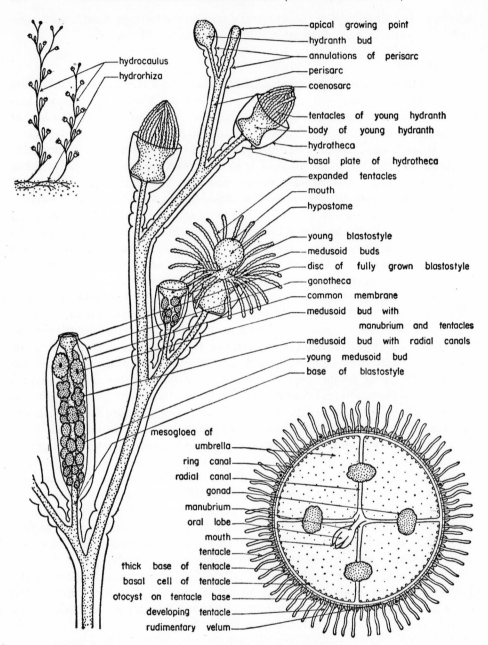

apical   growing   point
hydranth   bud
annulations   of   perisarc
perisarc
coenosarc
tentacles   of   young   hydranth
body   of   young   hydranth
hydrotheca
basal   plate   of   hydrotheca
expanded   tentacles
mouth
hypostome
young   blastostyle
medusoid   buds
disc   of   fully   grown   blastostyle
gonotheca
common   membrane
medusoid   bud   with
        manubrium   and   tentacles
medusoid   bud   with   radial   canals
young   medusoid   bud
base   of   blastostyle

hydrocaulus
hydrorhiza

mesogloea of
umbrella
ring   canal
radial   canal
gonad
manubrium
oral   lobe
mouth
tentacle
thick   base   of   tentacle
basal   cell   of   tentacle
otocyst   on   tentacle   base
developing   tentacle
rudimentary   velum

FIG. 38—*Obelia.*   A colony showing the method of branching (upper left), part of the hydrocaulus, and a medusa (lower right).

sheathed in a thin layer of ectoderm, the common membrane (early in development this membrane delaminates from the ectoderm of the blastostyle).
Examine stages in blastostyle development (the growing region is at the
base).

f. Examine a series of stages of **medusa formation**. The youngest medusoid
bud is a simple hollow outgrowth of the blastostyle; an older bud develops
four broad lobes, each of which contains a radial canal (an extension of the
enteron); later the four lobes fuse sideways, their canals join centrifugally to
form a ring canal, and at the same time a central swelling, the manubrium
appears; and in the oldest buds many blunt tentacles are visible (the medusae
finally escape when the common membrane ruptures, and when the blastostyle
disc shrinks to leave the top of the gonotheca open).

g. Examine a preparation of an *Obelia* **medusa**. It has the form of an
umbrella fringed with tentacles, the convex upper surface being the exumbrella
and the concave lower surface the subumbrella. The mouth opens through the
end of a manubrium which hangs from the centre of the subumbrella. The
edges of the mouth are enlarged as oral lobes (which contain large numbers of
nematocysts), and the manubrium contains the enteron cavity (in which digestion begins). From the upper end of the manubrium the enteron extends into
the umbrella through the four radial canals, which at their outer ends join into
the ring canal circling the edge of the umbrella (these canals are ciliated and carry
food particles in the process of digestion). Between the canals the substance of
the umbrella is largely mesogloea, and round the edge of the subumbrella is a
rudimentary velum (a muscular swimming organ which aborts almost completely during development). The four gonads (sexes are separate) lie in the
subumbrella ectoderm beneath the radial canals.

h. Through a high-power microscope the **tentacles of the medusa** can be
seen to have a similar structure to those of the hydranth. The row of large
endodermal cells is clearly visible, and the basal cell is so large that it extends
from the tentacle, across the ring canal, and into the mesogloea of the umbrella.
Distinguish stages in the growth of tentacles (they increase in number throughout
life). The base of each fully grown tentacle is greatly thickened to form a
tentacular bulb (digestive ferments are secreted from its endoderm, and great
numbers of nematocysts are formed in its ectoderm). Eight otocysts, two in
each interradial region, are attached to the subumbrella side of eight of the
thickened tentacular bulbs (they are hollow balance organs containing calcareous otoliths, but they are usually difficult to see in prepared specimens).

3. CONCLUSION

a. Observing the specimens, review the characteristics of the phylum, of the
class, and of the order.

b. Compare and contrast the structure of *Obelia* with that of *Bougainvillea.*

4. REFERENCE

For the structure of this and of other Calyptobiastea (Leptomedusae) see:

DELAGE, Y., and HÉROUARD, E. (1901).   Volume 2 and part 2 of " Traité de zoologie concrète."   Paris.

2.03.   Order **Trachylina**

Characteristics : Hydrozoa in which the hydroid generation is either reduced or eliminated; hydranth, if present, is a minute polyp and, if absent, the medusa develops directly from the fertilised egg.

The group is divisible into two suborders: the Trachomedusae (with umbrella margin smooth, with sense organs enclosed in pits or vesicles, and with gonads beneath the radial canals) and the Narcomedusae (with umbrella margin lobed, with sense organs naked, and with gonads on the wall of the central enteron chamber).   The members of both suborders are widely distributed in the warmer seas, species occurring at the surface and at depths down to more than 1000 fathoms.   A few species are also known in large inland rivers and lakes, particularly in Africa and North America.

Genus **Gonionemus**

1. GENERAL ACCOUNT

a. This genus is widespread in the warmer oceans, but the best-known species is *G. murbachi* Mayer, which occurs along the east coast of North America, and which is particularly abundant at Woods Hole, Massachusetts.   The hydroid generation is represented by a tiny solitary polyp which feeds on diatoms, protozoans, and other small animals.   It multiplies by budding, and in spring gives rise to tiny medusae (apparently also by budding).   The medusae feed by swimming to the surface, turning upside down, and sinking with snaring tentacles outspread.   In this way they catch small swimming animals such as crustaceans, but when the sun is bright they lie upside down at the bottom and feed like hydranths.   The gametes are shed in the evenings of July, August, and September, and the zygotes develop into ciliated planula larvae which settle, grow into hydranths, and in this form pass the winter.

2. ANATOMY

a. If a preparation of the **hydroid stage** is available, notice its close resemblance to *Hydra*.   The tiny body has a basal disc (by which it attaches itself), a ring of four long tentacles, and a conical hypostome on which opens the cross-shaped mouth.   In optical section distinguish the enteron (where digestion begins); the division of the body-wall into outer ectoderm, thin mesogloea, and inner endoderm; the upward projection of the endoderm of the basal disc to form a peduncle; and the solid tentacles. Nematocysts

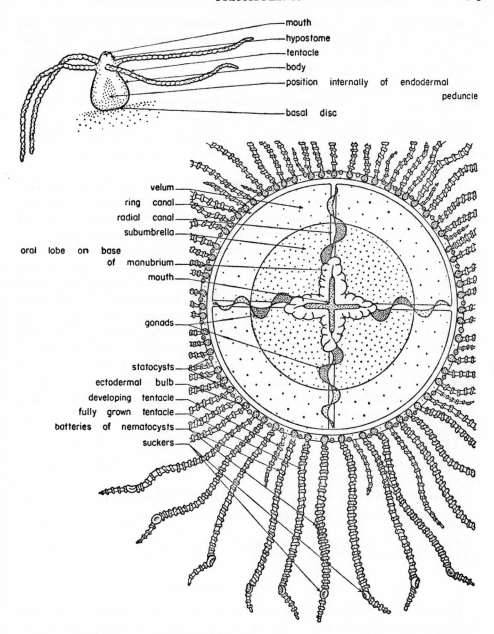

mouth
hypostome
tentacle
body
position internally of endodermal peduncle
basal disc

velum
ring canal
radial canal
subumbrella
oral lobe on base of manubrium
mouth
gonads
statocysts
ectodermal bulb
developing tentacle
fully grown tentacle
batteries of nematocysts
suckers

FIG. 23.—*Gonionemus.* The hydroid (above), and the medusa as seen from the oral side.

occur all over the tentacles and body, but not the basal disc. A bud (which does not develop mouth or tentacles until it separates) may be attached to the side of the body.

b. Through a lens examine a mature **medusa** which is transparent and bowl-shaped.   The manubrium bearing the mouth hangs from the centre of the subumbrella.   The mouth is cross-shaped, and its edges are prolonged into four frilled oral lobes (which grip the food passed in by the tentacles).   The enteron (where digestion begins) occupies the centre of the manubrium, extends through the thick mesogloea of the umbrella as four radial canals (in line with the four oral lobes), circles the edge of the umbrella as the ring canal, and penetrates to the ends of the tentacles.   Notice the strongly developed velum (swimming organ containing circular muscle fibres) extending inwards as a circular shelf from the edge of the subumbrella.

c. The four yellowish or brownish **gonads** appear as folded ribbons embedded in the surface ectoderm of the subumbrella beneath the radial canals (sexes are separate; the ovaries appear more granular and the testes more translucent; and the gametes are shed into the subumbrella space by rupture of the ectoderm).

d. Through a binocular microscope or a strong lens examine the edge of the umbrella.   Each **tentacle** is hollow, is based on the exumbrella surface just above the umbrella edge, and is connected with the edge itself by a solid ectodermal bulb (within which cnidoblast cells are formed to migrate out on to the tentacle).   Large numbers of cnidoblast cells, containing the nematocysts, are based in the ectodermal swellings which circle the tentacles, and through a high-power microscope their cnidocils can be seen protruding from the surface. On one side of the tentacle and towards its tip is a prominent sucker (by which the medusa anchors).   On the umbrella edge in many of the spaces between the ectodermal bulbs there are situated the statocysts (balance organs), each consisting of a hollow vesicle containing a calcareous otolith.

3.   CONCLUSION

a. Observing the specimens, review the characteristics of the phylum, of the class, and of the order.

b. Compare the medusa of *Gonionemus* with those of *Bougainvillea* and *Obelia*.

4.   REFERENCE

PERKINS, H. F. (1902).   "The development of *Gonionema murbachii.*"   *Proceedings of the Academy of Natural Sciences of Philadelphia*, Vol. 54, p. 750.

2.04.   Order **Siphonophora**

Characteristics : Pelagic Hydrozoa which form colonies composed of many highly polymorphic individuals; which never form complete medusae and rarely free those which are formed; and which move either by the efforts of one or more swimming bells or by the pressure of the sea and wind on a float.

The animals exhibit the highest degree of polymorphism to be found in the animal kingdom.   Both hydranths and medusae are extremely modified and are reduced to mere appendages of the colony, which, particularly in the more specialised species, appears and acts like an individual. Modern opinion suggests that their closest affinities are with gymnoblastic hydroids, especially of the type of *Tubularia*.

Genus **Physalia** (Portuguese man-of-war)

I. GENERAL ACCOUNT

a. The species of *Physalia* occur abundantly in all tropical and subtropical oceans. Each colony floats with its large gas-filled pneumatophore above the water surface, and so is blown along by the wind. When necessary the gas can be forced out through a tiny pore, and the colony sinks, to rise again by the secretion of more gas. The tentacles are capable of great extension, and those of large specimens may hang down to a depth of more than 40 feet. The poison in the nematocysts is so virulent that fish as large as mackerel can be caught as food. Asexual reproduction results in increasing colony size and in the production of medusoid buds which bear the gonads. *Physalia* is hermaphrodite, but each medusoid bud is either male or female. The female medusae are set free, but the males remain attached to the blastostyles. The eggs are shed into the sea, where they are fertilised and develop through planula larvae into new colonies.

2. ANATOMY

a. The most obvious feature is the enormous bladder-like **pneumatophore** (hydrostatic), which is elongated and surmounted by a prominent crest (it represents the greatly enlarged invagination of the base of the larva, and is therefore lined with ectoderm which is partly modified as a gas gland and elsewhere covered by a thin chitinous substance; the gas is about 10% oxygen and 90% nitrogen). Beneath hangs the rest of the colony, the individuals of which extend to one end of the pneumatophore (which, although morphologically apical, is often for convenience termed anterior), but not to the other (morphologically basal, but termed posterior). At the anterior end there opens the tiny apical pore (which is the opening of the invagination, and through which the gas can be released), and in the walls longitudinal muscle bands are visible (the contraction of these forces out the gas). Notice that, if the crest of the pneumatophore is regarded as dorsal, the individuals of the hanging colony are attached along a latero-ventral line either to the left or right according to individual variation. Internally the gas gland extends along the other latero-ventral line, and it can be seen as a thicker area when the bladder is held to the light.

b. Beneath the pneumatophore the pendant colony consists of a single row of **cormidia**, each of which is a large group of modified individuals which share a single, or apparently double, base. The oldest and largest cormidium is posterior, and the youngest and smallest is anterior.

c. Examine a large cormidium, and notice that its most prominent component part is a mouthless individual, a **dactylozooid**, which bears basally a single enormous tentacle (for food capture). This tentacle tends to hang down the outer side of the cormidium. It has a relatively straight axis to which is attached a narrow, transversely ribbed, and twisting ribbon (this ribbon

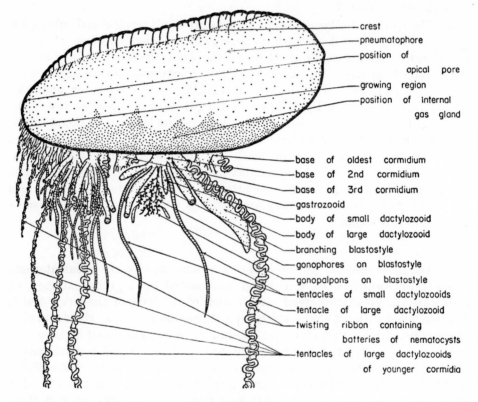

FIG. 40.—*Physalia.* The external features of a colony seen from the side on which the gas gland is situated. For clarity, the first and third cormidia are omitted, and the second cormidium is opened out and greatly simplified.

contains an extension of the enteron cavity, and is armed with batteries of large nematocysts).

d. Turn aside the large dactylozooid, and examine the rest of the cormidium, which is composed of many individuals of several types. The first type is a **small dactylozooid** similar in all but size to the large one. The second is a **gastrozooid** which lacks tentacles and is easily distinguished by its terminal mouth (the prey is drawn up to these gastrozooids which, being too small to swallow it, apply their mouths to its surface; their lips spread out, touch, and so form a cavity within which digestion begins). The third type is the branching moss-like blastostyle, sometimes termed a gonodendron (and best considered as a group of individuals).

e. Distinguish the details of a **blastostyle**. Its branches end either in small leaf-like plates called gonopalpons (apparently tiny mouthless individuals) or in considerably larger structures called gelatinous zooids (also apparently mouthless individuals). Its stalks bear the tiny, berry-like gonophores (which are degenerate medusae). The female gonophores are larger (they develop four radial canals and a velum, but lack a mouth and sense organs; when liberated they swim for only a short time, shed their ova, and die).

3. CONCLUSION

a. Observing the specimen, review the characteristics of the phylum, of the class, and of the order.

b. Compare the structure of *Physalia* with that of other colonial Hydrozoa such as *Obelia.*

4. REFERENCE

For the structure of this and of other Siphonophora see:

DELAGE, Y., and HÉROUARD, E. (1901). Volume 2 and part 2 of " Traité de zoologie concrète." Paris.

3.00. Class **Scyphomedusae (Scyphozoa)**

Characteristics : Solitary coelenterates in which the hydroid form has been either reduced to a scyphistoma with four mesenteries and no stomodaeum, or eliminated; medusa without a velum (but sometimes with a velarium as a substitute), and with gonads situated in the endoderm and discharging into the enteron.

The Scyphomedusae clearly originated through a specialisation of the medusoid form of some hydrozoan-like ancestor. The group includes the larger jelly-fish which occur abundantly in all the oceans.

3.01. Order **Stauromedusae**

Characteristics : Sedentary Scyphomedusae which resemble a scyphistoma in that they possess an aboral stalk and four mesenteries, and lack tentaculocysts.

This is a small and aberrant order which is often regarded as having arisen by the persistence and abnormal enlargement of the scyphistoma stage and by the suppression of the medusoid stage.

Genus **Haliclystus**

1. GENERAL ACCOUNT

a. Haliclystus occurs in shallow coastal waters attached particularly to the seaweeds *Laminaria* and *Zostera,* and less commonly to other seaweeds and to such objects as rocks and shells.   It is found most abundantly in the colder seas bordering the arctic and the antarctic.

b. Like the other Stauromedusae, *Haliclystus* cannot swim, but it can move about slowly by gliding on its aboral adhesive disc.   Asexual reproduction does not occur in the adult, but sexual reproduction is stated to continue through all seasons.   The sexes are separate, the gametes are shed into the enteron, they escape through the mouth, particularly at night, and fertilisation is external in the sea-water.   The resulting planulae settle to the bottom, crawl to a suitable site, develop a mouth and feed, and bud off other larvae by means of stolon development.   Thus the young forms occur in groups, and they act together in subduing relatively large animals, such as nematodes, rotifers, and copepods.

2.   ANATOMY

a. The **body** is trumpet-shaped, and is widest at the oral end, which bears a ring of modified tentacles.   Aborally it is based on a stalk, or peduncle, which ends in an adhesive disc.

b. Examine the membrane, the **subumbrella**, which lies within the ring of tentacles.   Its centre is pierced by the mouth, which, opening through a small quadrangular manubrium, is four-cornered and bordered by four small oral lobes.   Its surface is depressed to form four deep, blind-ending, subumbral pits (function unknown), which extend to the base of the body but not into the peduncle (they pass down within the four mesenteries which divide the enteron into four pockets).

c. The margin, where the subumbrella meets the exumbrella, is drawn out into eight lobes which are adradial in position.   The end of each lobe is swollen, and is covered with short **secondary tentacles** which also have swollen ends (bearing sting cells).   In the depressions between the adradial lobes (i.e. in the per- and inter-radii) are eight **marginal anchors**, also termed rhopalioid bodies or colletocystophores (which are in fact the reduced remnants of the four first formed, or perradial, tentacles and the four later formed, or interradial, tentacles).   Each marginal anchor consists of a short stalk surmounted by a cushion-like swelling (formed of large cells which secrete a sticky substance of doubtful function).   The perradial marginal anchors can be distinguished from the interradial, since they lie opposite the ridges separating the subumbral pits, and since the perradial depressions are often wider and deeper than the interradial.

d. Notice now that the oral lips are perradial, and that the subumbral pits, and therefore the internal mesenteries, are interradial.   In the walls of each of the four internal mesenteries two **gonads** are developed.   These bulge into the enteron in the space between the sides of the subumbral pits and the outer body-wall, and, being large, they are easily visible through the wall.   They are seen to lie one beneath each adradial lobe, and between each pair is the line of insertion of the interradial mesentery.

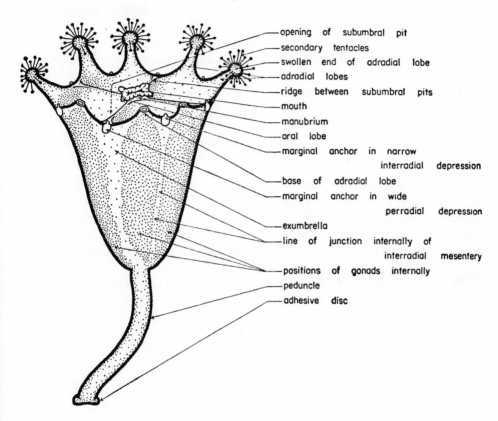

opening of subumbral pit
secondary tentacles
swollen end of adradial lobe
adradial lobes
ridge between subumbral pits
mouth
manubrium
oral lobe
marginal anchor in narrow
                          interradial depression
base of adradial lobe
marginal anchor in wide
                          perradial depression
exumbrella
line of junction internally of
                          interradial mesentery
positions of gonads internally
peduncle
adhesive disc

FIG. 41.—*Haliclystus.* To show the details of the subumbrella, three of the adradial lobes have been omitted.

3.   CONCLUSION

a. Observing the specimen, review the characteristics of the phylum, of the class, and of the order.

4.   REFERENCE

DELAGE, Y., and HÉROUARD, E. (1901).   Volume 2 and part 2 of " Traité de zoologie concrète."   Paris.

3.02.   Order **Discomedusae**

Characteristics : Free-swimming Scyphomedusae with the umbrella disc- or saucer-shaped; with either four or eight long oral lobes; and usually with eight marginal tentaculocysts, but occasionally with more.

To the order belong the great majority of the Scyphomedusae. They are relatively large forms, varying in size from a diameter of an inch or two to the huge *Cyanea*, the largest coelenterate known, with a diameter of over 7 feet and a marginal tentacle length of over 100 feet.   The shallow-water species possess a hydroid stage, but in the open-ocean forms the planula larva develops directly into the medusa.   The group is split into two important suborders, the Semostomae with four oral lobes and the Rhizostomae with eight partly fused oral lobes pierced by great numbers of tiny sucking mouths.

Genus **Aurelia**

1. GENERAL ACCOUNT

a. This jelly-fish has a world-wide distribution, especially in coastal regions. It swims close to the surface of the sea, living on small planktonic animals and plants caught by the ciliary feeding mechanism.   The sexes are separate, and the gametes are shed into the enteron, particularly in spring and summer. The spermatozoa escape to enter the females, and so fertilise the eggs internally. The segmenting zygotes lodge in the folds of the oral lobes until the planula stage is reached.   Then they swim free and settle on some rock or weed to grow into small hydroids called scyphistomae.   These feed and grow, and during autumn and winter they give rise by stolon formation to other scyphistomae.   In late winter and early spring they begin the process of strobilation (repeated transverse fission), which results in the production of tiny medusae called ephyrae.   A scyphistoma may live for years budding off medusae in winter and spring, and feeding and forming more scyphistomae in summer and autumn.

2. ANATOMY

a. Examine a preparation of a **scyphistoma**.   It has a *Haliclytus*-like, trumpet-shaped body set on a stalk which ends in an adhesive disc.   The oral end is fringed by sixteen tentacles (four first-formed perradial tentacles, four second-formed interradial tentacles, and eight last-formed adradial tentacles). The mouth is in the centre of the subumbrella, the membrane within the tentacle ring.   Focus into the body to see the enteron cavity within which four inter-radial subumbral pits may be visible (these pits extend downwards from the subumbrella, and lie inside the four interradial mesenteries which divide the enteron into four perradial pockets).   If possible, examine a scyphistoma with a basal extension, or stolon, on which a bud is growing, and another which is undergoing strobilation, and so forming ephyrae.   Each ephyra bears eight prominent balance organs called tentaculocysts (before the first ephyra is re-leased the sixteen tentacles are absorbed and eight tentaculocysts grow in the per- and inter-radial positions; later ephyrae develop only tenta-culocysts).

b. An *Aurelia* **medusa** has a disc-like umbrella and a pendant manubrium. The slightly convex exumbrella is featureless, but the slightly concave sub-umbrella bears the manubrium, and the four blind-ending subgenital pits (which are developed from the subumbral pits of the scyphistoma, are homo-logous with those of *Haliclystus*, and are of unknown function). In the centre of the manubrium is the four-cornered mouth. The lips at the four corners are greatly elongated as the oral lobes which are deeply grooved and fringed with tiny oral tentacles (these and the lobes are covered with nematocysts).

c. The **umbrella margin** (in which lie the circular muscle fibres which cause

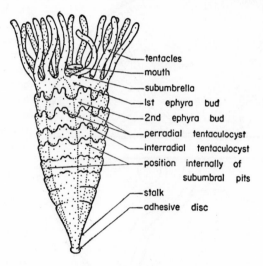

FIG. 42.—*Aurelia.* A strobilising scyphistoma.

the swimming pulsations) is fringed with numerous tiny marginal tentacles (these bear batteries of sting cells for protection rather than food capture). It also bears eight notches, at the base of each of which is a tentaculocyst (balance organ) bordered by two lappets. On the subumbrella side of the margin a narrow ridge, the velarium (which does not, however, contain circular muscle fibres), is cut into eight sections by the eight notches.

d. Dissect out a small piece of the umbrella margin containing a **tenta-culocyst**, mount it, and examine it through a microscope from the exumbrella side (the details are better seen in a stained permanent preparation; see method on p. 117). The base of the little, club-like tentaculocyst is hollow (containing an extension of the enteron), but its distal end is blocked by large endodermal cells (containing crystals mainly of calcium sulphate). A small hood covers the base, and the tip is supported by the inner edges of the two

I

large lappets (which are extensions of the umbrella margin, and contain sensory cells on which the tentaculocyst presses to give a sense of balance). At the end of the hollow part of the tentaculocyst is a tiny pigment spot called the ocellus (and presumed to be light sensitive). Lateral to the hood, and overlying the large lappets, are two smaller lappets (presumed to be sensory), and on the upper surface between their bases and the base of the hood is a small pit (lined by sensory cells). Another sensory pit is on the subumbrella surface at the base of the tentaculocyst.

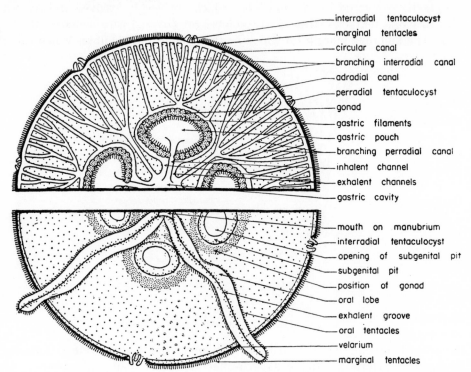

interradial tentaculocyst
marginal tentacles
circular canal
branching interradial canal
adradial canal
perradial tentaculocyst
gonad
gastric filaments
gastric pouch
branching perradial canal
inhalent channel
exhalent channels
gastric cavity

mouth on manubrium
interradial tentaculocyst
opening of subgenital pit
subgenital pit
position of gonad
oral lobe
exhalent groove
oral tentacles
velarium
marginal tentacles

FIG. 43.—*Aurelia*. The gastrovascular and reproductive systems seen through the exumbrella (above), and the details of the subumbrella (below).

e. Trace the course of the **gastrovascular system** (enteron), which lies embedded in the thick, jelly mass of the mesogloea (in its branching cavity digestion begins, and water is circulated by the action of cilia). Through the short, hanging manubrium, the mouth opens upwards into the central gastric cavity which is visible through the exumbrella surface (if necessary, part of this surface may be removed to obtain a clearer view). Four branches of the gastric cavity lead outwards into the four gastric pouches in which also lie the prominent, ring-like gonads. From the floor of each of these branches rise two long ridges which separate a central inhalent channel (through which water enters) from two lateral exhalent channels (through which water leaves). Notice also that close inside each gonad ring is a prominent row of gastric filaments (which contain nematocysts and kill prey swallowed alive). From the outer edge of each gastric pouch arise two straight, unbranching adradial canals (through which water and food particles pass centrifugally). These join into a canal which circles the umbrella margin, and which gives little, blind branches to each tentacle and tentaculocyst. From this circular canal there lead inwards four perradial and four interradial canals, all of which branch extensively (and along which the current flows centripetally). The perradial canals pass between the gastric pouches to open directly into the gastric cavity, but the interradial canals open into the gastric pouches (the water thus re-entering the gastric pouches flows round the outside of the gonad, and so reaches the gastric cavity through the exhalent channels). Notice again the four-cornered mouth and the grooves on the oral lobes, which are, in fact, exhalent grooves (water and waste are passed along them by ciliary action).

f. Notice now the **orientation** of the body. The oral lobes are perradial in position, and the subgenital pits are interradial. Four of the tentaculocysts are perradial and four are interradial.

g. Distinguish the **sexes.** In the male the edges of the oral lobes bear only the oral tentacles, but in the female these edges are highly convoluted, and within the convolutions the tiny developing larvae can be seen as white spots. Both testes and ovaries (situated in the floors of the gastric pouches) are lobed structures forming incomplete rings, and although they are superficially similar, the ovaries can be seen through a lens to contain eggs (these eggs, shed into the pouches and fertilised by the spermatozoa drawn in with the water current, pass with that current to the circular canal, and then back into the exhalent grooves of the oral lobes, where they fix themselves). Detach a portion of the oral lobe of a female, and examine the developing eggs through a microscope.

3. CONCLUSION

a. Observing the specimens, review the characteristics of the phylum, of the class, and of the order.

b. Compare the life history and structure of *Aurelia* with those of *Haliclystus.*

4. REFERENCE

Details of the structure of the semostome *Aurelia* and of the rhizostome *Rhizostoma* are given by:

DELAGE, Y., and HÉROUARD, E. (1901). Volume 2 and part 2 of " Traité de zoologie concrète." Paris.

APPENDIX TO THE COELENTERATA

I. CULTURE METHODS

a. Of all the coelenterates described above, only *Hydra* and *Actinia* can be easily kept for any length of time.   However, *Astrangia* may survive for a few months, and *Bougainvillea* and *Obelia* for a few weeks.

b. *Hydra* is obtained most easily by collecting weeds and dead submerged leaves from a pond or slow stream and letting these stand in small aquaria. In a day or two the animals move to the glass and to the surface film, when they can be seen easily and removed with a pipette.   A good culture can be kept for years with relatively little attention.   It should be started in a large aquarium already established with pond-mud and pond-water, with one or two pond-weeds of any kind that will grow, and from which all larger animals have been eliminated.   Add the *Hydra* together with some *Daphnia* or other small swimming crustacean, keep the tank in a window away from the sun, maintain the temperature at below 20° C., and cover with a glass plate to prevent evaporation. Feed by adding living *Daphnia* (culture method on p. 331) at intervals.   The more that are given the more numerous will the *Hydra* become, but several weeks of starvation will not kill the culture entirely.   If the water becomes cold (below 10° C.) in winter, the *Hydra* may disappear, but they usually survive in the form of winter eggs, and reappear in the spring.   If for no apparent reason the culture ceases to thrive, transfer the remaining individuals to a new tank with fresh water.

c. *Actinia* and other anemones collected from between tide-marks can be kept fairly easily and for long periods.   They should not be overcrowded, and the water must be well aerated mechanically.   The tank may be electrically lighted, and the temperature should be kept at about 10° C. (never lower than 4° C. nor higher than 15° C.).   In summer the temperature can be kept down by passing a constant stream of tap-water through a long, undulating or spiral glass tube immersed in the tank.   Loss of water by evaporation is reduced by covering with a glass plate, and any such loss should be made good with water distilled in glass apparatus.   *Actinia*, like other anemones, can be fed on small fragments of raw mussel, clam, fish (fresh-water or marine), and even pieces of earthworm (with the earth cleaned out of them) or of horse meat, which should be dropped directly on to the extended tentacles so that they do not lie about and rot.   One small piece weekly is sufficient for each animal, and they will tolerate long periods of starvation.

d. Colonies of *Astrangia* can be kept and fed in a similar manner to *Actinia*. However, if available, the best foods are small living marine crustaceans or tiny worms.   The colonies will not usually grow and spread, but they will survive for some months.

2. FIXATION METHODS

a. To obtain well-expanded specimens of all coelenterates, including medusae, it is usually necessary to narcotise them by adding crystals of menthol or of magnesium sulphate (Epsom salts) to the small volume of water in which they are confined. Alternatively, a drop or two of commercial formalin may be added at about ten-minute intervals until it makes up about a tenth of the total volume. Coelenterates are best stored in a 5% solution of neutralised formalin (which for marine forms should be made up in sea-water), but 70% alcohol may also be used.

3. STAINING METHODS

a. The structural details of small coelenterates such as *Bougainvillea* and *Obelia*, of the anthocodiae of the alcyonarians, and of such organs as the tentaculocysts of *Aurelia* are most easily seen after staining. If they are preserved in 70% alcohol, they can be transferred directly into borax carmine and over-stained (from thirty minutes to several hours). Extract the excess stain in a 1% solution of hydrochloric acid in 70% alcohol, wash in normal 70% alcohol, and then transfer through 90% alcohol, absolute alcohol, a mixture of absolute alcohol and xylol (five or ten minutes in each) to pure xylol. Mount in Canada balsam.

b. Alternatively, they may be transferred to water, either directly from formalin or via 50% and 30% alcohols from 70% alcohol, and then over-stained in a haematoxylin solution such as Ehrlich's, Delafield's, or Mayer's. Wash in 30%, 50%, and 70% alcohols (five or ten minutes in each), and extract the excess stain in acid 70% alcohol. Stop the extraction when necessary by placing the specimens in normal 70% alcohol, and then turn the stain blue in 70% alcohol to which a few drops of strong ammonia have been added. Transfer to xylol as described above, and mount in Canada balsam.

CHAPTER V

PHYLUM **CTENOPHORA**

Characteristics : Solitary free-living animals which are fundamentally bi-laterally symmetrical; with eight rows of ctenes; with a highly developed mesogloea containing parenchymatous cells which are apparently mesodermal; and with lasso cells but no nematocysts.

The ctenophores are all marine and almost all are pelagic. They are evidently unrelated to the coelenterates, and there are good reasons for suggesting that their origin was by neoteny from an eight-lobed planktonic larva similar to the Müller's larva of the modern polyclad turbellarians. Polyclads and ctenophores are similar in their method of development, in their form of gut, and in their possession of aboral sense organs, statoliths, paired tentacles, and ctenes.

1.00. Class **Tentaculata**

Characteristics : Ctenophora which possess tentacles.

1.01. Order **Cydippida**

Characteristics : Tentaculata possessing a spherical or ovoid body; and with two branching tentacles retractible into sheaths.

Genus **Pleurobrachia** (sea gooseberry)

1. GENERAL ACCOUNT

a. The sea gooseberries are common and cosmopolitan pelagic animals, and they are often found stranded by a receding tide. The genus extends southwards from within the arctic circle, and the individuals usually swim in huge shoals. They move mouth forwards and catch their prey by means of the long, trailing tentacles. Their food is stated to consist largely of various larvae, small copepods, and fish eggs which are transferred to the mouth by the contraction and bending of the tentacles. *Pleurobrachia* is hermaphrodite, and reproduction is entirely sexual. In temperate regions it takes place particularly in late summer and autumn, but in warmer waters it may occur all the year round. Fertilisation is external and development direct.

2. ANATOMY

a. The transparent gelatinous **body** is ovoid in form. At one end is the mouth, at the other is a small sense organ, and down the long axis pass eight prominent costae. Near the aboral end, and in the intercostal intervals, are

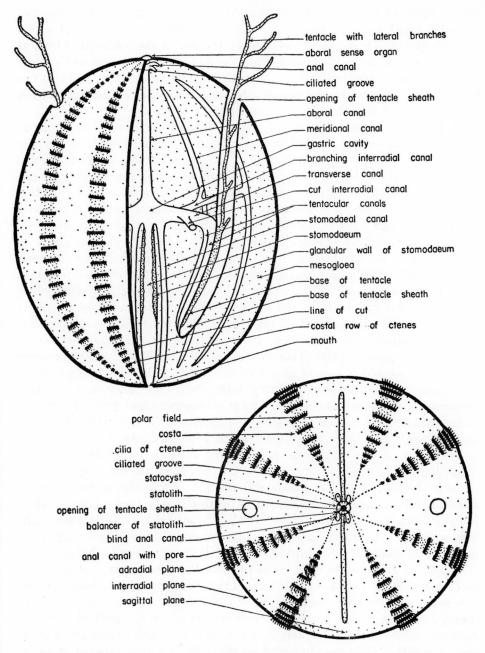

tentacle with lateral branches
aboral sense organ
anal canal
ciliated groove
opening of tentacle sheath
aboral canal
meridional canal
gastric cavity
branching interradial canal
transverse canal
cut interradial canal
tentacular canals
stomodaeal canal
stomodaeum
glandular wall of stomodaeum
mesogloea
base of tentacle
base of tentacle sheath
line of cut
costal row of ctenes
mouth

polar field
costa
cilia of ctene
ciliated groove
statocyst
statolith
opening of tentacle sheath
balancer of statolith
blind anal canal
anal canal with pore
adradial plane
interradial plane
sagittal plane

FIG. 44.—*Pleurobrachia*.   Above is a specimen seen from the side with part of the ectoderm removed to expose the gastrovascular canal system.   Below is a specimen seen from the aboral pole.

the openings of the two tentacle sheaths (in preserved specimens the two tentacles, which bear the sticky lasso cells, are usually found retracted within these sheaths).   These two openings mark the line of the tentacular plane, at right angles to which is the sagittal plane (along either of these planes the body can be cut, from aboral to oral end, into identical halves).   Between these two planes are the two interradial planes.   None of the costae lies in any of these planes, and they may therefore be considered as adradial.

b. Examine one of the **costae**.   It is made up of a single row of small plates, or ctenes, which stops short of both the oral and aboral poles (these ctenes beat in succession, the aboral one first, and so propel the animal mouth forwards). Carefully cut out a piece of the outer body-wall, including almost all of the two costae which flank one of the sagittal intercostal spaces (leave in place only a few of the aboral ctenes of these two costae).   Mount the excised tissue on a slide, and through a low-power microscope notice that each ctene consists of a transversely placed row of long cilia which are fused to each other basally.

c. Through the window cut in the ectoderm distinguish the two **tentacle sheaths**, which end blindly near the oral end and contain the retracted tentacles.

d. In the same way, trace the course of the **gastrovascular system**, which branches within the mass of the mesogloea (and is presumed to distribute oxygen in solution as well as food materials).   The mouth opens into an ecto-dermal stomodaeum which passes up to the centre of the animal and is flattened in the sagittal plane.   Parts of the stomodaeal walls are thickened (and contain glandular cells which secrete digestive enzymes).   The stomodaeum opens into a small endodermal gastric cavity, from which two transverse canals pass outwards in the tentacular plane.   Each transverse canal gives rise to five main branches : a stomodaeal canal passing down the flattened side of the stomodaeum ; two interradial canals which pass outwards, divide once, and so reach four of the meridional canals lying beneath the costae ; and two tentacular canals which turn down, side by side, along the inner border of the tentacle sheath.   All these canals end blindly.   From the gastric cavity a single aboral canal runs to a point just beneath the aboral sense organ.   There it divides into four small anal canals which pass outwards in the four interradii. Two of these, which are diagonally opposite, open through two small pores (indigestible matter is voided from them), while the others end blindly.

e. Cut off the aboral cap of ectoderm with the **sense organ**, a statocyst, in its centre, and the extreme upper ends of the costae on its periphery.   Mount it beneath a cover-glass, and examine it through a low-power microscope (its details can be seen even better after staining by one of the methods given for coelenterates on p.117).   The statocyst consists of a small depression contain-ing a statolith (calcareous) balanced on the ends of four interradial groups of long cilia which are called the balancers.   It is roofed by a transparent dome (apparently formed of a ring of fused cilia).   From the base of each balancer a ciliated groove (of doubtful function) passes outwards, and divides almost immediately into two adradial grooves which pass to the upper ends of two of the costae (these costae are to be regarded as highly specialised regions of the ciliated grooves). Extending from the sides of the statocyst in the sagittal plane are two long, ciliated depressions, the polar fields (presumed to be sensory). Emerging from beneath the statocyst are the four interradial anal canals, and the pores through which two of them open may be visible.

f. The **gonads** are not usually visible, but if they are well developed they may be seen as thickenings in the sides of the meridional canals (a testis extends along one side of the canal and an ovary along the other; in adjacent canals gonads of like nature face each other, the ovaries doing so across the tentacular and sagittal planes).

3. CONCLUSION

a. Observing the specimen, review the characteristics of the phylum, of the class, and of the order.

4. REFERENCES

CHUN, C. (1880). " Die Ctenophoren des Golfes von Neapel." *Fauna und Flora des Golfes von Neapel.* Vol. 1.
DELAGE, Y., and HÉROUARD, E. (1901). Volume 2 and part 2 of " Traité de zoologie concrète." Paris.

2.00. Class **Nuda**

Characteristics : Ctenophora which lack tentacles.

2.01. Order **Beroida**

Characteristics : Body conical and compressed, with greatly enlarged mouth and stomodaeum, and with branching meridional canals.

The principal genus of this, the only order of the class Nuda, is *Beroe.*

Genus **Beroe**

1. GENERAL ACCOUNT

a. This is a cosmopolitan genus, the species of which occur commonly in huge shoals in the plankton of all seas from the Arctic to the Antarctic. The animals are highly phosphorescent. Each swims with its large mouth directed forwards, and in this way catches its prey, which consists largely of small crustaceans and of other ctenophores. In the colder seas sexual reproduction takes place in summer and autumn, but elsewhere it probably occurs throughout the whole year. Fertilisation is external and development direct.

2. ANATOMY

a. The transparent **body** is elongated and flattened. It has a wide, slit-like mouth at one end, an apical sense-organ at the other, and eight costae (the length of which depends on the species). The narrow edges of the body are in the sagittal plane, and at right angle to this is the transverse plane (the tentacular plane of the Tentaculata). Between these are the interradial planes, and the costae are adradial.

b. Through a lens examine one of the **costae**. Notice that it consists of a single row of closely packed ctenes, each of which is a transverse row of partly

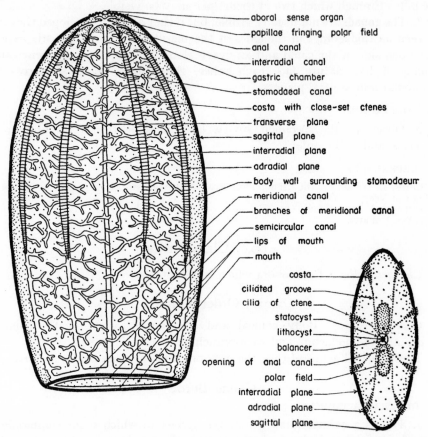

aboral sense organ
papillae fringing polar field
anal canal
interradial canal
gastric chamber
stomodaeal canal
costa with close-set ctenes
transverse plane
sagittal plane
interradial plane
adradial plane
body wall surrounding stomodaeum
meridional canal
branches of meridional canal
semicircular canal
lips of mouth
mouth

costa
ciliated groove
cilia of ctene
statocyst
lithocyst
balancer
opening of anal canal
polar field
interradial plane
adradial plane
sagittal plane

FIG. 45.—*Beroe.* On the left is a specimen seen from the flattened side with the internal organs showing through the transparent wall. On the right is a specimen seen from the aboral pole.

fused cilia (the ctenes in each row beat in succession with a metachronal rhythm, the wave starting from the aboral end).

c. Through a lens examine the aboral pole. The apical **sense organ** is a statocyst (with a calcareous lithocyst supported on four interradial balancers and covered by a dome), and from it in the sagittal plane there extend two polar fields (ciliated depressions which are probably sensory), fringed by tiny branching papillae (also probably sensory). From the statocyst there also emerge four interradial ciliated grooves which divide immediately to run in the adradii to the aboral ends of the costae.

d. Through the transparent body-wall trace as much as possible of the course of the **gastrovascular system**. The mouth has extensible lips (which close behind the prey), and it opens into a huge stomodaeal cavity (in which digestion begins). This cavity is so large that the body is thimble-like. Beneath the aboral sense-organ the stomodaeum opens into a small gastric cavity (endoderm lined), from which eight canals pass through the mesogloea to the various parts of the body. There are four interradial canals, which divide to form eight meridional canals running beneath the costae, two stomodaeal canals, which pass in an oral direction in the transverse plane, and two short anal canals, which pass outwards beneath the polar fields and open through two small pores visible within these fields (undigested waste is voided through these pores and through the mouth). The eight meridional canals have numerous side branches (which, according to the species, may or may not anastomose and join with the stomodaeal canals). Orally the four meridional canals and the one stomodaeal canal of each flattened side join into a semi-circular canal (which, again according to the species, may or may not communicate with the semicircular canal of the other side).

e. The **gonads**, which are not usually visible, occur on either side of the meridional canals. In any one canal the testis lies along one side and the ovary along the other.

3. CONCLUSION

a. Observing the specimen, review the characteristics of the phylum, of the class, and of the order.

b. Compare the structure of *Beroe* with that of *Pleurobrachia*.

4. REFERENCES

DELAGE, Y., and HÉROUARD, E. (1901). Volume 2 and part 2 of "Traité de zoologie concrète." Paris.

MAYER, A. G. (1912). "Ctenophores of the Atlantic coast of North America." *Publication of the Carnegie Institution of Washington, No.* 162.

CHAPTER VI

PHYLUM NEMERTEA

Characteristics : Bilaterally symmetrical, unsegmented animals; with a proboscis enclosed in a sheath, lying dorsal to the alimentary canal, and eversible through a pore situated above the mouth; epidermis ciliated; alimentary canal with both mouth and anus; a blood vascular system but no perivisceral body cavity; a protonephridial (flame-cell) excretory system; sexes separate and gonads simple and repeated; and sometimes with a planktonic pilidium larva.

The nemerteans are evidently closely related to the platyhelminths, but they are more highly organised especially in their development of an anus, of a blood vascular system, and of separate sexes. They are mostly marine but some occur in fresh water and on land, and a few are commensal.

1.00. Class Enopla

Characteristics : Nemertea with the mouth anterior to the cerebral ganglion; with the central nervous system internal to the body wall musculature; and with the proboscis often armed.

1.01. Order Hoplonemertini

Characteristics : Enopla with the proboscis armed with one or more stylets; intestine straight with lateral diverticula.

Genus Amphiporus

I. GENERAL ACCOUNT

a. One of the commonest species on the European coast is *A. lactifloreus* (Johnston), while on the North American coast is the essentially similar *A. ochraceus* Verrill. These animals are commonly found hiding under stones between tide-marks, and they can also be dredged in shallow water offshore. They are predaceous and carnivorous, attacking their prey and protecting themselves from their enemies by means of their proboscis. This organ is armed with sharp stylets and probably also secretes poison. The gonads develop in winter when breeding takes place. The ova and spermatozoa are released into the water, fertilisation is external, and development is direct.

2. ANATOMY

a. Examine the **body form** of a specimen which has been dorso-ventrally compressed, stained, and mounted (see method for Platyhelminthes on p. 76). The head is spatulate, and commonly the proboscis can be seen protruding from it. Also at the anterior end are numerous eyespots which on each side are arranged in two groups, one dorsal over the prominent cerebral ganglia and the other lateral.

b. The most prominent body organ is the **proboscis** (a tubular invagination of the anterior body wall), which may be retracted within the body or partially protruded through an anterior opening, the rhynchopore. The proboscis wall is muscular and its central cavity is lined by a glandular epithelium (ectoderm). The proboscis is divisible into anterior, central, and posterior regions. The anterior region is a thin tube, the rhynchodaeum, through which the central region can be everted. At the junction of the central and posterior regions is a constriction bearing one median stylet and two lateral pouches containing smaller accessory stylets (when the median region is fully everted these stylets protrude from its tip). The posterior region is not eversible (it probably secretes poison). When retracted the proboscis lies twisted inside a cavity, the rhychocoel (containing fluid), which is bounded by the muscular proboscis sheath (by contraction of this sheath and consequent pressure on the liquid the proboscis is forced to evert). The posterior end of the proboscis is continuous with a muscle strand, the retractor muscle, which turns forward before joining into the proboscis sheath.

c. The **alimentary canal** lies ventral to the proboscis sheath. The mouth opens from the ventral side of the rhynchodaeum, and a narrow oesophagus leads back into a capacious stomach. From the posterior end of the stomach a narrow straight pylorus passes back for some distance before turning downwards to join into the intestine. The intestine is thus divided into two regions, the one extending anterior to the pyloric–intestinal junction to form a blind-ending caecum, and the other leading posteriorly from the pyloric–intestinal junction to form the intestine proper. Throughout the full length of the caecum and the intestine proper there are large numbers of laterally placed blind-ending diverticula. The anus opens through the posterior tip of the body.

d. Notice that the proboscis sheath and the alimentary canal are embedded in a solid **mesenchyme**.

e. Distinguish as much as possible of the **vascular system** (the colourless blood contains nucleated corpuscles). There are two lateral vessels and one median vessel which runs dorsal to the alimentary canal but ventral to the proboscis sheath. Immediately posterior to the cerebral ganglia the median vessel branches left and right to fuse with the lateral vessels, which then pass forwards into the head to form a loop vessel (there is no heart and the blood is circulated by the movements of the body).

f. The **excretory system** is not usually visible in whole mounts.   There are

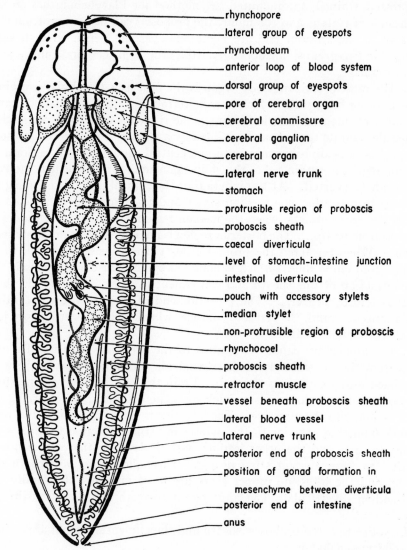

rhynchopore
lateral group of eyespots
rhynchodaeum
anterior loop of blood system
dorsal group of eyespots
pore of cerebral organ
cerebral commissure
cerebral ganglion
cerebral organ
lateral nerve trunk
stomach
protrusible region of proboscis
proboscis sheath
caecal diverticula
level of stomach-intestine junction
intestinal diverticula
pouch with accessory stylets
median stylet
non-protrusible region of proboscis
rhynchocoel
proboscis sheath
retractor muscle
vessel beneath proboscis sheath
lateral blood vessel
lateral nerve trunk
posterior end of proboscis sheath
position of gonad formation in
    mesenchyme between diverticula
posterior end of intestine
anus

Fig.45*a*.—*Amphiporus.*   Dorsal view of a whole mount with the body greatly foreshortened.

two lateral ducts (collecting the products of the protonephridial system) drained by lateral pores situated just posterior to the level of the cerebral ganglia.

g. The **reproductive system** is evident only during the breeding season. Sexes are separate and the numerous gonads develop along the full length of the intestine, arising from that part of the lateral mesenchyme which lies between the many caecal and intestinal diverticula. Each gonad has its own narrow duct which opens dorso-laterally (fertilisation is external).

h. Distinguish again the well-developed cerebral ganglia and trace as much as possible of the **nervous system**. There are in fact four cerebral ganglia, two dorsal and two ventral. On each side the dorsal and ventral ganglia are partially fused, while from side to side the dorsal ganglia are linked by a dorsal commissure and the ventral ganglia by a ventral commissure. The rhynchodaeum passes through the nerve ring so formed. Anteriorly from the dorsal ganglia numerous small nerves pass forwards to the eyespots, to a large lateral pair of cerebral organs (probably sensory and each opening by a lateral pore), and to a pair of dorsal cephalic grooves (probably sensory and more easily seen in living specimens). Posteriorly from the ventral cerebral ganglia there arise the two large lateral nerve trunks. The nerves from the ventral ganglia to the oesophagus and to the proboscis are difficult to see except in sections.

3. CONCLUSION

a. Observing the specimen, review the characteristics of the phylum, of the class, and of the order.

b. Compare and contrast the structure of *Amphiporus* with that of a polyclad turbellarian.

4. REFERENCE.

McINTOSH, W. C. (1873–74). "A monograph of the British annelids. Part I. The nemerteans." The Ray Society, London.

1.02. Order **Bdellonemertini**

Characteristics : Enopla with the proboscis unarmed; intestine sinuous without diverticula; commensal habit and with posterior sucker.

Genus **Malacobdella**

1. GENERAL ACCOUNT

a. The best-known species is *M. grossa* (Müll.), a leech-like nemertine which is to be found living alone in the mantle cavity of such lamellibranch molluscs as *Cyprina islandica*. *Malacobdella* anchors itself by a large posteroventral sucker, but it lives a commensal, not a parasitic, life feeding on small organisms extracted from the passing stream of water. The sexes are separate, fertilisation is external, and development is direct.

2. ANATOMY

a. The **body** is leech-like, but anteriorly there is neither sucker nor eyes. Examine a stained specimen mounted whole (see method for Platyhelminthes on p. 76).

b. Distinguish internally the **alimentary canal**. The large anterior mouth opens into a capacious foregut, which in turn leads into the intestine in such a way as to separate a short lateral caecum from the long coiled intestine proper. Notice the absence of intestinal diverticula. At the posterior end of the intestine another short lateral caecum is formed by the subterminal junction of the intestine with the rectum. The anus opens dorsal to the sucker.

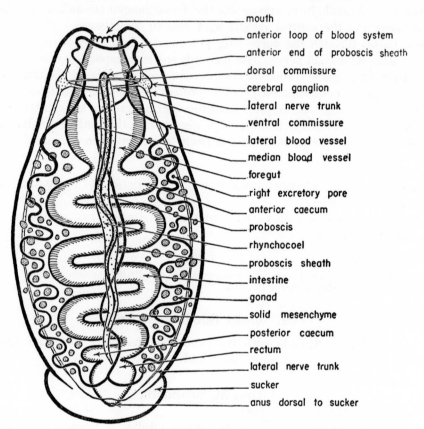

mouth
anterior loop of blood system
anterior end of proboscis sheath
dorsal commissure
cerebral ganglion
lateral nerve trunk
ventral commissure
lateral blood vessel
median blood vessel
foregut
right excretory pore
anterior caecum
proboscis
rhynchocoel
proboscis sheath
intestine
gonad
solid mesenchyme
posterior caecum
rectum
lateral nerve trunk
sucker
anus dorsal to sucker

FIG. 46.—*Malacobdella.* A dorsal view of a whole mount.

c. The **proboscis** opens anteriorly into the large foregut, and, when retracted, it leads back from this point along the dorsal side of the alimentary canal. Notice that the proboscis does not bear stylets, and that it is enclosed in a wide proboscis sheath (fluid filled).

d. A solid **mesenchyme** fills all the interstices of the body around the alimentary canal and the proboscis sheath.

e. The most prominent parts of the **vascular system** are the three longitudinal vessels, two lateral and one median. The median vessel runs between the alimentary canal and the proboscis sheath. All three vessels follow a sinuous course, and posteriorly they join dorsal to the rectum. Anteriorly the median vessel divides left and right, and these branches, joining with the lateral vessels, pass forward into the head to form a loop (the blood is kept in motion by the movements of the body).

f. The protonephridial **excretory system** is usually obscure and is confined to the region around the foregut. Its ducts coalesce to open through a pair of ventro-lateral pores close to the first intestinal loop.

g. The **reproductive system** is a simple one. The sexes are separate, and the numerous gonads develop in the mesenchyme as small discrete bodies which are arranged in two lateral zones in the intestinal region. Each gonad develops its own short duct to the exterior (fertilisation is external).

h. The **nervous system** is well developed. Locate the pair of large cerebral ganglia situated left and right of the foregut (each is formed of fused dorsal and ventral ganglia). They are linked by dorsal and ventral commissures, which pass respectively dorsal and ventral to the proboscis sheath. Many small nerves lead forwards from these ganglia, but there are no obvious sense organs in the head region. Posteriorly the two ganglia give rise to two large lateral nerve trunks which run the whole length of the body before meeting and joining dorsal to the anus.

3. CONCLUSION

a. Observing the specimen, review the characteristics of the phylum, of the class, and of the order.

b. Compare and contrast the structure of *Malacobdella* with that of the free-living *Amphiporus*.

4. REFERENCES

GERING, G. (1910). " Beiträge zur Kenntnis von *Malacobdella grossa* (Müll.)." Zeitschrift für wissenschaftliche Zoologie, Vol. 97, p. 673.
RIEPEN, O. (1933). "Anatomie und Histologie von *Malacobdella grossa* (Müll.)." *Zeitschrift für wissenschaftliche Zoologie*, Vol. 143, p. 323.

K

CHAPTER VII

PHYLUM NEMATODA

Characteristics : Bilaterally symmetrical, unsegmented, elongated, cylindrical worms; elastic cuticle usually moulted four times; body-wall muscles longitudinal and usually divided into four sections; peculiar body cavity, which in some species has been shown to be formed of the confluent vacuoles of a few enormous cells; alimentary canal straight with ectodermal fore- and hind-guts, and with endodermal midgut lacking muscles and glands; excretory system with single external pore and with either one or two glandular organs anteriorly, or one or two tubular structures lying inside the lateral lines, or both; sexes usually separate, there being usually two ovaries with a duct opening directly to the exterior, or one testis with a duct opening into the hindgut, which is then a cloaca; nervous system a circumoesophageal ring and longitudinal nerves, especially in the mid-dorsal and mid-ventral lines; sense organs simple; no cilia.

Both in numbers of individuals and in numbers of species, this is one of the largest animal phyla. Nematodes occur freely and abundantly almost everywhere in the sea, in fresh water, in the soil, and in decaying organic matter. In addition, they are commonly parasitic in both plants and animals, and are particularly abundant in the insects and the vertebrates. In spite of their numbers and of their widely different habitats, the anatomy of the various species is remarkably simple and uniform, and they may all be accommodated in five orders.

o.oi. Order **Ascaroidea**

Characteristics : Nematodes with three lips, one dorsal and two latero-ventral; often with one or two prominent oesophageal bulbs; free living and parasitic (usually in vertebrates).

The order contains all the free-living nematodes. These considerably outnumber the parasitic forms, and are considered to be more primitive.

Genus **Rhabditis**

I. GENERAL ACCOUNT

a. The members of the genus *Rhabditis* are all small, and they occur in great abundance in the soil. There they feed on the fluid formed by bacterial action in decaying organic matter. In some species the females sometimes develop as protandrous hermaphrodites and fertilise themselves, but separate sexes and cross fertilisation are the general rules. Each egg, laid in the soil, gives rise to a tiny worm which, during its growth, moults four times. After the second moult it may remain ensheathed in the old skin, cease feeding, become dormant, and resist desiccation. This is an " encysted larva ". Dormancy is broken by the proximity of decaying organic matter, and subsequent growth to sexual maturity is rapid. Living specimens can easily be obtained by the method described on p. 142.

2.   EXTERNAL ANATOMY

a. Mount living specimens in water on a microscope slide and add a coverglass. Through a microscope watch the stiff, wriggling movements of the **body**. Identify the anterior end by the terminal mouth which is flanked by three small lips, one dorsal and two latero-ventral, and the ventral side by the anal opening posteriorly.

b. Distinguish the **sexes**. The posterior end of the female is long and pointed, but the posterior end of the male bears a disc-shaped bursa which is directed ventrally.

3.   INTERNAL ANATOMY

a. Focusing through the transparent cuticle and body-wall, identify the parts of the **alimentary canal**. The mouth opens into a foregut, or stomodaeum (ectodermal and cuticle lined), which is made up of a short, thin-walled buccal cavity and a muscular oesophagus swollen to form two oesophageal bulbs (the posterior of which is sometimes called the pharynx). Watch the pulsations of the oesophageal bulbs (which suck in food liquefied by bacteria and ready for immediate absorption). The midgut (endodermal) is long, straight, and featureless (and through it absorption occurs). A short hindgut, or proctodaeum (ectodermal and cuticle lined), passes ventrally from the posterior end of the midgut to the anus.

b. Ventrally, just behind the mouth, distinguish the single external opening of the **excretory system** (this system is presumed to be excretory, but final proof is still lacking). Part of the terminal excretory canal can be seen passing upwards and backwards from this pore (the canal branches right and left to reach the two longitudinal excretory canals lying in the lateral lines, but these details may not be visible). Behind the excretory pore, beneath the junction of the oesophagus with the midgut, lies an excretory gland (in some species there are two). This is connected forwards with the terminal excretory canal (the whole system, canals and gland, is formed of only two cells, and the duct cavities are intracellular).

c. In a female worm identify the parts of the **female reproductive system**. There are two ovaries, the one anterior on one side of the alimentary canal, and the other posterior on the other. Each is U-shaped, and an oviduct arises from

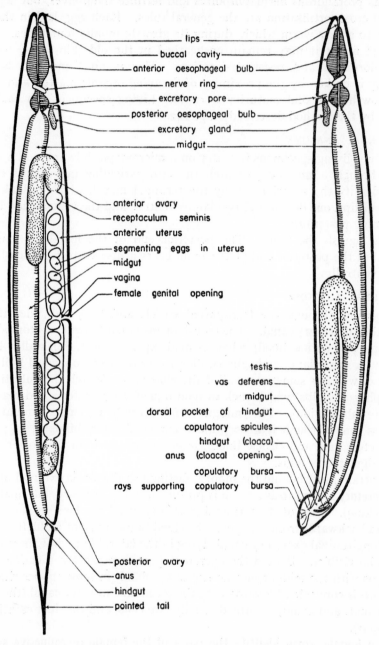

lips

buccal cavity

anterior oesophageal bulb

nerve ring

excretory pore

posterior oesophageal bulb

excretory gland

midgut

anterior ovary

receptaculum seminis

anterior uterus

segmenting eggs in uterus

midgut

vagina

female genital opening

testis

vas deferens

midgut

dorsal pocket of hindgut

copulatory spicules

hindgut (cloaca)

anus (cloacal opening)

copulatory bursa

rays supporting copulatory bursa

posterior ovary

anus

hindgut

pointed tail

FIG. 47.—*Rhabditis.*   A female seen from the right side, and a male seen from the left side.

one arm of the U. This duct is differentiated into two regions, the first being a small receptaculum seminis (in which spermatozoa are stored after copulation, and into which the eggs are passed singly to be fertilised and to receive a shell). The second part of the oviduct is the uterus (in which the shells harden, and the eggs within them begin development). The two uteri, one passing backwards and the other forwards, join near the middle point of the mid-ventral line, and open to the exterior through a short duct, the vagina (through which spermatozoa are introduced and the eggs laid).

d. In a male worm, identify the parts of the **male reproductive system**. The single U-shaped testis lies to one side of the alimentary canal in the posterior part of the body cavity. From one arm of the U a relatively wide vas deferens (usually filled with spermatozoa) passes back to open into the hindgut, which is therefore a cloaca. The dorsal wall of the cloaca forms a pocket, which contains two grooved spicules (these are protruded together and used as a penis during copulation). Around the cloacal opening, and set with sensory papillae, is a disc-like sucker, the copulatory bursa (by which the male grips the female during copulation).

e. The only visible part of the **nervous system** is the ring which surrounds the alimentary canal between the anterior and posterior oesophageal bulbs.

4. CONCLUSION

a. Observing the specimens, review as far as possible the characteristics of the phylum, and of the order.

5. REFERENCES

CHITWOOD, B. G., and CHITWOOD, M. B. (1937–40). Section 1 of " An introduction to nematology." Baltimore.
KÜKENTHAL, W., and KRUMBACH, T. (1928–34). Volume 2 and part 1 of " Handbuch der Zoologie." Berlin and Leipzig.

Genus **Ascaris**

1. GENERAL ACCOUNT

a. The largest common species are *A. equorum* Goeze from the small intestine of the horse and *A. lumbricoides* L. from the small intestine of the pig. Although it will not infect man, the latter, distinguished as var. *suis*, is morphologically indistinguishable from the human parasite *A. lumbricoides* var. *humanis*. It is not known with certainty what these worms eat, but it is usually presumed that they swallow, in liquid form, the already digested food of their host, together with some bacteria. Each female lays great numbers of eggs daily (more than 1000), and these pass out with the host's faeces. Lying on the ground for perhaps a month, the young worm develops and moults once inside the egg-shell, and is then ready to infect a new host. This happens when it is swallowed. The young worm then hatches, bores its way into the blood-stream, and passes via the liver and the heart to the lungs. It grows considerably during this journey, which takes about five days, and being then too large to pass through the lung capillaries, it breaks its way into the lung cavity and moults. It remains in the lung for about a week, moults again, and then migrates up the trachea and down the alimentary canal to the intestine. There, after growing for about a month and moulting for the fourth time, it becomes sexually mature.

2. EXTERNAL ANATOMY

a. Examine worms obtained from a slaughter-house (a method of preservation is given on p. 143). Notice the long, cylindrical shape of the **body**, which is pointed at both ends and encased in a thick cuticle. The cuticle shows four longitudinal streaks, two being narrow and white and dorsal and ventral in position, and two being broader and brown and lateral in position (these lines mark the internal divisions of the longitudinal muscles into four bands ; in the lateral lines there is brown excretory tissue). Distinguish the anterior end by the terminal mouth, and through a lens notice that it bears three lips, one dorsal and two latero-ventral. The ventral side is marked anteriorly by the single excretory pore, which is about two millimetres behind the mouth, and posteriorly by the slit-like anus, which is about the same distance from the posterior end.

b. Distinguish the **sexes**. The male is smaller, has its tail curved sharply in a ventral direction, and bears a group of tiny sensory papillae just behind the anal opening. The male genital duct opens through the hindgut and the anus (which is therefore a cloacal opening), from which two copulatory spicules may be seen protruding. In the female the tail is straight, and the ventral genital opening is about one-third of the distance from the anterior end.

3. INTERNAL ANATOMY

a. Open a female *Ascaris* by a longitudinal mid-dorsal incision into the body cavity, and pin aside the flaps of the body-wall. The **alimentary canal** is straight and almost featureless. The mouth opens into the foregut (an ectodermal stomodaeum lined with cuticle), which is modified anteriorly into a very short, thin-walled, buccal cavity, and posteriorly into a muscular oesophagus. A constriction marks the division between the oesophagus and the long, dorso-ventrally flattened midgut (endodermal and presumably absorptive in function), which runs dorsally for almost the full length of the body. A short, thinner hindgut (an ectodermal proctodaeum lined with cuticle) links the posterior end of the midgut with the subterminal anus.

b. The two lateral lines, which are prominent internally, contain what is considered to be excretory tissue surrounding two longitudinal **excretory ducts**. Anteriorly these two ducts are linked by a cross duct, from which a branch, the terminal canal, leads to the excretory pore (the whole system is composed of only three cells, the duct cavities being intracellular). In the anterior quarter

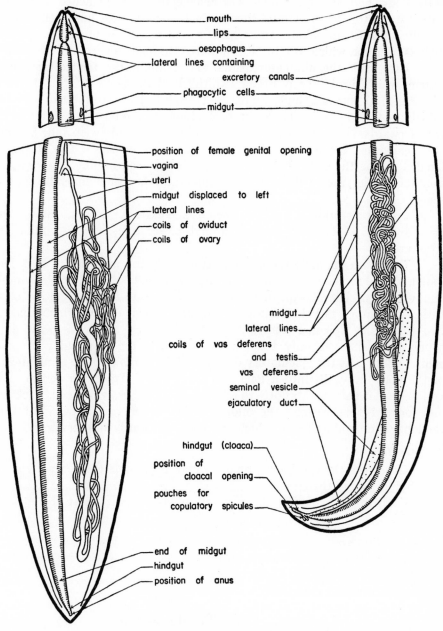

mouth
lips
oesophagus
lateral lines containing
excretory canals
phagocytic cells
midgut

position of female genital opening
vagina
uteri
midgut displaced to left
lateral lines
coils of oviduct
coils of ovary

midgut
lateral lines
coils of vas deferens
and testis
vas deferens
seminal vesicle
ejaculatory duct

hindgut (cloaca)
position of
cloacal opening
pouches for
copulatory spicules

end of midgut
hindgut
position of anus

FIG. 48.—*Ascaris.* A dissection of a female with the left reproductive organs omitted, and, on the right, a dissection of a male.

of the body there are also two pairs of **phagocytic organs** attached to the body-wall just ventral to the lateral lines. Each consists of a huge cell, which is usually brownish in colour (and which is said to collect unwanted particles, such as bacteria, which cannot be eliminated through the excretory canals).

c. Turn aside the alimentary canal and examine the **female reproductive system**, which lies in the posterior two-thirds of the body cavity. From the female genital pore the single vagina leads back to join into the two wide uteri (which are full of eggs). These run back almost to the posterior end, and then turn forwards as the narrower oviducts which coil and twist and, becoming even narrower, merge into the two filamentous ovaries. The ovaries lie tangled among the coils of the oviducts, and they end blindly (the eggs, shed from the ovaries, are fertilised in the oviducts and then surrounded by chitinous shells).

d. Cut out a section of a uterus, open it, and extract the **eggs**. Mount these in a drop of water, and through a high-power microscope examine their structure.

e. To expose the **male reproductive system**, open a male worm by a longitudinal dorsal incision along the straight part of the body, and by the complete removal of one lateral wall of the curved tail. Into the hindgut, or cloaca, within the curved tail there open dorsally the two small sacs which house the two copulatory spicules (these, protruded together, act as a penis during copulation), and ventrally the ejaculatory duct (the terminal part of the genital duct). As the ejaculatory duct passes forwards into the straighter part of the body, it swells into a long seminal vesicle. Trace the course of this vesicle until it narrows abruptly to join the vas deferens, which coils backwards and forwards, ensheathing the midgut. The vas merges imperceptibly into the long, blind-ending testis, which also coils backwards and forwards.

4. CONCLUSION

a. Observing the specimens, review as far as possible the characteristics of the phylum and of the order.

b. Compare and contrast the structure of *Ascaris* with that of the simpler *Rhabditis*.

5. REFERENCES

CHITWOOD, B. G., and CHITWOOD, M. B. (1937–40). Section 1 of " An introduction to nematology." Baltimore.
KÜKENTHAL, W., and KRUMBACH, T. (1928–34). Volume 2 and part 1 of " Handbuch der Zoologie." Berlin and Leipzig.

0.02. Order **Strongyloidea**

Characteristics : Nematodes with the oesophagus club-shaped and lacking definite oesophageal bulbs ; males with a copulatory bursa usually stiffened by one unpaired and six paired rays ; parasitic in vertebrates.

Genus **Ancylostoma** (hookworm)

(As an alternative, the essentially similar *Necator* may be used.)

I. GENERAL ACCOUNT

a. Hookworms are widely distributed in almost all tropical and sub-tropical countries. The two most important species, very similar in life-history and in structure, are *Ancyclostoma duodenale* Dub., which predominates in Europe, Africa, and Asia, and *Necator americanus* (Stiles), which predominates in the New World. The adults live in the intestine of man, and are only rarely recorded in such other animals as the gorilla, the pig, and the rhinoceros.

b. The eggs pass out with the host's faeces and hatch about a day later. The larvae feed on bacteria, moult, feed again, and moult a second time. They are then infective, and may live in moist soil for at least six months awaiting the opportunity to enter a new host. This they usually do by boring through the epidermis, a process which takes from a few minutes to about half an hour, but occasionally they may be swallowed. The larvae pass via the lymphatics to the blood, and so to the heart and to the lungs. After boring into the lung cavity they pass up the trachea and down the alimentary canal to the intestine. There they grow and undergo the third and fourth moults before becoming adults. Larvae entering the host through the mouth either bore into the mucosa and perform the usual lung migration, or pass directly to the intestine. For food, the worms bite away the intestinal mucosa.

2. EXTERNAL ANATOMY

a. Through a low-power microscope examine a preparation of a hook-worm. The **body** has the usual nematode shape, and is encased in a cuticle marked by transverse ridges, or striae. The anterior end curves dorsally, and the mouth opens obliquely upwards. The two lateral lines are marked by the positions of two cervical papillae (presumed to be sensory), and the ventral side by the positions of the anterior excretory pore and the posterior subterminal anus.

b. Distinguish the **sexes**. The longer female has a pointed tail, while the shorter male bears posteriorly the large, ventrally directed, copulatory bursa (which grips the female during copulation).

3. INTERNAL ANATOMY

a. The mouth opens downwards into the foregut, or **stomodaeum** (ectodermal and cuticle lined), which is divided into a buccal cavity and an oesophagus. The former is globular, and contains antero-ventrally two pairs of large pointed teeth, postero-dorsally one pair of smaller teeth, and in its floor a pair of saw-like teeth (all these teeth are the projecting parts of a single chitinous capsule, and are for gripping and tearing the intestinal mucosa). The muscular oeso-phagus broadens posteriorly, and a sharp constriction (containing valves) marks

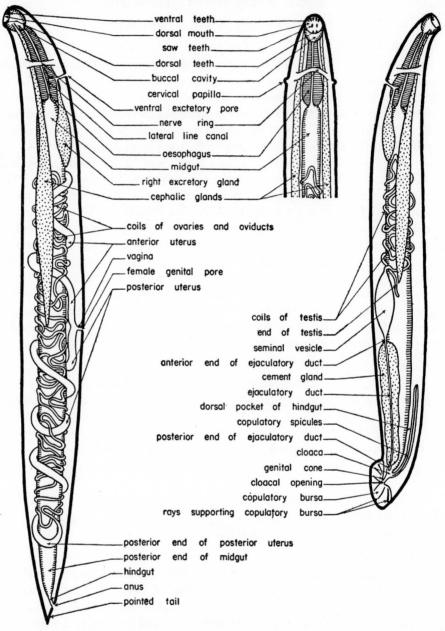

ventral teeth
dorsal mouth
saw teeth
dorsal teeth
buccal cavity
cervical papilla
ventral excretory pore
nerve ring
lateral line canal
oesophagus
midgut
right excretory gland
cephalic glands

coils of ovaries and oviducts
anterior uterus
vagina
female genital pore
posterior uterus

coils of testis
end of testis
seminal vesicle
anterior end of ejaculatory duct
cement gland
ejaculatory duct
dorsal pocket of hindgut
copulatory spicules
posterior end of ejaculatory duct
cloaca
genital cone
cloacal opening
copulatory bursa
rays supporting copulatory bursa

posterior end of posterior uterus
posterior end of midgut
hindgut
anus
pointed tail

FIG. 49.—*Ancylostoma*. On the left is a female seen from the right side, in the centre is the anterior end of a male seen from the dorsal side, and on the right is a male seen from the left side. In all cases, for clarity, the cephalo-oesophageal muscles are omitted, as are also the muscles linking the cement gland to the body wall in the male.

its posterior end. The anterior region of the oesophagus is partly obscured by the cephalo-oesophageal muscle-bands which anteriorly join into the sides of the mouth, and posteriorly are inserted into the oesophagus just behind its middle point. Lateral and external to these muscle-bands lie the two cephalic glands (possibly digestive glands), which anteriorly open into the buccal cavity, and posteriorly are prominent latero-dorsally until they end about half-way down the body (each gland is a single cell).

b. Trace the course of the **rest of the alimentary canal**. The midgut (endodermal) is straight and featureless, and is largely obscured by the reproductive system. It joins into a short hindgut, or proctodaeum (ectodermal and cuticle lined), which in the male is a cloaca, and which opens ventrally through the anus.

c. The so-called **excretory system** consists of two lateral line canals (not easily visible), which, on a level with the cervical papillae, are joined by a cross duct passing beneath the oesophagus; of two latero-ventral excretory glands, or cervical glands (each a single cell), which are attached anteriorly to the cross duct, and which extend almost a third of the way down the body; and of a single median duct, which leads from the cross duct to the excretory pore.

d. In the **female reproductive system** the single female genital pore opens just in front of the mid-ventral point. It leads into a short vagina, into which open two wide, egg-filled uteri. One uterus passes forwards and the other backwards to coil and twist around the midgut. On approaching the ends of the midgut each uterus turns and joins into a narrower oviduct. The oviducts, and the filamentous ovaries into which they merge, also coil and twist around the midgut.

e. In the **male reproductive system** the single testis is easily seen as a coiled filament surrounding the midgut. After twisting forwards and then backwards, it opens into a spindle-shaped seminal vesicle (in which spermatozoa are stored). This in turn opens into the long, narrow ejaculatory duct, which is almost entirely enveloped in a large cement gland (the products of this gland pass into the ejaculatory duct, and serve to cement the bursa of the male to the body of the female during copulation). Obliquely directed muscle-strands join the cement-gland to the body-wall. The ejaculatory duct opens into the ventral side of the hindgut, which is therefore a cloaca, and a long sac, containing two wand-like copulatory spicules (which are inserted into the vagina of the female during copulation), opens into the dorsal side of the hindgut. The cloacal opening of the male is on a small papilla, the genital cone, which is situated towards the centre of the large copulatory bursa. Notice that the flanges of the bursa are supported by six paired rays and one unpaired, or dorsal, ray (the rays are fleshy tactile structures).

f. The only part of the **nervous system** that is easily visible is the nerve-ring encircling the oesophagus.

4. CONCLUSION

a. Observing the specimens, review the characteristics of the phylum and of the order.

b. Compare the structures and life histories of *Ancylostoma* and *Ascaris.*

5. REFERENCE

Looss, A. (1905). " The anatomy and life history of *Agchylostoma duodenale* Dub." *Records of the Egyptian Government School of Medicine,* Vol. 3, p. 1.

o.o3. Order **Trichinelloidea**

Characteristics : Nematodes with the body usually divided into a narrow anterior region containing the stomodaeum and a wider posterior region containing the other organs ; with the oesophagus passing through the centre of a single row of large cells ; with one ovary and one uterus in the female ; and with one copulatory spicule, or none at all, in the male.

Only a small number of families and genera belong to this order, and all of them are parasitic in the alimentary canal of vertebrates.

Genus **Trichinella**

1. GENERAL ACCOUNT

a. Trichinella spiralis (Owen), one of the smallest of the nematodes, is widespread in temperate regions.   It is a common parasite of the rat and the pig, and it also occurs in man, particularly in the United States.   The adults live in the small intestine, where they feed on the mucosa, grow, reproduce, and die within a few weeks.   The female is ovoviviparous, and as soon as they are born the larvae penetrate into the blood-stream to reach the skeletal muscles. They burrow into and along the muscle fibres, which degenerate as they pass, and there they grow, and finally encyst.   The times of the cuticle moults are not known, but the coiled encysted larvae are ready to infect a new host when eaten together with the surrounding muscles.   The cyst then dissolves, and the young worm emerges to burrow into the intestinal mucosa and grow rapidly to maturity.   A method of culture is described on p. 143.

b. This life cycle is unique among parasitic nematodes in that the larvae neither come into the open nor enter an intermediate host.   This is made possible by the ovoviviparous habit of the female and the cannibalistic habit of the hosts.   The usual source of human infection is under-cooked pork, the pigs being themselves infected by feeding on uncooked pork scraps or on rats which are, perhaps, the original hosts.

2. ANATOMY

a. Examine a prepared section of pig or rat muscle containing **encysted larvae**.   One, or occasionally two, larvae lie coiled within each lemon-shaped, transparent cyst, which also contains a mass of waste products and of degener-

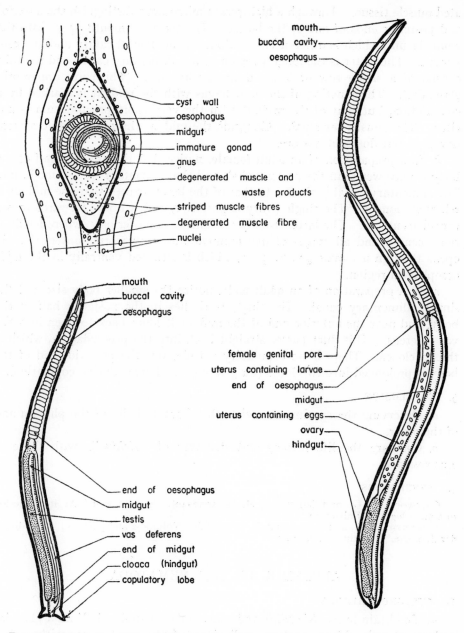

cyst wall
oesophagus
midgut
immature gonad
anus
degenerated muscle and
          waste products
striped muscle fibres
degenerated muscle fibre
nuclei

mouth
buccal cavity
oesophagus

mouth
buccal cavity
oesophagus

female genital pore
uterus containing larvae
end of oesophagus
midgut
uterus containing eggs
ovary
hindgut

end of oesophagus
midgut
testis
vas deferens
end of midgut
cloaca (hindgut)
copulatory lobe

FIG. 50.—*Trichinella*. The coiled larva encysted in striped muscle (upper left), the adult
        male (lower left), and the adult female.

ated muscle tissue.   Through a high-power microscope distinguish the anterior and posterior ends of one of the larvae.   The terminal mouth opens into the stomodaeum, which is differentiated into a narrow buccal cavity and an oesophagus.   The latter is the longest region of the alimentary canal, and its walls consist of a single row of large, drainpipe-like cells (which are apparently glandular).   The junction of the oesophagus with the midgut is marked by a constriction, but that of the midgut with the very short proctodaeum is not clear.   The anus is terminal.   Alongside the midgut the reproductive system develops, but does not mature.

b. In a preparation of an **adult female**, notice that the anterior half of the body is narrower than the posterior half and that it contains the stomodaeum. The alimentary canal is similar to that of the larva, except that the midgut is relatively longer.   The single ovary is posterior, and it opens forwards into a capacious uterus.   The latter usually contains eggs posteriorly (where fertilisation occurs), and all stages of development into tiny worms anteriorly.   It opens through a female genital pore, which is situated ventrally in the mid-oesophageal region.

c. In a preparation of an **adult male**, notice the smaller body size and the similar alimentary canal.   The single testis lies in the posterior half of the body, and near the anterior end of the midgut it loops back to open into the vas deferens.   This duct passes straight back into the proctodaeum, which is thus a cloaca.   There is no copulatory spicule, but the posterior end of the body is prolonged into two lobes (for gripping the female during copulation).

3. CONCLUSION

a. Observing the specimens, review the characteristics of the phylum and of the order.

b. Compare the life history and structure of *Trichinella* with those of *Ancylostoma.*

4. REFERENCES

CHITWOOD, B. G., and CHITWOOD, M. B. (1937–40).   Section 1 of " An introduction to nematology."   Baltimore.
KÜKENTHAL, W., and KRUMBACH, T. (1928–34).   Volume 2 and part 1 of " Handbuch der Zoologie."   Berlin and Leipzig.

APPENDIX TO THE NEMATODA

1. CULTURE METHODS

a. To obtain living *Rhabditis* and other soil nematodes, half fill a glass jar with moist soil, add one or two small pieces of raw meat, cover with a glass plate to prevent evaporation, and keep at room temperature.   The " encysted larvae " in the soil become active and feed on the juices produced as the meat rots.   Within a week they develop into adults, which are found most abundantly on the underside of the meat. The worms will continue living for a week or two in these conditions, but if a pure culture is required, isolate one or more mature females containing eggs and (with a drop of dirty water to supply bacteria) put them on to agar jelly (a 2% aqueous solution of agar allowed to cool and set in a covered dish). Within a few days the agar will be covered with hundreds of developing worms.

b. It is difficult to culture parasitic nematodes unless they are kept inside their natural hosts. The stages of *Trichinella* can easily be obtained by feeding infected pork to rats. Within two or three days the larvae grow to sexual maturity among the villi of the upper part of the small intestine. After about seven days the males die, but the females continue to live for as long as two months. The larvae are common in the blood between the eighth and twenty-fifth days as they pass to the muscles. The muscles particularly infected are those of the diaphragm, ribs, larynx, tongue, and eye, and once inside the muscle the larvae take about fourteen more days before they coil up and begin to encyst.

2. FIXATION METHODS

a. Nematodes are difficult to fix owing to their very resistant cuticles. The best fixative is steaming hot (almost boiling) 70% alcohol (remember that alcohol vapour is highly inflammable), but steaming hot 5% formalin can also be used. Parasitic worms should be fixed as soon as possible after they are removed from their host, but they should be given a preliminary wash in a 0·9% aqueous solution of sodium chloride. The dishes used for fixation should be large enough to allow the worms to straighten out.

b. When the fixing fluid has cooled, store the specimens either in fresh fluid of the same kind with 5% of glycerine added, or in a mixture made up of 85 parts of 70% alcohol, 10 parts of 10% formalin, and 5 parts of glycerine.

3. MOUNTING METHODS

a. Nematodes are not easily stained. Those required for microscopic examination should be placed in lactophenol solution (see p. 474), and left there until, after about a day, they become transparent. Permanent mounts may then be made by putting the worms on slides and adding melted glycerine jelly and a cover-glass. Alternatively, they may be examined in lactophenol, and then returned to the preserving fluid.

CHAPTER VIII

PHYLUM ACANTHOCEPHALA

Characteristics: Bilaterally symmetrical, unsegmented, elongated round-worms which are parasitic in the intestines of vertebrates; body usually divisible into a proboscis armed with hooks, a neck, and a trunk; body-wall composed of cuticle, syncytial epidermis, and circular and longitudinal muscle layers; large body cavity of doubtful nature; glandular lemnisci; no alimentary canal; excretory organs, when present, are a pair of nephridia with flame cells; sexes separate and gonads on a tubular ligament; nervous system a cephalic ganglion and two lateral nerves.

The systematic position of these, the thorny-headed worms, is doubtful. Those species infecting aquatic vertebrates pass their larval stage in some small crustacean, while those infecting land vertebrates make use of insects as alternate hosts.

Genus **Macracanthorhynchus** (**Echinorhynchus**)

I. GENERAL ACCOUNT

a. *M. hirudinaceus* Pallas (*E. gigas* Bloch), which occurs when adult in the small intestine of the pig, is common in southern Europe and in North America, but rare in the British Isles. Lacking an alimentary canal, it absorbs through its body-wall the already digested food of its host. The eggs, by the time they leave the female worm, contain well-developed embryos with pro-bosces and hooks, but they do not hatch until swallowed by some particular species of dung-eating beetle larva. Then they bore into the insect's body cavity and encyst. A pig is infected when it swallows the beetle larva, the young worm fixing itself into the wall of the small intestine and growing directly into an adult. The methods of fixation, preservation, etc., are the same as those of the nematodes (see p. 143).

2. EXTERNAL ANATOMY

a. The pink cylindrical **body** is widest near the anterior end, and tapers gradually to the posterior end. The anterior end is also marked by the small apical proboscis, and the posterior end by the terminal genital pore.

b. The **body-wall** is covered by a thin cuticle beneath which is the epidermis (a syncytium). In well-expanded specimens a canal system can be seen within the epidermis. There are two prominent lateral line canals, and each gives

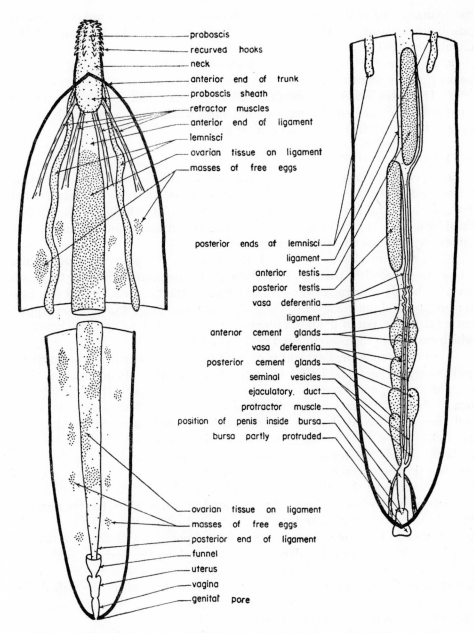

proboscis
recurved hooks
neck
anterior end of trunk
proboscis sheath
retractor muscles
anterior end of ligament
lemnisci
ovarian tissue on ligament
masses of free eggs

posterior ends of lemnisci
ligament
anterior testis
posterior testis
vasa deferentia
ligament
anterior cement glands
vasa deferentia
posterior cement glands
seminal vesicles
ejaculatory duct
protractor muscle
position of penis inside bursa
bursa partly protruded

ovarian tissue on ligament
masses of free eggs
posterior end of ligament
funnel
uterus
vagina
genital pore

FIG. 51—*Macracanthorhynchus* (*Echinorhynchus*). The anterior and posterior ends of a dissection of a female, and the posterior end of a dissection of a male.

L

rise to many small side branches (the function of the system is unknown, but is possibly circulatory). Through the epidermis the ring-like markings of the circular muscle layer are visible.

c. Examine the structure of the **proboscis**. It bears six rows of recurved hooks (for gripping the intestine wall), and is set on a neck which lacks hooks.

d. The **sexes** are distinguishable, the male being less than a quarter the length of the female, and having a genital bursa which is often found to be partly evaginated through the terminal genital pore.

3. INTERNAL ANATOMY

a. Open the worm by a longitudinal incision through the body-wall along a line running between the two lateral lines (dorsal and ventral sides are not recognisable), and pin aside the flaps. Notice the large **body cavity**, which is lined by a layer of longitudinal muscle fibres (the cavity is not coelom, and the muscle layer is not covered by an epithelium).

b. At the anterior end of the body cavity is the **proboscis sheath** (into which the proboscis is partially retractible). To the posterior end of the sheath are attached four retractor muscles which cross the body cavity and join into the longitudinal muscle layer of the body-wall; two long, thin lemnisci (apparently glandular, but of unknown function); and a tubular organ, the ligament, which extends to the posterior end of the animal.

c. In the **female** the ligament is covered by whitish granular ovarian tissue, and masses of eggs also lie freely in the body cavity. Mount some of these eggs on a slide, and examine them through a microscope. They include ripe ova ready for fertilisation, and developing eggs in two, four, eight, and many cell stages. Each of these is surrounded by a single shell (secreted by the zygote). There are also larger and darker eggs, each of which contains an embryo already possessing a proboscis with hooks and surrounded by a roughened capsule composed of three shells (the outer of which was secreted by the zygote and the others by the embryo ectoderm). At the posterior end of the body cavity is a single oviduct, the anterior end of which has the form of a funnel (inside this funnel the ligament ends, and into it the eggs pass; at the posterior end of the funnel are two tiny lateral pores, not easily seen, through which the small undeveloped eggs are returned to the body cavity). The rest of the oviduct is modified into a so-called uterus and a vagina, and the latter opens through the genital pore (and receives the penis of the male during copulation). The regions of the oviduct are more easily seen if the contained eggs are squeezed gently back out of the funnel.

d. In the **male** the tubular ligament is diaphanous. Anteriorly it bears two long white testes, one in front of the other. A vas deferens emerges from the anterior end of each testis, and the two vasa pass back side by side until, near the posterior end of the body, they join to form an ejaculatory duct.

The posterior ends of the vasa pass through a group of eight cement glands (function doubtful), and from the point at which the vasa join there emerge several narrow seminal vesicles (for the storage of spermatozoa), which run forwards alongside the cement glands and end blindly. The ejaculatory duct, which is joined to the body-wall by two narrow protractor muscle strands, ends in a small penis, which projects into the sac-like bursa (this bursa, which is protrusible through the genital pore, perhaps envelops, and so grips, the posterior end of the female during copulation).

e. The excretory and nervous systems are not easily distinguished in a dissection.

4. CONCLUSION

a. Observing the specimens, review the characteristics of the phylum.

b. Contrast the structure of *Macracanthorhynchus* with that of *Ascaris*.

5. REFERENCES

For the structure of this and of other genera see :

HAMANN, O. (1891). "Monographie der Acanthocephalen (Echinorhynchen). Ihre Entwicklungsgeschichte, Histogenie und Anatomie." *Jenaische Zeitschrift für Natur-wissenschaft*, Vol. 25, p. 113.

KAISER, J. E. (1893). "Die Acanthocephalen und ihre Entwickelung." *Bibliotheca Zoologica*, Vol. 2, p. 1.

CHAPTER IX

PHYLUM **ROTIFERA**

Characteristics : Small, bilaterally symmetrical, unsegmented animals, usually with a head, trunk, and postanal foot ; ciliated trochal disc for loco-motion and food capture ; mouth antero-ventral and cloacal opening postero-dorsal ; pharynx containing jaws ; flame-cell excretory system discharging into cloaca ; large perivisceral cavity which is not coelom ; no blood system ; no special respiratory organs ; cerebral ganglion and simple nervous system ; sexes separate, but males usually degenerate or absent and parthenogenesis common.

The Rotifera, the smallest of the Metazoa, have a relatively constant structure, but their affinities are doubtful. They are very widespread, the great majority occurring in fresh waters, where they are either free living or sedentary. Only a few are parasitic or marine.

0.01. Order **Monogonata**

Characteristics : Rotifera with lateral sensory papillae ; females with only one ovary ; and males usually present but degenerate.

The great majority of the common species belong to this order.

Genus **Hydatina (Epiphanes)**

1. GENERAL ACCOUNT

a. One of the commonest and largest of the rotifers, *Hydatina* is found abundantly in such places as farm pools which are contaminated with manure and green with *Euglena* or *Chlamydomonas*. It swims freely with its cilia, but when feeding it fixes itself by its foot, and the cilia then drive unicellular plants and animals into its mouth. There are two types of females, amictic and mictic. The former produce eggs which develop parthenogenetically and give rise to females of both types. The mictic females produce eggs which, if they develop parthenogenetically, give rise to males or, if they are fertilised, form thick shells and lie dormant. These resting eggs resist freezing and desiccation, and ultimately give rise to amictic females. A culture method is described on p. 151.

2. EXTERNAL ANATOMY

a. Mount living specimens in an uncovered drop of water, and watch their **movements** through a low-power microscope. They either swim actively by means of their cilia, or walk with a looping action by gripping the substratum alternately with foot and head, or remain sedentary and use the cilia to set up a feeding current.

b. Add a cover-glass, and if necessary arrest movement by the agar method (described for protozoans on p. 35). The **body** consists of a head, which is

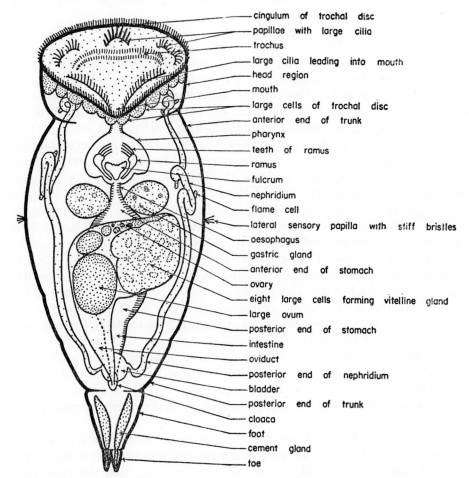

cingulum of trochal disc
papillae with large cilia
trochus
large cilia leading into mouth
head region
mouth
large cells of trochal disc
anterior end of trunk
pharynx
teeth of ramus
ramus
fulcrum
nephridium
flame cell
lateral sensory papilla with stiff bristles
oesophagus
gastric gland
anterior end of stomach
ovary
eight large cells forming vitelline gland
large ovum
posterior end of stomach
intestine
oviduct
posterior end of nephridium
bladder
posterior end of trunk
cloaca
foot
cement gland
toe

FIG. 52.—*Hydatina* (*Epiphanes*). A female seen from the ventral side with the circular and oblique muscle bands omitted.

flattened anteriorly to form the ciliated trochal disc, a rotund trunk, and a posterior foot, which terminates in two toes. It is covered by a thin cuticle (secreted by the syncytial ectoderm, which is the only complete cell layer in the body-wall). The dorsal side is marked by a sensory papilla on the head, by a hump on the trunk, and by the cloacal opening just in front of the foot

There is also a sensory papilla on each side of the trunk, and all three papillae are crowned with stiff bristles.

c. The **trochal disc**, composed of very large cells, bears two main groups of cilia, the inner, the trochus, forming a double transverse row, and the outer, the cingulum, encircling the edge of the disc. Between them is a shallow groove containing a series of papillae bearing especially large cilia, which lead into the ventral mouth.

3. INTERNAL ANATOMY

a. In females (which are larger and far commoner than males) held steady by agar or made into a permanent preparation (method on p. 151), notice the large body cavity and distinguish the **alimentary canal**. The mouth opens into a stomodaeum (lined by ectoderm and cuticle), which has the form of a muscular pharynx, or mastax, containing three chitinous teeth, or trophi (which break up the food). Two of these teeth, the rami, are lateral and hinge on the central and ventral tooth, the fulcrum. From the pharynx a short, narrow, ciliated oesophagus leads to the large, ciliated stomach (in which digestion takes place). The wall of the stomach can be seen to be composed of a single layer of large cells. Into the anterior end of the stomach open two lateral gastric glands with cell nuclei clearly visible, and from its posterior end emerges a short, ciliated intestine, which leads to the small cloaca.

b. Trace the course of the **excretory system**. It consists of two tubes, the nephridia (formed of drainpipe-like cells), one on each side of the alimentary canal. Each tube is relatively straight except where it is thrown into coils on a level with the gastric glands, and again close behind the trochal disc (it is difficult to see that the two nephridia are joined by a cross duct which passes between the large cells of the trochal disc). Anteriorly and at irregular intervals, tiny, blind-ending flame-cells can be seen protruding from the sides of the nephridia, and in living specimens the flickering action of the cilia within them is visible. The posterior half of each nephridium does not bear flame-cells, but leads into a ventral bladder (which pulsates to drive the excreted liquid upwards into the cloaca).

c. Identify the **brain**, a large swelling between the base of the dorsal sensory papilla and the pharynx ; the narrow **muscle bands** which encircle the body at intervals and pass obliquely across the body cavity ; and the two **cement glands** lying within the foot and the toes (they open through pores in the tips of the toes, and secrete a sticky material to anchor the animal while it feeds).

d. The **female reproductive system** lies ventral to the alimentary canal. It consists mainly of a vitelline gland (yolk secreting), which is usually displaced laterally and is composed of eight large cells with prominent nuclei, and of an ovary, which lies sandwiched between the vitelline gland and the stomach. The ovary usually protrudes both anteriorly and laterally, and in addition there is usually one very large egg lying in the broad, thin-walled oviduct which passes back to open into the ventral side of the cloaca.

e. If a **male** is available, notice that it is only about half the length of the female, that it lacks an alimentary canal, and that it contains a single large testis. This testis discharges into the cloaca, which is elongated and opens through the end of a large dorsal penis (which is inserted through the cloaca and into the oviduct of the female during copulation).

4. CONCLUSION

a. Observing the specimens, review the characteristics of the phylum and of the order.

5. REFERENCES

DELAGE, Y., and HÉROUARD, E. (1897). Volume 5 of " Traité de zoologie concrète." Paris.

KÜKENTHAL, W., and KRUMBACH, T. (1928–34). Volume 2 and part 1 of " Handbuch der Zoologie." Berlin and Leipzig.

APPENDIX TO THE ROTIFERA

1. CULTURE METHODS

a. Rotifers of many genera are readily obtained from ponds, small pools, or damp moss, and they will live for weeks in aquaria. *Hydatina* itself is most easily obtained from pools, such as those in farm-yards, which are green with flagellate protozoans and unicellular plants. However, it may prove most convenient to collect the baked mud from the bottoms of dried-up ponds or farm-yard pools, and to put it into water a few days before the animals are required.

b. Because of these simple collecting methods more permanent culture is rarely necessary, but if required rotifers such as *Hydatina* will live indefinitely if fed with cultures of *Euglena* or *Chlamydomonas* (see p. 34).

2. FIXATION METHOD

a. All rotifers require special fixation. They should first be narcotised by adding drops of a solution of eucain hydrochloride (1 gm. dissolved in 10 c.c. of 90% alcohol with 10 c.c. of distilled water added) to the small volume of water (less than 10 c.c.) in which the animals are confined. When they have sunk to the bottom, add and mix rapidly a solution of osmic acid, one drop to each c.c. of water (use a 1% aqueous solution of osmic acid with 1% of chloro-platinic acid added). After ten minutes replace the fixing fluid with water, and renew the water several times during the next few hours. Finally store in 5% formalin.

3.   STAINING METHODS

   a. Rotifers can be stained alive by pipetting them into a 1 : 50,000 solution of neutral red.

   b. Alternatively, for permanent preparations, specimens fixed as above can be stained for about twenty-four hours in alum carmine diluted to a pale pink colour, or in one of the haematoxylin solutions such as Delafield's, diluted to the point of transparency.   After haematoxylin, differentiation is in a 1% solution of hydrochloric acid in 90% alcohol, followed by blueing in 90% alcohol to which a drop of ammonia has been added.   Finally, the specimens should be dehydrated and mounted in Canada balsam.

CHAPTER X

PHYLUM **ENDOPROCTA**

Characteristics : Small unsegmented solitary or colonial animals which are stalked and sessile; with distal circle of non-retractible tentacles, the lophophore; a U-shaped alimentary canal with both mouth and anus opening within the lophophore; no coelom, the space between body wall and alimentary canal being filled by a gelatinous substance containing mesenchyme cells; a protonephridial excretory system but no vascular system; usually hermaphrodite and reproduction also by budding; and with a free-swimming ciliated larva.

Although originally grouped with the Ectoprocta in the phylum Polyzoa (Bryozoa), the Endoprocta must be considered a separate phylum. Perhaps their closest relationships may be with the pseudocoelomate rotifers, which they resemble in shape of body and of alimentary canal and in the possession of a protonephridial system. The endoprocts are common in the sea, frequently being found attached to other animals or plants, and the genus *Urnatella* is also found in fresh water in North America.

Genus **Pedicellina**

(The anatomy of all the members of this phylum is remarkably constant, and other genera, such as the solitary *Loxosoma*, may be used as alternatives.)

I. GENERAL ACCOUNT

a. The genus *Pedicellina* is apparently cosmopolitan, the colonies being found between tide-marks and in shallow seas firmly attached to almost any solid object. The individual zooids are connected by a stolon, which also gives rise to new buds. The tentacles are ciliated and so maintain a current of water from which diatoms, desmids, and protozoans are filtered for food. In adverse conditions the bodies of the zooids may degenerate, leaving only the stolon and the stalks. New bodies may later regenerate on the ends of the stalks, and similar regeneration also occurs readily after injury. Some species are hermaphrodite, while others appear to be dioecious, but when more is known these latter may prove to be protandric hermaphrodites. Fertilisation is internal, early development is inside a brood pouch, and the embryos finally escape as free-swimming ciliated larvae.

153

2. ANATOMY

a. The **colony** consists of numerous zooids, or polyps, each attached by a stalk to a basal stolon (which adheres closely to the substratum). Buds are especially evident at the tips of the stolon. Notice that the stolon tube is subdivided by septa at short intervals, and that of the compartments so formed only the alternate ones bear zooids.

b. An individual, or **zooid**, consists of a stalk, a body containing the essential organs, and a distal crown of tentacles called the lophophore. Within the stalk is a central strand of retractor muscle.

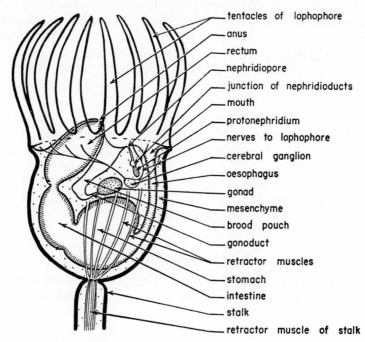

tentacles of lophophore
anus
rectum
nephridiopore
junction of nephridioducts
mouth
protonephridium
nerves to lophophore
cerebral ganglion
oesophagus
gonad
mesenchyme
brood pouch
gonoduct
retractor muscles
stomach
intestine
stalk
retractor muscle of stalk

FIG. 53.—*Pedicellina.* A zooid as seen in optical section from the side. For clarity, the various body organs have been more widely spaced than is natural.

c. Examine the **lophophore.** Viewed from above, the tentacle bases form an oval because the body is slightly flattened bilaterally, and at the ends of the oval, opposite the mouth and the anus respectively, the gap between adjacent tentacles is wider. The tentacles vary in number according to the species and to the age of the zooid (food particles are passed down a ciliated track on the inner side of each tentacle to enter either the left or right vestibular groove, which leads forwards to enter the left or right corner of the mouth).

d. Inside the body of a zooid viewed from the side (for methods of fixation and staining see as for Ectoprocta on p. 161) distinguish the U-shaped **alimen-**

tary canal. The mouth opens through a narrow oesophagus into a capacious stomach, which is situated basally within the body. From this the intestine rises to join into the rectum, which opens at the anus. Notice that there is no muscle coat in the wall of the alimentary canal, although sphincter muscles are present at the junction of the intestine and rectum and at the anus (the food is moved by the cilia which line the whole canal; part of the stomach epithelium is glandular).

e. Notice that the space between the body wall and the alimentary canal is filled by a loose **mesenchyme** (which is embedded in a gelatinous matrix; this mesenchyme also extends up the centres of the tentacles).

f. The **excretory system** is not easily visible in whole mounts. There are two protonephridia close behind the oesophagus, and these open by a common duct to a single nephridiopore just behind the mouth.

g. The most prominent part of the **reproductive system** is the pair of large gonads. In dioecious species of *Pedicellina* these may be either testes or ovaries; in hermaphrodite species the pair of testes is situated posterior to the pair of ovaries. The two ducts from the gonads unite in the centre line to open through a single gonopore; in hermaphrodite species the sperm duct and the oviduct of each side unite to form a common duct before joining with the common duct from the other side. The gonopore opens into a deep recess, which in females and in hermaphrodites acts as a brood pouch (the eggs remain there until they develop into ciliated larvae).

h. The **nervous system** is extensive but usually only the cerebral ganglia can be distinguished in the region above the stomach. Three pairs of nerves extend upwards to give branches to the tentacles.

3. CONCLUSION

a. Observing the specimen, review the characteristics of the phylum.

b. Compare and contrast the structure of *Pedicellina* with that of a rotifer such as *Hydatina*.

4. REFERENCE

KÜKENTHAL, W., and KRUMBACH, T. (1928–33) Volume 2, Part I of " Handbuch der Zoologie. Kamptozoa." Leipzig.

CHAPTER XI

PHYLUM **ECTOPROCTA**

Characteristics : Small unsegmented sessile colonial animals; with a circle of tentacles, the lophophore, retractible into a sheath; a U-shaped alimentary canal with the mouth opening inside and the anus outside the lophophore; coelomic body cavity; no excretory system and no vascular system; hermaphrodite and reproduction also by budding; and commonly with a free-swimming ciliated larva.

This very ancient group must be regarded as a phylum in its own right, and the composite phylum, the Polyzoa (Bryozoa), should be abandoned. The resemblances between the Ectoprocta and the Endoprocta are superficial and probably mainly due to convergence. The ectoprocts are primarily marine, but many genera also occur in fresh water.

o.oi.   Order **Gymnolaemata**

Characteristics : Ectoprocta which are mainly marine and which show polymorphism; with a circular lophophore; no epistome; and no statoblasts.

Genus **Bugula**

I.   GENERAL ACCOUNT

a. The species of *Bugula* occur all over the world, and are found commonly in shallow seas up to the low-tide mark. The upright branching colonies are attached to rocks, wooden piles, seaweeds, or various animals such as sponges or molluscs. The food, consisting mainly of unicellular plants and animals, is caught by the lophophore, which is also a respiratory structure. Asexual reproduction results in increased colony size. Sexual reproduction takes place in temperate regions in summer and autumn. The eggs are retained, one to each ovicell, until they develop into ciliated larvae, and these are released each day about dawn to swim free for about five hours before they settle to grow into the first individuals of new colonies.

2.   ANATOMY

a. The **colony,** or zooarium, is erect and flexible, and is fixed to the substratum by rooting filaments. It is made up largely of feeding individuals, or zooids, which are placed alternately. The branching is dichotomous, and the whole is ensheathed in an exoskeleton of calcified chitin (secreted by the ectoderm).

b. In a stained preparation (see methods of fixation and staining on p. 161) notice that the body of each **zooid** is encased in an elongated, cup-shaped

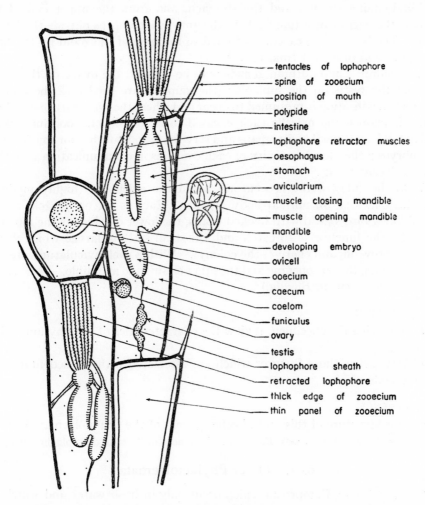

tentacles of lophophore
spine of zooecium
position of mouth
polypide
intestine
lophophore retractor muscles
oesophagus
stomach
avicularium
muscle closing mandible
muscle opening mandible
mandible
developing embryo
ovicell
ooecium
caecum
coelom
funiculus
ovary
testis
lophophore sheath
retracted lophophore
thick edge of zooecium
thin panel of zooecium

FIG. 54.—*Bugula.* Part of a colony showing the structure of a zooid, an ovicell, and an avicularium.

exoskeleton, the zooecium, which has thickened edges, thin sides, and one or more spines (depending on the species) on its upper edge. That part of the zooid which protrudes is called the polypide, and it bears the ring of tentacles, the lophophore, which surrounds the mouth (the tentacles are strongly ciliated on their inner sides, and they contain extensions of the coelom). When retracted, the walls of the polypide form a lophophore sheath. Retractor muscles join the base of the lophophore to the body-wall.

c. In an extended zooid the **alimentary canal** is easily visible hanging within the large coelom. The swollen oesophagus opens into the junction of the blind-ending caecum and the stomach, and from the upper end of the stomach the narrow intestine leads to the anus, which opens outside the lophophore. The base of the caecum is joined to the base of the zooid by the funiculus (a strand of mesodermal tissue).

d. In summer and autumn **gonads** may be present, the ovary on the body-wall and the testis on the funiculus (the gametes are shed into the coelom, where self-fertilisation is presumed to occur and where the eggs start to develop).

e. Distinguish the **ovicells** each encased in an exoskeletal ooecium (these individuals lack normal body organs and serve as brood pouches for the developing embryos; the coelomic cavity of each ovicell is in communication with that of the adjacent zooid).

f. On the sides of the zooecia are based the **avicularia** (highly modified individuals lacking all normal body organs). Each is set on a neck, and is shaped like a bird's head with hooked beaks, the lower of which is the movable mandible (the function is to catch and kill small settling larvae which would otherwise grow on, and encrust, the colony). Within each avicularium are two strong muscles, the one opening and the other closing the mandible. (Nb. vibracularia do not occur in *Bugula*.)

3.   CONCLUSION

a. Observing the specimen, review the characteristics of the phylum and of the order.

b. Also review those features which are associated with the sedentary and colonial mode of life.

4.   REFERENCE

For the structure of this and of other genera of the Gymnolaemata see:

DELAGE, Y., and HÉROUARD, E. (1897). Volume 5 of "Traité de zoologie concrète." Paris.

o.o2.   Order **Phylactolaemata**

Characteristics: Ectoprocta which occur only in fresh water and which do not show polymorphism; with a horseshoe-shaped lophophore and an epistome; and with resistant winter buds, called statoblasts.

Genus **Pectinatella**

I.   GENERAL ACCOUNT

a. Pectinatella is a common genus with a world-wide distribution in the quiet waters of slow rivers, lakes, and ponds. By asexual reproduction, large colonies, sometimes reaching several feet in diameter, are built up around a variety of supports such as reeds and logs, molluscs and crustaceans. The individuals forming the colonies are very voracious and feed on rotifers, flagellate and ciliate protozoans, and on diatoms and desmids. Sexual reproduction takes place in spring and summer, and in late summer and autumn asexual buds,

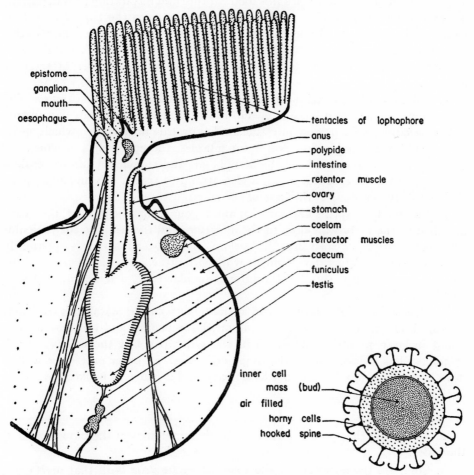

epistome
ganglion
mouth
oesophagus

tentacles of lophophore
anus
polypide
intestine
retentor muscle
ovary
stomach
coelom
retractor muscles
caecum
funiculus
testis

inner cell mass (bud)
air filled horny cells
hooked spine

Fig. 55.—*Pectinatella.* A zooid as seen in optical section with the zooecium and half of the lophophore omitted. Lower right is a statoblast.

called " winter eggs " or statoblasts, are produced. These are very resistant to adverse conditions, and survive the winter.

2. ANATOMY

   a. The **colony** is gelatinous and often massive, and its shape varies according to that of the object which it envelops. The gelatinous zooecia are completely fused together to form a common exoskeleton, but the relatively large individuals, or zooids, are distinct, and can be seen through the transparent jelly.

b. In an expanded **zooid** (seen either alive or as a preparation made according to the methods described on p. 161) the protruded part of the body, the polypide, can be seen to bear the horseshoe-shaped lophophore, which is composed of a double row of ciliated tentacles (for food capture and respiration; and containing extensions of the coelom). The mouth lies between the two rows of tentacles, and to one side of it is the epistome (which can close over the mouth). Close beneath the epistome is a prominent ganglion, the " brain ", and the base of the polypide is joined internally to the body-wall by a ring of retentor muscles.

c. The **alimentary canal** is suspended in a capacious coelomic cavity. The oesophagus opens into a large stomach, the base of which extends downwards as the caecum, and a narrow intestine leads upwards to the anus, which opens on the side of the polypide. Retractor muscles, the upper ends of which are attached mainly to one side of the oesophagus and stomach, cross the coelom to join into the base of the zooid, and a strand of tissue, the funiculus, joins the base of the caecum to the base of the zooid.

d. Especially in spring and early summer, **gonads** may be present, the ovary attached to the body-wall close to the intestine, and the testis to the funiculus (the spermatozoa are shed into the coelom, and self-fertilisation is apparently the rule; the eggs start development while still attached to the ovary, and the ciliated larvae escape through the intertentacular tube, a temporary opening within the lophophore).

e. Especially in late summer and autumn, lens-shaped **statoblasts** (resistant asexual buds) may be seen developing on the funiculus, and they can also be found in large numbers embedded in the older parts of the colony. Each statoblast has a dark centre (the living cell mass), an outer protective wall of dead horny cells (air filled to act as a float), and a fringe of hooked spines (an anchoring device).

3. CONCLUSION

a. Observing the specimen, review the characteristics of the phylum and of the order.

b. Compare the structure of the zooid of *Pectinatella* with that of *Bugula*, and the structure and function of the statoblast of *Pectinatella* with those of the gemmule of *Ephydatia*.

4. REFERENCES

For the structure of this and of other genera of the Phylactolaemata see :

DELAGE, Y., and HÉROUARD, E. (1897). Volume 5 of " Traité de zoologie concrète." Paris.

HYATT, A. (1866–68). " Observations on Polyzoa. Suborder Phylactolaemata." Salem.

APPENDIX TO THE ECTOPROCTA

1. CULTURE METHODS

a. Marine Ectoprocta are not easily kept in aquaria for long, since the constant addition of sea-water containing a food supply of unicellular organisms is necessary.

b. Fresh-water Ectoprocta are more easily cultured, although well-grown colonies usually die quickly when brought into the laboratory. The best way to obtain healthy living animals is to collect the statoblasts in late summer and autumn, either by catching with a fine mesh net those floating at the surface of a pond, or by letting an old colony die and disintegrate until the statoblasts float free. Until they are required they can be kept dormant in some cold place. When brought into the warmth (about 20° C.) they hatch in about a month. Each statoblast then quickly develops into a single zooid, and small colonies may be grown by adding *Euglena* or *Paramecium* cultures (see p. 34), dried and powdered *Elodea*, or even malted milk. However, for an examination of the internal structure the newly hatched single zooids are best, since they have not yet secreted gelatinous zooecia.

2. FIXATION METHODS

a. For all Ectoprocta narcotisation is preferable before fixation. Colonies of *Bugula* or single zooids of *Pectinatella*, obtained as described above, should be kept quiet in a small volume of water and allowed to expand their tentacles. Then add a few crystals of menthol, and when the tentacles no longer contract when touched, kill the animals by adding enough commercial formalin to make up a 5% solution. Store either in fresh 5% formalin, or wash in water and pass slowly through 30% and 50% alcohols and store in 70% alcohol.

3. STAINING METHODS

a. Material preserved in alcohol is most easily stained in borax carmine, into which it can be directly transferred. Overstain and then remove the excess in a 1% solution of hydrochloric acid in 70% alcohol. Wash in normal 70% alcohol, and then pass the animals slowly (about 5 or 10 minutes in each) through 90% alcohol, absolute alcohol, a mixture of absolute alcohol and xylol, and xylol, and mount in Canada balsam.

b. Alternatively, the specimens may be transferred to water, either direct from formalin or via 50% and 30% alcohols from 70% alcohol, and overstained in a haematoxylin solution such as Delafield's. Then wash in water and take slowly through 30% and 50% alcohols to 70% alcohol (five to ten minutes in each). As before, remove the excess stain in acid 70% alcohol, and then turn the remainder of the stain blue in 70% alcohol made alkaline with a few drops of ammonia. Finally pass the specimens through 90% alcohol, absolute alcohol, and xylol, and mount in Canada balsam.

M

CHAPTER XII

PHYLUM **BRACHIOPODA**

Characteristics : Unsegmented sedentary animals which are usually anchored by a peduncle ; with the body enclosed by dorsal and ventral mantle lobes which secrete the bivalve shell ; large coiled circumoral lophophore ; coelom and haemocoel well developed ; one or two pairs of excretory nephridia, which also serve as gonoducts ; sexes usually separate ; and larvae ciliated and free swimming.

This is a very ancient and conservative phylum which has flourished in all geological ages from the Cambrian to the present time. Today it is marine and cosmopolitan.

0.01. Order **Ecardines**

Characteristics : Brachiopoda with the shell mainly chitinous and the valves not hinged ; with no internal skeleton ; and with an anus present.

Genus **Lingula**

1. GENERAL ACCOUNT

a. This is the oldest animal genus known, and it has apparently existed unchanged since the Cambrian. Today the species are tropical and subtropical, and they live in muddy sand between and just below tide-marks. Each animal is anchored by a long peduncle, the contraction of which pulls it to safety beneath the surface. The anterior edges of the two valves project from the mud, and by the action of the cilia of the lophophore, two inhalent currents are drawn in at the sides and a single exhalent current leaves in the centre. In this way oxygen is obtained and tiny food particles, such as unicellular animals and plants, are caught. *Lingula* is hermaphrodite, fertilisation is external, and ciliated larvae are produced.

2. EXTERNAL ANATOMY

a. The body is encased in two identical greenish **shell-valves**, which are marked by concentric lines of growth and are dorsal and ventral in position. Between the valves the edges of the two mantle lobes are visible, and embedded in these edges (and secreted by them) is a fringe of horny setae.

b. The posterior end of the body protrudes as a long **peduncle** (highly contractile) encased in a thick semi-transparent cuticle through which a central muscle band can be seen.

3. INTERNAL ANATOMY

a. Carefully detach both valves by separating them from the mantle lobes and cutting the two anterior and one posterior adductor muscles (which close

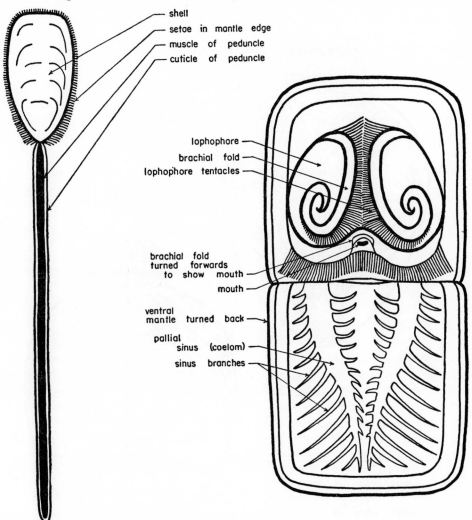

shell
setae in mantle edge
muscle of peduncle
cuticle of peduncle

lophophore
brachial fold
lophophore tentacles

brachial fold
turned forwards
to show mouth
mouth

ventral
mantle turned back

pallial
sinus (coelom)
sinus branches

FIG. 56.—*Lingula.* A whole specimen to show the length of the peduncle, and, on the right, a ventral view with the ventral mantle fold turned back to show the lophophore, the mouth, and the sinus system.

the valves). Turn back the ventral mantle fold (see figure 56) to expose the **lophophore** within the mantle cavity. It is composed of two spiral projections of the anterior body-wall and bears a row of ciliated tentacles. Along the bases of the tentacles a deep ciliated groove leads to the mouth (it carries the food particles caught by the tentacles). One side of this groove is formed by the brachial fold, which also normally covers the mouth.

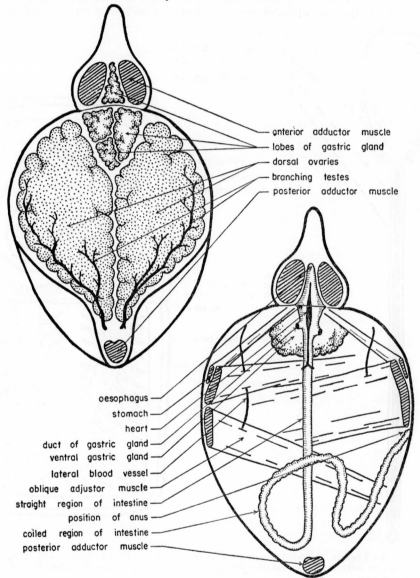

anterior adductor muscle
lobes of gastric gland
dorsal ovaries
branching testes
posterior adductor muscle

oesophagus
stomach
heart
duct of gastric gland
ventral gastric gland
lateral blood vessel
oblique adjustor muscle
straight region of intestine
position of anus
coiled region of intestine
posterior adductor muscle

FIG. 57.—*Lingula*. A dorsal view of a specimen from which the dorsal mantle has been removed (above). A dorsal view of a specimen from which the dorsal ovaries and gastric glands have been removed (below).

b. Within the inner surface of the ventral mantle fold notice the large branching **sinus system** (probably respiratory), which is an extension of the perivisceral coelom.   Notice that a similar system is also present inside the dorsal mantle fold.

c. Cut away the dorsal mantle lobe together with the thin membrane which covers the visceral mass and forms the upper wall of the perivisceral coelom. Distinguish the dorsal pair of large **ovaries** from the greenish lobes of the dorsal gastric gland.   On the surface of the ovaries, particularly posteriorly, the **testes** can be seen as colourless or orange branching threads (another pair of ovaries bearing branching testes are situated ventral to the visceral mass ; the gametes are shed into the coelom and escape through the nephridioducts).

d. Uncover the **alimentary canal** and the ventral gastric glands by gently removing the dorsal ovaries and the dorsal gastric glands.   The oesophagus opens into a swollen stomach, into which also open the ducts of the dorsal and ventral gastric glands.   From the stomach the intestine leads straight to the posterior end of the body cavity, and then coils forwards to the anus, which is on the right side.

e. Dorsal to the stomach lies the **heart**, and lateral blood-vessels are also prominent where they perforate the three large oblique **adjustor muscles** and pass dorsal to the two small anterior adjustor muscles (the course of the circulation is doubtful).

f. Cut through the outer ends of the three large adjustor muscles, and displace them to expose the two broad **nephridioducts** which lie lateral to the two ventral ovaries.

4.   CONCLUSION

a. Observing the specimen, review the characteristics of the phylum and of the order.

b. Also review those features which are associated with a sedentary life spent buried in sand.

5.   REFERENCES

For the structure of this and of other Ecardines see :

DELAGE, Y., and HÉROUARD, E. (1897).   Volume 5 of " Traité de zoologie concrète." Paris.
    HANCOCK, A. (1858).   " On the organisation of the Brachiopoda." *Philosophical Transactions of the Royal Society of London*, Vol. 148, p. 791.

0.02.   Order **Testicardines**

Characteristics : Brachiopoda with the shell mainly calcareous and with the valves hinged together ; with an internal skeleton ; and with no anus.

Genus **Terebratella**

(*Waldheimia*, *Terebratulina*, and other similar genera may be used as alternatives.)

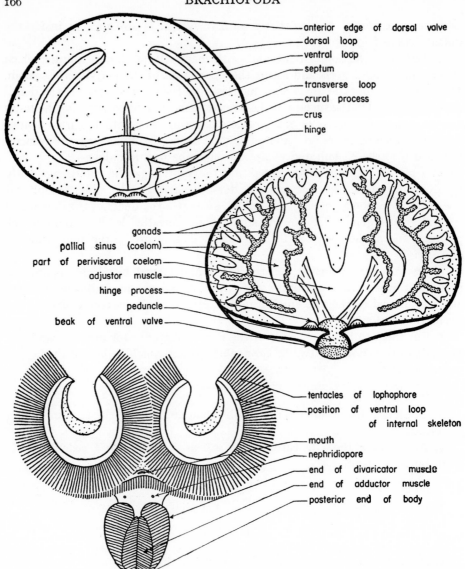

anterior edge of dorsal valve
dorsal loop
ventral loop
septum
transverse loop
crural process
crus
hinge

gonads
pallial sinus (coelom)
part of perivisceral coelom
adjustor muscle
hinge process
peduncle
beak of ventral valve

tentacles of lophophore
position of ventral loop
　　　　of internal skeleton
mouth
nephridiopore
end of divaricator muscle
end of adductor muscle
posterior end of body

FIG. 58.—*Terebratella.* An internal view of the dorsal valve to show the skeleton, an internal view of the ventral mantle lobe to show the coelomic sinus system and the gonads, and a ventral view of the body with the dorsal and ventral mantle lobes removed.

I. GENERAL ACCOUNT

a. Terebratella has a world-wide distribution, and is a common circumpolar form. It occurs particularly on rock or gravel bottoms from near the low-tide mark to depths of more than 100 fathoms. Each individual is fixed by a short peduncle, and its ciliated lophophore sets up water currents which bring oxygen and food. Through the gape of the shell two inhalent currents enter laterally and one exhalent current leaves centrally. The food sieved from the water consists mainly of tiny larvae and of unicellular plants and animals. The sexes are separate, fertilisation is external, and ciliated free-swimming larvae are formed.

2. EXTERNAL ANATOMY

a. The body is encased in two **shell-valves**, which show concentric lines of growth. The ventral valve is larger and has a projection, the beak, which is posterior to the hinge and which is perforated for the passage of the peduncle. This perforation, called the foramen, has an incomplete margin. The gape of the shell is anterior, and when closed the two valves fit perfectly together.

b. The dark brown **peduncle** is short, thick, and of a horny nature (and is normally cemented firmly to some support).

3. INTERNAL ANATOMY

a. In a cleaned specimen (method of cleaning on p. 169) a delicate **internal skeleton** can be seen attached within the dorsal valve. It consists of a ridge-like septum and two crura, which are based lateral to the hinge and which bear the crural processes and the dorsal, ventral, and transverse skeletal loops (which support the lophophore). In the ventral valve notice the hinge processes, and the foramen for the peduncle.

b. Pull back the ventral valve of a preserved specimen (method of preservation on p. 169) until the hinge breaks (because of the internal skeleton the animal remains attached to the dorsal valve). In the ventral mantle lobe (detached with the ventral valve) identify the large branched **pallial sinuses** (extensions of the perivisceral coelom, and probably respiratory), and the pair of large **adjustor muscles** which join the ventral valve to the base of the peduncle.

c. In the walls of the pallial sinuses lie the **gonads**, either testes or ovaries (the gametes are shed into the coelom and escape via the nephridia).

d. Examine the coiled structure of the **lophophore**, and its fringe of ciliated tentacles. Trace the course of the ciliated groove (food carrying), which passes between the bases of the tentacles and a prominent brachial fold, and which leads to the crescentic mouth. Feel for the positions of the dorsal and ventral loops of the internal supporting skeleton.

e. Carefully detach the dorsal valve and mantle lobe by cutting through the adductor muscles and breaking the connexions of the internal skeleton. Cut away the enlarged dorsal ends of the adductor muscles to expose the two gastric glands, and remove the right gastric gland to uncover the **alimentary canal** (which is ciliated throughout). The oesophagus, rising dorsally, turns back to join the swollen stomach, into which there open laterally the ducts of the gastric glands and posteriorly the short, blind-ending intestine.

f. Lateral to the intestine distinguish the two **adductor muscles** (which joined the two shell valves), and the two divaricator muscles (which joined the ventral valve to the crura).

g. Above the posterior end of the stomach is the globular **heart,** from which several vessels emerge (the course of the circulation is doubtful).

h. Postero-lateral to the heart are the two prominent **nephrostomes,** with thick, folded lips, and from them two diaphanous nephridioducts lead down-

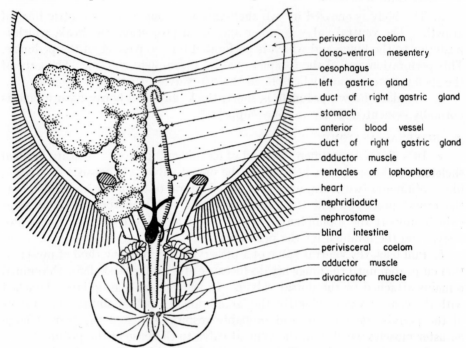

periviscerol   coelom
dorso-ventral   mesentery
oesophagus
left   gastric   gland
duct   of   right   gastric   gland
stomach
anterior   blood   vessel
duct   of   right   gastric   gland
adductor   muscle
tentacles   of   lophophore
heart
nephridioduct
nephrostome
blind   intestine
periviscerol   coelom
adductor   muscle
divaricator   muscle

FIG. 59.—*Terebratella.*   A dissection made from the dorsal side and from which the right gastric gland has been removed.

wards to the nephridiopores (they serve both as excretory ducts and as gono-ducts).

4.   CONCLUSION

a. Observing the specimens, review the characteristics of the phylum and of the order.

b. Compare the mode of life and structure of *Terebratella* with those of *Lingula.*

5.   REFERENCES

For the details of the structure of this and of related genera of the Testi-cardines see :

DELAGE, Y., and HÉROUARD, E. (1897).   Volume 5 of " Traité de zoologie concrète." Paris.

HANCOCK, A. (1858). "On the organisation of the Brachiopoda." *Philosophical Transactions of the Royal Society of London*, Vol. 148, p. 791.

APPENDIX TO THE BRACHIOPODA

I. METHOD OF FIXATION AND PRESERVATION

a. It is recommended that brachiopods be killed by slowly adding 90% alcohol up to a maximum of a tenth part of the volume of sea-water in which they are confined. When the shell-valves open easily insert chips of wood, and store the specimens in 70% alcohol.

2. METHOD OF EXPOSING THE INTERNAL SKELETON

a. Slowly transfer a large preserved specimen through 50% and 30% alcohols (twenty-four hours in each) to water. Add potassium hydroxide to make a concentrated solution, and keep hot, but not boiling, until all the soft parts have dissolved. Allow to cool, and wash in water.

CHAPTER XIII

PHYLUM **CHAETOGNATHA**

Characteristics : Elongated, unsegmented, coelomate animals with body divisible into head, trunk, and tail ; head with eyes and chitinous spines and jaws ; trunk and tail with lateral and caudal fins ; alimentary canal straight and simple ; no special excretory, respiratory, or vascular systems ; nervous system with dorsal cerebral and ventral trunk ganglia joined by commissures ; cross-fertilising hermaphrodite with no larval stage.

The chaetognaths form an aberrant but homogeneous group, which is considered to be ancient and to represent an early offshoot from the coelomate stock. They are exclusively marine.

Genus **Sagitta** (arrow worm)

I. GENERAL ACCOUNT

a. The cosmopolitan species of *Sagitta* occur in huge numbers in the plankton close to the surface of the sea, and also down to depths of more than 100 fathoms. For protection they are almost completely transparent. They swim rapidly and feed predaciously on almost all other planktonic plants and animals from diatoms to small fishes. They are cross-fertilising hermaphrodites, and the spermatozoa, in some way unknown, enter the oviducts to fertilise the eggs internally. The eggs are then laid, and float near the surface to develop directly into small worms, which are essentially like the adults.

2. ANATOMY

a. In a stained preparation (method of staining on p. 172) distinguish the regions of the **body**. The head is small, and the long trunk and tail bear two anterior lateral fins, two posterior lateral fins, and a caudal fin (each fin is an ectodermal fold containing a gelatinous substance and a series of stiffening chitinous rays). The division between the trunk and tail regions is marked internally by the position of a posterior transverse septum. The body-wall, covered by a thin epithelium, contains four bundles of longitudinal muscles, two of which are dorsal and two ventral.

b. The **head** is partly enclosed in a hood, a fold of the body-wall which is most prominent laterally, and which bears and partly sheaths the two lateral groups of chitinous jaws. Anteriorly the head also bears a series of short, chitinous spines, dorsally a pair of small dark eyes, and ventrally the elongated mouth.

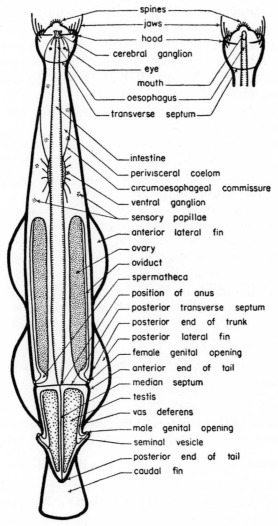

FIG. 60.—*Sagitta*. A stained specimen seen from the dorsal side, and a head seen from the ventral side.

c. The cavity of the **coelom** within the head is small, and is separated from that of the trunk by the anterior transverse septum. The trunk coelom is spacious; it extends back to the posterior transverse septum, and it is incompletely divided into right and left compartments by a perforated median septum. In the tail the coelom is also extensive, and the median septum is prominent.

d. The **alimentary canal** is almost featureless, but the narrower anterior region within the head is called the oesophagus, and the posterior region, which passes through the trunk and is supported by the median septum, is called the intestine. The anus opens ventrally at the junction of trunk and tail.

e. The two **ovaries** lie posteriorly in the trunk, and they are supported by two narrow lateral mesenteries. Along the outer surface of each ovary there passes an oviduct which, particularly posteriorly, acts as a spermatheca (for the reception of spermatozoa from another individual). The oviducts open laterally on a level with the posterior transverse septum and dorsal to the bases of the posterior lateral fins.

f. The two **testes** are in the tail, and in fully mature individuals the tail coelomic cavities are entirely filled with developing spermatozoa. Each of the two lateral vasa deferentia swells into a seminal vesicle, which protrudes laterally and opens just in front of the base of the caudal fin.

g. The **nervous system** consists of a cerebral ganglion above the mouth, and a large ventral ganglion beneath the intestine. The two are connected by circumoesophageal commissures. Each ganglion gives rise to numerous nerves, which pass especially to the head and body-walls. The most prominent sense-organs are the eyes, already seen, and the numerous dark staining papillae (presumed to be tactile) which are scattered irregularly over the surface of the trunk and tail and surmounted by bundles of fine chitinous spines.

3. CONCLUSION

a. Observing the specimen, review the characteristics of the phylum.

b. Review also those features which are associated with the predaceous pelagic mode of life.

4. REFERENCES

For further details of the structure of this and of related genera see :

BURFIELD, S. T. (1927). " *Sagitta.*" *Memoirs of the Liverpool Marine Biological Committee*, Vol. 28.
DELAGE, Y., and HÉROUARD, E. (1897). Volume 5 of " Traité de zoologie concrète." Paris.

APPENDIX TO THE CHAETOGNATHA

1. FIXATION METHODS

a. Chaetognaths should preferably be killed by immersion in Bouin's fluid, although a mixture of 1 part of commercial formalin to 10 parts of sea-water may also be used. They should be stored either in the Bouin's fluid or in 5% formalin. Alcohol should not be used.

2. STAINING METHOD

a. Wash in water to remove the formalin, and over-stain in a haematoxylin solution such as that of Delafield or Ehrlich. Wash in 30% alcohol, and then transfer slowly through 50% alcohol to 70% alcohol (from fifteen to thirty minutes in each). Remove the excess stain in a 1% solution of hydrochloric acid in 70% alcohol, and then turn the remaining stain blue in 70% alcohol to which a few drops of concentrated ammonia have been added. Pass slowly through 90% alcohol, absolute alcohol, a mixture of absolute alcohol and xylol, and xylol, and mount in Canada balsam under a long cover-glass.

 CHAPTER XIV

PHYLUM **ANNELIDA**

Characteristics : Metamerically segmented worms with a single preoral segment, the prostomium ; body-wall with outer circular and inner longitudinal muscle layers ; extensive perivisceral coelom ; usually a closed blood system ; double ventral nerve-cord with a pair of ganglia in each segment and a pair of preoral cerebral ganglia ; nephridial excretory organs ; and larva, if present, a trochosphere.

Originally marine, the Annelida is a highly successful phylum whose members are modified for active, sedentary, or ectoparasitic lives in the sea, in fresh-water, and on the land.

1.00. Class **Chaetopoda**

Characteristics : Annelida with well-defined segmentation ; with setae ; and with a perivisceral coelom usually divided into compartments by intersegmental septa.

In this class are included the most primitive and most typical of the annelids.

1.01. Order **Polychaeta**

Characteristics : Chaetopoda with setae mounted on parapodia ; with head usually distinct and bearing eyes, palps, and tentacles variously modified ; and with sexes usually separate and gonads in most segments.

This order, which includes swimming, crawling, burrowing, and tube-dwelling worms, is almost exclusively marine. Of the few fresh-water genera known, an example is *Manayunkia* in the Great Lakes of North America.

Genus **Nereis** (rag worm or clam worm)

I. GENERAL ACCOUNT

a. The common and cosmopolitan species of *Nereis* are among the least modified of the polychaets. They are all of the crawling type, and they build loose tubes of mucus in sandy places and in rock crevices from between tide-marks to depths of more than 100 fathoms. The food includes other worms and crustaceans, and many species also eat algae such as *Fucus* and *Ulva*. In temperate regions the breeding season is mainly in spring and summer. Most species then develop into the heteronereis type, when they either remain on the bottom or swim to the surface to spawn by a rupture posteriorly of the body-wall. The zygotes develop into free-swimming trochosphere larvae which may also be obtained by artificial fertilisation (see p. 205).

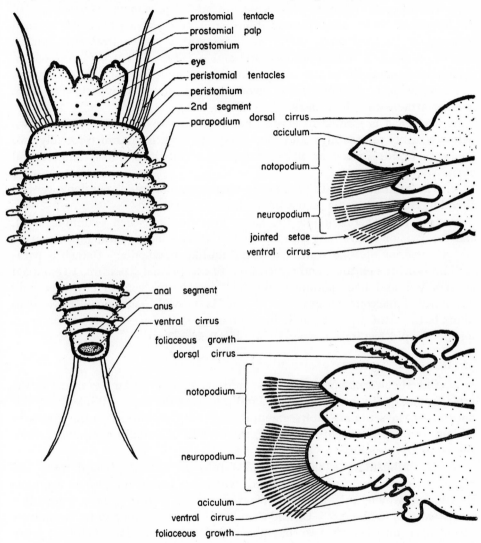

prostomial tentacle
prostomial palp
prostomium
eye
peristomial tentacles
peristomium
2nd segment
parapodium

dorsal cirrus
aciculum
notopodium
neuropodium
jointed setae
ventral cirrus

anal segment
anus
ventral cirrus
foliaceous growth
dorsal cirrus
notopodium
neuropodium
aciculum
ventral cirrus
foliaceous growth

FIG. 61.—*Nereis*. A dorsal view of the anterior and posterior segments, and, on the right, detached parapodia of the normal and heteronereis forms.

2.   EXTERNAL ANATOMY

   a. The **body** is clearly segmented and has a prominent head.   The mouth is directed ventrally and the anus is terminal.   The buccal region and pharynx are often everted, and protrude in front of the head, so that the black serrated pharyngeal teeth are visible (such eversion takes place during normal feeding, and is common at death).

b. Each typical segment bears a pair of lateral **parapodia**. Detach one of the largest of these, and examine it in water or make a permanent stained preparation (method on p. **207**). It bears dorsal and ventral cirri (tactile organs), a bilobed dorsal notopodium and a bilobed ventral neuropodium (which act both as limbs and as gills), and long jointed setae. Internally are two long acicula (modified setae), which act as skeletal supports and have muscles attached to their bases.

c. The **head** is formed of a prostomium with two tentacles (tactile), two palps (possibly for tasting), and four eyes, and a peristomium (probably two segments fused) with four pairs of tentacles (modified dorsal and ventral cirri).

d. The **anal segment** is peculiar in that it is elongated, has long ventral cirri, but lacks notopodia, neurodia, and dorsal cirri.

e. In a **heteronereis** notice the larger eyes (needed when swimming free), and the division of the body into an anterior atoke which is normal in structure and a posterior epitoke which has large fin-like parapodia. Detach a parapodium from the epitoke, and notice that its exceptional size is due to enlarged notopodium and neuropodium, branched dorsal and ventral cirri, specially developed foliaceous outgrowths of the body-wall, and oar-like terminal joints to the setae (apart from its function as a fin, the larger surface also serves for more rapid respiration when swimming free).

3. INTERNAL ANATOMY

a. Cut the worm open along the mid-dorsal line as far forwards as the prostomium, gently break the septa, and pin aside the flaps. While doing this notice that the septa are intersegmental, and that they subdivide the extensive **coelom** into compartments (however, the coelom is actually continuous, since the septa are perforated).

b. The **alimentary canal** is modified into an anterior buccal mass and pharynx (ectodermal and cuticle lined) which are bound together in a muscle sheath, and which, unless they are everted, can be seen to occupy segments 1 (peristomium) to about 6. Behind them, in about segments 7 to 12, is a narrow oesophagus into which two oesophageal glands (function doubtful) open anteriorly. It in turn leads into the long intestine, which is constricted intersegmentally and which extends to the anus. Dissect the muscle-sheath from the buccal mass and pharynx, and cut open these chambers longitudinally. In the pharynx are two long, curved, pointed, and serrated teeth, and in both chambers are numbers of small teeth called paragnaths.

c. The **blood system** is well developed. A dorsal blood-vessel runs the full length of the body above the alimentary canal (it is contractile, driving the blood forwards). In each segment it is joined by two alimentary vessels, which encircle the alimentary canal to reach a ventral blood-vessel, and by two

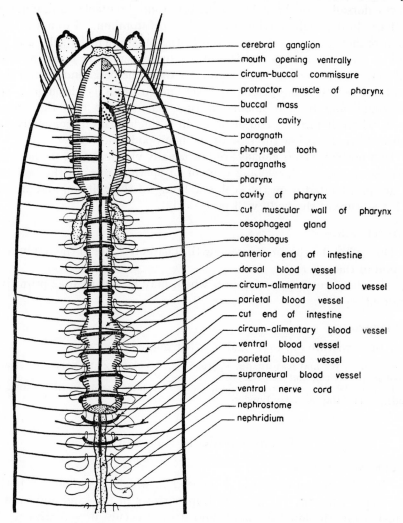

cerebral ganglion
mouth opening ventrally
circum-buccal commissure
protractor muscle of pharynx
buccal mass
buccal cavity
paragnath
pharyngeal tooth
paragnaths
pharynx
cavity of pharynx
cut muscular wall of pharynx
oesophageal gland
oesophagus
anterior end of intestine
dorsal blood vessel
circum-alimentary blood vessel
parietal blood vessel
cut end of intestine
circum-alimentary blood vessel
ventral blood vessel
parietal blood vessel
supraneural blood vessel
ventral nerve cord
nephrostome
nephridium

FIG. 62.—*Nereis*. A dorsal view of a general dissection from which the right halves of the buccal mass and the pharynx have been removed to show the paragnaths and teeth.

parietal vessels which extend to the parapodia and body-wall (to obtain oxygen). Turn aside the intestine to expose the ventral blood-vessel, which also runs the full length of the body (it is contractile in lesser degree and passes the blood back). Beneath the ventral vessel is a narrow supra-neural blood-vessel.

N

d. Examine the ventral **nerve cord**, which appears single, but is in fact double. In each segment it swells slightly to form a ganglion from which lateral nerves arise. Anteriorly it divides into two circumbuccal commissures which rise dorsally, give branches to the peristomial tentacles, and join into the bilobed cerebral ganglion lying within the prostomium. From the cerebral ganglion branches pass to the eyes and to the prostomial tentacles and palps.

e. The **excretory system** consists of a pair of nephridia lying immediately lateral to the nerve-cord in every segment except the peristomium and the anal segment. The internal opening of each nephridium is through a ciliated nephrostome, and from it a ciliated tube passes back into the succeeding segment, where it forms a coil enclosed in a single mass of connective tissue. It opens externally below the base of the neuropodium.

f. In a normal *Nereis* **gonads** are not usually visible, but in the heteronereis form loose masses of developing eggs or of spermatozoa fill the body cavity (they are proliferated from the coelomic lining of the epitoke, and are usually shed by rupture of the body wall posteriorly).

4. CONCLUSION

a. Observing the specimens, review the characteristics of the phylum, of the class, and of the order.

b. Also distinguish those features which may be regarded as primitive and generalised.

5. REFERENCES

For the structure of *Nereis* and of other related genera see :

Kükenthal, W., and Krumbach, T. (1928–34). Volume 2 and part 2 of " Handbuch der Zoologie." Berlin and Leipzig.

McIntosh, W. C. (1908–10). Volume 2 of " A monograph of the British marine annelids." The Ray Society, London.

Genus **Arenicola** (lug worm)

I. GENERAL ACCOUNT

a. The best-known species is *A. marina* L. which is common on both sides of the North Atlantic. It lives in deep burrows in the sand and mud above and just below the low tide mark, and it even occurs in estuaries where the water is less saline. It constructs a J-shaped burrow lined with a mucus secretion to prevent collapse, and in this it appears to live for the most part head downwards. For food the sand is swallowed, and its organic content digested. The breeding seasons are in February and March and again in late summer. The sexes are separate, fertilisation is external, and the eggs develop into modified trochospheres, which remain attached to the substratum until they develop into small worms and start to burrow.

2. EXTERNAL ANATOMY

a. The **body** is thickest near the anterior end, and its external segmentation is confused by the presence of annuli. The true number of segments is indicated

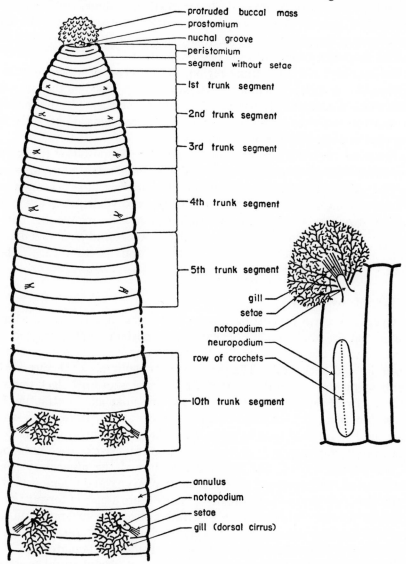

protruded buccal mass
prostomium
nuchal groove
peristomium
segment without setae
1st trunk segment
2nd trunk segment
3rd trunk segment
4th trunk segment
5th trunk segment
gill
setae
notopodium
neuropodium
row of crochets
10th trunk segment
annulus
notopodium
setae
gill (dorsal cirrus)

FIG. 63.—*Arenicola.* A dorsal view of the head and trunk regions to show the annulation, and a side view of one of the trunk annuli to show the structure of a parapodium.

by the parapodia present on all segments except the first two and those of the tail region. The dorsal side is marked by the prominent branching gills.

b. The **head** lacks tentacles and palps, and the tiny eyes are indistinguishable externally. The prostomium is small and trilobed, and is usually retracted into the nuchal groove (a sensory intucking of the epidermis). The peristomium and the succeeding segment lack parapodia and setae, and each contains two ill-defined annuli. The buccal mass usually protrudes from the mouth, and is covered with curved, blunt, vascular papillae (in life its constant eversion and withdrawal carry sand into the oesophagus).

c. Behind the head is the **trunk region**, the segments of which contain from 3 to 5 annuli. In each segment a pair of parapodia is based on the last but one annulus which is also slightly wider. The first six segments bear simple parapodia, but the last thirteen segments also have branching dorsal gills (which are not cirri but out-growths of the body wall).

d. Examine the structure of a **parapodium** in the posterior trunk region. The prominent notopodium bears elongated, unjointed setae, which are serrated at the tip. The ventral neuropodium is a long, low swelling bearing a row of small curved setae called crochets. Both dorsal and ventral cirri are lacking.

e. The segments of the narrower **tail region** lack parapodia, but have irregularly placed epidermal papillae which may resemble notopodia. Annulation may or may not be present, and the anus opens through the last segment.

3. INTERNAL ANATOMY

a. Open the worm by cutting up the mid-dorsal line to the peristomium, but do not cut the prostomium. The extensive **coelom** is uninterrupted except by three septa at the anterior end of the trunk and by an irregular number at the posterior end of the tail. The three anterior septa mark the anterior limits of trunk segments 1, 3, and 4. Part of the first septum bulges posteriorly to form a pair of septal pouches (which are muscular and contractile, but of unknown function), and the third septum is fenestrated. In the body-wall can be seen the longitudinal muscle layer, an incomplete ventral layer of oblique muscle strands, and muscle fibres radiating from the base of each notopodium.

b. The buccal cavity, the anterior chamber of the **alimentary canal**, is usually everted, and posterior to it is a short pharynx and a long oesophagus. Opposite the sixth parapodium the oesophagus bears a pair of forward directed oesophageal pouches (which probably secrete a digestive enzyme), and then it merges with the long intestine which is yellow due to a covering of chloragogen cells (modified peritoneal cells which collect and store waste material).

c. The **blood system** is very well developed. A dorsal vessel (contractile) drives the blood forwards from tail to head, and a ventral vessel takes it back. In the tail and posterior trunk regions, intestinal vessels carry blood from the ventral to the dorsal vessel, and in those segments with gills, afferent branchial vessels leave the ventral vessel and efferent branchial vessels enter

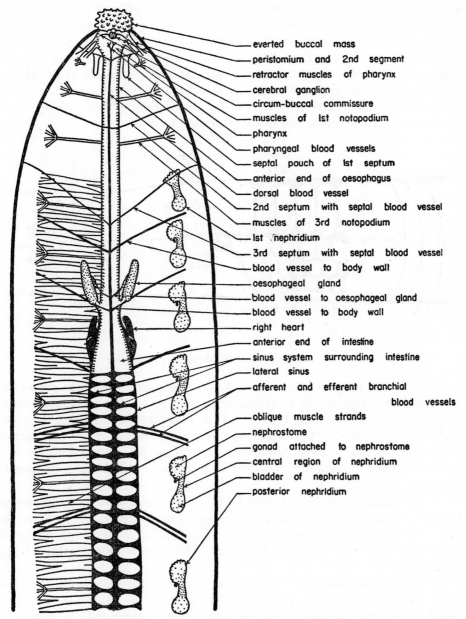

everted buccal mass

peristomium and 2nd segment

retractor muscles of pharynx

cerebral ganglion

circum-buccal commissure

muscles of 1st notopodium

pharynx

pharyngeal blood vessels

septal pouch of 1st septum

anterior end of oesophagus

dorsal blood vessel

2nd septum with septal blood vessel

muscles of 3rd notopodium

1st nephridium

3rd septum with septal blood vessel

blood vessel to body wall

oesophageal gland

blood vessel to oesophageal gland

blood vessel to body wall

right heart

anterior end of intestine

sinus system surrounding intestine

lateral sinus

afferent and efferent branchial

blood vessels

oblique muscle strands

nephrostome

gonad attached to nephrostome

central region of nephridium

bladder of nephridium

posterior nephridium

FIG. 64.—*Arenicola.* A dorsal view of a general dissection from which, on the right, the oblique muscle strands have been removed to uncover the nephridia.

the dorsal vessel. However, in the mid-trunk region the efferent branchial vessels pass instead to the subintestinal sinus, the ventral part of the extensive system of sinuses which surrounds the intestine in this region. The well defined lateral sinuses receive blood partly from the dorsal vessel and partly from the ventral sinus. Each lateral sinus passes blood forwards to a lateral heart where, via the auricle, it goes to the lateral oesophageal vessel or, via the ventricle, to the ventral vessel. Distinguish these vessels and sinuses, and also in the anterior trunk region find the vessels passing to the oesophageal glands, to the three septa, and to the pharyngeal region.

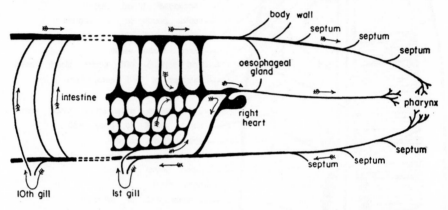

Fig. 65.—*Arenicola*. A diagram of the blood system as seen from the right side.

d. From one side carefully remove the oblique muscle strands to expose the six **nephridia** which belong to trunk segments 4 to 9. Each nephrostome is large and red with convoluted lips, and the first protrudes through the third septum into the third trunk segment. Behind the nephrostome is a narrow dark brown central region (containing excretory cells), and posteriorly is a paler bladder. The external opening is just above and behind the neuropodium.

e. The **gonads** are extremely small, but in large specimens they can be seen through a lens attached to the posterior tip of each nephrostome except the first. In the breeding season the whole of the coelom is filled with masses of developing eggs or of spermatozoa (which, when mature, escape through the nephridia).

f. Leaving the pharynx temporarily in place, cut through the anterior end of the oesophagus and turn it to one side. Remove the ventral blood-vessel, and find the ventral **nerve cord**. Removing the pharynx and any obscuring muscle-strands and septa, follow the cord forwards to find the circumbuccal commissures which converge beneath the prostomium. With great care, skin the top of the prostomium to expose the minute cerebral ganglia.

4. CONCLUSION

a. Observing the specimen, review the characteristics of the phylum, of the class, and of the order.

b. Identify those characteristics which are associated with the burrowing mode of life.

5. REFERENCES

ASHWORTH, J. H. (1904). *"Arenicola."* *Memoirs of the Liverpool Marine Biological Committee*, Vol. 11.

McINTOSH, W. C. (1915). Volume 3 of "A monograph of the British marine annelids." The Ray Society, London.

Genus **Amphitrite**

1. GENERAL ACCOUNT

a. The genus has a world-wide distribution, and it extends from the low-tide mark to depths of more than 800 fathoms. The various species are modified for living in tubes constructed of mud, sand, or shell fragments cemented together, and are hidden in rock crevices, in mud or sand, or among the holdfasts of large algae. The ciliated tentacles protruding from the tube catch tiny food particles, which, as far as is known, normally consist of such organisms as unicellular plants and animals. The sexes are separate, fertilisation is external, and in temperate regions the breeding season is in spring.

2. EXTERNAL ANATOMY

a. The **body** is divisible into a small head with a crown of long tentacles, a trunk bearing dorsal gills anteriorly, and a tail the segments of which lack notopodia.

b. The **head** is formed of a prostomium and a peristomium fused together. The prostomium extends into two lateral lobes, and bears large numbers of unbranched tentacles (modified prostomial palps). On one side of each tentacle is a ciliated food-groove (which also contains mucus-secreting cells). The prostomium has no eyes, and the peristomium bears no appendages.

c. In the **trunk** the first three segments bear branching dorsal gills (modified dorsal cirri), and the 3rd also bears a notopodium, but no neuropodium. The 4th and succeeding segments lack gills and cirri, but have prominent notopodia with normal setae and long, low neuropodia with crochets. Small papillae, through which open the nephridioducts, are visible between the notopodia and neuropodia of the 2nd to the 14th or 15th trunk segments. The ventral regions of the same segments are thickened to form the gland-shield (which secretes the mucus used in building the tube).

d. The segments of the **tail** lack notopodia, but possess neuropodia, and the elongated anus opens through the last segment.

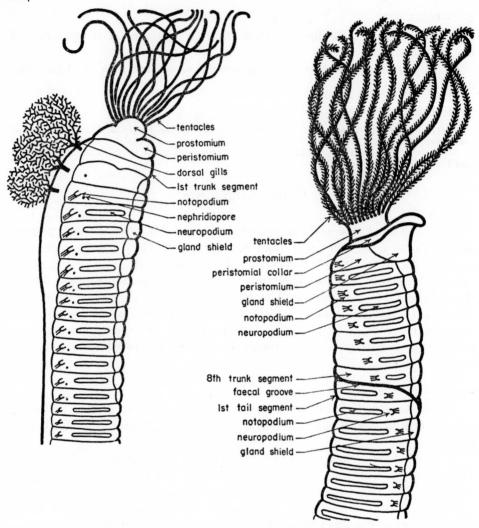

tentacles
prostomium
peristomium
dorsal gills
1st trunk segment
notopodium
nephridiopore
neuropodium
gland shield

tentacles
prostomium
peristomial collar
peristomium
gland shield
notopodium
neuropodium

8th trunk segment
faecal groove
1st tail segment
notopodium
neuropodium
gland shield

Fig. 66.—*Amphitrite* (left). The head and part of the trunk seen from the right side. *Sabella* (right). The head, trunk, and anterior tail region seen from the right side.

3. CONCLUSION

   a. Observing the specimen, review as far as possible the characteristics of the phylum, of the class, and of the order.

   b. Distinguish those special features which are modifications for the tube-dwelling mode of life.

4. REFERENCES

McIntosh, W. C. (1915). Volume 3 of " A monograph of the British marine annelids." The Ray Society, London.

THOMAS, J. G. (1940). " *Pomatoceros, Sabella,* and *Amphitrite.*" *Memoirs of the Liverpool Marine Biological Committee,* Vol. 33.

Genus **Sabella**

I. GENERAL ACCOUNT

a. Sabella, like *Amphitrite,* is modified for a tube-dwelling mode of life, but here the modification is carried to greater extreme. Species are found throughout the world from the low-tide mark to depths of at least 100 fathoms, particularly on a muddy bottom. The rubbery tube, composed of grains of mud and sand cemented together, may reach a length of 2 feet. It lies on, or protrudes from, the sea bottom, and commonly serves as a base for colonies of coelenterates. The food consists of tiny particles, such as unicellular plants and animals, which are caught by the ciliated tentacles. The sexes are separate, fertilisation is external, and in temperate regions breeding takes place in summer.

2. EXTERNAL ANATOMY

a. The **body** is composed of a small head with a crown of tentacles, a trunk with prominent notopodia, and a tail with prominent neuropodia.

b. The **head** is formed of the prostomium alone, and the tentacles represent modified prostomial palps (they serve for respiration as well as for food capture). Each tentacle is fringed with two rows of pinnules (which are ciliated and contain mucus-secreting cells), and it is strongly pigmented.

c. There are usually eight segments in the **trunk**, but there is some individual variation. The 1st segment, the peristomium, has a flanged collar (for moulding the top of the tube), a large ventral gland-shield (for secreting mucus for tube construction), a dorsal notopodium with normal setae, but no neuropodium. In each of the other seven trunk segments there is, in addition to a notopodium and a gland-shield, a long, low neuropodium with small bent setae called crochets. Along the dorsal side of the trunk is the ciliated faecal groove which passes to the ventral side between the last trunk and first tail segments (and which carries faeces from the anus to the mouth of the tube). At the anterior end of this groove there opens the single median nephridiopore (common to the only two nephridia in the body).

d. In the long **tail** the notopodia and neuropodia show a reversal of type, the notopodia being long, low swellings with crochets and the neuropodia prominent with normal setae. The ventral gland-shield extends from segment to segment, and down its centre the faecal groove passes to the terminal anus.

3. CONCLUSION

a. Observing the specimen, review as far as possible the characteristics of the phylum, of the class, and of the order.

b. Compare the specialisations of *Sabella* and *Amphitrite* for the tube-dwelling mode of life.

4. REFERENCES

McIntosh, W. C. (1915).   Volume 3 of " A monograph of the British marine annelids." The Ray Society, London.

Thomas, J. G. (1940).   " *Pomatoceros, Sabella,* and *Amphitrite.*"   *Memoirs of the Liverpool Marine Biological Committee,* Vol. 33.

1.02.   Order **Oligochaeta**

Characteristics : Chaetopoda which lack parapodia and have relatively few setae ;   head small and usually without appendages ;   always hermaphrodite, with only two or three pairs of gonads in fixed segments, and with the testes always anterior to the ovaries ;   with special gonoducts which are coelomoducts ; and, when mature, with spermathecae and clitellum.

Almost all the oligochaets are land or fresh-water animals modified for burrowing, crawling, or free-swimming modes of life.   However, a few genera, such as *Enchytraeus,* can exist on the seashore just below the high-tide mark.

Genus **Lumbricus**

(The description given below is of *L. terrestris* L., but other species are commonly dissected, and differ slightly in the number of segments and the position of the clitellum.   The other common genus is *Allolobophora* (*Eisenia*), in which differences occur, particularly in the form of the prostomium and the position of the clitellum.)

1. GENERAL ACCOUNT

a. This large, cosmopolitan, and well-known terrestrial genus inhabits soils which do not dry out, which are not too acid, and which contain organic matter for food.   The burrows are formed partly by pushing the earth aside and partly by swallowing it, and they are lined by a cement of defaecated earth. They sometimes extend downwards for more than 6 feet, and each usually ends in a small chamber.   The deepest burrows are constructed in cold weather, when the worms seek warmth, and in hot weather, when they must avoid desiccation.   A worm normally emerges only at night, when, with its tail anchored in the mouth of its burrow, it gathers vegetable débris for food. Copulation takes place commonly on wet nights in the warmer seasons of the year, and the eggs are later laid in cocoons, which are deposited on or near the surface.   Culture methods are described on p. 205.

2. EXTERNAL ANATOMY

a. Examine a fully-grown worm freshly killed with chloroform.   The **body** has a cylindrical, pointed, anterior end and a flattened, blunt, posterior end, and the mouth and anus are terminal.   The dorsal side is marked by darker pigmentation and by the dark line of the dorsal blood-vessel, which shows through the body-wall.   There are about 150 well-marked segments, of which numbers 32 to 37 are swollen to form a clitellum (which secretes the cocoon).

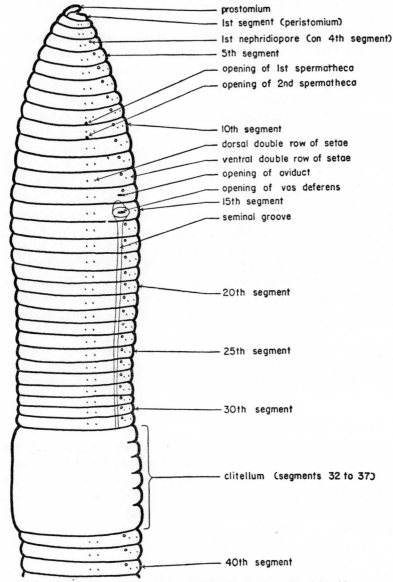

prostomium
Ist segment (peristomium)
Ist nephridiopore (on 4th segment)
5th segment
opening of Ist spermatheca
opening of 2nd spermatheca

I0th segment
dorsal double row of setae
ventral double row of setae
opening of oviduct
opening of vas deferens
I5th segment
seminal groove

20th segment

25th segment

30th segment

clitellum (segments 32 to 37)

40th segment

FIG. 67.—*Lumbricus.*   The anterior end seen from the right side.

   b. The **head** is composed of a prostomium and a peristomium, which is the 1st segment.   The prostomium is dorsal, forms an upper lip to the mouth, and extends back over the peristomium to touch the 2nd segment (in *Allolo-bophora* the prostomium does not extend back to touch the 2nd segment). The peristomium forms the sides and base of the mouth.

c. Notice the thin, iridescent **cuticle** (chitinous) which covers the whole body surface, and with fine forceps strip off a small piece. Four pairs of setae (local thickenings of the cuticle) are present on each segment except the first and the last. They are set in pits, but their protruding points can be seen through a lens and felt by drawing a finger along the ventral surface towards the head (they can be extracted by boiling the body-wall in a concentrated aqueous solution of potassium hydroxide).

d. Distinguish the **openings** of the vasa deferentia on the 15th segment. They are latero-ventral and have prominent lips. The other external openings are most clearly seen in a preserved specimen from which the cuticle has been stripped, and they should be searched for through a lens or binocular micro-scope. They are the openings of the oviducts on segment 14 on a level with the openings of the vasa deferentia ; the openings of the spermathecae in the folds between segments 9 and 10, and 10 and 11, on a level with the dorsal row of setae ; the openings of the nephridia, in all segments except the first three and the last, dorsal to and in front of the ventral double row of setae ; and the dorsal pores which open directly from the coelom in the mid-dorsal line in the grooves between all the segments behind segment 10. The presence of all these apertures, if too small to see, can be demonstrated by thoroughly drying the outer surface, and then gently squeezing the body so that fluid oozes from them.

e. Notice the **seminal grooves** which pass back across the segments between the openings of the vasa deferentia and the anterior edge of the clitellum (during copulation spermatozoa pass along these grooves to the spermathecae of the other worm).

3.   INTERNAL ANATOMY

a. Open the worm from end to end by cutting through the body-wall along the mid-dorsal line. Notice the large perivisceral **coelom**, which is subdivided into compartments by intersegmental septa. Gently break these septa, and pin aside the flaps of the body-wall. To help in the later location of various body organs, pins should be carefully fixed through the 5th, 10th, 15th, and 20th segments.

b. At the anterior end of the **alimentary canal** is the buccal region (segments 1 to 3), and this leads into the thick-walled pharynx (segments 4 and 5), which is joined to the body-wall by muscle strands. The thin-walled oesophagus (segments 6 to 13 or 14) is dilated laterally in segments 10 and 13 to form the oesophageal pouches, and in segments 11 and 12 to form the even more pro-minent sausage-shaped oesophageal glands (both pouches and glands produce masses of tiny crystals of calcium carbonate which probably aid digestion). In segments 14 or 15 to 16 is the thin-walled crop (for food storage), and usually

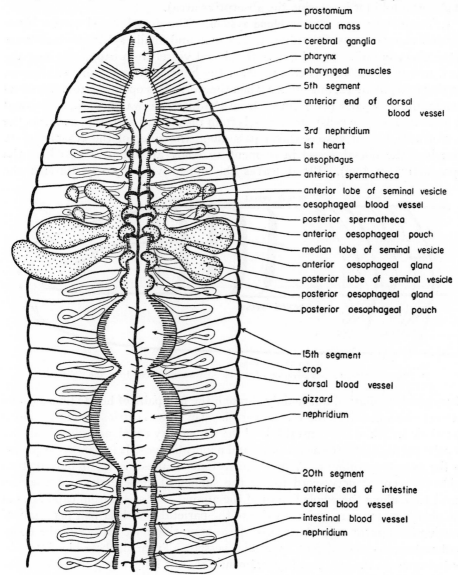

- prostomium
- buccal mass
- cerebral ganglia
- pharynx
- pharyngeal muscles
- 5th segment
- anterior end of dorsal blood vessel
- 3rd nephridium
- 1st heart
- oesophagus
- anterior spermatheca
- anterior lobe of seminal vesicle
- oesophageal blood vessel
- posterior spermatheca
- anterior oesophageal pouch
- median lobe of seminal vesicle
- anterior oesophageal gland
- posterior lobe of seminal vesicle
- posterior oesophageal gland
- posterior oesophageal pouch
- 15th segment
- crop
- dorsal blood vessel
- gizzard
- nephridium
- 20th segment
- anterior end of intestine
- dorsal blood vessel
- intestinal blood vessel
- nephridium

Fig. 68.—*Lumbricus.* A dorsal view of a general dissection.

in segments 17 to 19 is the thick-walled muscular gizzard (which grinds the food with the help of small stones). Through the rest of the body runs the long intestine, which is yellow due to its loose covering of chloragogen cells (modified peritoneal cells full of waste material).   Remove a section of the intestine, cut it open ventrally, wash out its contents, and notice the typhlosole (a longitudinal dorsal fold for increasing the absorptive area).

c. Trace the course of the **blood system**.   The dorsal vessel carries blood forwards along the top of the alimentary canal, and finally splits into capillaries in the pharynx wall.   Blood enters the dorsal vessel from capillaries near the anus, from parietal vessels coming from the body-wall (one pair per segment starting in segment 12, but broken when the worm was opened), from intestinal vessels (the two pairs per segment from the intestine wall are often obscured by loose chloragogen cells), from vessels from the gizzard and crop, and from the pair of oesophageal vessels which pass along the sides of the oesophagus to open into the dorsal vessel in segment 10 (they are often obscured by the reproductive system).   Blood leaves the dorsal vessel partly through the

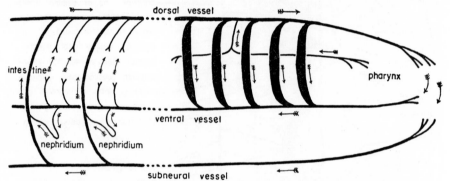

Fig. 69.—*Lumbricus*.   A diagram of the blood system as seen from the right side.

pharyngeal capillaries, but mainly through the five pairs of hearts (in segments 7 to 11) which pass it to the ventral vessel.   This vessel carries blood back along the whole length of the ventral side of the alimentary canal, and gives branches (2 pairs per segment) to the intestine and nephridial vessels (1 pair per segment) to the excretory tubules.   Where the section of intestine was removed, turn aside the ventral nerve-cord to see the subneural vessel, which also carries blood back along the whole length of the animal.   It arises from capillaries in the pharyngeal region, and gives rise to the parietal vessels (1 pair per segment starting in segment 12), which pass upwards on the inner surface of the body-wall and receive the efferent nephridial vessels.   Trace all these blood-vessels, and also notice the two small lateral neural vessels lying along the sides of the nerve-cord.

d. The **excretory system** consists of one pair of nephridia in each segment except the first three and the last.   Carefully remove a nephridium together with the mid-ventral part of the septum anterior to it.   Mount it in water and examine it through a microscope.   The tiny nephrostome, attached to the anterior face of the septum, is an open funnel with a fringe of cilia. It leads back through the septum into a coiled and ciliated tube (which lay in the segment behind). This tube makes three loops, the first two being narrow and the last wide (with muscular walls), before opening through the nephridiopore (to see the action of the cilia within the tube it is necessary to carry out the dissection and the mounting in normal saline solution).

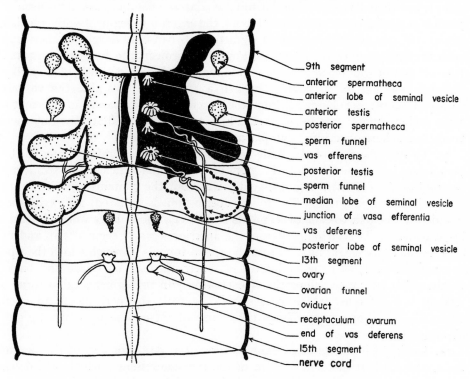

9th segment
anterior spermatheca
anterior lobe of seminal vesicle
anterior testis
posterior spermatheca
sperm funnel
vas efferens
posterior testis
sperm funnel
median lobe of seminal vesicle
junction of vasa efferentia
vas deferens
posterior lobe of seminal vesicle
13th segment
ovary
ovarian funnel
oviduct
receptaculum ovarum
end of vas deferens
15th segment
nerve cord

FIG. 70.—*Lumbricus.* A dorsal dissection of the reproductive system with the seminal vesicles opened and partly removed.

e. The **female reproductive system** is simple but obscure. Distinguish segment 13, and, pushing the oesophagus and seminal vesicles to one side, search through a lens or binocular microscope to find the tiny ovary hanging from the anterior septum close to the mid-ventral line. Also in segment 13 find the funnel which projects forwards from the posterior septum at a point opposite to the ovary, and which in segment 14 leads via the little receptaculum ovarum (which contains mature ova) to the short oviduct. Remove the ovary by cutting away the septum to which it is attached, mount it in water on a slide, and through a microscope observe the developing oocytes. The other organs of the female system are the two pairs of yellowish, pear-shaped spermathecae in segments 9 and 10. Remove one of these, break it open in a drop of water on a slide, and through a microscope see the masses of filamentous spermatozoa (which were received from another worm).

f. In the male reproductive system the most obvious organs are the lobed **seminal vesicles** in the cavities (coelom) of which the spermatozoa develop. The main parts of these seminal vesicles are situated ventrally in segments 10 and 11, but their lobes, passing dorsally, overlap the oesophagus. It is usually possible to distinguish three pairs of lobes, the anterior in segment 9, the median in segment 11, and the posterior in segment 12 (when fully developed they may push the septa before them, and so appear to project into further segments). Tear off one of the lobes, and on a slide make and stain a smear of its milky contents (method on p. 207). Through a microscope examine the various stages of sperm development from the blackberry-like masses of spermatogonia and spermatocytes to the thread-like spermatozoa still attached by their heads to a sphere of residual cytoplasm called the cytophore.

g. To find the rest of the **male reproductive system**, carefully remove the oesophagus to expose the ventral regions of the seminal vesicles. Dissect away the roof of these ventral regions, gently wash out the contents, and look into the cavity through a lens. The foliose sperm funnels (ciliated) are easily distinguished (one pair to each of segments 10 and 11), and in large worms the tiny lobed testes can be seen hanging from the anterior septa of segments 10 and 11 close to the mid-ventral line. From the sperm funnels (through which the ripe spermatozoa pass) thin, convoluted vasa efferentia lead outwards and backwards. The two vasa efferentia of each side join in segment 12 to form a straight vas deferens, which passes back beneath the peritoneum to open externally on segment 15. Trace the course of these vasa by removing any obscuring tissue.

h. Distinguish the cerebral ganglia above the posterior end of the buccal mass, and without disturbing them or the two commissures which lead down from them, remove the pharynx and the remnants of the seminal vesicles. The main part of the **nervous system** consists of these ganglia, the circumpharyngeal commissures, a pair of subpharyngeal ganglia, and a long ventral nerve-cord. Through a lens notice the double nature of this cord, the ganglia, which are slight swellings towards the centre of each segment (and are especially prominent posteriorly), and the three pairs of branch nerves per segment.

4. CONCLUSION

a. Observing the specimen and the drawings made, review the characteristics of the phylum, of the class, and of the order.

b. Notice also those features which are associated with the active burrowing mode of life, and compare the structure of *Lumbricus* with that of *Arenicola*.

5. REFERENCE

For further details of the habits and structure of this and other oligo-chaets see :

Stephenson, J. (1930). " The Oligochaeta." Oxford.

Genus Enchytraeus

1. GENERAL ACCOUNT

a. The species of this cosmopolitan genus are small worms which are semi-aquatic in habit, the best known being the widely distributed *E. albidus* Henle. This worm occurs commonly near fresh water, where it feeds on decaying vegetation, in the filter-beds of sewage works, where it feeds on algae, and on the seashore around the high-water mark, where it feeds on decaying sea-weed. It breeds whenever the temperature is high enough, and the eggs are laid in cocoons. Its extraordinary tolerance both of conditions and foods makes its culture relatively easy (see p. 206).

2. EXTERNAL ANATOMY

a. Watch the **movements** of a living worm in a drop of water on a glass slide. To restrict these movements as much as possible, add a cover-glass, and, using blotting-paper, withdraw the water until most of the weight of the glass is borne by the worm. After about ten or fifteen minutes it usually becomes quiet, but if necessary it may be embedded in agar by the method described for protozoans on p. 35.

b. Through a microscope notice the **segmentation** of the body. The prostomium is prominent, and together with the peristomium it forms the head. Both the peristomium and the anal segment lack setae, but all the other segments bear short, curved setae in groups. There are two pairs of groups per segment, one pair being latero-ventral and the other lateral.

3. INTERNAL ANATOMY

(The worms are best examined alive, and since they normally come to rest with the dorsal side uppermost, the following description is mainly concerned with the features which can be seen through that side. The worms should be examined by transmitted light, the intensity of which should be cut down to the point at which the details of internal structure are most clearly visible.)

a. Trace the course of the **alimentary canal**. Anteriorly the buccal mass (in segment 1) and the eversible pharynx (in segments 2 and 3) are joined to the body-wall by long muscle-strands which lead diagonally backwards across the perivisceral cavity. Opening into the posterior end of the pharynx is a pair of salivary glands (also known as peptonephridia, although they are not derived from nephridia). The oesophagus (in segment 4) is short, and like the buccal mass and pharynx is almost colourless. In contrast, the long intestine (from segment 5 to the end) is clearly visible because of its covering of yellow

o

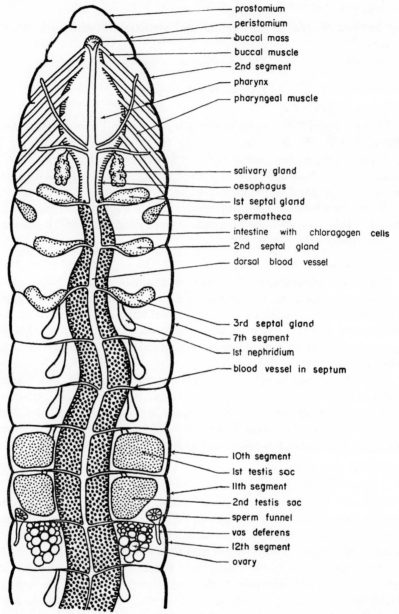

prostomium
peristomium
buccal mass
buccal muscle
2nd segment
pharynx
pharyngeal muscle

salivary gland
oesophagus
lst septal gland
spermatheca
intestine with chloragogen cells
2nd septal gland
dorsal blood vessel

3rd septal gland
7th segment
lst nephridium
blood vessel in septum

lOth segment
lst testis sac
llth segment
2nd testis sac
sperm funnel
vas deferens
l2th segment
ovary

FIG. 71.—*Enchytraeus.* A dorsal view of the organs in the anterior region of a living specimen.

chloragogen cells (which contain granules of waste material). Attached to the anterior faces of the posterior septa of segments 4, 5, and 6 are three pairs of septal glands (which secrete mucin into the anterior end of the intestine).

b. Watch the **peristaltic movement** of the anterior region of the intestine (pushing the food backwards), and the antiperistaltic movement of the posterior region of the intestine (sucking water in through the anus for intestinal respiration).

c. In the perivisceral coelomic cavity are large numbers of **coelomic corpuscles**, some floating free in the coelomic fluid and some attached to the coelomic lining. The most easily distinguishable are the so-called discoid corpuscles, which are usually ovoid or spindle-shaped, but which may be circular and plate-like (they apparently collect and contain waste material). Some of them, free in the coelomic fluid, are grouped together to form blackberry-like masses, while others, attached to the coelomic lining (from which they are derived), are anchored by a short stalk. Also present, though in much smaller numbers, are amoebocytes (phagocytic), which are sometimes spherical and sometimes seen with fine pseudopodia.

d. Distinguish the **septa** which separate all segments behind the 4th. Notice also that the coelomic corpuscles stream to and fro through the segments as the worm moves, thus demonstrating that the septa are all incomplete and that the coelom is actually continuous from head to tail.

e. The **excretory system** consists of the corpuscles and chloragogen cells already seen, and of the nephridia, of which there is one pair in each segment except the first six. The first nephrostome opens into segment 6, the body of the nephridium being in segment 7. The ciliated nephrostomes are not usually visible, but the nephridia, hanging back from each septum in a latero-ventral position, are easily seen. Each is a solid structure perforated by a thin branching tube.

f. Of the **blood system**, the dorsal vessel is particularly clear as a transparent line along the top of the anterior end of the intestine. It is contractile, and with an irregular beat it drives the blood forwards. This vessel is not continuous along the whole length of the body, but arises from capillaries in the anterior half of the intestine. It continues forwards along the top of the oesophagus and the pharynx to the buccal region. Notice the paired vessels which join into it on a level with each septum, and the two pairs of large branches in the posterior pharyngeal region.

g. The **female reproductive system** consists of a pair of ovaries which, with oocytes arranged like bunches of grapes, almost fills the coelomic cavity of segment 12. There are no ovarian funnels or oviducts (the eggs, when ripe, escape by a rupture of the body wall), and the only other organs of the female system are the two spermathecae in segment 5 (they store spermatozoa received from another worm).

h. In the **male reproductive system** there are two pairs of testes, one in segment 10 and the other in segment 11. The epithelium is lifted from the surface of each testis to form a capacious testis sac, inside which the developing blackberry-like groups of spermatogonia and spermatocytes can be seen floating free. A single pair of large sperm funnels is situated posteriorly and laterally in segment 11, and from each a short vas deferens passes through the septum to open externally in segment 12 (since the funnels are outside the testes, they can only pass the spermatozoa when these are released by the bursting of the sacs).

i. The broad ventral **nerve-cord** is only visible when the worm turns on to its side or back. It is separate from the body-wall, and, although double, it appears superficially to be single and its ganglia are not prominent.

4. CONCLUSION

a. Observing the specimen, review the characteristics of the phylum, of the class, and of the order.

b. Make a comparison of the habits and structure of *Enchytraeus* with those of *Lumbricus*.

5. REFERENCE

For details of the structure of *Enchytraeus* and of the various aquatic oligochaets see :

STEPHENSON, J. (1930). " The Oligochaeta." Oxford.

2.00. Class **Hirudinea**

Characteristics : Annelida with a small fixed number of segments which externally are subdivided into annuli, and which bear neither parapodia nor setae ; suckers present both anteriorly and posteriorly ; mouth ventral and inside the anterior sucker, but anus dorsal and outside the posterior sucker ; coelom much reduced by the ingrowth of botryoidal tissue ; hermaphrodite and eggs laid in cocoons.

Closely related to the oligochaets, the leeches are mainly fresh-water animals, but some live in the sea and some in moist earth. They are either predacious, feeding for instance on worms and snails, or they are ectoparasites of aquatic vertebrates.

Genus **Hirudo**

1. GENERAL ACCOUNT

a. *H. medicinalis* L. is a European species, but since it was once used extensively in medicine for blood-letting, it has been introduced into most other continents. It lives in marshes, ponds, and streams, where it either swims by vertical undulations or grips with its suckers and walks by looping. Its food is the blood of vertebrates, and one meal suffices for months. Copulation takes place in the warmer months, and the eggs are laid inside cocoons, from which they hatch as small leeches. Culture methods are described on p. 206.

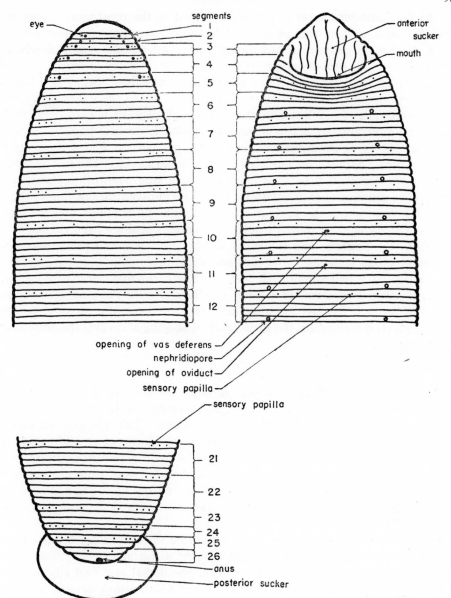

FIG. 72.—*Hirudo*. Dorsal and ventral views of the external features.

2. EXTERNAL ANATOMY

a. Examine a leech freshly killed by the method given on p. 207. The dorsal side of the **body** is heavily and variably pigmented, and the anterior end bears a small sucker containing the mouth.

b. This **anterior sucker** is probably formed of the prostomium, projecting forwards as a hood in front of the mouth, and of part of the peristomium.

c. Notice the prominent **annulation**. The first annulus, most clearly seen on the dorsal side, probably represents that part of the peristomium not involved in the sucker, and segment 2 also has only one annulus. Segment 3 has two annuli, segments 4, 5, and 6 have three annuli each, and the following segments have five annuli each. The first annulus of each segment is marked, both dorsally and ventrally, by a row of sensory (probably tactile) papillae, of which there are up to 14 arranged as shown in fig. 72. In the first 5 segments five pairs of dorsal papillae are modified into small dark eyes. The last annulus of each of the segments 6 to 22 is marked by the latero-ventral nephridiopores, the second annulus of segment 10 by the single mid-ventral opening of the vas deferens (from which the penis is often seen to be protruding), and the second annulus of segment 11 by the single mid-ventral opening of the vagina.

d. At the **posterior end** the usual number of five annuli per segment continues as far as segment 22. Segment 23 has three annuli, and segments 24, 25, and 26 have two annuli each. As elsewhere, the first annulus of each segment is marked by a row of sensory papillae. Notice the anus opening mid-dorsally through the last annulus, and the large ventrally directed posterior sucker which is formed by the fusion and telescoping of several (possibly seven) posterior segments.

3. INTERNAL ANATOMY

a. Steady the leech by two pins through the sides of the anterior sucker and one through the posterior sucker, and then open it by means of a shallow cut made longitudinally along the mid-dorsal line. Take the greatest care not to damage the thin-walled alimentary canal which lies close underneath and which is bound to the body-wall by botryoidal tissue. Gently cutting through the botryoidal tissue, separate the flaps of the body-wall from the top of the alimentary canal, and pin them out. Along the top of the alimentary canal lies the **dorsal sinus** and its lateral branches (remnants of the coelom, but containing blood).

b. Remove any botryoidal tissue obscuring the **alimentary canal**. Distinguish the buccal mass anteriorly, and without disturbing the cerebral ganglia, open it to find the three chitinous jaws, one dorsal and two latero-ventral. Behind the buccal mass is the pharynx, from which muscle-strands radiate to the body-wall. Among the muscle-strands are the diffuse salivary glands which consist of masses of very large cells. Extract some of these cells, and through a microscope notice their ducts which are processes of the cells. From the pharynx a short oesophagus leads into the large, thin-walled crop which is made up of eleven chambers, each with a pair of lateral caeca (and which contains stored blood). The last two caeca turn back to reach the posterior end of the body.   The stomach is small and globular, and leads into a narrow, straight intestine which passes via the rectum to the anus.   Open the intestine to see the spiral folding of its inner lining.

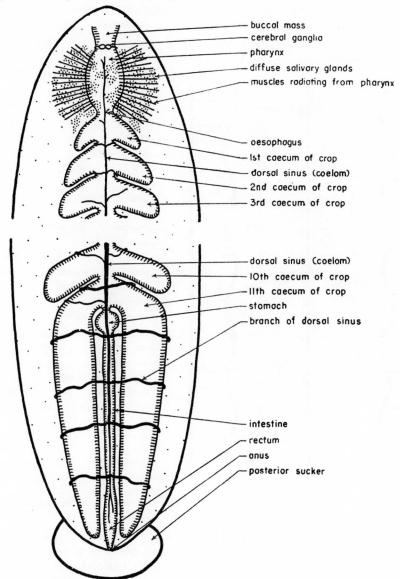

FIG. 73.—*Hirudo*.   A dorsal view of a general dissection.

c. With great care remove the crop, stomach, and intestine, the lower walls of which are closely applied to the underlying tissues.   This exposes the remainder of the **circulatory system**, consisting of two undulating lateral blood-vessels (which are contractile and have a haemocoelic cavity) and a narrow ventral sinus (which, like the dorsal sinus, has a coelomic cavity containing blood, and is in communication with the lateral vessels through the botryoidal tissue).

d. The **female reproductive system** lies in segment 11. There is a pair of coiled ovaries, each enclosed in a small coelomic pouch, and from them two short oviducts converge, the right passing beneath the ventral sinus, to join into a

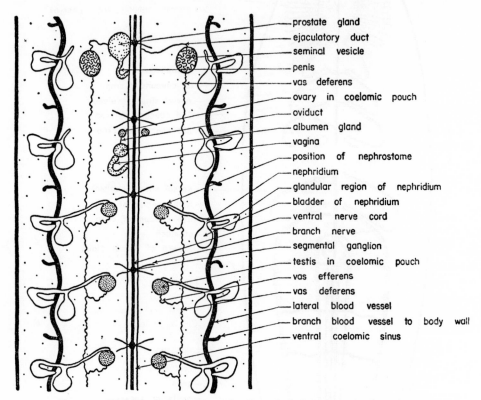

prostate gland
ejaculatory duct
seminal vesicle
penis
vas deferens
ovary in coelomic pouch
oviduct
albumen gland
vagina
position of nephrostome
nephridium
glandular region of nephridium
bladder of nephridium
ventral nerve cord
branch nerve
segmental ganglion
testis in coelomic pouch
vas efferens
vas deferens
lateral blood vessel
branch blood vessel to body wall
ventral coelomic sinus

Fig. 74.—*Hirudo.* A dorsal view of a dissection of the reproductive system.

common duct. Around the common duct is a bulbous albumen gland, and from it a vagina leads to the exterior.

e. The **male reproductive system** consists of nine pairs of spherical testes (in segments 12 to 20), each enclosed in a small coelomic pouch. A twisting vas efferens leads from each testis to the lateral vas deferens, which at its anterior end coils to form a seminal vesicle. From each seminal vesicle an ejaculatory duct turns inwards, the right passing beneath the ventral sinus. The two ducts join into the swollen prostate gland, from which a muscular penis emerges posteriorly.

f. The **excretory system** contains seventeen pairs of nephridia (in segments 6 to 22). Each nephridium has a nephrostome opening into a coelomic pouch, which in those segments possessing testes is also the testis pouch. Each nephridium also has a reflexed or coiled glandular region, and a muscular bladder (which discharges the waste through the nephridiopore).

g. The ventral cord of the **nervous system** lies within the ventral sinus. It is superficially single, but actually double, and it bears a series of ganglia, each of which corresponds to a segment and gives off branch nerves. The cord passes forwards beneath the pharynx, which now may be carefully removed, until it reaches the first, or subpharyngeal, ganglion. This is large and composed of several ganglia fused, and from it two circumbuccal commissures pass to the two dorsal cerebral ganglia. The posterior ganglion of the body also consists of several ganglia fused.

4. CONCLUSION

a. Observing the specimen and the drawings made, review the characteristics of the phylum, of the class, and of the order.

b. Also review those features which are associated with the semi-parasitic blood-sucking mode of life.

5. REFERENCES

BOURNE, A. G. (1884). " Contributions to the anatomy of the Hirudinea." *Quarterly Journal of Microscopical Science*, Vol. 24, p. 419.
KÜKENTHAL, W., and KRUMBACH, T. (1928–34). Volume 2 and part 2 of " Handbuch der Zoologie." Berlin and Leipzig.

3.00. Class **Gephyrea**

Characteristics : Relatively large annelids with little or no trace of segmentation.

The gephyreans, which are all marine, may be regarded as aberrant chaetopods specialised for a sluggish life hidden in rock crevices or buried in sand. In all probability they do not form a homogeneous group, and they are classed together merely for convenience.

3.01. Order **Echiuroidea**

Characteristics : Gephyrea with the prostomium enlarged as a proboscis ; with the anus posterior and terminal ; and with a pair of ventral setae.

Genus **Bonellia**

1. GENERAL ACCOUNT

a. The best-known species, *B. viridis* Rolando, is common along the coasts of the Mediterranean. The animal's body lies concealed in some hole, while the ciliated proboscis is extended, sometimes to a length of 3 feet, to catch tiny food particles. This form is the female, and as the male is slender, and not more than 2 mm. long, there is great sexual dimorphism. The eggs are shed into the sea, where they hatch to produce ciliated larvae with clear signs of segmentation. These, if they develop alone, grow to produce females, but if they come into contact with an adult female, to which they are attracted, their growth is repressed and they become parasitic males. This latter effect is due to the secretion by the female of an unknown chemical substance. In the female the males are found attached to the proboscis, to the lining of the alimentary

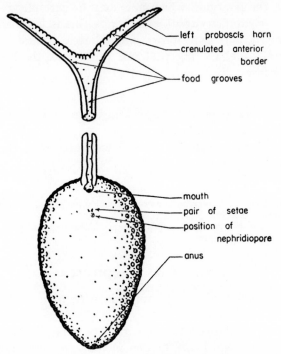

—left proboscis horn
—crenulated anterior
                border
—food grooves

—mouth
—pair of setae
—position of
        nephridiopore
—anus

FIG. 75.—*Bonellia*. A ventral view of the external anatomy of a female with the proboscis greatly shortened by the removal of its middle section.

canal, and particularly within the single enormous nephridium, which also acts as an oviduct, and they fertilise the eggs before they are shed.

2. EXTERNAL ANATOMY

   a. The **body** of the female is ovoid, and has a rough, warty surface with a greenish-brown pigmentation. Its anterior end is clearly marked by the long proboscis. The mouth opens ventral to the base of the proboscis, and from it a narrow streak of paler pigmentation passes along the mid-ventral line to the posterior terminal anus. In preserved specimens the ventral side of the body is usually slightly concave, while the dorsal side is convex. There is no evidence of segmentation.

b. The **proboscis** (considered to represent the prostomium) is considerably longer than the body (and is capable of rapid movement and of great expansion and contraction). It terminates in two horns, which extend outwards to the left and right, and which have crenulated anterior borders. Food grooves (ciliated) pass along the posterior borders of these horns to join centrally and deepen into a single groove, which continues back along the ventral side of the proboscis to the mouth.

c. Close behind the mouth in the mid-ventral line is a single pair of dark setae set in pits, and immediately behind and to the left of these (to the right in *B. minor* Marrion) the single **nephridiopore** opens through the end of a small but prominent papilla.

3.   CONCLUSION

a. Observing the specimen, review the characteristics of the phylum, of the class, and of the order.

4.   REFERENCES

For further descriptions of the anatomy of *Bonellia*, and for descriptions of *Echiurus* and other echiuroids see :

DELAGE, Y., and HÉROUARD, E. (1897).   Volume 5 of " Traité de zoologie concrète." Paris.

KÜKENTHAL, W., and KRUMBACH, T. (1928–34).   Volume 2 and part 2 of " Handbuch der Zoologie."   Berlin and Leipzig.

LACAZE–DUTHIERS, H. (1858).   " Recherches sur la Bonellie (*Bonellia viridis*)." *Annales des Sciences Naturelles : Zoologique*, Vol. 10. p. 49.

3.02.   Order **Sipunculoidea**

Characteristics : Gephyrea with the prostomium lacking in the adult stage ; with the anterior part of the body capable of invagination ; with the anus anterior and dorsal ; and without setae.

Genus **Sipunculus**

1.   GENERAL ACCOUNT

a. The genus has a world-wide distribution, and is especially common in the warmer seas, where it is found particularly in shallow water at and below the low-tide mark.   Individuals are sometimes discovered in rock clefts, but usually they lie in sand or mud, which is swallowed in large quantities so that its organic content can be digested.   For defence the body contracts, and the anterior end is withdrawn inside the posterior end.   The sexes are separate but similar, fertilisation is external, and the eggs develop into free-swimming larvae which show no clear signs of segmentation.

2.   EXTERNAL ANATOMY

a. The **body** is long, club-like, and pale brown in colour.   It is covered by a thick, chitinous cuticle, which is transparent and iridescent, and which overlies a glandular epidermis (the secretion escapes through pores in the cuticle). The body is sharply divided into a shorter anterior region, which has a thin wall bearing numbers of blunt, backward-pointing papillae, and a longer posterior region, which has a thick wall decorated by a regular lattice-like pattern of grooves (these are the outward signs of the crossing pattern made by the strands of outer circular and inner longitudinal muscles in the body wall). There is no evidence of segmentation.

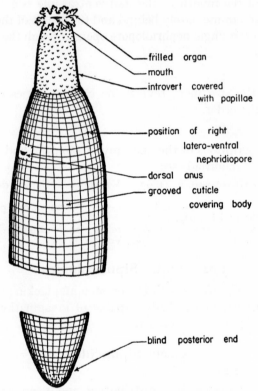

frilled organ
mouth
introvert covered with papillae
position of right latero-ventral nephridiopore
dorsal anus
grooved cuticle covering body
blind posterior end

FIG. 76.—*Sipunculus.* A dorso-lateral view of the external anatomy with the body considerably shortened by the omission of its middle region.

b. The anterior thin-walled region is the **introvert** (invaginable within the posterior region), and it is pierced by the terminal mouth. This is surrounded by the frilled membrane, so called because of its fringe of short, unbranched tentacles (it is not a prostomium, and its function is to push sand into the mouth).

c. On the dorsal surface, and a short distance posterior to the base of the introvert, is the slit-like opening of the **anus**. The only other external openings are the two tiny and obscure **nephridiopores** situated slightly closer to the base of the introvert and latero-ventral in position.

3. CONCLUSION

a. Observing the specimen, review the characteristics of the phylum, of the class, and of the order.

4. REFERENCES

For details of the internal anatomy of *Sipunculus*, and for descriptions of other genera see :

DELAGE, Y., and HÉROUARD, E. (1897). Volume 5 of " Traité de zoologie concrète." Paris.
KÜKENTHAL, W., and KRUMBACH, T. (1928–34). Volume 2 and part 2 of " Handbuch der Zoologie." Berlin and Leipzig.

APPENDIX TO THE ANNELIDA

1. CULTURE METHODS

a. None of the marine annelids mentioned above is easily maintained in the laboratory unless unusual facilities are available. However, worms such as *Nereis* may survive for several days or weeks if the aquarium is large. If the worms are available in breeding condition, the rearing of the larvae is relatively easy. During late spring and summer the eggs and spermatozoa should be collected separately by cutting open the worms in small bowls containing from 25 c.c. to 50 c.c. of sea-water. Artificial fertilisation is then carried out by adding a few c.c. of a soup of active spermatozoa to the water containing the eggs. It is necessary to keep the temperature down to about that of the sea from which the worms came, and at least for the first day or two, to change the water every few hours. Cleavage can be observed after about three hours, the small ciliated gastrulae begin to rotate within the egg membranes after about twelve hours, and the trochosphere larvae are fully developed after about thirty-six hours. As early as possible the young larvae should be separated from the residual egg-jelly and put into clean sea-water. They will then continue their growth without feeding, and at the end of a week the first few segments of the body will have developed. If still further development is required, feeding with a diatom culture is necessary.

b. Healthy specimens of the earthworm *Lumbricus* may be stored for a week or two in boxes of moist grass cuttings or of *Sphagnum* moss. To maintain a culture, however, they should be kept in large wooden boxes filled with loamy (not clayey) soil and old dead leaves to a depth of at least 12 inches. The soil and leaves should be damp (not wet), the temperature should not exceed 15° C., and, to prevent evaporation, the box should be covered by a sheet of glass. Overcrowding must be avoided (about 25 worms per cubic foot of soil is a maximum), and all injured and unhealthy worms must be immediately removed. The worms eat the decaying leaves, but if these are lacking, breadcrumbs or corn meal, added sparingly about once a fortnight and buried an inch deep, may be given.

c. The other common earthworm *Allolobophora* (*Eisenia*), which is recognised by the fact that the prostomium does not extend across the peristomium to touch the second segment, may also be kept as described above, but it should be fed, in addition, with rotted cow or horse manure. In the laboratory this genus is much hardier than *Lumbricus*, and it more readily copulates and lays eggs.

d. Although aquatic oligochaets, such as *Tubifex*, are easily kept in aquaria which are fitted with slowly running water and which have mud and decaying leaves mixed into the sandy bottom, the semi-aquatic *Enchytraeus* should be cultured like an earthworm. A small wooden box containing some 3 or 4 inches of damp (not wet) loamy soil is sufficient, and the worms can be fed sparingly on small pieces of bread soaked in milk, or on mashed potatoes, buried an inch deep. The temperature should not exceed 18° C. If small white cocoons are found in the soil of the culture, they may be taken out and kept in a petri dish on damp filter-papers. Since these cocoons are transparent, the development and method of hatching can be watched through a microscope.

e. In the past, and particularly in France, the medicinal leech *Hirudo* has been cultured on a large scale. It will live for years, and will breed in aquaria, or even in earthenware jars, which are kept half full of fresh water in a cool, shady place. The aquaria must have well-fitting lids, as the leeches leave the water and wander. They can be kept for at least a year without food, and in any case they need not be fed more often than once in six months. They will suck the blood of any mammal or, more conveniently, of a frog, which can be added to the aquarium.

f. The large horse leech *Haemopsis*, which is common in ponds and streams, can be similarly cultured, but it does not normally suck blood, and it should be fed on such small animals as earthworms or tadpoles.

2. FIXATION METHODS

a. Marine annelids should always be narcotised before fixation in order to prevent any sudden contraction from causing distortion or even fragmentation. Allow the worms to settle down and become fully expanded in a small dish of water, and then slowly add crystals of menthol or of magnesium sulphate or add small amounts of 95% alcohol up to a maximum of 1 part of alcohol to 9 parts of sea-water. When the worms react only slightly to a touch, they should be straightened out and the sea-water replaced by 70% alcohol. Change the alcohol after one day and again after two days, when the worms may remain in it for storage. It is recommended that exceptionally delicate worms, such as many pelagic species, should be fixed after narcotisation in a mixture of 1 part of commercial formalin and 10 parts of sea-water, and that they should be stored in the same solution.

b. Earthworms can be killed quickly with chloroform water, or narcotised slowly in water to which crystals of menthol or magnesium sulphate are added. When they become limp they should be dissected immediately. They may also be preserved, after narcotisation, in 5% formalin or 70% alcohol, but they are not so easily dissected afterwards.

c. Fresh-water worms and enchytraeids are best studied alive, but they also may be narcotised and preserved. They should be put into a watch-glass or petri dish and just covered with water, over which chloroform vapour is then blown. When they are limp, pick them out, straighten each in turn in the crack between two slides, and add a small drop of Bouin's solution. After about half an hour they can be transferred to and stored in 70% alcohol.

d. All leeches have the power of extreme contraction, and they must therefore be carefully narcotised. Place them in a small jar filled to the brim with water, add a few crystals of menthol or magnesium sulphate, and cover with a lid which does not trap any air-space into which they can climb. When after many hours they become quite limp, they can be dissected immediately. Alternatively they can be fixed and stored in either 5% formalin or 70% alcohol, but this makes dissection more difficult.

3. STAINING METHODS

a. Small whole worms, or separate heads or parapodia, are most easily stained in picrocarmine, being transferred directly into the stain from 70% alcohol. After over-staining, the excess is extracted in a 1% solution of hydrochloric acid in 70% alcohol, and when just sufficient stain remains, the extraction is stopped by transference to normal 70% alcohol. The specimen is then passed slowly through 90% alcohol, absolute alcohol, and xylol, and mounted in Canada balsam. As an alternative the specimens can be transferred to water and over-stained in either Delafield's or Ehrlich's haematoxylin. Excess stain is removed, as before, in acid 70% alcohol, and the remaining stain is turned blue in 70% alcohol to which a few drops of ammonia have been added. Finally dehydrate, and mount in Canada balsam.

b. To make a smear of the seminal vesicle contents of an earthworm, remove one of the vesicle lobes and dab its cut end on to a clean slide which has been moistened with the breath. Allow the milky contents of the vesicle to flow out evenly, but do not attempt to flatten the smear with another slide. Fix the smear by putting it (for about five minutes) into 70% alcohol, and then pass it through 50% and 30% alcohols (two minutes in each) to water. Stain in Delafield's or Ehrlich's haematoxylin (the time depending on the activity of the stain), and then turn the stain blue in slightly alkaline water. Counter-stain in an aqueous solution of eosin (for about two minutes), wash in water, and pass through 30%, 50%, 70%, 90%, and absolute alcohols (two minutes in each) to xylol. Put a small drop of Canada balsam over the smear, and add a cover-glass.

CHAPTER XV

PHYLUM **ARTHROPODA**

Characteristics : Bilaterally symmetrical segmented animals with the body usually encased in a tough, chitinous, jointed exoskeleton, and consequently with the body-wall reduced and with growth by ecdysis ; typically with a pair of jointed appendages on each segment ; with the coelom reduced and the haemocoel enlarged as the perivisceral cavity ; without nephridia, but often with coelomoducts as excretory organs ; and with a double ventral nerve-cord with a pair of ganglia in each segment and a pair of preoral cerebral ganglia.

This is the largest and most successful animal phylum, and its members, emerging from the sea, have invaded all possible environments. In all probability the original marine forms evolved from the same stock as did the annelids.

1.00. Class **Onychophora**

Characteristics : Arthopoda with the exoskeleton thin and soft, and therefore with the body and limbs unjointed ; head poorly defined and formed of three segments, the 1st preoral with preantennae, the 2nd with jaws, and the 3rd with oral papillae ; body of uniform segments each with two parapodia-like limbs ending in claws ; body-wall well developed, with outer circular and inner longitudinal muscle layers ; tracheal respiratory system with spiracles scattered irregularly ; segmental pairs of ciliated excretory coelomoducts ; sexes separate, ciliated gonoducts formed of modified excretory tubules, and development direct.

The Onychophora are the most primitive living arthropods, and apart from the haemocoelic body cavity and the tracheal respiratory system, their structure is mainly annelidan. They are sometimes considered to form a separate phylum. All the present-day forms are terrestrial with a discontinuous distribution in tropical and subtropical forests, but the mid-Cambrian *Aysheaia*, although very similar in appearance to the modern forms, was marine.

Genus **Peripatus**

I. GENERAL ACCOUNT

a. The species of this genus occur locally in the damp forests of Africa, Malaya, Australasia, the East and West Indies, and Central and South America.

b. P. Novae-Zealandiae Hutton, the New Zealand species, may be taken as the type.   The animals avoid light, and by day they remain beneath leaves, stones, and rotten tree-stumps.   By night they emerge to feed on such animals

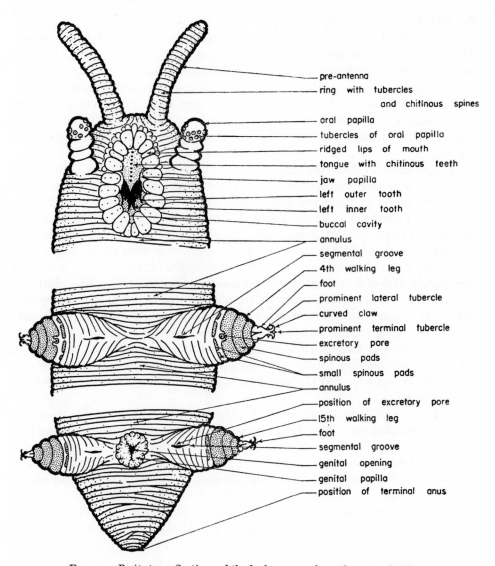

pre-antenna
ring with tubercles
             and chitinous spines
oral papilla
tubercles of oral papilla
ridged lips of mouth
tongue with chitinous teeth
jaw papilla
left outer tooth
left inner tooth
buccal cavity
annulus
segmental groove
4th walking leg
foot
prominent lateral tubercle
curved claw
prominent terminal tubercle
excretory pore
spinous pads
small spinous pads
annulus
position of excretory pore
15th walking leg
foot
segmental groove
genital opening
genital papilla
position of terminal anus

FIG. 77.—*Peripatus*.   Sections of the body as seen from the ventral side.

as small insects, which are killed by the sharp jaws, and they can protect themselves by throwing out a jet of sticky slime.   Apparently copulation takes place mainly in spring, the spermatozoa, bound into spermatophores, being deposited on the female's body, whence they make their own way to the oviducts.   The
P

yolked eggs are retained, and the young develop inside the oviducts for almost a year before they are born.

2.   EXTERNAL ANATOMY

a. The **body** is caterpillar-like, and encased in a thin, chitinous cuticle. The anterior end is marked by the preantennae and by the ventrally directed mouth, while the posterior end, extending behind the last pair of legs, bears the terminal anus.   There are fifteen pairs of legs attached latero-ventrally (the number is different in other species), and these are the only external signs of segmentation.   The body is ringed by annuli, on which are tubercles set in rows.   Each tubercle ends in a tiny chitinous spine (and is presumed to be tactile).

b. Examine the **head** through a lens or binocular microscope.   The blunt-ending preantennae (appendages of segment 1) are ringed by ridges set with tubercles ending in chitinous spines (they are tactile and are the main sense organs).   A small eye is situated dorsally behind the base of each pre-antenna, and has a shining spherical lens.   The elongated mouth is surrounded by ridged, unpigmented lips, which converge into it, each ridge bearing a row of tubercles. In the sides of the mouth are two jaws (appendages of segment 2).   Each is a low papilla, and in it are embedded two backward-pointing, claw-like, chitinous teeth.   The roof of the anterior end of the mouth is thickened to form a muscular ridge, the tongue, which is armoured with a row of small chitinous teeth (and acts as a rasping organ).   Through the posterior end of the mouth the buccal cavity is visible.   Lateral to the mouth are the oral papillae (of segment 3), which are prominently ringed and bear large tubercles distally (they are presumed to be sensory, and through their ends open the ducts of the defensive slime-glands).

c. In the middle region of the body examine from the ventral side the structure of a **walking leg**.   Basally it consists of a cone, the leg proper, ringed by ridges studded with tubercles, while distally it terminates in a foot which bears two curved claws and three prominent tubercles.   Ventrally, on the three distal ridges of the leg proper are three pads (formed of fused tubercles), and on the fourth ridge are a number of smaller pads all closely studded with chitinous spines (for gripping the ground).   In the base of each leg is a groove, transverse to the long axis of the body, and on all legs except the 4th and 5th an excretory pore opens into its inner end.   Grooves are present on the 4th and 5th pairs of legs, but the excretory pores of these segments open through the centres of the third spinous pads.   There are no crural glands in this species.

d. Between the last pair of legs is the **genital opening**, surrounded by tumid lips which form a genital papilla.   In the female these lips are also called the vulvae, but the appearance is the same in both sexes (the only distinguishing feature is the smaller size of the male).

3. CONCLUSION

a. Observing the specimen, review as far as possible the characteristics of the phylum and of the class.

b. Distinguish those features which are of the annelidan type and those which are of the arthropod type.

4. REFERENCES

For further details of this and of other species of *Peripatus*, and for a description of the internal anatomy see :

BALFOUR, F. M. (1883). " The anatomy and development of *Peripatus capensis.*" *Quarterly Journal of Microscopical Science*, Vol. 23, p. 213.

SEDGWICK, A. (1888). " A monograph of the species and distribution of the genus *Peripatus* (Guilding)." *Quarterly Journal of Microscopical Science*, Vol. 28, p. 431.

CHAPTER XVI

PHYLUM **ARTHROPODA** (*continued*)

2.00. Class **Crustacea**

Characteristics : Typically aquatic Arthropoda which possess gills ; head formed of 6 segments, the 1st disappearing, the 2nd and 3rd both preoral with antennae, the 4th with mandibles, and the 5th and 6th with maxillae ; body divisible into a thorax (the region anterior to and including the segment with the genital opening) and an abdomen ; limbs modified for food capture, swimming, walking, respiration, and reproduction ; excretion by antennal and maxillary glands (which are partly coelomoducts) ; sexes usually separate, and development usually via a nauplius stage.

The crustaceans are primarily and almost exclusively aquatic animals which abound in the sea and in fresh water, as the insects do on land. For the most part they are free living either as herbivores, predators, or scavengers, but a few are ecto- or endo-parasites.

2.10. Subclass **Branchiopoda**

Characteristics : Free-living and mainly fresh-water Crustacea ; head with compound eyes and with mandibles usually lacking palps ; thorax with a variable number of segments, usually with a carapace, and with limbs which are phyllopodia ; abdomen either with a large number of segments or greatly reduced ; parthenogenesis frequent, and development either through a nauplius stage or direct.

These are the most primitive living crustaceans, and they feed in what is possibly the primitive manner by sieving the water with their bristle-fringed limbs to extract tiny particles of detritus or plankton.

2.11. Order **Anostraca**

Characteristics : Branchiopoda in which the head bears stalked eyes and, in the male, prehensile second antennae ; thorax of either 12 or 20 segments, all similar except the last, and with a carapace ; abdomen long, with terminal unjointed rami ; and development through a nauplius stage.

The usual habitat of these, the most primitive of the branchiopods, is shallow, stagnant water, especially such as appears in winter and spring and evaporates to dryness in summer.

212

Genus **Eubranchipus** (fairy shrimp)

(Another fairy shrimp *Chirocephalus*, which occurs in Britain, may be used as an alternative. It is recognised by the fact that the appendage of the antenna of the male is jointed and bears secondary processes.)

I. GENERAL ACCOUNT

a. The distribution of *Eubranchipus* is irregular, as is that of related genera, but the animals are so widespread as to be almost cosmopolitan. They are found especially in shallow ponds which are formed by melting snow or early spring rain and which dry up in summer. They are transparent, and swimming with the ventral side uppermost, they sieve food-particles from the water by means of their thoracic limbs. This food, which consists especially of organic detritus, diatoms, and protozoans, is passed forwards along the ventral food-groove by a water current induced by the movements of the limb bases. Close to the mouth it is bound into balls by a sticky secretion of the labrum, chewed by the mandibles, and then swallowed. The sexes are separate, and fertilisation is internal. The eggs have resistant shells, and they remain in the mud until the following year when the pond reforms. Development from the egg is then very rapid, and the life cycle is completed in a few weeks.

2. ANATOMY

a. The long, clearly segmented **body** is divided into a head, a thorax bearing phyllopodia and appendages modified for reproduction, and a slender, limbless abdomen ending in a telson.

b. The **head** is slightly swollen and clearly distinguishable from the thorax. Laterally it bears two large, stalked, compound eyes, while anteriorly there is a small, unstalked, median eye (the eye of the nauplius larva). Mid-dorsally is the nuchal sense organ (function unknown). Postero-laterally the maxillary glands (excretory organs opening by the bases of the maxillae) are clearly visible through the body-wall, and they also extend into the sides of the 1st thoracic segment (antennal glands are absent from the adult, having functioned as the excretory organs of the larva). Ventrally the mouth is covered by the prominent backward-pointing labrum. It leads into a short foregut (ecto-dermal and cuticle lined), which rises vertically, but which is usually obscure. The long midgut (endodermal) starts in the dorsal side of the head, where it also bears two many-lobed diverticula (of unknown function, but possibly secreting digestive enzymes).

c. The **segmentation of the head** is shown mainly by its appendages. The 1st segment disappears in the embryo, and the 2nd therefore bears the 1st appendages which are thin, unjointed, uniramous antennules each ending in a tuft of sensory bristles. The 2nd appendages (segment 3) are stout uniramous antennae, unjointed in the female but 2-jointed in the male. Each male antenna also carries internally a prominent unjointed appendage (by which the female is gripped during copulation; it is a new outgrowth and not an

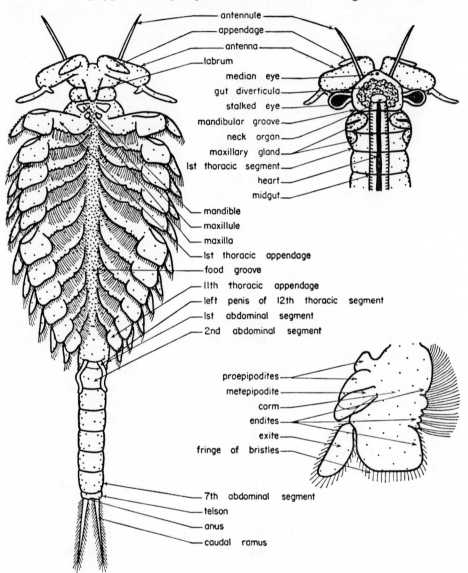

antennule
appendage
antenna
labrum
median eye
gut diverticula
stalked eye
mandibular groove
neck organ
maxillary gland
1st thoracic segment
heart
midgut
mandible
maxillule
maxilla
1st thoracic appendage
food groove
11th thoracic appendage
left penis of 12th thoracic segment
1st abdominal segment
2nd abdominal segment

proepipodites
metepipodite
corm
endites
exite
fringe of bristles

7th abdominal segment
telson
anus
caudal ramus

FIG. 78.—*Eubranchipus.* A ventral view of a male, and, on the right, a dorsal view of the anterior end of a male, and an isolated phyllopodium.

endopodite). The 3rd appendages (segment 4) are the mandibles, the bases of which can be seen latero-ventrally as they turn inwards to end bluntly in the middle line. The 4th appendages (segment 5) are the maxillules, which are visible ventrally as two small triangular plates fringed with bristles, and immediately posterior to them are the 5th appendages (segment 6), which are greatly reduced maxillae each bearing three bristles. A further sign of segmentation is the mandibular groove, which passes up the sides of the head to separate the first four segments (which probably formed the primitive head) from the last two (which were only later added to this region).

d. The **thorax**, convex above, has 12 segments, the first 11 of which carry similar pairs of phyllopodia (functioning in locomotion, respiration, and food capture). Ventrally between the bases of the appendages the segments are concave to form a long groove (into which, the animal being on its back, the food-particles fall). Dorsally, through the transparent wall, the long heart (with a pair of ostia in each segment) can be seen passing along the top of the featureless midgut. On the 12th thoracic segment, which ventrally is partly fused to the 1st abdominal segment, are the openings of the gonoducts. In the female the appendages of this segment are fused together to form a single prominent egg-pouch (in which the eggs are carried for a time). In the male the appendages remain separate as two eversible penes (through which the vasa deferentia open).

e. Detach a **phyllopodium** and mount it on a slide. It is a broad, flat, unjointed limb, the axis of which is called the corm. Internal to this axis is a series of 6 lobes, the endites, and external to it is a series of 4 larger lobes, of which the distal is the exite (or exopodite, or flabellum), the next the metepipodite (or branchia), and the two basal the proepipodites. Except for these three epipodites, all the lobes are closely fringed with bristles, which are themselves fringed with finer bristles (the food sieving mechanism).

f. The **abdomen** consists of 7 limbless segments (the 1st partly fused to the 12th thoracic) and a telson bearing two unjointed caudal rami fringed with bristles. Through the transparent wall the posterior ends of the midgut and of the long dorsal heart are visible. The short hindgut (ectodermal and cuticle lined) lies within the telson, and the anus opens between the bases of the caudal rami. The two gonads, particularly if they are ovaries, may also be visible lateral and ventral to the alimentary canal in the anterior part of the abdomen.

3. CONCLUSION

a. Observing the specimen, review the characteristics of the phylum, of the class, of the subclass, and of the order.

b. Also review those features which may be considered as primitive.

4. REFERENCE

CLAUS, C. (1873). " Zur Kenntniss des Baues und der Entwicklung von *Branchipus stagnalis* und *Apus cancriformis*." *Abhandlungen der königlichen Gesellschaft der Wissenschaften zu Göttingen*, Vol. 18, p. 93.

2.12. Order **Notostraca**

Characteristics : Branchiopoda in which the head bears sessile eyes and rudimentary antennules and antennae ; thorax of 11 segments covered by a broad, horseshoe-shaped carapace ; anterior abdominal segments each with 1 to 6 pairs of limbs, posterior segments limbless, and telson with many-jointed rami ; parthenogenesis common, and development through a nauplius stage.

This order contains only the genera *Apus* and *Lepidurus*, which, like the anostracans, usually reach the adult stage in temporary ponds, and survive the summer drought as resistant eggs.

Genus **Apus**

(The various species of *Apus* and *Lepidurus* are all essentially alike.)

1. GENERAL ACCOUNT

a. The habitat and habits of *Apus* are similar to those of *Eubranchipu*s. The genus has a world-wide distribution in shallow fresh water, especially that which is temporary, but it is unpredictably local in occurrence. Swimming upside down, the animals feed by sieving the water through the bristles of their phyllopodia, and they also occasionally settle on and wriggle along the bottom. The food-particles taken consist of any small animals, plants, or organic débris. Males are very rare, and reproduction is normally parthenogenic. The eggs are carried for some time in a pouch, and they can survive prolonged drought. The young hatch as metanauplius larvae which develop quickly.

2. ANATOMY

a. The **body** is divided into a head, the posterior edge of which is developed as a carapace ; a clearly segmented thorax, which is covered by the carapace ; and an abdomen, which protrudes posteriorly and ends in a telson with two caudal rami.

b. The dorsal side of the **head** bears two close-set, sessile eyes, between and behind which is the dorsal organ (function unknown, and not homologous with the nuchal sense organ of *Eubranchipus*). Immediately posterior to this are two transverse grooves, the anterior being the mandibular groove, which separates the four anterior from the two posterior head segments, and the posterior being the cervical groove, which marks the division between head and thorax. Inside the head, in the region anterior and lateral to the eyes, the diverticula of the midgut may be visible (these possibly produce digestive enzymes). The dorsal covering of the head projects back behind the cervical groove to form the thin carapace, inside which the coils of the two large maxillary glands (excretory) are clearly visible. The ventral side of the head is

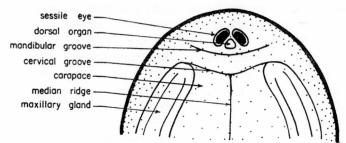

sessile eye
dorsal organ
mandibular groove
cervical groove
carapace
median ridge
maxillary gland

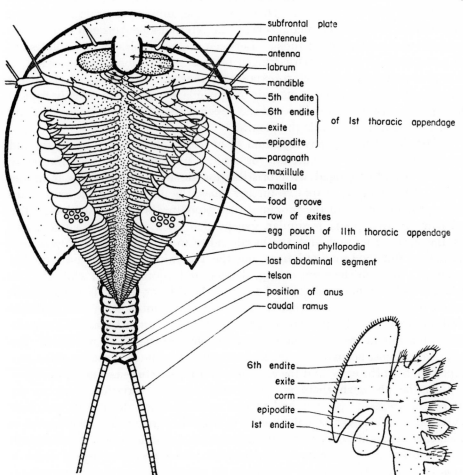

subfrontal plate
antennule
antenna
labrum
mandible
5th endite ⎫
6th endite ⎬ of 1st thoracic appendage
exite
epipodite ⎭
paragnath
maxillule
maxilla
food groove
row of exites
egg pouch of 11th thoracic appendage
abdominal phyllopodia
last abdominal segment
telson
position of anus
caudal ramus

6th endite
exite
corm
epipodite
1st endite

FIG. 79.—*Apus.*   A dorsal view of the anterior end, a ventral view of a female, and an abdominal phyllopodium.

protected anteriorly by the subfrontal plate, from the posterior edge of which the labrum projects to cover the mouth and form an upper lip.

c. The 1st of the 6 head segments is limbless and indistinguishable, and thus there are only 5 pairs of **head appendages**. The first two of these are the small 2-jointed antennules (tactile) and the even smaller, hook-like, unjointed antennae (vestigial structures which are absent from some species of both *Apus* and *Lepidurus*). The 3rd pair (of segment 4) are the large mandibles, the serrated edges of which bite together beneath the labrum. The 4th and 5th pairs (segments 5 and 6) are the maxillules and maxillae (which may help in passing food into the mouth). They are simple, unjointed structures fringed with bristles, but each maxilla also bears an external lobe (through which open the ducts of the maxillary glands). Between the mandibles and maxillules are the paragnaths, a pair of bristle-fringed processes which form the lower lip.

d. Cut away the carapace to expose the **thorax**. It consists of 11 clearly defined segments, each with one pair of appendages, which are mostly typical phyllopodia. Between the bases of the appendages a food-groove passes along the mid-ventral line towards the mouth.

e. Detach a **thoracic phyllopodium** from one of the segments 3 to 10, and examine its shape. The main axis, or corm, is unjointed, and bears internally a row of 6 endites edged with bristles (for sieving food-particles from the water). Externally it bears two further lobes, the distal being the exite (exopodite or flabellum) and the proximal the epipodite (bract or branchia). The 2nd pair of phyllopodia is similar, except that each is more elongated, and has the corm 2-jointed and the basal endite more strongly developed as a gnathobase (for food manipulation), but the 1st pair of phyllopodia is highly modified. In them the corm is long, slender, and 4-jointed, and while the 1st, or basal, endite remains a gnathobase and the 6th, or distal, is reduced, the 2nd to the 5th endites are greatly elongated and jointed (they are probably tactile organs ; their length is much greater in *Apus* than in *Lepidurus*). In the female, but not in the male, the 11th pair of phyllopodia is also modified. The endites are almost normal, the epipodite is reduced, while the broad corm is cup-shaped (to hold the eggs) and the exite fits over its aperture as a movable lid.

f. In the **abdomen** there is considerable specific variation, both in the number of segments present and in the number which do and do not bear phyllopodia. However, a subdivision is possible into an anterior region in which each segment bears 1 pair of phyllopodia, a middle region in which each segment bears up to 6 pairs of phyllopodia, and a posterior region which is limbless (the lengths of these regions in *A. cancriformis* Schaeffer are respectively 2, 15, and 5 segments). The segments are clearly defined, and bear rows of backward-pointing spines. The abdomen terminates in a telson with two long caudal rami, between the bases of which the anus opens (in *Lepidurus* there is also a flat postanal plate based dorsal to the anus).

3. CONCLUSION

a. Observing the specimen, review the characteristics of the phylum, of the class, of the subclass, and of the order.

b. Distinguish those features which are primitive and compare them with those of *Eubranchipus*.

4. REFERENCES

CLAUS, C. (1873). "Zur Kenntniss des Baues und der Entwicklung von *Branchipus stagnalis* und *Apus cancriformis.*" *Abhandlungen der königlichen Gesellschaft der Wissenschaften zu Göttingen*, Vol. 18, p. 93.

LANKESTER, E. R. (1881). "Observations and reflections on the appendages and on the nervous system of *Apus cancriformis.*" *Quarterly Journal of Microscopical Science*, Vol. 21, p. 343.

2.13. Order **Cladocera**

Characteristics : Small, laterally compressed Branchiopoda in which the head bears sessile eyes and large biramous antennae ; thorax of from 7 to 9 segments, the first 2 fused to the head and the last 3 limbless, and with the female opening on segment 7 and the male opening on the telson which has unjointed rami ; no true abdominal segments ; development direct.

It is thought that the cladocerans, the most specialised and successful of the branchiopods, may have originated by neoteny from some metanauplius such as that of the notostracans. Characterised by their small size, they are mainly fresh-water forms, but a few live in brackish water and a few in the sea.

Genus **Daphnia** (water flea)

(*Simocephalus*, the other common genus, is similar except that it possesses a cervical groove and lacks a posterior spine on the carapace.)

I. GENERAL ACCOUNT

a. Daphnia is almost cosmopolitan, and is one of the commonest inhabitants of ditches and ponds. It swims by means of the large antennae, and sieves animal and vegetable food-particles from the water by means of its bristle-fringed thoracic limbs. In favourable conditions the female lays thin-shelled eggs which contain little yolk and develop parthenogenetically, but in adverse conditions thick-shelled resistant eggs are produced which contain much yolk and require fertilisation. The parthenogenetic eggs are carried in a brood-pouch until they hatch, and the larvae also remain there for a time. The fertilised eggs, produced two at a time, are fertilised in the brood-pouch, and are shed at the next moult, when they remain inside the specially thickened cuticle of the brood-pouch, which forms a box, the ephippium, for their extra protection. When, after freezing or desiccation, better conditions return, these eggs hatch into parthenogenetic females. Sexual individuals appear particularly in spring and autumn. A culture method is described on p. 331.

2. ANATOMY

a. The animals should be examined through a microscope while still alive. They can be held steady by the weight of a small cover-glass or by embedding in agar jelly (the method is given for protozoans on p. 35). The bilaterally compressed **body**, which is often reddish in colour (due to the presence of haemoglobin), consists of a head on which are based the large antennae, and a thorax which is entirely encased in a large carapace.

b. The **head** is not clearly divided from the thorax (but a cervical groove is present in *Simocephalus*). It is flexed ventrally so that the beak-like rostrum points downwards and the single large compound eye (formed of a pair fused) is directed forwards. Notice that this eye is continually vibrating. Within the head the large cerebral ganglion can be seen giving one nerve to the compound eye and another to a small degenerate median eye seen as a streak of black pigment (which is the remains of the simple nauplius eye). Two nuchal organs (groups of club-shaped cells associated with ganglia and presumed to be sensory) are present in the sides of the head, and are joined to the ventral side of the cerebral ganglion by two slender nerves. Due to the flexure of the head, the mouth is directed posteriorly into the space enclosed by the carapace. The narrow foregut (ectodermal and cuticle lined) passes forwards through the nerve-ring, immediately in front of which it opens into the wider midgut (endodermal). In this region the midgut gives rise to two unbranched curved diverticula (which possibly secrete digestive enzymes), and then it loops back to enter the thorax.

c. The **head appendages** belong to segments 2, 3, 4, and 5. Segment 1 is limbless and indistinguishable, and segment 6 is limbless in the adult (a rudimentary maxilla is present in the embryo). The 1st appendages (segment 2) are the tiny antennules, which are unjointed, end in a bunch of sensory bristles, and are based on the posterior surface of the rostrum. The 2nd appendages are the large antennae (used for swimming), each with a basal joint bearing two rami. One ramus is 3-jointed and the other 4-jointed, and both carry long, jointed, feather-like bristles. The 3rd appendages, the large mandibles, are prominent close to the mouth, and immediately posterior to them the 4th appendages, the maxillules (segment 5), can be seen.

d. The **carapace** is exceptionally large, and with its lobes joined above and separated below, it is shaped like a bivalve shell (in addition to its protective function, it serves to canalise the stream of water bringing food-particles, and to assist respiration). Its surface is marked by two crossing series of ridges, and its posterior edges bear rows of tiny spines as well as the single large spine (which is absent in *Simocephalus*). Anteriorly, within each carapace lobe, is a large, coiled, maxillary gland (an excretory structure, the ducts of which open immediately behind the maxillules). Antero-dorsally the carapace is attached to the head and to the first two thoracic segments, but postero-dorsally, be-

tween it and the thorax, there is a space which serves as the brood-pouch.   In
this pouch eggs and developing embryos may be present, and these are prevented from escaping posteriorly by two dorsal thoracic spines.

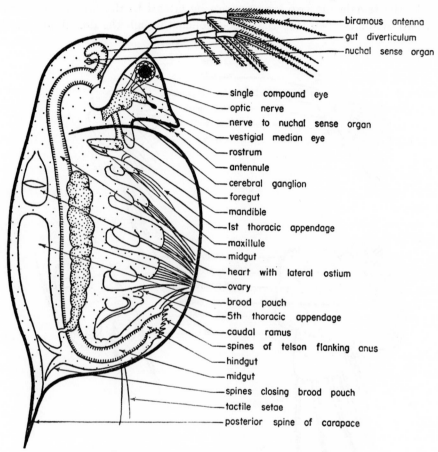

biramous antenna
gut diverticulum
nuchal sense organ

single compound eye
optic nerve
nerve to nuchal sense organ
vestigial median eye
rostrum
antennule
cerebral ganglion
foregut
mandible
1st thoracic appendage
maxillule
midgut
heart with lateral ostium
ovary
brood pouch
5th thoracic appendage
caudal ramus
spines of telson flanking anus
hindgut
midgut
spines closing brood pouch
tactile setae
posterior spine of carapace

FIG. 80—*Daphnia*.   A female seen from the right side.

e. The **thorax**, visible through the transparent carapace, comprises all the
postcephalic segments, there being no true abdomen.   A row of 6 ill-defined
segments, all but the 5th bearing limbs, passes straight back to the posterior
end of the carapace.   The last 3 segments, limbless and ill-defined, turn downwards and forwards to end in the telson.   The telson carries two unjointed rami
and two spine-bearing plates, one on each side of the anus.   In the last segment
the midgut joins into a short hindgut (ectodermal and cuticle lined) which
opens through the anus (water is sucked in through the anus by antiperistalsis,
probably as an aid to respiration).   The bulbous heart is in front of the brood-
pouch, and in its wall can be seen muscle-cells and a single pair of ostia.   Watch

the blood corpuscles passing in through the ostia and being pumped forwards into the head, whence they make their way back through the flaps of the carapace and through the body ventral to the midgut.

f. In the **female** the two long ovaries lie lateral to the midgut, and from them two oviducts open into the brood-pouch through the dorsal side of the

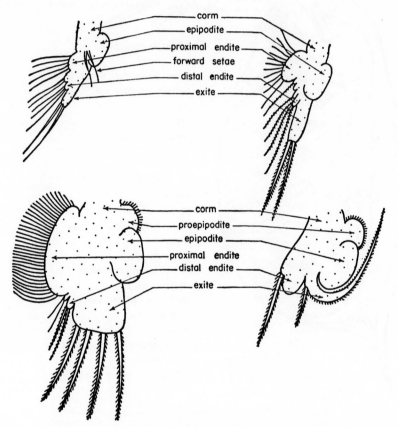

FIG. 81.—*Daphnia.* The 1st and 2nd thoracic appendages (above), and the 3rd (or 4th) and 5th thoracic appendages (below).

7th thoracic segment. In the **male**, which is smaller, the testes are similarly placed, but their ducts open ventrally on the telson.

g. Kill the animal with a drop of alcohol, and then tear off the flaps of the carapace to uncover the 5 pairs of thoracic **phyllopodia**. The 1st phyllopodia (segment 1) are relatively small and simple, and have a corm supporting a row of endites, an exite, and an epipodite (or bract). The endites and the exite bear bristles, and there are also two forward-pointing setae based on the corm. The 2nd pair is similar, but larger. The largest phyllopodia are the

3rd and 4th pairs (of segments 3 and 4). In them the basal endite (or gnatho-base) is large and closely fringed with fine bristles (for food capture), and there is also a proepipodite. The 5th phyllopodia (segment 6) are more modified, with only one endite and with a narrow curved exite. (By the beating of the 3rd and 4th limbs, water is drawn into the carapace space antero-ventrally, and at the same time unduly large particles are excluded by the backward-pointing bristles of the first two pairs of limbs. Finer particles are then trapped by the bristles of the proximal endites of the 3rd and 4th pairs of limbs, and the water leaves postero-ventrally past the barrier formed by the 5th limbs. The food-particles are then moved forward along a mid-ventral food groove, and glued into balls by a secretion of the labrum before being swallowed.)

3. CONCLUSION

a. Observing the specimen and the drawings made, review the character-istics of the phylum, of the class, of the subclass, and of the order.

b. Compare the specialised form of *Daphnia* with the simpler form of *Eubranchipus.*

4. REFERENCE

CLAUS, C. (1876). "Zur Kenntniss der Organisation und des feinern Baues der Daphniden und verwandter Cladoceren." *Zeitschrift für wissenschaftliche Zoologie,* Vol. 27, p. 362.

2.20. Subclass **Copepoda**

Characteristics : Free-living and parasitic Crustacea ; head with or without compound eyes, with large antennules and antennae, and with mandibles with or without palps ; thorax of 5 or 7 segments without a carapace, but with 5 or 7 pairs of stenopodia of which the 1st is uniramous, the 2nd to the 5th biramous, the 6th often uniramous, and the 7th reduced to a mere process ; abdomen of 3 limbless segments and a telson with rami ; development usually through a nauplius stage.

Although the copepods are common in fresh water, the majority are marine and abound in both the plankton and the bottom fauna. While the free-living forms are tiny, the many parasitic forms are larger (*Penella* is 12 inches long), and the majority attach themselves to fishes. The semiparasitic Branchiura, the fish lice, are included in this subclass. The copepods may have originated by neoteny from the protozoean larva of an early decapod.

2.21. Order **Eucopepoda**

Characteristics : Free-living and parasitic Copepoda ; head without com-pound eyes, and with mouth-parts for chewing or sucking ; thorax of 7 segments with 7 pairs of appendages ; and females usually with ovisacs.

Genus **Cyclops**

I.　GENERAL ACCOUNT

a. The genus *Cyclops* is cosmopolitan in fresh and brackish waters, and a great number of species is known.　Individuals occur commonly in quiet pools and backwaters, where they creep along the bottom or over plants and occasionally swim free with great rapidity.　They are known to eat diatoms, but exactly how these are caught is not understood.　Probably they also swallow protozoans, which then become unrecognisable, and they are also described as attacking and injuring small fish and as feeding on dead animals. The females are larger and more abundant.　In copulation the male fastens one or two spermatophores to the genital segment of the female, and this supply is adequate for many successive batches of eggs.　Each batch is fertilised internally, and then covered with a secretion which, in contact with the water, hardens to form the ovisacs.　The eggs hatch as nauplius larvae, which then swim free.　Many species can be found breeding in spring, summer, and autumn, but some which live in casual water breed only in winter and early spring. These latter survive the summer drought buried in the baked mud either as eggs or as unencysted half-grown or adult animals.　A culture method is given on p. 331.

2.　ANATOMY

a. The animals should first be examined alive, when they can be held steady by the weight of a cover-glass or, better, embedded in agar jelly (see method for protozoans on p. 35).　The **body** is divided into an anterior region encased in a single shield of chitin, and a posterior region which is segmented.　The anterior region includes the head and first 2 thoracic segments, and is therefore called the cephalothorax.　The other 5 thoracic segments are free and bear limbs, and in the female, two large ovisacs are attached to the last of them. The abdomen consists of 3 limbless segments and a telson with two long caudal rami.　In the female, but not in the male, the 1st abdominal segment is fused to the last thoracic.

b. On the anterior edge of the **cephalothorax** is a ventrally-directed rostrum, above which is the single median eye containing only three ocelli, two lateral and one ventral (it is the nauplius eye).　Within this region, and extending to the abdomen, two great muscle-bands (which flex the body) are visible latero-ventrally.

c. The **reproductive system** can be seen through the dorsal body-wall.　In the **female** it consists of a single median transparent ovary ; two prominent lateral oviducts opening externally through the sides of the 7th thoracic segment and having numerous blind-ending caeca (which are usually full of opaque eggs) ; a mid-ventral spermatheca within the 7th thoracic segment (for sperm storage after copulation) with two lateral ducts opening into the bases of the

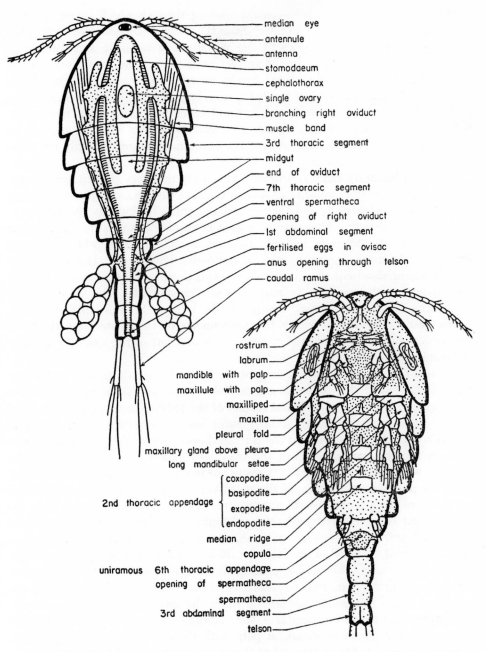

median eye
antennule
antenna
stomodaeum
cephalothorax
single ovary
branching right oviduct
muscle band
3rd thoracic segment
midgut
end of oviduct
7th thoracic segment
ventral spermatheca
opening of right oviduct
1st abdominal segment
fertilised eggs in ovisac
anus opening through telson
caudal ramus

rostrum
labrum
mandible with palp
maxillule with palp
maxilliped
maxilla
pleural fold
maxillary gland above pleura
long mandibular setae
coxopodite
basipodite
2nd thoracic appendage
exopodite
endopodite
median ridge
copula
uniramous 6th thoracic appendage
opening of spermatheca
spermatheca
3rd abdominal segment
telson

FIG. 82.—*Cyclops.* Dorsal and ventral views of a female, from which the 3rd, 4th, and 5th pairs of thoracic appendages have been removed.

Q

oviducts (and also a single mid-ventral opening through which sperm enters) ; and two ovisacs (formed of a secretion from the walls of the posterior ends of the oviducts) attached to the sides of the 7th thoracic segment and containing groups of developing eggs.   In the smaller **male** the system comprises a single transparent testis similarly placed to the ovary ; two vasa deferentia which arise from the anterior end of the testis and, lateral to it, coil backwards, forwards, and backwards again (in this last and wider part of the duct the spermatozoa are bound into spermatophores) ; and two swollen seminal vesicles (in which the spermatophores are stored) lying in, and opening through, the sides of the 7th thoracic segment.

d. The **alimentary canal** is simple.   Anteriorly the stomodaeum (ectodermal and cuticle lined) rises dorsally as a narrow gullet (into which open two glands lying above the labrum), and then swells and turns backwards ventral to the reproductive system.   This swollen region continues through the thorax, but its posterior two-thirds is midgut (the endodermal walls of which store oil droplets and secrete brown granules of unknown significance ; the movements of this region also help to circulate the blood, there being no heart).   Within the abdomen the midgut is narrow and transparent.   The proctodaeum (ectodermal and cuticle lined) lies inside the telson, through which the anus opens postero-dorsally.   Watch the movements of the posterior end of the alimentary canal by which water is passed in and out of the anus (apparently for respiratory purposes).

e. Kill the specimen with a drop of alcohol or by gentle heat over a lamp. Support it ventral side uppermost in a blob of agar jelly, and carefully add a cover-glass.   Examine the **ventral surface of the body**.   The cephalothorax and free thoracic segments have lateral pleural folds which turn downwards and inwards.   Through the sides of the cephalothorax, above the pleural folds, can be seen the transparent coils of the maxillary glands (excretory organs, the ducts of which open through the bases of the maxillae).   In the female, distinguish the mid-ventral opening of the spermatheca on the 7th thoracic segment.

f. There are 5 pairs of **head appendages** (belonging to segments 2 to 6, the 1st segment being indistinguishable and limbless).   The 1st appendage is the 17-jointed antennule (sensory and used for swimming), which in the male is bent sharply at the level of the 8th joint (to form a hook for gripping the female during copulation).   The 2nd appendage is the 4-jointed antenna (sensory and used for clinging).   Internal to the bases of these limbs, and posterior to the rostrum, is the triangular labrum, forming the anterior edge of the mouth. Behind this are the 3rd appendages, the mandibles, each with a toothed biting projection, the gnathobase, and a palp with three setae, one short and two which trail back as far as the end of the cephalothorax.   The 4th appendages, the maxillules, lie immediately behind the mandibles, bite together by means of toothed gnathobases, and bear a small basal palp with two lobes (which may represent exo- and endo-podites). The 5th appendages are the uniramous maxillae based immediately external to the smaller 1st thoracic appendages.

g. The 1st **thoracic appendages** are the uniramous maxillipeds (which function with the mouth-parts). The 2nd to the 5th appendages are all similar (and are used in rapid swimming). Each consists of a broad, flattened protopodite, subdivided into a proximal coxopodite and a distal basipodite, on which are borne flattened 3-jointed exo- and endo-podites fringed with large setae. Each pair of coxopodites is linked by a flat plate, the copula (to help co-ordinate the beat). The 6th appendages are reduced, 2-jointed, and uniramous, while the 7th are even further reduced, and are represented only by small flaps, one overlying each genital opening.

3. CONCLUSION

a. Observing the specimen, review the characteristics of the phylum, of the class, of the subclass, and of the order.

4. REFERENCES

GURNEY, R. (1931–33). Volumes 1 and 3 of " British fresh-water Copepoda." The Ray Society, London.

HARTOG, M. M. (1888). " The morphology of *Cyclops* and the relations of the Copepoda." *Transactions of the Linnean Society*, Vol. 5, p. 1.

2.30. Subclass **Cirripedia**

Characteristics : Crustacea which are sessile when adult ; head without compound eyes, with vestigial antennules, without antennae, and with mandibles usually possessing palps ; thorax typically of 6 segments each with a pair of biramous stenopodia ; abdomen vestigial, but with rami ; usually hermaphrodite, and with development through nauplius and cypris stages.

The cirripedes, or barnacles, are usually found in groups attached to such objects as algae, rocks, ships, whales, turtles, decapod crustaceans, etc. In addition, many are parasitic, and like *Sacculina*, may undergo extreme degeneration in the adult stage.

2.31. Order **Thoracica**

Characteristics : Cirripedia with a carapace of calcareous plates ; with 6 pairs of thoracic appendages ; and not parasitic.

Genus **Lepas** (goose barnacle)

I. GENERAL ACCOUNT

a. This large barnacle is common all over the world, and is usually found attached to floating objects such as loose seaweed, logs, turtles, and ships. It feeds by beating its bristle-fringed, thoracic limbs, which sieve planktonic animals and plants from the sea-water. It is hermaphrodite, but, since it usually occurs in groups, cross-fertilisation is possible, and seems to be the

general rule.   The eggs develop within the mantle cavity and hatch to escape
as typical nauplius larvae, which, after swimming freely and moulting several
times, are transformed into cypris larvae.   These are encased in bivalve shells,
and each of their antennules ends in a disc on which opens a cement gland.   By
these discs the larvae attach themselves to some object, after which they
metamorphose to the adult form and grow rapidly.   The method of fixation
is described on p. 333.

2. EXTERNAL ANATOMY

a. The bilaterally compressed body, or **capitulum**, is enclosed between two
leathery mantle folds, the carapace, in which are embedded five calcareous
plates.   The dorsal plate is the unpaired, keel-like carina, the two largest
plates are the anterior scuta, and the two remaining plates are the terga.   The
mantle cavity can be seen through the slit-like gap between the ventral edges
of the carapace, and within it are the feathery limbs.

b. The capitulum is mounted on a long, stout **peduncle**, which is the preoral region of the body (and by which the animal was attached).

c. Remove the right half of the carapace, noticing at the same time the point
of insertion of the adductor muscle (the contraction of which pulls together the
two halves of the carapace).   The **head** consists of 6 segments, the 1st of which
is missing in the adult.   The 2nd segment comprises the peduncle, on the
adhesive end of which the two small, disc-shaped antennules may be found (at
their bases open the two cement glands by the secretion of which the animal is
anchored).   The 3rd segment is not distinguishable, since its limbs, the
antennae, are lacking.   Distinguish the prominent posteriorly directed mouth.
It is bounded anteriorly by a swollen labrum, laterally by the two toothed
mandibles (segment 4) each with a lateral palp, postero-laterally by the two
simple maxillules (segment 5) each with a bristle fringe, and posteriorly by
the two simple maxillae (segment 6) which are based close together (and
probably act in passing food particles to the mouth ; on their bases open the
ducts of the excretory maxillary glands).

d. A **thorax** of 6 segments, each with a pair of limbs, constitutes most of
the rest of the body.   These limbs, or cirri, increase in size posteriorly, but
otherwise they are all similar.   Each has a basal coxopodite and a basipodite
which carries two long many-jointed rami, the inner the endopodite and the
outer the slightly longer exopodite.   Each ramus, which curves forwards towards the mouth, bears a single fringe of bristles, one bristle to each joint (by a
grasping motion of the limb the sea-water is sieved through these bristles).
Laterally on each of the coxopodites of the 1st pair of cirri is a filamentous
epipodite (function doubtful).   Between the 6th pair of cirri is a single long
penis closely covered with fine bristles (this can reach into the mantle cavities
of adjacent individuals).

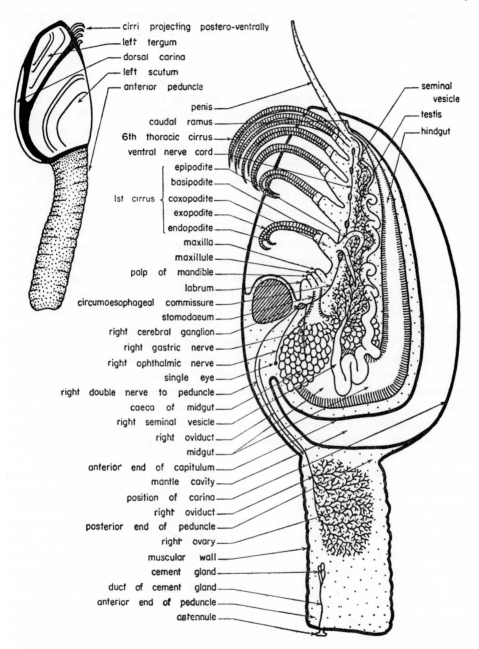

cirri projecting postero-ventrally
left tergum
dorsal carina
left scutum
anterior peduncle

seminal vesicle
testis
hindgut

penis
caudal ramus
6th thoracic cirrus
ventral nerve cord
epipodite
basipodite
1st cirrus { coxopodite
exopodite
endopodite
maxilla
maxillule
palp of mandible
labrum
circumoesophageal commissure
stomodaeum
right cerebral ganglion
right gastric nerve
right ophthalmic nerve
single eye
right double nerve to peduncle
caeca of midgut
right seminal vesicle
right oviduct
midgut
anterior end of capitulum
mantle cavity
position of carina
right oviduct
posterior end of peduncle
right ovary
muscular wall
cement gland
duct of cement gland
anterior end of peduncle
antennule

FIG. 83.—*Lepas*. A whole specimen seen from the left side, and a general dissection seen from the right side (the adductor muscle, ventral to the mouth, is marked by cross shading).

e. Immediately posterior to the penis base is the **anus**, flanked by a pair of tiny caudal rami (this region is the last remnant of the abdomen).

3.   INTERNAL ANATOMY

a. Dissect away the right side of the peduncle, noticing the muscle-strands in its wall.   In the anterior region of the **peduncle** the two tiny cement glands may be visible (although they are usually obscure), and from each a fine duct passes along the muscle-wall to open by one of the antennules.   Based posteriorly, but spreading forwards throughout the whole peduncle, are the tubules of the paired **ovaries**.   The two oviducts pass backwards close together along the ventral line into the capitulum (where they open on the bases of the 1st pair of cirri).

b. Gently remove the thin skin covering the right side of the capitulum. The branching tubules of the right **testis** obscure everything else, and also extend into the bases of the cirri.   Gently pick away these tubules to uncover the male ducts and the alimentary canal.   The many vasa deferentia of the right side join together into a large seminal vesicle, which coils first forwards and then backwards to reach the base of the penis.   There it joins the seminal vesicle of the left side to form the single ejaculatory duct, which runs within the penis.

c. Trace the course of the **alimentary canal**.   The mouth leads forwards into the stomodaeum (cuticle lined and also called the oesophagus), which in turn leads into a large thin-walled midgut, or stomach.   On the first part of the stomach are large numbers of small caeca, the so-called hepatic diverticula (which are possibly secretory).   The second part curves dorsally and then tapers posteriorly to join, without any constriction, into the hindgut (cuticle lined and also called the intestine or rectum), which passes straight to the anus.

d. In the **nervous system** the two cerebral ganglia are easily distinguished in the region between the stomodaeum and the adductor muscle.   From each of them a double nerve runs forwards into the peduncle, passing close alongside the oviducts.   Between the bases of these double nerves there arise two fine ophthalmic nerves, which pass forwards to join into a tiny black eye (the nauplius eye) based on the antero-ventral end of the mass of caeca.   The circumoesophageal commissures are long, and at their anterior ends they each give off a small bunch of nerves to the stomach.   At their posterior ends they join the large 1st thoracic ganglion situated above the 1st pair of cirri.   Other ganglia are associated with the bases of the other pairs of cirri, but those of the 5th and 6th pairs are fused together.   The thoracic ganglia give branches to their associated cirri, and they are linked by a double nerve cord.   The 1st thoracic ganglion also gives two prominent nerves into the viscera, while branches of the last supply the penis.

4. CONCLUSION

a. Observing the specimen, review the characteristics of the phylum, of the class, of the subclass, and of the order.

b. Also review those modifications in structure which are associated with the sessile mode of life.

5. REFERENCE

DARWIN, C. (1851). " A monograph on the sub-class Cirripedia. The Lepadidae; or, pedunculated cirripedes." The Ray Society, London.

2.40. Subclass **Malacostraca**

Characteristics : Free-living Crustacea of great diversity ; head with eyes compound and usually stalked, antennules often biramous, and mandibles with or without a palp ; thorax of 8 segments with stenopodia, with or without a carapace, and with the female openings on the 6th and the male openings on the 8th segments ; abdomen usually of 6 segments, all with stenopodia, and ending in a telson, which usually lacks rami ; development usually direct.

The malacostracans are a very numerous group, and they include the largest and most successful of the Crustacea. They are almost entirely aquatic, the majority being marine. However, large numbers have invaded fresh water, and a few have successfully colonised the land. Complete emancipation from the water is rare, and is confined to the Oniscoida (wood lice) of the Isopoda and the Talitridae (sand hoppers) of the Amphipoda. Parasitism is also rare.

2.41. Order **Leptostraca**

Characteristics : Marine Malacostraca in which the head bears stalked eyes and biramous antennules, and has its exoskeleton extended backwards to form a large bivalve carapace ; thoracic segments distinct, unattached to the carapace, not forming a brood-pouch, and bearing similar biramous foliaceous appendages ; abdomen of 7 segments and a telson, with appendages biramous on segments 1 to 4, uniramous on segments 5 and 6, lacking on segment 7, and with pointed rami on the telson.

This small order contains a few genera which are commonly considered to be the most primitive of the Malacostraca. However, although the structure and function of their thoracic limbs are reminiscent of those of the Branchiopoda and Copepoda, it has been suggested that the resemblance is superficial. There is a closer resemblance to the mysids, from which these animals may conceivably have been derived.

Genus **Nebalia**

1. GENERAL ACCOUNT

a. The genus *Nebalia* is common throughout almost the whole world in the shallow water of the littoral zone. It occurs particularly abundantly among

deposits of organic mud and silt, and it can withstand very foul conditions.   It
lives gregariously among seaweeds, under stones, and buried in sand and mud,
the food consisting of particles of organic matter sieved from the water by the
setae of the thoracic appendages.   By their beating these appendages set up a

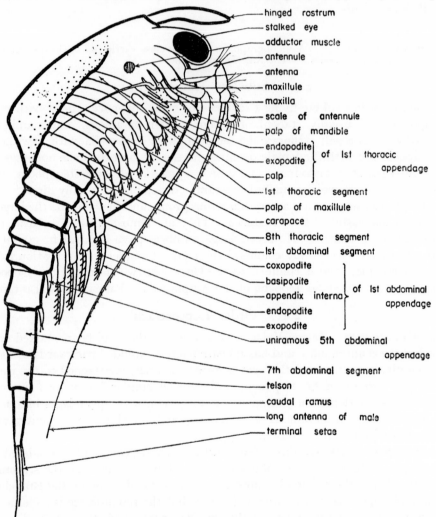

FIG. 84.—*Nebalia*.   A male with the right carapace lobe removed to show the appendages.

series of feeding currents within the carapace cavity.   Breeding occurs in
spring and summer.   The eggs are carried by the female between the thoracic
appendages, where they are not attached but are prevented from falling out
by the fringe of setae.   Development is direct, and the young have the adult
form when they leave their mothers.

2. ANATOMY

a. The **body** consists of a head, part of which is covered by the transparent shield of the bilobed carapace, and part of which projects forwards ; a thorax which is wholly enclosed within the carapace ; and an abdomen, some segments of which project posteriorly.

b. The anterior end of the **head** bears a long, hinged rostrum and two large, stalked eyes, and its exoskeleton extends posteriorly and ventrally as the carapace. Remove the right half of the carapace, and examine the animal through a strong lens or binocular microscope. The posterior margin of the head is marked by the groove between it and the 1st thoracic segment, and just anterior to the groove is an adductor muscle (which pulls together the two halves of the carapace). The 1st of the cephalic appendages, the antennule, belongs to segment 2. It has 4 basal joints, on the distal of which is set an outer scale and an inner multiarticulate ramus (these do not represent exo- and endo-podites). The 2nd appendage is the antenna, which is as long as the body in the male, but shorter in the female. The mandible has a basal segment with a gnathobase, and a large 3-jointed palp. The 4th appendage is the maxillule, which at its base bears inward directed setae (for food manipulation), and terminally is reflexed to form a long, slender, jointed palp (which lies within, and is presumed to clean, the carapace cavity). The last appendage is the maxilla (segment 6), which also bears inward directed setae, but which is biramous.

c. The 8 closely crowded **thoracic segments** are easily distinguishable, and their foliaceous appendages are all alike. A basal protopodite carries externally a large, flat epipodite, which appears to be divided into two lobes, and distally a flat, oval exopodite and a long, narrow endopodite. The inner edges of the protopodite and the endopodite are closely set with setae (for straining and manipulating food particles).

d. Of the 7 **abdominal segments**, the first 5 are relatively short, while the last 2 and the telson are long. The first 4 pairs of appendages are large (and are used for swimming). They have a short basal coxopodite, a longer basipodite, and two rami fringed with setae, and internally from the endopodite base there arises a short lobe known as the appendix interna. The 5th and 6th appendages are small and uniramous, and there are no appendages on segment 7. On the telson the two caudal rami are hinged posteriorly, and between them opens the anus.

3. CONCLUSION

a. Observing the specimen, review the characteristics of the phylum, of the class, of the subclass, and of the order.

b. Compare and contrast the structure of *Nebalia* with that of *Eubranchipus*.

4. REFERENCES

CLAUS, C. (1872). " Über den Bau und die systematische Stellung von *Nebalia*, nebst Bemerkungen über das seither unbekannte Männchen dieser Gattung." *Zeitschrift für wissenschaftliche Zoologie*, Vol. 22, p. 323.

CLAUS, C. (1888). " Über den Organismus der Nebaliden und die systematische Stellung der Leptostraken." *Arbeiten aus dem Zoologischen Institute der Universität Wien*, Vol. 8, p. 1.

PACKARD, A. S. (1883). " A monograph of North American phyllopod Crustacea. I. The anatomy and development of *Nebalia*." *12th Annual Report of the U.S. Geological and Geographical Survey of the Territories*, part 1, p. 433.

2.42. Order **Mysidacea**

Characteristics : Mainly marine Malacostraca in which the head bears stalked eyes or no eyes at all, biramous antennules, and antennae which usually have a flat, scale-like exopodite ; thorax with the first 3 segments fused to the carapace, with a brood-pouch in the female, with all limbs usually biramous, and with the 1st, and sometimes also the 2nd, limbs specialised as maxillipeds ; 6th abdominal segment with uropods which, with the telson, form a tail fan.

These animals are mainly found in the cold and temperate seas bordering the Arctic and the Antarctic, occurring in the surface plankton and extending down to great depths. However, a few members of the family Mysidae have invaded fresh water, and are found in the colder lakes of Europe, Asia, and North America.

Genus **Mysis**

1. GENERAL ACCOUNT

a. Species of this genus are common in all the cold and temperate seas of the world, abounding in coastal, surface, and deep waters. The well-known fresh-water *M. relicta* Lovén also occurs in many lakes in Europe, Asia, and North America. For protection the animals have a glass-like transparency. They are mainly carnivorous, and eat their food either in large pieces or, by filtering the currents set up by the constant beating of their limbs, they obtain tiny planktonic animals and plants. Breeding is in spring and summer, and in some cases is reported to continue throughout the whole year. The developing eggs are carried by the female inside a brood-pouch, and when the young escape they already have the adult form.

2. ANATOMY

a. The **body** is divided into a head ; a thorax, which is almost completely covered by the carapace ; and a long, free abdomen, bearing relatively short limbs and ending in a telson.

b. The **head** carries a pair of prominent stalked eyes anteriorly. Between these are based the 1st cephalic appendages, the biramous antennules (of segment 2), each with a 3-jointed peduncle and multi-articulate rami. The antenna (segment 3) is also biramous, the 3-jointed protopodite carrying a scale-like exopodite and a multi-articulate endopodite. The mandible (segment 4) is large, and bears a long 2-jointed palp fringed with setae. Imme-

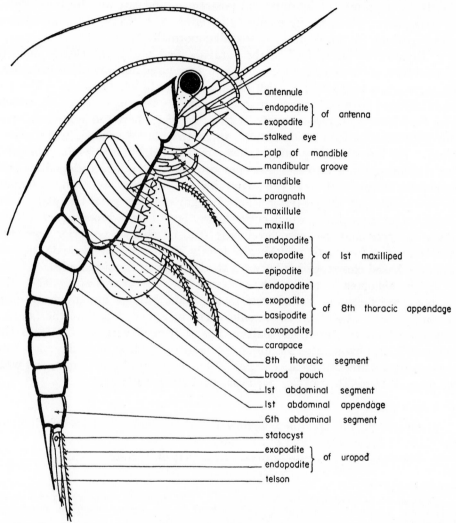

antennule

endopodite
} of antenna
exopodite

stalked eye

palp of mandible

mandibular groove

mandible

paragnath

maxillule

maxilla

endopodite
exopodite } of 1st maxilliped
epipodite

endopodite
exopodite
basipodite } of 8th thoracic appendage
coxopodite

carapace

8th thoracic segment

brood pouch

1st abdominal segment

1st abdominal appendage

6th abdominal segment

statocyst

exopodite
} of uropod
endopodite

telson

FIG. 85.—*Mysis.* A female seen from the right side and with the 2nd to the 7th thoracic appendages omitted.

diately behind the mandible is the mandibular groove, which divides the head into an anterior region of 4 segments (which are believed to represent the primitive head ; the first of them is indistinguishable except in the embryo) and a posterior region of 2 segments. The first of these 2 segments (segment 5) carries the maxillule, which is small, flattened, 3-jointed, and with inward directed setae (for food manipulation). The maxilla (segment 6) is larger, also flattened, 6-jointed, probably biramous, and fringed with inward directed setae. From the ventral side it can be seen that the mouth is bounded anteriorly by a prominent labrum, and posteriorly and laterally by two ridges, the paragnaths, which are immediately anterior to the bases of the maxillules and over which the maxillules and maxillae normally lie.

c. Remove the right half of the carapace and notice the clearly defined segmentation of the **thorax**. Segments 1 to 3 are fused dorsally to the carapace, but segments 4 to 8 are free. All the thoracic limbs are biramous. The 1st is a maxilliped with the coxopodite and basipodite bearing an epipodite which turns back into the carapace cavity, with a relatively short and jointed endopodite (with setae for food manipulation), and with a plumose exopodite (for swimming). The larger 2nd appendage is also a maxilliped, but it lacks the epipodite. The remaining limbs also lack the epipodite, and have long endopodites and exopodites fringed with setae (for swimming and food capture). In the female the coxopodites of the posterior thoracic segments bear petal-like plates, the oostegites (or epipodites), which curve forwards to form a brood-pouch within which embryos may be seen developing (the number of posterior segments involved varies from 2 to 7 within the family Mysidae). In the male the two penes are based close together between the last pair of thoracic limbs.

d. The **abdomen** is long and has 6 segments. The first 5 appendages, the pleopods, are biramous swimmerets in the male, but are unjointed and uniramous (or even absent) in the female. The 6th appendages are the fan-like uropods, which are biramous, flattened, and fringed with setae. Both the endopodite and exopodites are unjointed, and in the base of each endopodite is a spherical statocyst (balance organ). The telson is also flattened, and with the uropods forms the tail fan (for rapid backward swimming).

3. CONCLUSION

a. Observing the specimen, review the characteristics of the phylum, of the class, of the subclass, and of the order.

b. Compare the structure of *Mysis* with that of *Nebalia*.

4. REFERENCES

CANNON, H. G., and MANTON, S. M. (1927). " On the feeding mechanism of a mysid crustacean, *Hemimysis lamornae.*" *Transactions of the Royal Society of Edinburgh,* Vol. 55, p. 219.
SARS, G. O. (1867). " Histoire naturelle des Crustacés d'eau douce de Norvège. I. Les Malacostracés." Christiania.

2.43. Order **Isopoda**

Characteristics : Marine, fresh-water, and terrestrial Malacostraca which are usually dorso-ventrally compressed ; head with sessile eyes, small uniramous antennules, and antennae sometimes possessing minute exopodites ;

thorax without a carapace, with segment 1 fused to the head, with a brood-pouch in the female, and with uniramous appendages all alike except the 1st which are maxillipeds; abdomen of 6 segments with biramous pleopods plate-like and respiratory, and with uropods of varying structure.

This is a large, widespread, and successful order which includes a wide variety of free-living and parasitic forms. The members of the suborder Oniscoidea, the woodlice or sowbugs, are the most successful of the few terrestrial Crustacea.

Genus **Oniscus** (woodlouse)

(Similar alternative genera are the terrestrial *Porcellio* and *Armadillidium*; the fresh-water *Asellus* in which all the abdominal segments are fused; the marine *Ligia*; and the marine *Idotea* in which the last 4 segments are fused with the telson while the uropods turn forward to protect the pleopods.)

1. GENERAL ACCOUNT

a. Oniscus and other closely related genera are of common and widespread occurrence all over the world. The various species are able to live in fairly dry places beneath stones, dead trees, and matted tangles of vegetation. Their food consists mainly of vegetable matter such as young leaves, ripe fruit, or rotting material, but a small amount of animal matter, such as tiny arthropods or any carrion, is also taken. Breeding occurs during the warmer months, and about three broods are produced each year. The eggs and developing embryos are carried in the brood-pouch for about five weeks until they attain the adult shape and can fend for themselves. *Oniscus* has been known to live for four years in captivity, breeding for the first time in the year in which it was born.

2. ANATOMY

a. The three regions of the compressed **body** are the head flanked by the black sessile eyes, and with the 1st segment of the thorax incorporated into its hinder margin; a region consisting of the remaining 7 thoracic segments carrying walking legs; and the abdomen composed of 6 smaller segments, the last of which is fused to the telson. The edges of the thoracic and abdominal segments are expended laterally into pleural folds.

b. The **head** is compact, and the most prominent head appendages are the antennae. The 1st appendages (segment 2) are the rudimentary 3-jointed antennules internal to the bases of the antennae. The antennae themselves (segment 3) are 8-jointed. The mouth is bordered anteriorly by the labrum, and laterally by the mandibles (segment 4), which have strong, brown, serrated cutting edges. The two remaining head appendages overlie the bases of the mandibles, and are in turn covered by the maxillipeds (of the 1st fused thoracic segment). Turn back the maxillipeds to uncover the narrow, curved, spine-tipped maxillae (segment 6), beneath which are the membranous maxillules (segment 5).

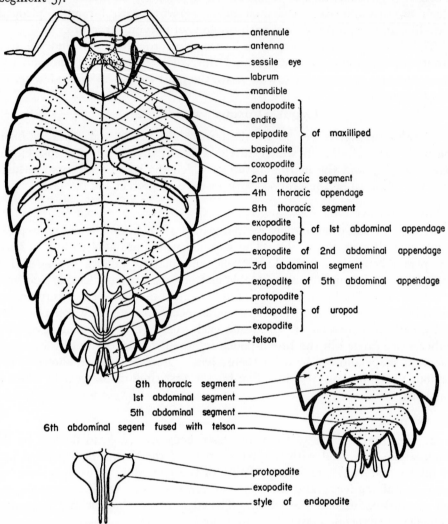

FIG. 86.—*Oniscus*.   A ventral view of a male from which all but one of the pairs of walking legs have been removed, a dorsal view of the posterior end of the body, and the modified 2nd abdominal appendage of a male.

c. The first of the **thoracic appendages** is the maxilliped.   It consists of two flat, triangular plates, the outer being the epipodite and the inner and larger the basipodite (they form an operculum to protect the delicate mouth parts). They are both mounted on a short but broad coxopodite, and distally the basipodite carries a small endite internally and a small jointed endopodite externally.

Each of the 2nd to the 8th thoracic segments has a pair of 6-jointed walking legs, of which the proximal joints, the coxopodites, are fused to the body and the distal joints, the dactylopodites, each end in a hook. In the mature female the 2nd to the 6th pairs of limbs develop large epipodites, the oostegites, which form the brood-pouch.

d. The first 5 **abdominal segments** are distinct, but the 6th segment is fused to the telson. The first 5 pairs of abdominal appendages, the pleopods, are biramous, and in the female each consists of a short protopodite bearing an anterior and tougher exopodite (protective, and containing air spaces which are possibly respiratory) which overlies a posterior and softer endopodite (respiratory). In the male the endopodite of the 1st pleopod is long and pointed, while the endopodite of the 2nd pleopod bears a long style, the appendix masculinus (these two pleopods function in the transference of bundles of spermatozoa to the female). The 6th limb is the uropod, consisting of a large protopodite with an unjointed exopodite distally and an unjointed endopodite internally. The telson is short and pointed.

3. CONCLUSION

a. Observing the specimen, review the characteristics of the phylum, of the class, of the subclass, and of the order.

4. REFERENCES

For the structure of this and of other isopods see :

BATE, C. S., and WESTWOOD, J. O. (1868). Volume 2 of " A history of the British sessile eyed Crustacea." The Ray Society, London.
SARS, G. O. (1867). " Histoire naturelle des Crustacés d'eau douce de Norvège. I. Les Malacostracés." Christiania.
TSCHETWERIKOFF, S. (1910). " Beiträge zur Anatomie der Wasserassel (*Asellus aquaticus*, L.)." *Bulletin de la Société Impériale des Naturalistes de Moscou*, Vol. 24, p. 377.
VANDEL, A. (1943). " Essai sur l'origine, l'évolution et la classification des Oniscoidea." *Bulletin Biologique de France et de Belgique*, supplement 30.

2.44. Order **Amphipoda**

Characteristics : Marine, fresh-water, and terrestrial Malacostraca which are usually laterally compressed ; head with sessile eyes, with antennules usually biramous, and with antennae uniramous ; thorax without a carapace, with segment 1, and rarely also segment 2, fused to the head, with a brood-pouch in the female, and with the appendages uniramous, the 1st being maxillipeds, the 2nd and 3rd prehensile gnathopods, and the 4th to the 8th walking legs ; abdomen of 6 segments with the appendages biramous, the first 3 with jointed and the last 3 with unjointed rami.

These are widespread and successful animals both in the sea and in fresh water, and they are particularly abundant in the Arctic and Antarctic. They are mostly free-living, but there are a few parasitic forms. Two common genera, *Orchestia* and *Talitrus* (sand hoppers), have invaded the land. They usually remain near the high-tide mark, and can flourish only in damp places, but there are records of them reaching heights of several thousand feet and distances of many miles from the sea.

Genus **Gammarus**

I. GENERAL ACCOUNT

a. The genus *Gammarus* is common in salt, brackish, and fresh waters, but it does not occur in the tropics. The animals live gregariously, and are particularly abundant on the sea-shore and in fresh-water streams. For protection they burrow into the sand or live under stones or thick vegetation. They swim upright, but often lie on one side when crawling. They are mainly scavengers, eating dead and decaying animal and vegetable matter, but they also take smaller living animals, and are even cannibalistic. In many sea-shore forms reproduction apparently occurs during winter and early spring, while in the fresh-water *Gammarus* the season is during spring and summer. Fertilisation is external, and the developing embryos are carried by the females, which, in turn, are carried by the males. The young have the adult form when they leave the brood-pouch.

2. ANATOMY

a. Notice the division of the bilaterally compressed **body** into a head with black, or sometimes red, sessile eyes, and with the 1st thoracic segment fused indistinguishably to it ; a region of 7 free thoracic segments ; and a prominent, ventrally flexed abdomen composed of 6 segments and a free telson.

b. Emerging straight forwards from the front of the **head** are the antennules and antennae. As usual, the 1st head segment is indistinguishable and limbless, and the antennules belong to segment 2. Each has a 3-jointed base and two multi-articulate rami, the outer long and the inner short. The antenna has a 5-jointed base and a single ramus. Hold the specimen on its back, and through a lens or binocular microscope distinguish the large labrum in front of the mouth, the flanking mandibles each with a 3-jointed palp, and the two ridge-like paragnaths which form the posterior border of the mouth. Overlying each paragnath is a complex maxillule with a 3-jointed base bearing an endite, a small 2-jointed endopodite, and rows of setae (for gripping the food particles). The maxilla (segment 6) is smaller and simpler, and the homologies of its two main lobes are not understood.

c. There is no carapace, and the 1st segment of the **thorax** (fused to the head) bears the maxillipeds. The coxopodites of the maxillipeds are fused together to form a single plate, but the basipodites are separate, and each bears an endite and a 5-jointed endopodite of which the basal joint, the ischiopodite, also bears an endite. The other 7 thoracic segments have uniramous 7-jointed limbs, each with a coxopodite expanded externally into a large coxal plate. Internally many of the coxopodites are also expanded to form branchiae, accessory branchiae, and in the female, oostegites (these structures, which are epipodites, are most easily seen in specimens which have been split in two

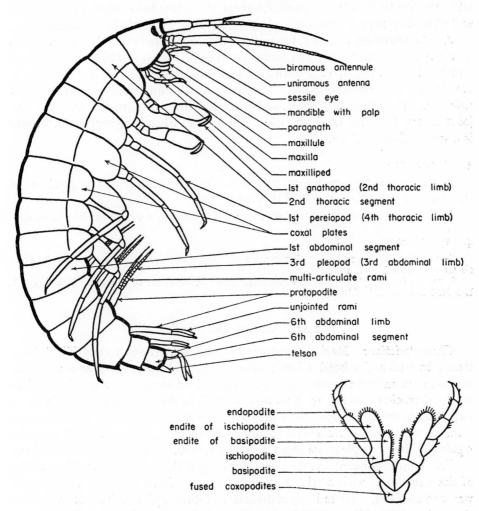

biramous antennule
uniramous antenna
sessile eye
mandible with palp
paragnath
maxillule
maxilla
maxilliped
1st gnathopod (2nd thoracic limb)
2nd thoracic segment
1st pereiopod (4th thoracic limb)
coxal plates
1st abdominal segment
3rd pleopod (3rd abdominal limb)
multi-articulate rami
protopodite
unjointed rami
6th abdominal limb
6th abdominal segment
telson

endopodite
endite of ischiopodite
endite of basipodite
ischiopodite
basipodite
fused coxopodites

FIG. 87.—*Gammarus.* A specimen seen from the right side, and the 1st thoracic appendages, or maxillipeds.

longitudinally). Depending on the species, there may be as many as 6 branchiae (segments 3 to 8) and 7 accessory branchiae (segment 3 to abdominal segment 1), or as few as 3 branchiae (segments 6 to 8) and no accessory branchiae. In the female there are usually 4 pairs of oostegites on segments 3 to 6. In the male two small papillae (through which the vasa deferentia open) can be seen on

R

the sternum of the 8th segment.   The limbs of segments 2 and 3 are prehensile gnathopods with the terminal joint, the dactylopodite, reflexed on the stout subterminal propodite (to form a gripping, chela-like structure).   The 4th and 5th pairs of limbs are pereiopods (locomotory, and also assisting in feeding), while the 6th to the 8th are similar, except that they have smaller coxal plates and that they turn backwards and upwards (they are entirely locomotory).

d. The **abdomen** is flexed ventrally, particularly between the 3rd and 4th segments.   The first 3 pairs of limbs are typical pleopods which turn forward and consist of a protopodite with two multi-articulate seta-fringed rami (they are the chief swimming organs).   The last 3 pairs of limbs are sometimes called uropods.   They turn backward, and possess a stout protopodite with two un-jointed rami (they are used for kicking the ground when jumping).   Posteriorly is a small bilobed telson.

3. CONCLUSION

a. Observing the specimen, review the characteristics of the phylum, of the class, of the subclass, and of the order.

b. Compare and contrast the structure of *Gammarus* with that of *Oniscus.*

4. REFERENCES

DELLA VALLE, A. (1893). " Gammarini del Golfo di Napoli." *Fauna und Flora des Golfes von Neapel,* Vol. 20.
    SARS, G. O. (1867). " Histoire naturelle des Crustacés d'eau douce de Norvège.   I. Les Malacostracés." Christiania.

2.45. Order **Decapoda**

Characteristics :   Marine, fresh-water, and sometimes terrestrial Malaco-straca in which the head bears stalked eyes, and antennules and antennae which are usually biramous ; thorax encased in a carapace, which is fused to all the thoracic segments, with no brood-pouch in the female, with limbs 1 to 3 biramous maxillipeds, and with limbs 4 to 8 usually uniramous pereiopods, some of which are often chelate ; abdomen of 6 segments, primitively with 5 pairs of biramous pleopods and 1 pair of biramous uropods, and with a telson.

This large order contains the most highly specialised and successful members of the Crustacea, with a wide variety of habitat from the sea through fresh water to the land.   There is great diversity of form, and a division is made into three main suborders : the Macrura which includes the prawns, shrimps, lobsters, and crayfishes, and which is characterised by a well-developed, elongated, and extended abdomen ending in a tail-fan formed of flattened uropods and telson ; the Anomura, which includes the squat lobsters, hermit crabs, and cocoa-nut crabs, and which is characterised by a reduced abdomen, usually carried flexed forwards, and by reduced uropods ; and the Brachyura, which includes the true crabs, and which is characterised by a greatly reduced abdomen carried permanently flexed beneath the thorax, and by the absence of uropods.

Genus **Astacus** (crayfish)

(Alternatives are the fresh-water *Cambarus*, which has 17 pairs of gills, the marine lobster *Nephrops*, which has 19 pairs of gills, and the marine lobster *Homarus*, which has 20 pairs of gills.)

I. GENERAL ACCOUNT

a. Crayfishes are common in streams and rivers, and even in some lakes and marshes, in many parts of Europe, Asia, North and South America, and Australasia, the most important factor favourable to their presence being a sufficiently high concentration of dissolved calcareous matter. During the day they avoid the light by hiding in crevices or in burrows which they excavate themselves. Activity begins in the evening, when they search for their food, which consists of almost anything organic, animal or vegetable, dead or alive. They are also cannibals, and snail-shells and calcareous algae are often eaten for their calcareous content. In winter they burrow deeper, and remain inactive during the coldest weather. Mating takes place commonly in the autumn, the eggs being carried glued to the pleopods of the female until the spring. After hatching the young crayfishes still lack some of the abdominal appendages, and for some further time they maintain their grip on the pleopods by means of the peculiarly hooked tips of their chelae.

2. EXTERNAL ANATOMY

a. Anteriorly the **body** is enclosed in a cephalothoracic shield, but posteriorly the segmentation is obvious. The head is the region anterior to the cephalic groove, and it is prolonged anteriorly into a pointed rostrum, lateral to which are the two stalked eyes. The thorax is covered by the carapace, and its segmentation is shown by the presence of pairs of limbs, of which the chelae and walking legs are especially prominent. The abdomen comprises the 6 posterior segments and the telson. Each of these segments is divided into a ventral sternum and a dorsal tergum, which, on each side, projects into a flange, the pleuron. The anus is the longitudinal slit beneath the telson.

b. The 1st head segment is seen only in the embryo, and it is limbless. The 1st of the **anterior head appendages** (segment 2) are the relatively short biramous antennules. Each has a peduncle of 3 joints, the basal of which is the largest and contains a statocyst (balance organ) with a triangular opening dorsally. The long antenna (segment 3) has a coxopodite and basipodite, a scale-like exopodite, and a multi-articulate endopodite with the three basal joints enlarged. On the ventral side of the coxopodite is a prominent papilla, with the excretory opening (of the antennary gland) on its posterior surface. Between the bases of the antennae is the heavily calcified epistome (formed of fused cephalic sterna), from the ridged posterior edge of which the soft labrum over-hangs the mouth. The mandibles (segment 4) meet over the mouth, each

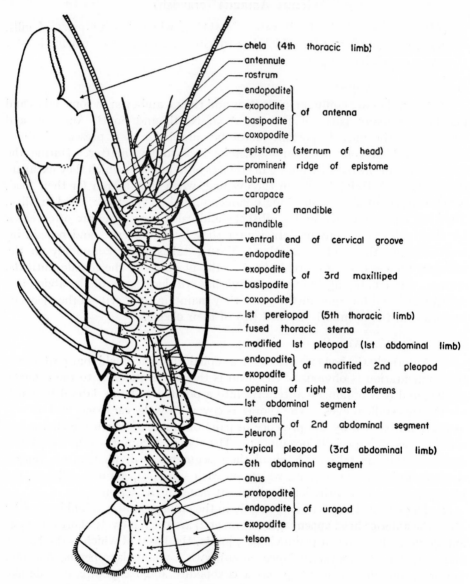

chela (4th thoracic limb)
antennule
rostrum
endopodite ⎤
exopodite ⎬ of antenna
basipodite ⎨
coxopodite ⎦
epistome (sternum of head)
prominent ridge of epistome
labrum
carapace
palp of mandible
mandible
ventral end of cervical groove
endopodite ⎤
exopodite ⎬ of 3rd maxilliped
basipodite ⎨
coxopodite ⎦
1st pereiopod (5th thoracic limb)
fused thoracic sterna
modified 1st pleopod (1st abdominal limb)
endopodite ⎤ of modified 2nd pleopod
exopodite ⎦
opening of right vas deferens
1st abdominal segment
sternum ⎤ of 2nd abdominal segment
pleuron ⎦
typical pleopod (3rd abdominal limb)
6th abdominal segment
anus
protopodite ⎤
endopodite ⎬ of uropod
exopodite ⎦
telson

FIG. 88.—*Astacus*. A ventral view of a male with the left thoracic and right abdominal appendages omitted.

consisting of a powerful tooth (modified protopodite) bearing a 3-jointed endo-podite, or palp.

c. The **posterior head appendages** lie obscured by the maxillipeds (thoracic appendages). Starting with the 3rd maxilliped, which is immediately anterior to the chela, carefully detach all the mouth appendages from one side. Working anteriorly they are the 3rd, 2nd, and 1st maxillipeds of the thorax, and the maxilla, maxillule, and mandible of the head. Between the bases of the maxillule and the mandible notice the small, plate-like paragnath, which forms the posterior edge of the mouth. The maxillule (segment 5) is small and flattened, and has two basal joints, which may be the coxopodite and basipodite, and which extend inwards as setae-fringed endites (for food manipula-

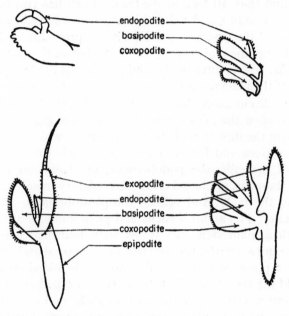

Fig. 89.—*Astacus*. The mandible and maxillule (above), and the 1st maxilliped and the maxilla.

tion). It also has a small, unjointed endopodite. The maxilla (segment 6) is more complex. It may be considered as consisting of a coxopodite and basipodite, each expanded internally into bilobed endites, a small, unjointed endopodite, and a greatly elongated exopodite (or perhaps epipodite), which is also called the scaphognathite (and which by its constant beating keeps a current flowing out of the anterior end of the gill chamber).

d. The **thoracic segments** are fused to the carapace, which, as the branchiostegite, overhangs on each side to enclose a gill chamber. The segments are also fused to each other, with the exception of the 8th which articulates with the 7th (it is fused in *Nephrops* and *Homarus*), but some of the narrow segmental sternal plates can be distinguished between the bases of the walking legs.

e. The **anterior thoracic appendages** are the 1st maxillipeds with the coxo-podite and basipodite extended inwards as endites, and with a large external epipodite, a tiny, 2-jointed endopodite, and a long, many-jointed exopodite. The 2nd and 3rd maxillipeds have a coxopodite bearing a gill (epipodite), and a basipodite bearing endo- and exopodites. Each endopodite is large, and, as in the succeeding thoracic limbs, it consists of 5 joints, which are from the base the ischio-, mero-, carpo-, pro-, and dactylopodites. The exopodite is slender and multi-articulate.

f. The **posterior thoracic appendages** are the cheliped and pereiopods (walking legs), and they all lack exopodites. Each has two basal joints, the coxopodite and basipodite, and 5 distal joints, which have been named above. In the cheliped and the first two pereiopods the propodite and dactylopodite form chelae (for gripping and tearing the food), but in the last two pereiopods they do not. The coxopodites of the 2nd pereiopods of the female and of the 4th pereiopods of the male are perforated by the genital pores.

g. From one side cut away the overhanging lobe, the branchiostegite, of the carapace, and so open the gill-chamber to expose the **gills** (epipodites), which curve forwards (in the direction of the water current which enters posteriorly). Examine the positions and forms of these gills while carefully detaching the limbs. Some of the gills, the podobranchs, are based on the coxopodites, some, the arthrobranchs, are based on the articulatory membranes between the coxopodites and the body, and others, the pleurobranchs, are based on the side of the thorax. The arthrobranchs and pleurobranchs are all similar and plume-like, with a main stem closely set with branchial filaments, but the podobranchs are in two parts, the anterior being typical and plume-like, while the posterior is a plate, or lamina. This lamina is folded once, and into the space of the fold fits the plume of the next posterior podobranch (the laminae deflect the current upwards over the arthrobranchs and pleurobranchs). The numbers of these different gills vary in different genera, but in *Astacus* there is none on the 1st maxilliped, 1 podobranch and 1 arthrobranch on the 2nd maxilliped, 1 podobranch and 2 arthrobranchs on all limbs from the 3rd maxilliped to the 3rd pereiopod, and 1 pleurobranch on the 8th segment (the absence of this pleurobranch distinguishes *Cambarus*).

h. The **abdominal appendages** consist of 5 pairs of pleopods (or swimmerets) and 1 pair of uropods. The pleopods of the female are all similar (and serve to carry the eggs), except that the 1st pair is reduced. Each consists of a coxo-podite and an elongated basipodite, to which are hinged the flattened endo- and exo-podites fringed with setae. In the male the 3rd to the 5th pleopods are similar to those of the female, but the 1st and 2nd are modified. The 1st is reduced to an unjointed grooved rod, while the 2nd has a normal coxopodite, basipodite, and exopodite, and only the endopodite is stiffened (they both serve in passing spermatozoa to the female). The 6th appendage, the uropod, has a broad, unjointed protopodite, which carries flat, plate-like endo- and exo-podites, the latter being transversely hinged. Together with the telson the uropods form the tail-fan (used in rapid backward swimming to escape danger).

3. INTERNAL ANATOMY

a. Taking great care not to penetrate the soft tissues beneath, cut forwards from the posterior edge of the carapace along the upper and outer edges of the thorax to the base of the rostrum. Gently remove the dorsal piece of the carapace. Next cut along the outer edges of the abdominal terga and detach these also. Strip away any remaining parts of the sheet of epidermal cells (which underlie and secrete the exoskeleton). The organs lie in a **haemocoelic body cavity**, which, in the dorsal side of the thorax, forms a large pericardial sinus (blood enters it laterally from the gills). Within this sinus lies the muscular polygonal heart with three pairs of ostia, one antero-dorsal, one lateral, and one ventral (through these ostia blood enters the heart). Blood leaves the heart either anteriorly through the median ophthalmic and the lateral antennary arteries, antero-ventrally through the two hepatic arteries, or posteriorly through the dorsal abdominal and sternal arteries (the sternal artery passes ventrally, and is not easily seen at this stage).

b. To expose the **reproductive system** carefully cut away one of the chitinous sides of the thorax as far down as the bases of the legs. In the **female** the single ovary is bilobed anteriorly, and from its ventral surface the two oviducts pass almost straight to the coxopodites of the 2nd pereiopods. In the **male** the white testis has a similar shape, but the two vasa deferentia which lead from its ventral surface are highly convoluted. They end in the coxopodites of the 4th pereiopods. If the vasa deferentia are distended with white masses of spermatozoa, place some of this material in water on a slide, and through a microscope notice the curious shape of the spermatozoa, which have disc-like centres and stiff tangential projections.

c. Remove one of the gonoducts and distinguish the **sternal artery** passing ventrally from the posterior end of the heart. Cut this artery where it leaves the heart.

d. Identify the two large digestive glands which form a branching green or brown mass around the midgut (they secrete digestive enzymes and absorb the digested food). Carefully remove one of these glands together with the heart, gonad, and any other tissues which obscure the **alimentary canal**. The mouth leads into a stomodaeum (ectodermal and chitin lined) consisting of a vertical oesophagus and a capacious proventriculus with a large anterior, or cardiac, chamber and a small posterior, or pyloric, chamber (the chitin forms a series of articulating ossicles and crushing teeth in the cardiac chamber, and rows of sieving setae in the pyloric chamber). Notice the two pairs of stout muscles

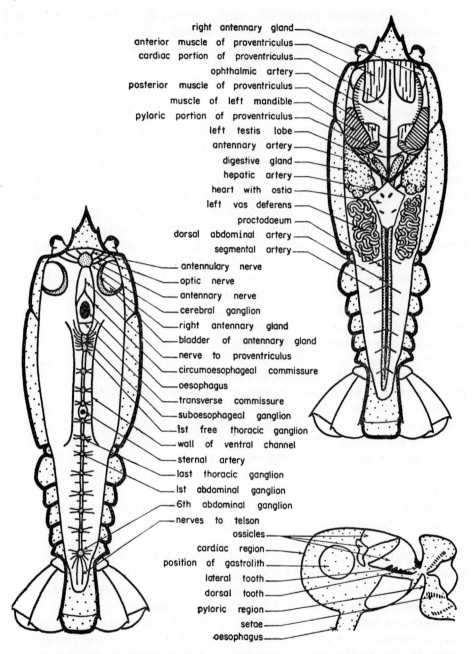

right antennary gland
anterior muscle of proventriculus
cardiac portion of proventriculus
ophthalmic artery
posterior muscle of proventriculus
muscle of left mandible
pyloric portion of proventriculus
left testis lobe
antennary artery
digestive gland
hepatic artery
heart with ostia
left vas deferens
proctodaeum
dorsal abdominal artery
segmental artery

antennulary nerve
optic nerve
antennary nerve
cerebral ganglion
right antennary gland
bladder of antennary gland
nerve to proventriculus
circumoesophageal commissure
oesophagus
transverse commissure
suboesophageal ganglion
1st free thoracic ganglion
wall of ventral channel
sternal artery
last thoracic ganglion
1st abdominal ganglion
6th abdominal ganglion
nerves to telson
ossicles
cardiac region
position of gastrolith
lateral tooth
dorsal tooth
pyloric region
setae
oesophagus

FIG. 90.—*Astacus*.   Dorsal views of a general dissection of a male, and of a dissection of the
nervous system.   Lower right is the interior of the right half of the proventriculus.

which pass from the proventriculus to the dorsal carapace. The midgut (endodermal) is short, but it is expanded laterally into the digestive glands and antero-dorsally into a short caecum. The proctodaeum (ectodermal and chitin lined) is long and narrow, and it leads straight to the anus. Remove the proventriculus and open it under water to see, in the cardiac portion, the ossicles, the circular position of the gastrolith (a calcareous mass which is periodically formed and is of doubtful significance), and the one median and two lateral teeth (which chew the swallowed food), and, in the pyloric portion, the narrow cavity lined by filtering setae (which allow only the finest food particles to pass into the midgut). Distinguish the powerful muscles which pass down to the mandibles.

e. Identify the two large, flattened **antennary glands** (excretory) lying ventrally in the region in front of the mouth. Each consists of a ventral glandular region overlain by a swollen, bladder-like duct, which opens through the coxopodite of the antenna (and the cavity of which is coelom).

f. While removing the remnants of the alimentary canal, follow the **course of the sternal artery**, which passes straight down to the right or left of the proctodaeum to disappear into a ventral muscle-sheet. The ventral nervous system and the ventral part of the blood system of the thorax lie in a deep channel formed partly by upward-directed processes of the sterna (this is the endophragmal skeleton, to which the leg and tail muscles are joined) and partly by muscle tissue, which also forms a roof to the channel. Open the channel to follow the sternal artery as it passes between the two ventral nerve-cords, and then splits into an anterior ventral thoracic artery and a posterior ventral abdominal artery, both of which run beneath the nerve-cord.

g. Trace the course of the **nervous system**. It consists of pairs of segmental ganglia joined together by a double nerve-cord. Each pair of ganglia is closely fused, and throughout most of their length the two cords are also closely apposed. The fused cerebral, or supra-oesophageal, ganglia are based on the anterior wall of the body cavity in the region between the bases of the antennae. From them nerves pass to the antennules, the eyes, and the antennae. Two long, circumoesophageal commissures pass back to the suboesophageal ganglion. Anterior to the oesophagus they give off nerves which join and pass to the proventriculus, and posterior to the oesophagus they are linked by a transverse commissure. The suboesophageal ganglion supplies the mandibles, maxillules, maxillae, and the 1st and 2nd maxillipeds (and is thus probably composed of 5 pairs of ganglia fused). The first of the 6 free thoracic ganglia supplies the 3rd maxillipeds, while the others supply the chelae and pereiopods. Each of the 6 abdominal segments has a separate ganglion, the last being the largest and supplying the uropods and the telson.

4. CONCLUSION

a. Observing the specimen and the drawings made, review the characteristics of the phylum, of the class, of the subclass, and of the order.

b. Compare and contrast the structure of *Astacus* with that of *Mysis*.

5. REFERENCES

HERRICK, F. H. (1895). " The American lobster : a study of its habits and development." *Bulletin of the United States Bureau of Fisheries*, Vol. 29, p. 149.

HUXLEY, T. H. (1880). " The crayfish." London.

CHAPTER XVII

PHYLUM **ARTHROPODA** (*continued*)

3.00. Class **Myriapoda**

Characteristics : Terrestrial Arthropoda with a tracheal system, and with pairs of segmentally arranged spiracles; head of either 5 or 6 segments with the first 3 preoral, the 1st disappearing, the 2nd with antennae, the 3rd limbless, the 4th with mandibles, and the 5th and 6th (when present) with maxillae; body usually elongated with numerous segments, most of which bear walking legs; excretion by Malpighian tubules opening into the hindgut; sexes separate and development direct.

This class is so similar in many respects to the great class Insecta that it is clear that the two must have evolved from a common stock, which was perhaps the first large group of land arthropods. The two orders of the Myriapoda are probably not so closely related as they appear superficially.

3.01. Order **Chilopoda**

Characteristics : Carnivorous Myriapoda which are flattened dorso-ventrally; head of 6 segments, the 5th and 6th bearing maxillae; indefinite number of body segments each with one pair of walking legs, except the 1st, which has limbs modified as poison claws, and the last two, which usually lack appendages; gonads dorsal to the alimentary canal, and genital opening posterior.

Genus **Lithobius** (centipede)

(An alternative is the large tropical *Scolopendra*, with the body segments similar, with 21 pairs of walking legs, and with 9 pairs of spiracles.)

I. GENERAL ACCOUNT

a. *Lithobius* is widespread and common throughout both temperate and tropical regions. It is an active predatory animal, but since it requires an atmosphere saturated with moisture, it normally lives under the cover of stones, thick vegetation, or the bark of trees. At anything less than 100% humidity it loses water through its spiracles and dies. Its food consists of any small animals killed by means of the poison claws, and to some extent it may also eat carrion. Reproduction takes place during spring and summer, but will also occur in warm conditions in winter. The method of copulation is appar-

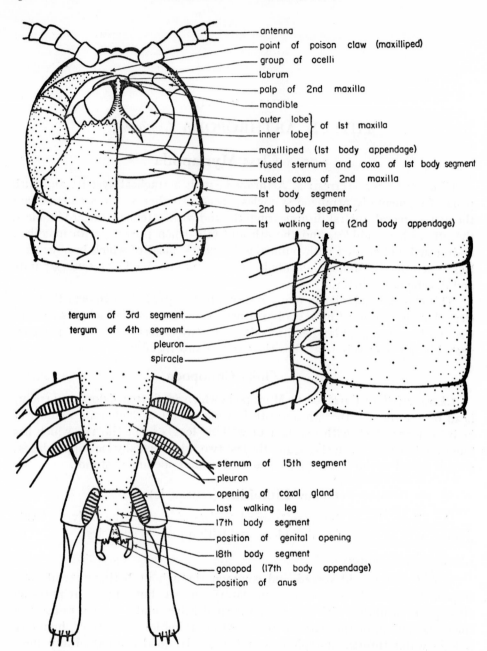

FIG. 91.—*Lithobius*. A ventral view of the head with the left maxilliped removed to uncover the mouth-parts, a latero-dorsal view of the 3rd to the 5th body segments, and a ventral view of the posterior end of the body of a female.

ently unknown, but the eggs are laid singly. Each is covered with a sticky secretion, and then rolled about until, unrecognisably dirty, it is abandoned. The young hatch with the adult form, but with a reduced number of segments. Individuals can live for several years, and regeneration of lost limbs is rapid.

2. EXTERNAL ANATOMY

a. The long, segmented **body** is flattened dorso-ventrally, and is divisible into a small head and a long region of 18 segments, which is also known as the body (the number of segments is different in other genera).

b. The 6 segments of the **head** are closely fused. The 1st and 3rd segments, visible in the embryo, are indistinguishable in the adult. The many-jointed antennae (segment 2) are the main sense organs, since the eyes are mere groups of ocelli on the sides of the head. The other head appendages are partly obscured by the large poison claws (of the 1st body segment). Pull these aside to uncover the mouth flanked anteriorly by the narrow labrum, laterally by the mandibles (segment 4) and the 1st maxillae (segment 5), and posteriorly by the bases of the 1st and 2nd maxillae (segment 6). Through a binocular micro-scope the mandibles can be seen as toothed plates which lack palps, while each 1st maxilla has a basal joint bearing two short lobes, the outer and larger being 2-jointed. The 2nd maxillae are larger, and their basal joints are fused to-gether to form a broad, labium-like structure. Each carries a 3-jointed palp which ends in a small claw.

c. Each of the **body segments** has a dorsal tergal plate separated laterally by soft pleural membranes from a sternal plate to which the limbs are attached. The terga are alternatively short and long, this sequence being broken only between segments 8 and 9, but the sterna are all similar. Spiracles (per-manently open and leading into the tracheal system) are visible in the pleural membranes of segments 4, 6, 9, 11, 13, and 15, which all have long terga.

d. The first **body appendages** are the powerful poison claws, or maxillipeds, which are directed forwards, curved inwards, and end in sharp points (each pierced by the opening of a poison-gland). Each maxilliped has 4 free joints, and a basal joint which is fused to the sternum of the segment to form a large plate bearing teeth anteriorly. The 2nd to the 16th limbs are all similar walk-ing legs, each having 7 joints, which, from the base, are termed the coxa, trochanter, femur, tibia, and 3 tarsi. On the posterior surfaces of the coxal joints of the last 4 pairs of walking legs are the prominent openings of the coxal glands (of unknown function). In the female, but not in the male, the 17th segment bears small limbs, or gonopods, flanking the mid-ventral genital opening (gonopods are absent in *Scolopendra*). Each gonopod has a basal joint bearing two tiny lobes internally and a 2-jointed palp externally (they hold each egg after it is laid and until it is covered with dirt). The 18th segment in small and limbless, and it carries the terminal anus.

3.   CONCLUSION

a. Observing the specimen, review the characteristics of the phylum, of the class, and of the order.

b. Contrast the structure of *Lithobius* with that of *Peripatus*.

4.   REFERENCE

Kükenthal, W., and Krumbach, T. (1926–29).   Volume 4 and part 1 of " Handbuch der Zoologie."   Berlin and Leipzig.

3.02.   Order **Diplopoda**

Characteristics : Myriapoda which are usually herbivorous, and which have a cylindrical body; head of 5 segments, the 5th bearing maxillae; body divisible into a thorax composed of the 4 anterior segments, and an abdomen composed of the remaining indefinite number of segments; gonads ventral to the alimentary canal, and the genital opening on the 3rd thoracic segment.

Genus **Iulus** (millepede or wireworm)

1.   GENERAL ACCOUNT

a. Iulus and other closely related genera form a cosmopolitan family, the Iulidae, which includes some very large tropical species.   The animals live sluggishly in dark, damp places under stones and the bark of dead trees. For protection they can roll into a ball or spiral and emit a noxious smell. Their food consists mainly of decaying vegetable, and even animal, matter, but they also feed on the roots of living plants and on fruit lying in contact with the soil.   In temperate regions reproduction is apparently most common in late spring and early summer, and the eggs are deposited in groups of up to 100 in a spherical cavity dug in the soil by the female.   The eggs are watched over by the female until they hatch into young animals possessing 3 pairs of legs and 3 or 4 apodous body segments.

2.   EXTERNAL ANATOMY

a. The **body** consists of a small head ; a thorax composed of 4 single segments, the last 3 of which bear walking legs ; and an abdomen composed of the remaining segments which are actually double and which, except posteriorly, carry two pairs of walking legs each.

b. The **head** is covered by a cephalic shield, which curves downwards anteriorly to end in a sharp edge formed of the fused labrum.   Segments 1 and 3, visible in the embryo, have no limbs, and are indistinguishable in the adult. The 7-jointed antennae (segment 2) are on the front of the head, and posterior to their bases are groups of ocelli forming the eyes.   Ventrally, the mouth and parts of the mandibles are obscured by a large plate, the gnathochilarium. The outer parts of this plate are formed of the maxillae (segment 5), while the

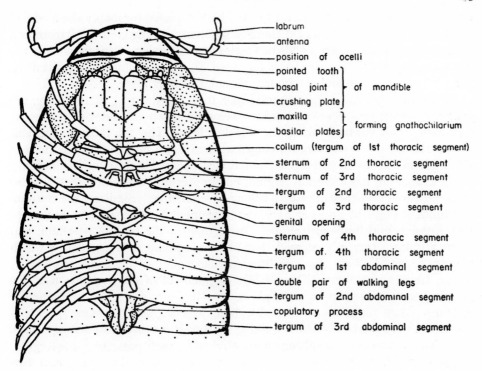

labrum
antenna
position of ocelli
pointed tooth
basal joint   } of mandible
crushing plate
maxilla
basilar plates   } forming gnathochilarium
collum (tergum of 1st thoracic segment)
sternum of 2nd thoracic segment
sternum of 3rd thoracic segment
tergum of 2nd thoracic segment
tergum of 3rd thoracic segment
genital opening
sternum of 4th thoracic segment
tergum of. 4th thoracic segment
tergum of 1st abdominal segment
double pair of walking legs
tergum of 2nd abdominal segment
copulatory process
tergum of 3rd abdominal segment

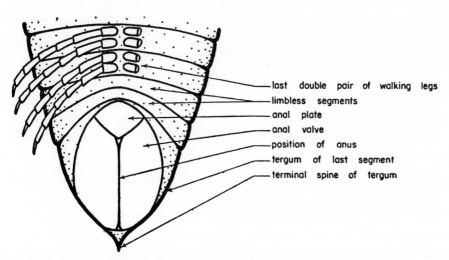

last double pair of walking legs
limbless segments
anal plate
anal valve
position of anus
tergum of last segment
terminal spine of tergum

FIG. 92.—*Iulus.* A ventral view of the anterior end of a male, and a ventral view of the posterior end.

internal and basal parts are formed of the basilar plates (probably the modified sternites of the 5th head and 1st thoracic segments). The gnathochilarium is a labium-like structure, and it ends in a series of short palps. It is flanked by the large basal joints of the mandibles (segment 4), each of which bears distally a hinged, pointed tooth and a rounded, ridged, crushing plate.

c. The 4 segments of the **thorax**, like those of the rest of the body, are cylindrical with well-developed terga extending down the sides of the body, and with small sterna bearing the walking legs. The 1st thoracic segment has an abnormally broad tergum known as the collum (apparently the limbs of this segment are absent and the sternum is incorporated in the gnathochilarium). The 2nd segment has a normal tergum, but its sternum and limbs are displaced so far forwards that they appear to belong to segment 1. Similarly the sternum and limbs of segment 3 appear to belong to segment 2, while segment 3 seems to lack sternum and limbs altogether. In segment 4 the tergum, sternum, and limbs are more correctly aligned (but in some species it is segment 4 which appears to lack limbs). Each walking leg has 7 joints : the coxa, trochanter, femur, tibia, and 3 tarsi. The 1st legs (segment 2) of the male are used for gripping the female during copulation, and in both sexes the reproductive openings are on the coxae of the 2nd walking legs (segment 3). One spiracle is associated with the base of each walking leg, but it is difficult to distinguish.

d. The segments of the **abdomen** are all double, each possessing one tergum, but two small, closely applied sterna, two pairs of walking legs, and two pairs of obscure spiracles. An exception is the 3rd abdominal segment of the male, which lacks walking legs and bears short copulatory processes of complex shape (they are of great importance in classification, and they function in the transference of spermatozoa to the female ; they are not homologous with limbs). The other exceptions are the last 3 abdominal segments, which are apodous (although in some species the 1st or 2nd of them may have one or even two pairs of legs). The last segment is highly modified with a large tergum ending in a spine, with a sternum probably represented by the anal plate, and with two large anal valves flanking the anus. On the sides of most of the terga are the dark openings of the odoriferous glands (which secrete a noxious substance).

3. CONCLUSION

a. Observing the specimen, review the characteristics of the phylum, of the class, and of the order.

b. Contrast the structure of *Iulus* with that of *Lithobius*.

4. REFERENCES

Krug, H. (1907). "Beiträge zur Anatomie der Gattung *Iulus.*" *Jenaische Zeitschrift für Naturwissenschaft Jena*, Vol. 42, p. 485.

Kükenthal, W., and Krumbach, T. (1926–29). Volume 4 and part 1 of " Handbuch der Zoologie." Berlin and Leipzig.

CHAPTER XVIII

PHYLUM **ARTHROPODA** (*continued*)

4.00.   Class **Insecta**

Characteristics : Typically terrestrial Arthropoda with a tracheal system, and with pairs of segmentally arranged spiracles ; head of 6 segments, with the first 3 preoral, the 1st disappearing, the 2nd with antennae, the 3rd limbless, the 4th with mandibles, and the 5th and 6th with maxillae ; body divisible into a thorax of 3 segments, each with a pair of walking legs, and an abdomen of not more than 12 segments, most of which are limbless ; excretion by Malpighian tubules opening into the hindgut ; sexes separate, and development either direct or via a larval stage.

The insects may have originated by neoteny from the six-legged larva of some early myriapod.   They have been most successful, and both in species and individuals they far outnumber any other group of land animals.   However, they are all small in size, and their distribution and activity are limited by environmental temperature.   Some have invaded fresh water, but very few spend their whole lives in that medium.   They are almost without representatives in the sea.

4.10.   Subclass **Apterygota**

Characteristics : Insects which are primitively wingless, and which do not undergo metamorphosis.

4.11.   Order **Thysanura**

Characteristics : Apterygota with or without compound eyes ; with an abdomen of 11 segments, many of which bear styliform appendages ; and with anal cerci which are usually many-jointed, but which occasionally form unjointed forceps.

Although this is the most primitive order of the insects, its members are common and very widely distributed.   They live obscure lives in the soil, under cover of stones and fallen leaves, in ants' nests, and in houses.

Genus **Petrobius (Machilis)**

(Less suitable alternatives are the house-living *Lepisma*, with simple eyes, and the soil-living *Campodea*, with mouth-parts retracted into the head, with no median cerciform process, and usually with no eyes.)

I. GENERAL ACCOUNT

a. The genera *Petrobius* and *Machilis*, once counted as a single genus, include a cosmopolitan group of species which generally live under stones or fallen leaves.

b. The species *P. maritimus* Leach, described below, is abundant on rocky shores above the high-tide mark.   It lives beneath stones, and it runs and jumps with great rapidity when disturbed.   Its spiracles have no closing mechanism to prevent water loss, and therefore it requires a highly humid atmosphere. Like other related species, *Petrobius* is a scavenger feeding on decaying vegetable matter.   Little appears to be known about its breeding habits, but the newly hatched young have a form resembling that of the adult, and during development they apparently pass through five ecdyses.

2. EXTERNAL ANATOMY

a. The segmented **body** is divisible into a head with two long, jointed antennae, a thorax of 3 segments, each with a pair of walking legs, and a long abdomen with three long cerciform processes posteriorly.   The surface of the body, and much of that of the limbs, is closely covered by tiny, loosely attached scales.

b. Examine the **head** through a lens or binocular microscope, or make a preparation on a microscope slide after boiling in caustic potash (method on p. 316).   Dorsally the most prominent features are the two large, closely adjacent, compound eyes, and anteriorly there are 3 small eyes (which have been described as intermediate between the simple and compound types).   Of the 6 head segments, the 1st and 3rd are limbless and indistinguishable.   The limbs of the 2nd segment are the long, many-jointed antennae.

c. The group of **mouth-parts** projects ventrally.   A labrum forms an anterior lip, which covers the points of the 2-jointed mandibles (of segment 4). Each maxilla (segment 5) has two basal joints, the cardo and stipes, the latter bearing internally the 2-jointed spinous lacinia, and externally a small plate, the palpifer, on which is mounted a simple galea and a long, 7-jointed palp.   In the labium (or fused 2nd maxillae of segment 6) there is a single basal plate, the postmentum.   On each side this plate carries a prementum, on which there are mounted internally the two lobes of the glossa, medially the two lobes of the paraglossa, and externally a poorly defined plate, the palpiger, with a 3-jointed labial palp attached.   Altogether the glossae and paraglossae are termed the ligula.

d. The **thorax** consists of 3 similar segments, the pro-, meso-, and metathoracic segments, each with a dorsal tergum, the edges of which project outwards and downwards, and a ventral sternum with legs attached.   Each leg has 8 joints, a small subcoxa hidden by the overhanging tergum (this is a primitive basal joint which is reduced or lacking in most insects), a stout coxa,

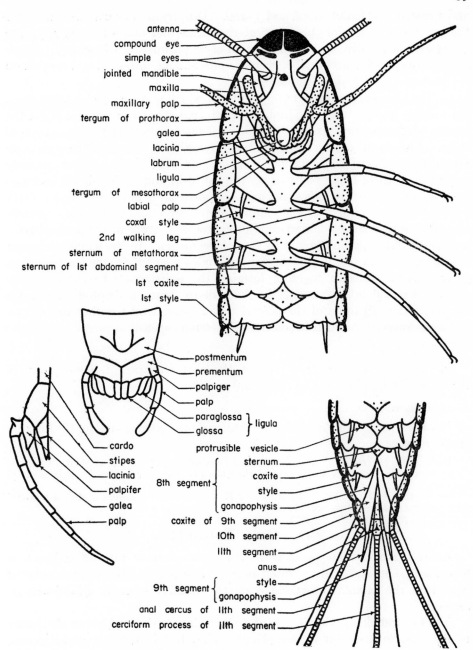

FIG. 93.—*Petrobius (Machilis)*. A ventral view of the anterior end, details of the maxilla and labium, and a ventral view of the posterior end of a female.

and a trochanter, femur, tibia, and 3 tarsi. Distally are two claws, often called the pretarsus. Each of the coxae of the meso- and meta-thoracic segments also carries a slender, backward-directed style (of unknown function). There is a pair of spiracles laterally between the pro- and meso-thorax, and another on the posterior border of the mesothorax.

e. The long **abdomen** has 11 segments, of which numbers 1 to 9 carry short appendages (reduced but true limbs). Each consists of a large basal plate, the coxite, which on segments 2 to 9 carries a slender style tipped with a group of setae. Also on the coxites, immediately internal to the bases of the styles, are protrusible vesicles (which can be extended or withdrawn, and are possibly respiratory), there being one pair on the 1st, 6th, and 7th segments and two pairs on the 2nd to the 8th segments. Segment 10 is limbless, but the small segment 11 carries a pair of long, many-jointed cerci, and its tergum is greatly elongated into a many-jointed cerciform process. Pairs of obscure spiracles are present laterally on the 2nd to the 8th segments. In the **female** the inner edge of each of the coxites of segments 8 and 9 is greatly extended to form a gonapophysis, the four together forming the ovipositor (the single female opening is on the 8th sternum). In the **male** the four gonapophyses are much shorter, and inner lobes of the posterior pair have fused together to form an aedeagus (or penis through which the vas deferens opens).

3. CONCLUSION

a. Observing the specimen, review the characteristics of the phylum, of the class, of the subclass, and of the order.

4. REFERENCES

For the structure of *Petrobius*, *Lepisma*, and other genera, and for the internal anatomy, see :

ESCHERICH, K. (1905). " Das System der Lepismatiden." *Zoologica*, Vol. 18, no. 43.
LUBBOCK, J. (1873). " Monograph of the Collembola and Thysanura." Ray Society, London.
OUDEMANS, J. T. (1888). " Beiträge zur Kenntniss der Thysanura und Collembola." *Bijdragen tot de Dierkunde*, Vol. 16, p. 147.

4.12. Order **Collembola**

Characteristics : Apterygota without compound eyes ; with an abdomen of 6 segments, usually with 3 fused pairs of appendages (the ventral tube of segment 1, the hamula of segment 3, and the furcula of segment 4), and with no anal cerci.

The Collembola are tiny insects abundant all over the world from the Arctic to the Antarctic, except in dry places. They live in the soil, under stones, vegetation, or the bark of trees, or in the nests of ants, termites, or birds. Some live on the surface of fresh water, and a few have colonised the seashore and are submerged by each tide. There are two suborders : the Arthropleona, with elongate form and clear segmentation, and the Symphypleona, with globular form and indistinct segmentation.

Genus Tomocerus

(Almost any springtail will serve as an alternative, but some of the Arthropleona are less typical in lacking a furcula, and all of the Symphypleona have obscure segmentation.)

I. GENERAL ACCOUNT

a. Tomocerus and other related genera form a cosmopolitan group which are common in open country, in woods and forests, and in caves. They live under cover in any crevices where the humidity is high enough to prevent desiccation, and they feed on decaying vegetable matter and on cells stripped from the leaves of young seedlings. The life-span of the adult is probably only a week or two. Reproduction is rapid, and, as is common among Collembola, young and old are often found living gregariously in large numbers. The reason for this habit is unknown.

2. EXTERNAL ANATOMY

a. Examined through a microscope, the **body** can be seen to be divided into a head, a thorax of 3 segments, each with a pair of walking legs, and an abdomen of 6 segments.

b. Prominent in front of the **head** are the 4-jointed antennae (of segment 2). Posterior to each antennal base is a group of black ocelli, and in many Collembola, but not *Tomocerus*, a small post-antennal organ (probably sensory) lies between the antennal base and the eye. The mandibles and maxillae are hidden within the head. They are guarded in front by the labrum, laterally by downgrowths of the sides of the head, and posteriorly by the labium, which is reduced and lacks glossae, paraglossae, and palps.

c. In the **thorax** the prothoracic segment is reduced (in many other genera it is normal in size), but the meso- and meta-thoracic segments are well developed, with clearly defined terga and sterna. The legs lack a tarsus, but possess a subcoxa, and are therefore 5-jointed. The distal tibia carries two claws. Along the mid-ventral line of the thorax is a narrow ventral groove (which carries back to the 1st abdominal segment a sticky secretion produced by cephalic glands behind the labium).

d. The 6 **abdominal segments** are distinct, especially dorsally. The limbs of segment 1 are fused to form a prominent bilobed structure, the ventral tube (which is thought to be an adhesive organ, since the sticky secretion from the ventral groove passes on to it ; in its tip are a pair of protrusible vesicles of unknown function, but possibly respiratory). The 2nd segment is apodous, but the limbs of the 3rd segment are fused to form the tiny hamula which has a basal corpus and two distal rami. The last limbs (of segment 4) are fused to form the furcula (which when folded forwards is held in position by the hamula ; by its sudden backward kick the animal is driven into the air). It has a stout basal joint, the manubrium, and two distal joints, the dentes, each of which carries a terminal claw-like process, the mucro. The obscure reproductive openings are on the sternum of segment 5, but there are no gonapophyses, and

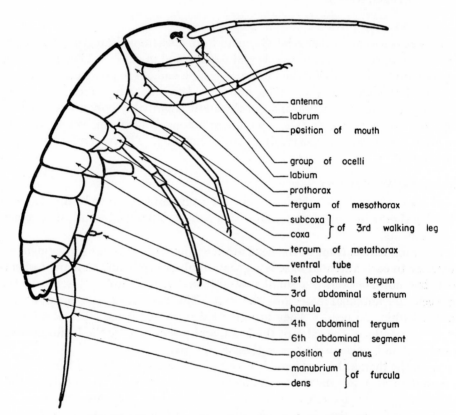

antenna
labrum
position of mouth

group of ocelli
labium
prothorax
tergum of mesothorax
subcoxa } of 3rd walking leg
coxa
tergum of metathorax
ventral tube
1st abdominal tergum
3rd abdominal sternum
hamula
4th abdominal tergum
6th abdominal segment
position of anus
manubrium } of furcula
dens

Fig. 94.—*Tomocerus.* A specimen seen from the right side.

the sexes appear similar. The anus opens on segment 6. There are no spiracles (and no tracheal system).

3. CONCLUSION

a. Observing the specimen, review the characteristics of the phylum, of the class, of the subclass, and of the order.

b. Contrast the specialised structure of *Tomocerus* with the more primitive structure of *Petrobius.*

4. REFERENCES

For the structure of this and of other genera, see :

LUBBOCK, J. (1873). "Monograph of the Collembola and Thysanura." Ray Society, London.
OUDEMANS, J. T. (1888). "Beiträge zur Kenntniss der Thysanura und Collembola." *Bijdragen tot de Dierkunde*, Vol. 16, p. 147.

4.20. Subclass **Exopterygota (Heterometabola)**

Characteristics : Insecta which develop wings externally, which pass through unspecialised larval stages, and which therefore show incomplete metamorphosis.

4.21. Order **Orthoptera**

Characteristics : Exopterygota in which the head carries biting mouth-parts and a 4-lobed ligula ; thorax with hardened forewings and membranous hindwings ; abdomen usually with jointed cerci and well-developed gonapophyses.

There are two suborders : the Cursoria, which includes the running forms, the cockroaches, mantids, and stick insects ; and the Saltatoria, which, with modified hind legs, includes the jumping forms, the crickets, grasshoppers, and locusts.   They form the least specialised order of winged insects, and the most primitive and generalised of them are the cockroaches, which also have the longest geological record, being known since the mid-Palaeozoic.

Genus **Blatta** (cockroach)

(The common alternative is the essentially similar *Periplaneta*, in which both sexes are winged and capable of flight.)

I. GENERAL ACCOUNT

a. Whatever were the original homes of *Blatta* and *Periplaneta*, they are now cosmopolitan, having been carried to all parts of the world in caravans and in ships. *Blatta* arrived in England in Elizabethan times, and although it cannot live out of doors, it has thrived ever since, living gregariously, and often in very large numbers, in the artificial warmth of such places as bakehouses, hospitals, distilleries, and zoological gardens. By day it remains hidden in crevices, and by night it feeds as a scavenger on almost any animal or vegetable débris. Unlike *Periplaneta*, it cannot fly, and in the female the wings are vestigial. Breeding continues throughout the year. The eggs are produced in groups of 16, encased in a hard capsule, and carried for about a week before being deposited in some corner. The young animals, or nymphs, resemble the adults, and their development takes about a year.

2. EXTERNAL ANATOMY

a. In a specimen freshly killed with chloroform, notice that the **body** is divisible into a head, a thorax of 3 segments, each with a pair of walking legs, and an abdomen. The whole is encased in a thick, brown, chitinous exo-skeleton.

b. The **head** is elongated dorso-ventrally. There are two large com-pound eyes, and between them, on top of the head, are two epicranial plates, or sclerites, separated by a median suture (not visible in *Periplaneta*). Anteriorly this suture splits into two, which pass outwards to the white oval fenestrae (function unknown) close to the antennal bases. The front of the head is protected by a single sclerite, the clypeus, to the base of which is hinged the labrum, while the sides of the head are covered by the genae.

c. The 1st **head appendages** are the long, many-jointed antennae (of seg-ment 2) based in the centres of articulating membranes in front of the eyes. The mouth is protected by the labrum in front, is flanked by the mandibles (segment 4) and the maxillae with palps (segment 5), and is backed by the labium with shorter palps (segment 6). Distinguish these three limbs, and then, using fine forceps and starting with the labium, detach them at their bases. Mount them in glycerine beneath a cover-glass, and examine them through a microscope. The simple mandibles are strong toothed plates (and they work sideways). Each maxilla has two basal joints, the cardo and stipes, and the latter carries internally the lacinia, with its curved toothed tip (for assisting in biting the food), medially the galea, and externally the 5-jointed maxillary palp (a tasting organ). The labium (formed of the two 2nd maxillae fused) has three basal plates, the submentum, the smaller postmentum, and the distal bilobed prementum. Each premental lobe carries internally a glossa, medially a paraglossa, and externally a partly fused plate, the palpiger, on which is mounted the 3-jointed labial palp (also a tasting organ). The two glossae and two paraglossae are together called the ligula (and help in food manipulation).

d. The 3 segments of the **thorax** are called the pro-, meso-, and meta-thorax. Each has a prominent tergum, a small sternum, and a series of lateral pleural sclerites. The 1st tergum is the large pronotum. Except in the female (of *Blatta*), the 2nd, or mesonotum, is extended into two movable lobes, the hard, protective forewings, or tegmina. Also except in the female (of *Blatta*), the 3rd, or metanotum, is similarly developed to form hindwings, which, however, are broader, thinner, and more movable (they normally lie folded beneath the tegmina). A pair of spiracles is present laterally between the pro- and meso-thorax, and another between the meso- and meta-thorax.

e. The **thoracic appendages** are the 3 pairs of walking legs, each of which articulates with a pleural sclerite (probably the remnant of a subcoxal joint). Each leg consists of five parts : the coxa (which also affords ventral protection to the thorax), trochanter, femur, tibia, and tarsus. The tarsus is itself sub-divided into five parts, each with a gripping pad of fine setae distally and ven-

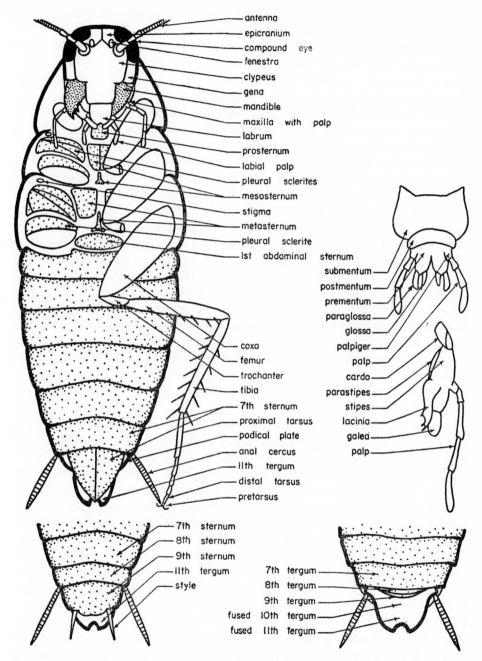

antenna
epicranium
compound eye
fenestra
clypeus
gena
mandible
maxilla with palp
labrum
prosternum
labial palp
pleural sclerites
mesosternum
stigma
metasternum
pleural sclerite
Ist abdominal sternum

submentum
postmentum
prementum
paraglossa
glossa
palpiger
palp
cardo
parastipes
stipes
lacinia
galea
palp

coxa
femur
trochanter
tibia
7th sternum
proximal tarsus
podical plate
anal cercus
IIth tergum
distal tarsus
pretarsus

7th sternum
8th sternum
9th sternum
IIth tergum
style

7th tergum
8th tergum
9th tergum
fused 10th tergum
fused 11th tergum

FIG. 95.—*Blatta.* Ventral views of a female and of the end of the male abdomen (left), a dorsal view of the end of the female abdomen (lower right), and details of the labium and maxilla.

trally, and it also bears yet another joint, the pretarsus, consisting of a gripping pad, or pulvillus, and a pair of claws.

f. The **abdomen** has 11 segments, but posteriorly they are telescoped, and the last two are much reduced. The first 7 are always distinct, having clear terga and sterna, between which are segmental pairs of spiracles (segment 8 also has a pair of spiracles). In the **female** segments 8 and 9 are hidden within segment 7, and the 7th sternum is extended backwards to form a hinged, keel-like process. In the **male** the 8th and 9th segments are distinct (but in *Periplaneta* this only applies to the sterna). The tergum of the 10th segment is fused to that of the 11th, which is prolonged backwards and notched posteriorly. The sternum of the 10th segment is obscure, but that of the 11th is represented by the pair of podical plates which flank the anus.

g. **Abdominal appendages** are mostly lacking, but those of segment 11 are the cerci. The other appendages subserve reproduction. In the **female**, by pulling down or cutting away the 7th sternum, a large cavity, the genital pouch, is exposed (spermatozoa are placed here by the male, and here also the egg capsule is moulded). In it are six backward-directed processes, the gonapophyses, of which the anterior pair (of segment 8) is large and flattened, while the posterior two pairs (of segment 9) are smaller and pointed (altogether they form the ovipositor). In the **male** conditions are more complex, and the gonapophyses (of segment 9 only) are modified into chitinous prongs and a series of asymmetrical plates. The male also bears two styles on the 9th sternum.

3. INTERNAL ANATOMY

a. Fix the specimen dorsal side uppermost either by means of pins passed through the edges of the mesothorax and abdomen, or, better, by drying the ventral surface, floating the animal in melted paraffin wax, and allowing the wax to set. Detach the elytra and wings, and continue the dissection under water. Without penetrating the soft tissues, carefully cut up the right edges of the terga, across the front of the pronotum and the back of the 7th abdominal tergum, and hinge aside and pin down the flap so formed. The heart and pericardial sinus usually remain attached to the terga. The **heart** is a chain of 13 narrow chambers, 3 thoracic and 10 abdominal, passing along the mid-dorsal line (in each segment there is a pair of obscure ostia through which blood enters ; it leaves anteriorly to the head). The pericardial sinus is a space as wide as the body, its roof being the terga and longitudinal tergal muscles, and its floor a fine, fenestrated membrane, the pericardial diaphragm (blood enters the sinus through the fenestrae). In this diaphragm a series of large intersegmental tracheae pass inwards towards the heart. Ventral to these tracheae, and also in the diaphragm, are the fine intersegmental alary muscles (which do not join the heart, but passing beneath it, join each other).

b. Having distinguished the alary **muscles**, notice the longitudinal tergal muscles, which are broad in the abdomen but narrow in the thorax ; the tergosternal muscles placed laterally in the abdomen (which they compress) ; the 3 pairs of lateral thoracic muscles ; and the 3 pairs of leg muscles

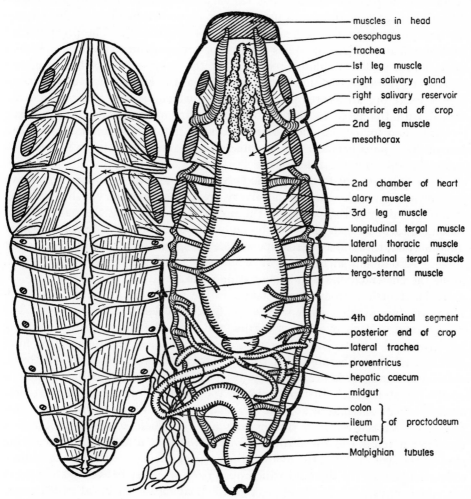

muscles in head
oesophagus
trachea
1st leg muscle
right salivary gland
right salivary reservoir
anterior end of crop
2nd leg muscle
mesothorax

2nd chamber of heart
alary muscle
3rd leg muscle
longitudinal tergal muscle
lateral thoracic muscle
longitudinal tergal muscle
tergo-sternal muscle

4th abdominal segment
posterior end of crop
lateral trachea
proventricus
hepatic caecum
midgut
colon
ileum } of proctodaeum
rectum
Malpighian tubules

FIG. 96.—*Blatta.*   A general dissection in which the terga, with the heart attached, have been hinged to the left.

passing ventrally from the coxae to their points of origin on the thoracic terga.

c. Gently move aside any obscuring fatty tissue and distinguish the **alimentary canal.**   Anteriorly the stomodaeum (ectodermal and cuticle lined) has the form of a narrow oesophagus, medially it swells into the large, thin-walled crop which extends into the abdomen, and posteriorly it ends in the small gizzard (which has thick muscular walls, six internal teeth for chewing the food, and a straining mechanism of setae to ensure that only fine particles pass on to the midgut). On the anterior end of the crop are a pair of white branching salivary glands and a pair of bladder-like salivary reservoirs. The midgut (endodermal) is relatively short and narrow. At its anterior end are 8 diverticula, the hepatic caeca (which increase the absorptive surface). The proctodaeum (ectodermal and cuticle lined) has an anterior narrow ileum, a median and wider colon, and a posterior dilated rectum. At the anterior end of the ileum are some 60 or 70 yellowish, thread-like diverticula, the Malpighian tubules (ectodermal excretory structures producing urates which, as uric acid crystals, are voided with the faeces). Cut through the alimentary canal, turn the crop forwards, and follow the ducts of the salivary glands and reservoirs. Each pair of ducts joins beneath the oesophagus, and the two ducts so formed also join before opening into the mouth.

d. Taking care not to disturb the nerve-ring round the oesophagus, remove the alimentary canal. Notice the silvery branching **tracheae**, which, beginning at the lateral spiracles, penetrate the body-tissues (and, by the pulsations of abdomen, carry oxygen in and carbon dioxide out). Remove one of the larger tracheae, and, through a microscope, notice the spiral thickening of its cuticular lining. Also mount small pieces of such tissues as salivary glands, muscle, etc., to see the fine trachioles branching within them.

e. The **female reproductive system** is in the posterior part of the abdomen. There are two ovaries, each with eight finger-like lobes, the ovarioles. The anterior end of each ovariole is narrow and bead-like (with small developing eggs), while the posterior end is swollen (with large eggs; 16 eggs, one from each ovariole, are liberated at a time). Two short wide oviducts lead back, unite, and disappear beneath the upraised 9th sternum (the genital opening is on the 8th sternum). Just posterior to the point of junction of the oviducts are two small spermathecae, one globular and the other filamentous (they store spermatozoa received during copulation). Their common duct passes through a notch in the 9th sternum to open into the genital pouch. Occupying most of the space around the oviducts and spermathecae are the two branching colleterial glands, the ducts of which open close together between the bases of the gonapophyses (these glands secrete the coagulating material which forms the egg capsule). If an egg capsule is present, detach it, and cut it open longitudinally to expose the two staggered rows, each of 8 eggs.

f. In the **male reproductive system** the two thread-like testes are dorsolateral in the 4th and 5th segments, but are obscurely embedded in the fatty tissue (they are never easy to find, and in older males they tend to disappear altogether). The two fine vasa deferentia loop back to the seminal vesicle, which, from the dorsal side, is hidden by a mass of tubules, the accessory

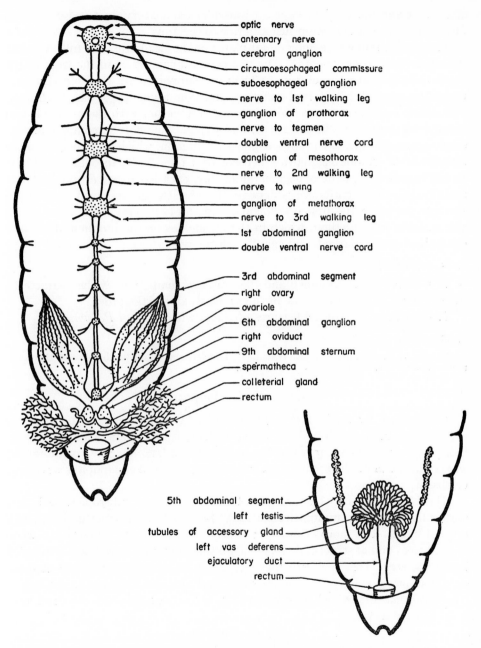

optic nerve
antennary nerve
cerebral ganglion
circumoesophageal commissure
suboesophageal ganglion
nerve to 1st walking leg
ganglion of prothorax
nerve to tegmen
double ventral nerve cord
ganglion of mesothorax
nerve to 2nd walking leg
nerve to wing
ganglion of metathorax
nerve to 3rd walking leg
1st abdominal ganglion
double ventral nerve cord

3rd abdominal segment
right ovary
ovariole
6th abdominal ganglion
right oviduct
9th abdominal sternum
spermatheca
colleterial gland
rectum

5th abdominal segment
left testis
tubules of accessory gland
left vas deferens
ejaculatory duct
rectum

FIG. 97.—*Blatta.* Dorsal views of the nervous system, the female reproductive system, and the male reproductive system.

glands. From the seminal vesicle a muscular ejaculatory duct passes back to open behind the 9th sternum just anterior to the anus.

g. Finally, remove the epicranial plates of the head, and carefully uncover the whole ventral **nerve-cord**. The two cerebral ganglia lie in the front of the head, close beneath the clypeus. They are supported by the thin chitinous tentorium (part of the internal skeleton), and from them nerves pass to the eyes and antennae. Remove one side of the head, together with the mandible and maxilla (if these are still attached), and expose the short circumoesophageal commissures leading to the suboesophageal ganglion, which gives nerves to the mouth-parts. A double ventral nerve-cord passes back through the body. In the thorax the 3 pairs of segmental ganglia, each fused, are especially large, and the two nerve-cords are widely separated. In the abdomen there are 6 smaller ganglia in the first 6 segments, and the two nerve-cords lie close together. The 6th ganglion, which in the female lies on the junction of the oviducts, is slightly enlarged, and supplies all the posterior end of the body.

4. CONCLUSION

a. Observing the specimen and the drawings made, review the characteristics of the phylum, of the class, of the subclass, and of the order.

b. Compare the external features of *Blatta* with those of *Petrobius*.

5. REFERENCE

MIALL, L. C., and DENNY, A. (1886). " The structure and life-history of the cockroach (*Periplaneta orientalis*)." London and Leeds.

4.22. Order **Isoptera**

Characteristics : Social Exopterygota which are polymorphic with a variety of fertile and sterile castes ; head with biting mouth-parts and a 4-lobed ligula ; thorax either wingless or with two pairs of similar, elongate, membranous wings which can be shed ; abdomen with short cerci, and gonapophyses reduced or absent.

The isopterans are the termites of the tropics and subtropics, and they always live in large communities with a well-defined social structure based on a caste system. The more primitive termites live in galleries bored in the wood of dead trees and of structural timbers, and they do immense damage to wooden buildings, etc. The more advanced termites build large termitaria of mud, sand, and faecal matter. They are particularly highly developed in Africa and Northern Australia, where the termitaria may reach a height of 20 feet and have walls as hard as rock.

Genus **Termes**

I. GENERAL ACCOUNT

a. This genus belongs to the most specialised family, the Termitidae, and is common in Africa and Ceylon, where it builds large termitaria. Within these is a maze of passages and chambers with special cells for storing dried vegetable food collected by nocturnal foraging parties, and with other cells for the 'gardens' in which fungus food is grown. A colony is established by a single pair, the so-called king and queen, whose first offspring are workers. The queen then increases greatly in size, is tended by the workers, is fed on fungus, and lays 3,000 or 4,000 eggs a day. The eggs hatch into nymphs, which are fed on fungus and on vegetable matter partly predigested by adults. In this way they become infected with the symbiotic protozoans which are always present in the alimentary canal and which assist in the digestion of cellulose. The nymphs develop either into fertile males and females, which can leave and start new colonies, or into sterile males and females, which are soldiers of various kinds for the defence of the colony, or workers which tend the queen and the young, build the termitarium, and provision the colony.

2. EXTERNAL ANATOMY

a. Examine first the winged **reproductive forms** (which have the more generalised structure). Notice the usual division of the body into a head, a thorax with two pairs of wings and 3 pairs of walking legs, and an abdomen.

b. The **head** is ovoid and of normal proportions, and laterally it bears well-developed compound eyes. Distinguish the suture separating the epicranial plates, the two fenestrae anterior to the eyes, and the anterior sclerites which are the postclypeus, the preclypeus, and the labrum. The 1st limbs (segment 2) are the antennae, the 2nd (segment 4) the prominent mandibles, the 3rd (segment 5) the typical maxillae, and the 4th (segment 6) the 2nd maxillae fused to form the labium. In the neck are two prominent lateral sclerites.

c. The 3 segments of the **thorax** are distinct. The 1st has a prominent pronotum, but the prosternum is reduced or absent. The 2nd and 3rd have both terga and sterna, but the latter are only weakly chitinised. The two pairs of wings are similar in size and form, with the veins of the anterior edges strongly chitinised. Notice on each wing the basal suture (the line of weakness along which the wing breaks when it is shed after the mating flight). The 3 pairs of legs are also similar with stout coxae, which in the 2nd and 3rd pairs are deeply grooved, the outer lobe so formed being called the meron. The tarsi are each composed of 3 short basal joints and 1 large distal joint with which the claws articulate.

d. The **abdomen** has 10 segments, all of which have distinct terga, but the 1st of which lacks a sternum. In the male the remaining sterna are distinct, the 9th carrying two tiny anal styles close to its posterior border, and the 10th with short lateral anal cerci. In the female the 7th sternum projects back as a subgenital plate to obscure the succeeding sterna, the anal styles are absent, but the cerci are present.

e. Examine also an **older queen**, noticing the broken stumps of the wings

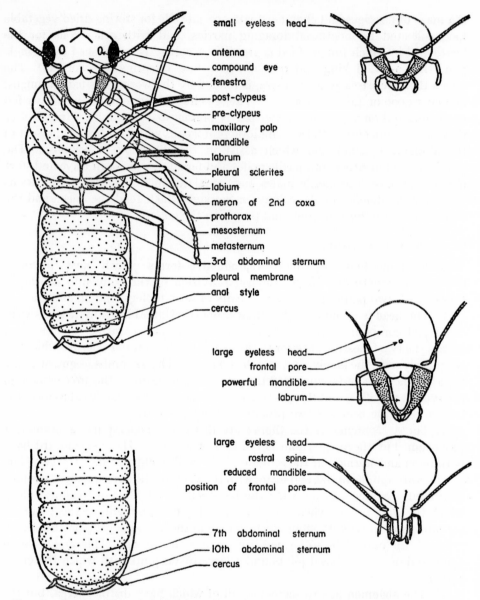

small eyeless head

antenna
compound eye
fenestra
post-clypeus
pre-clypeus
maxillary palp
mandible
labrum
pleural sclerites
labium
meron of 2nd coxa
prothorax
mesosternum
metasternum
3rd abdominal sternum
pleural membrane
anal style
cercus

large eyeless head
frontal pore
powerful mandible
labrum

large eyeless head
rostral spine
reduced mandible
position of frontal pore

7th abdominal sternum
10th abdominal sternum
cercus

FIG. 98.—*Termes.* Ventral views of a male, and of the end of the abdomen of a female (left). The heads of a worker, a mandibulate soldier, and a nasute soldier (right).

and the enormously swollen abdomen (due to the greatly increased size of the reproductive system). The sclerites have remained small, but the pleural membranes between them are greatly expanded.

f. Examine next the **sterile castes**, the **workers** and soldiers, which have in common their smaller size, absence of compound eyes and fenestrae, absence of wings, and poorer chitinisation of both thorax and abdomen. Apart from these features, the form of the worker is generally similar to that of the king or queen.

g. The **soldiers** are characterised by their large and strongly chitinised heads, and they are of two kinds : the mandibulate and the nasute. The mandibulate type possesses large mandibles (for offence and defence) and a frontal pore (through which, to repel enemies, a viscid secretion oozes, this being particularly effective if it is directed on to their antennae). In the nasute type the mandibles are reduced, and the frontal region of the head is drawn out into a rostrum which bears the frontal pore on its apex (in this type the viscid secretion is the sole means of attack and defence).

3. CONCLUSION

a. Observing the specimens, review the characteristics of the phylum, of the class, of the subclass, and of the order.

b. Contrast the external anatomy of *Termes* with that of *Blatta*.

4.23.   Order **Ephemeroptera**

Characteristics : Exopterygota in which the head bears vestigial mouth-parts ; thorax with membranous wings, the hind pair of which is small ; abdomen with very long cerci, and often with a long caudal filament ; and with the aquatic nymph developing into an active winged subimago which moults to release the adult.

The mayflies are of world-wide occurrence, the adults being common along the margins of lakes and rivers. The life of the adult often lasts for only a few hours or days, but the nymphs live for two or three years before transforming into the subimago, a stage unique among insects, and leaving the water. Apparently, in past ages this was a more extensive order than it is today, and it is known to have existed since the Permian.

Genus **Ephemera**

(Other common genera may be used as alternatives and are essentially similar.)

1. GENERAL ACCOUNT

a. This genus occurs abundantly throughout the palaearctic and nearctic regions. The adults take no food, and the alimentary canal is curiously modified to hold air, which apparently functions to reduce the specific gravity. Each female lays thousands of eggs, which are scattered on to the water surface and then sink to the bottom. After a week or two they hatch as nymphs, and burrow into the mud, which they eat for its contained diatoms, etc. (nymphs of

T

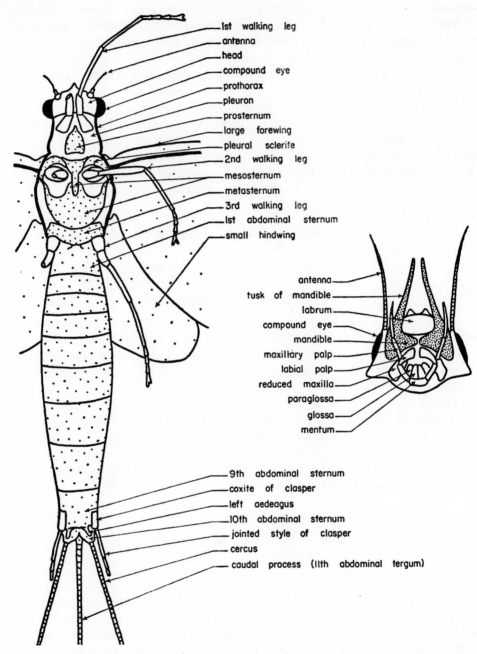

1st walking leg
antenna
head
compound eye
prothorax
pleuron
prosternum
large forewing
pleural sclerite
2nd walking leg
mesosternum
metasternum
3rd walking leg
1st abdominal sternum
small hindwing

antenna
tusk of mandible
labrum
compound eye
mandible
maxillary palp
labial palp
reduced maxilla
paraglossa
glossa
mentum

9th abdominal sternum
coxite of clasper
left aedeagus
10th abdominal sternum
jointed style of clasper
cercus
caudal process (11th abdominal tergum)

FIG. 99.—*Ephemera.*　A ventral view of a male, and of the head of a nymph.

other common genera live as creeping forms, or swimming forms, or are much flattened for life under stones in rapid currents). When fully grown the nymph makes its way to the water surface, and its skin then splits along the back to release the subimago, which flies free. After a short time the subimago sheds its dull pellicle to release the adult, which mates and quickly dies.

2. EXTERNAL ANATOMY

a. The adult fly, or **imago**, has a small head, 3 thoracic segments carrying the legs and wings, and a long abdomen of 11 segments.

b. The **head** bears two large compound eyes and three ocelli; two tiny antennae (belonging to segment 2); and mouth-parts which are almost completely degenerate, but of which the maxillary palps and the labium with small palps are recognisable.

c. In the **thorax** there is a small prothorax, a large mesothorax, and a small metathorax, all possessing clearly developed terga and sterna. The forewings are large and the hindwings small, and all are delicate (since they are needed for so short a time). The legs are all similar, each with a coxa, trochanter, femur, tibia, and 4-jointed tarsus (they are used only for clinging; in some genera there are varying degrees of reduction particularly of the 2nd and 3rd pairs). A pair of spiracles is situated antero-dorsal to the bases of both the 2nd and 3rd pairs of legs.

d. The **abdomen** contains 10 obvious segments, the first 8 of which each bears a pair of lateral spiracles. The 10th segment carries the exceedingly long cerci, and the tergum of a reduced 11th segment is represented by the median caudal process. In the **male** the 9th segment bears a pair of jointed claspers (modified limbs), each with a basal coxite and a jointed style, and a double aedeagus (the two parts of which carry the openings of the vasa deferentia and fit into the two oviducts of the female; they are formed of two gonapophyses, which are inner extensions of the two limbs). In the **female** there are no gonapophyses, and the two oviducts open separately into the space between the 7th and 8th terga.

e. Examine a **nymph** and notice the generally similar form. However, on the head there are well-developed mouth-parts, including curious mandibles with large, forward-directed tusks (which are absent in non-burrowing genera), reduced maxillae with palps, and a labium with glossae, paraglossae, and palps; on the thorax the legs are squat and strong (for burrowing) and the wings are rudimentary; and on the abdomen feathery gills are attached to segments 1 to 7, the 1st being rudimentary, and all being carried reflexed over the back (these gills are not present in smaller younger nymphs).

3. CONCLUSION

a. Observing the specimens, review the characteristics of the phylum, of the class, of the subclass, and of the order.

4. REFERENCE

For details of the external and internal anatomy, see :

NEEDHAM, J. G., TRAVER, J. R., and HSU, Y. (1935). "The biology of mayflies." New York.

4.24. Order **Odonata**

Characteristics : Predaceous Exopterygota in which the head bears very large eyes, very short antennae, and biting mouth-parts ; thorax with two similar pairs of membranous wings ; long abdomen with cerci reduced or absent and with unique genitalia ; and nymph aquatic and with a highly developed prehensile labium.

The dragon flies are cosmopolitan, but they are especially common in the tropics. They are diurnal, sun-loving animals, and a feature of the group is the brilliance of the body coloration. They have a long history, and in the Carboniferous the genus *Meganeura* had a wing span of more than 2 feet. To-day there are two suborders : the Anisoptera, with wings held open on landing, with eyes approaching each other dorsally, and with nymphs having rectal gills, and the Zygoptera, with wings closing over the body on landing, with eyes widely separated, and with nymphs having caudal gills.

Genus **Libellula**

(Other genera of the Anisoptera are similar and may be used as alternatives ; the Zygoptera differ as described above.)

1. GENERAL ACCOUNT

a. The genus *Libellula* is common in the northern hemisphere, and related genera occur elsewhere throughout the world. In spring and summer the adults are commonly seen hovering or flying at high speed to catch their prey, which consists of gnats, mosquitoes, and other small flies taken on the wing. The eggs are laid in water, and from each emerges a pronymph, which in a few minutes sheds its skin to appear as a typical nymph. This is coloured like the mud in which it passes a sluggish life waiting for the approach of its prey. It feeds particularly on other nymphs and larvae of its own and other orders, but when almost fully grown it may also take tadpoles, and even small fishes. Finally it climbs out of the water, and moults to release the imago.

2. EXTERNAL ANATOMY

a. The body of the **imago** is divided into a head, which is freely movable on a slender neck strengthened by cervical sclerites, a swollen thorax, and a long abdomen.

b. The **head** is extraordinary for the large size of the compound eyes (associated with fast flight and predaceous habits). Anterior to these are three ocelli and two tiny antennae (the reduction of which is also associated with the speed of flight). On the front of the head is a series of four plates, the frons dorsally, the post- and ante-clypeus, and the labrum ventrally. The mouth is bordered anteriorly by the labrum ; laterally by the powerful toothed mandibles (segment 4) and the two maxillae (segment 5), each of which consists of a cardo, a stipes, a toothed mala, and an unjointed palp ; and posteriorly by the compact and highly modified labium (segment 6), the palps of which are strongly chitinised and plate-like. Turn back the labium to expose the large, soft hypopharynx at its base (this projects into the buccal cavity and is probably sensory).

c. The 3 segments of the **thorax** have undergone an oblique twist to throw the sterna and legs forward (so that the prey can be held to the mouth while being torn to pieces by the mouth-parts), and the terga and wings backward. At the same time the terga and sterna have become reduced and the pleural sclerites greatly enlarged. Distinguish the small pronotum anteriorly, and the small meso- and metanota which lie between the bases of the wings. The pro- and meso-nota are widely separated by the meeting of two pleural sclerites in the centre line. Notice also that the space behind the metasternum is occupied by extra sternal sclerites, called the post-sterna. The 3 pairs of legs are attached to the 3 sterna. Each leg is spinous (it is not used for walking, but only for clinging or climbing, or for food capture), and consists of the usual joints with 3 tarsi, the distal of which bears 2 claws. The wings are large, strong, and all similar. There are two pairs of spiracles, the 1st between the pro- and meso-thorax, and the 2nd on the metathorax.

d. The **abdomen** has 10 complete segments, each with a large arched tergum and a narrow sternum. There is also a reduced 11th and a vestigial 12th segment, the latter being represented in both sexes by one dorsal (the tergum) and two latero-ventral (the divided sternum) laminae which surround the anus. Also in both sexes the 10th segment carries a pair of supra-anal appendages. In the pleural membranes of each of the segments 1 to 8 is a pair of spiracles.

e. In the **male** the supra-anal appendages are especially large (and act as claspers during copulation), and there is also an inferior anal appendage (the tergum of segment 11) based just dorsal to the anus (in the Zygoptera there are instead two inferior anal appendages based ventral to the anus ; they are outgrowths of the 11th sternum). The male ducts open separately through the 9th sternum, their openings being covered by a pair of small plates, the gonopods (which are not appendages, but are outgrowths of the 9th sternum), but the copulatory organs are on the 2nd sternum (to which spermatozoa are transferred prior to copulation). Examine the 2nd sternum to see the genital fossa within which lies the median penis (partly formed from the 3rd sternum), and lateral to which are an anterior pair of claspers, or hamuli (which grasp the ovipositor during copulation), and a posterior pair of genital lobes (both claspers and lobes are formed from the 2nd sternum).

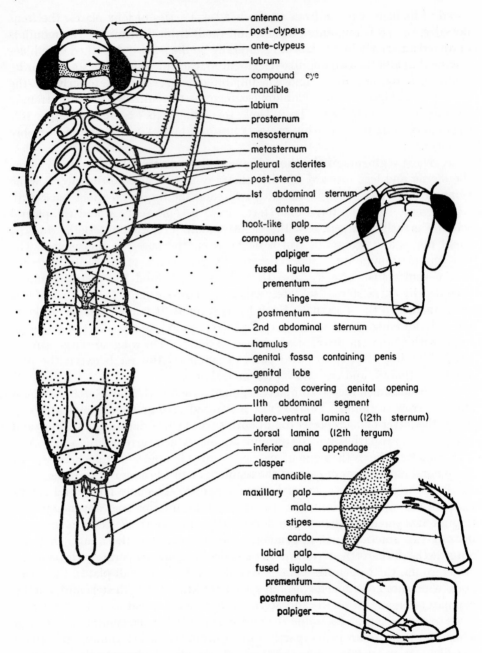

antenna
post-clypeus
ante-clypeus
labrum
compound eye
mandible
labium
prosternum
mesosternum
metasternum
pleural sclerites
post-sterna
1st abdominal sternum
antenna
hook-like palp
compound eye
palpiger
fused ligula
prementum
hinge
postmentum
2nd abdominal sternum
hamulus
genital fossa containing penis
genital lobe
gonopod covering genital opening
11th abdominal segment
latero-ventral lamina (12th sternum)
dorsal lamina (12th tergum)
inferior anal appendage
clasper
mandible
maxillary palp
mala
stipes
cardo
labial palp
fused ligula
prementum
postmentum
palpiger

FIG.100.—*Libellula*. A ventral view of a male (left), a ventral view of the head of a nymph (right), and details of the mouth-parts of an adult (lower right).

f. In the **female** the genital opening is on the 8th sternum and is flanked by two scale-like gonopods, which form a small ovipositor (they are probably not appendages, but are outgrowths of the 8th sternum).

g. Compare the external anatomy of the fully grown **nymph** with that of the adult. In the head the labium, or mask, is highly specialised by the lengthening of the pre- and post-menta and by the development of hook-like palps (by the sudden extension of this structure the prey is reached and is seized by the hooks). In the thorax the segmentation is clearer and the limbs longer (they have an autotomy joint between the femur and trochanter). In the abdomen the 10th segment carries a pair of short cercoids (which become the superior anal appendages); the 11th segment carries a median dorsal appendage (which in the male develops into the inferior anal appendage; in the female it disappears) and a pair of prominent cerci (which are missing in the adult); and the 12th segment is represented by the 3 anal laminae (as in the adult).

3. CONCLUSION

a. Observing the specimens, review the characteristics of the phylum, of the class, of the subclass, and of the order.

b. Review those special features of the imago which are associated with fast flight and predaceous habit.

4. REFERENCE

For details of the external and internal anatomy of this and of other genera, see :

TILLYARD, R. J. (1917). " The biology of dragonflies (Odonata or Paraneuroptera)." Cambridge.

4.25. Order **Hemiptera**

Characteristics : Exopterygota in which the head bears short antennae, and mouth-parts which lack palps and are modified for piercing and sucking, the labium forming a sheath in which the needle-like mandibles and maxillae work ; thorax usually with 2 pairs of wings, the anterior pair being the tougher ; abdomen lacking cerci, and with gonapophyses either well developed or reduced.

The bugs which compose this order are specialised primarily for sucking the sap of plants, but some families feed instead on the blood of animals. They are of great economic importance for the damage they cause and for the diseases they transmit. There are two suborders : the Homoptera, with the pronotum small and with uniformly horny forewings, and the Heteroptera, with the pronotum large and with only the bases of the forewings horny. Many of the Homoptera, as for example the parthenogenetic aphides, have an extraordinarily high rate of reproduction.

Genus **Cicada** (**Tibicen**)

1. GENERAL ACCOUNT

a. The species of this genus are the largest members of the suborder Homoptera, and they occur particularly in the forests of tropical, subtropical, and warmer temperate countries.

b. There is one British species occurring rarely in the New Forest, but the best-known species is *C. septemdecim* L. of North America. The eggs are laid in slits made in the twigs of trees, and the young nymphs, emerging several weeks later, fall to the ground. They spend their lives burrowing through the soil about a foot beneath the surface, using for this purpose their highly developed, powerful forelegs. They feed on sap sucked from the finer tree roots, and they grow for a period of from 13 years in the south of their range to 17 years in the north. The fully grown nymphs come to the surface in May, and climb up some tree-trunk or plant-stem before casting their skins for the last time. The adults have a fast direct flight, and the males produce an intense sound resembling the whine of a circular saw. They live for some 30 or 40 days, flying during the warmer part of the day and feeding on the sap of trees.

2. EXTERNAL ANATOMY

a. The body of the **imago** is clearly divisible into a head, thorax, and abdomen.

b. The **head** is broad, and carries prominent compound eyes laterally, three ocelli forming a triangle mid-dorsally, and two short antennae anteriorly. Between the antennae is the transversely ridged clypeus, ventral to which is the labrum, flanked by two plates, the lorae (which are extensions of the clypeus).

c. From beneath the labrum there project the long, narrow **mouth-parts**, which are carried flexed under the thorax. The most obvious of these is the long, jointed rostrum (the modified labium of segment 6), which has an open groove along its morphologically dorsal side. Using a needle point, ease the other mouth-parts out of this groove. The outer and stouter are the mandibles (segment 4), which, distally, are serrated on their outer edges (for cutting into twigs to obtain the sap). Each mandible is grooved internally, and into these grooves fits the pair of maxillae (these in turn are doubly grooved, so that when they are together two tubes are formed, the narrower being ventral for passing saliva outwards, and the wider being dorsal for sucking up the sap). Proximally, where it passes beneath the labrum, the labium is not grooved, and here a fine-pointed extension of the labrum, called the epipharynx, covers the bases of the mandibles and maxillae. Distally the labium bears tufts of setae (which are sensory).

d. Dorsally the 3 segments of the **thorax** are visible in the large pronotum and mesonotum and the small metanotum. Of the two pairs of wings, the anterior are larger and tougher. Ventrally the sterna are small but distinct,

and the metasternum has a backward projection, the post-sternum.   In the
males of many species (but not *C. septemdecim*) the post-sternum itself bears two
large, backward-directed projections, the opercula (which cover the sound-

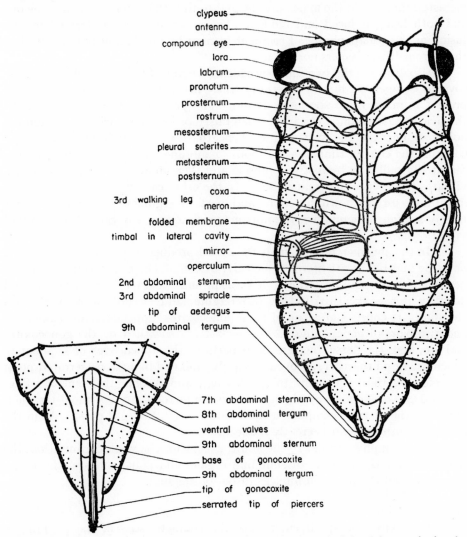

clypeus
antenna
compound eye
lora
labrum
pronotum
prosternum
rostrum
mesosternum
pleural sclerites
metasternum
poststernum
coxa
3rd walking leg
meron
folded membrane
timbal in lateral cavity
mirror
operculum
2nd abdominal sternum
3rd abdominal spiracle
tip of aedeagus
9th abdominal tergum

7th abdominal sternum
8th abdominal tergum
ventral valves
9th abdominal sternum
base of gonocoxite
9th abdominal tergum
tip of gonocoxite
serrated tip of piercers

FIG. 101.—*Cicada*.   A ventral view of a male, and of the posterior end of the abdomen of a female.

producing organs).   The legs have the usual number of joints, including 3
tarsi, and the coxae of the last pair each bears a posteriorly projecting meron.
Laterally, the pleural sclerites are prominent, and among them the 1st pair of
spiracles can be seen on the 1st segment, while the 2nd pair lies between the 2nd
and 3rd segments.

e. In the **abdomen** there are 10 segments, the first 8 each having a pair of spiracles. However, only 9 terga are visible dorsally, the tiny 10th being hidden beneath the 9th. Ventrally the 1st sternum is fused to the thoracic metasternum, and in the **male** only the 2nd to the 8th sterna are visible, the 9th and 10th being reduced and hidden. The aedeagus (a penis formed by the fusion of the gonapophyses of segment 9) may be protruding posteriorly, but there are neither claspers nor cerci.

f. Also examine the two **sound-producing organs** of the male, which may be covered by opercula hinged anteriorly (these are absent in *C. septemdecim*, but present in many other species). Remove an operculum (which is part of the thoracic metasternum, and which, when raised or lowered, varies the volume of noise) to uncover the two cavities beneath it. The smaller lateral cavity contains the convex timbal (a chitinous membrane, part of segment 2, which, repeatedly pulled in by a strong muscle and then allowed to spring out again, vibrates to produce the great noise). In the other cavity is an anterior folded membrane (of unknown function, and part of segment 1) and a posterior tightly stretched membrane, the mirror (which apparently can perceive sound vibrations).

g. In the **abdomen of the female** the sound-producing organs are absent, and only the 2nd to the 7th sterna are clearly visible. The 8th sternum is hidden beneath the 7th, and posterior to it is the prominent ovipositor. Dorsally and laterally this is sheathed by the 9th tergum, and laterally also by the 9th sternum. It consists of a pair of stout gonocoxites (appendages of segment 9) and two pairs of gonapophyses. These last are sheathed by the gonocoxites and are, first, the dorsal piercers (also parts of the appendages of segment 9) which are fused together, grooved ventrally, and end in a strong serrated point (for piercing the twigs prior to egg laying), and second, the ventral valves (appendages of segment 8) which underlie the piercers, are not fused together, and with the piercers complete a tube (down which the eggs pass). As in the male, the 10th segment is greatly reduced.

h. The **nymph** is similar to the adult, except for the weak chitinisation, the reduced eyes, the absence of sounding organs and gonapophyses, the larger antennae, and the powerful forelegs (used for digging).

3. CONCLUSION

a. Observing the specimen, review the characteristics of the phylum, of the class, of the subclass, and of the order.

4. REFERENCES

BALFOUR–BROWNE, F. (1932). "A text-book of practical entomology." London.
SNODGRASS, R. E. (1921–27). "The head and mouth parts of the *Cicada*." *Proceedings of the Entomological Society of Washington*, Vol. 23, p. 1; Vol. 29, p. 1.

Genus **Cimex** (bed bug)

I. GENERAL ACCOUNT

a. This important genus belongs to the suborder Heteroptera, but it is not typical, since it is practically wingless. It includes the almost cosmopolitan species *C. lectularius* L., as well as the more tropical *C. rotundatus* Sign., both of which are similar in habits and structure. They are parasites of man, and have been carried by him all over the world, but they have many alternative hosts, including such domestic animals as mice, rats, guinea-pigs, rabbits, cats, and dogs. They may also feed on bats, sparrows, and swallows. They often abound in dirty crowded houses, particularly in the bedrooms, where they remain hidden by day and emerge to feed at night. In warm houses breeding continues throughout the year. The development of the embryos has already begun before the eggs are laid in crevices, often of bedsteads, and they hatch in a week or two, depending on the temperature. Also depending on the temperature, growth, involving five moults, may be completed in seven weeks or take longer than a year. They are capable of surviving a period of at least six months without food.

2. EXTERNAL ANATOMY

a. The **body** is strongly flattened dorso-ventrally (to allow a firmer grip of the host by night, and an easier retreat into crevices by day). It is divided into a small head and a clearly segmented thorax and abdomen. The posterior end of the abdomen is rounded in the female and bluntly pointed in the male.

b. The **head** bears compound eyes laterally, and consists of the usual 6 segments, of which the 2nd carries the slender 5-jointed antennae. The 4th, 5th, and 6th segments bear the mandibles, maxillae, and labium respectively, and these are together modified to form a proboscis, which projects back as far as the bases of the 1st pair of walking legs. Anterior to the base of the proboscis is the labrum, while anterior to this, and extending on to the top of the head, is the clypeus.

c. To see the **mouth-parts**, examine a preparation of a head which has been cleared in potash (see method on p. 334). The jointed labium is deeply grooved to contain externally the two, fine, blade-like mandibles with serrated tips (for piercing the skin), and internally the two stouter maxillae which, when closely apposed, form two tubes (down the ventral tube flows the saliva, while up the dorsal tube passes the food).

d. The **thorax** has a large pronotum with lateral expansions which turn forward alongside the head. The mesonotum is small, and carries the pair of elytra which overlap the small metanotum (these elytra are the basal regions of the 1st pair of wings, the 2nd pair being entirely absent). Ventrally are the pro-, meso-, and meta-sterna, but there are only two pairs of pleural sclerites

which belong to the meso- and meta-thorax.   There are also two pairs of lateral
spiracles.   The legs are all similar, with the usual structure, the tarsus being 3-
jointed and bearing two hooks distally.

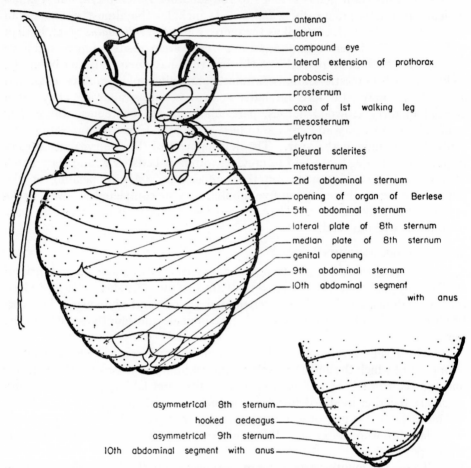

antenna
labrum
compound eye
lateral extension of prothorax
proboscis
prosternum
coxa of 1st walking leg
mesosternum
elytron
pleural sclerites
metasternum
2nd abdominal sternum
opening of organ of Berlese
5th abdominal sternum
lateral plate of 8th sternum
median plate of 8th sternum
genital opening
9th abdominal sternum
10th abdominal segment
with anus

asymmetrical 8th sternum
hooked aedeagus
asymmetrical 9th sternum
10th abdominal segment with anus

FIG. 102.—*Cimex*.   A ventral view of a female, and of the posterior end of the abdomen of a male.

e. Of the 10 segments of the **abdomen** only the 2nd to the 9th are easily
visible, and there are pairs of spiracles only on segments 2 to 8.   Segment 1 is
represented only by a tergum, which is almost indistinguishably fused to the
anterior edge of the 2nd tergum (it is more distinct in the nymph).   Segment 10
is tiny and surrounds the anus.   In the **male** the 8th and 9th sterna are asymmetrical, and from the left side of the 9th there protrudes the hooked aedeagus
(formed of the fused gonapophyses of segment 9 ; it is grooved, and assists in
passing spermatozoa to the female).   In the **female** there is a deep cleft on the
right side of the 5th sternum (this is the opening of the organ of Berlese, into

which spermatozoa are introduced by the aedeagus of the male; thence the spermatozoa bore their way into the haemocoel and pass via the blood-stream to the oviducts). The 8th sternum is divided into two pairs, and the 9th into one pair of plates, and between them in the middle line is the opening of the oviducts (there are two pairs of short gonapophyses, of which those of segment 8 may be partly visible).

f. The **nymph** is similar, but lacks the elytra and the aedeagus or gonapo·physes, and has a more distinct abdominal tergum.

3. CONCLUSION

a. Observing the specimen, review the characteristics of the phylum, of the class, of the subclass, and of the order.

b. Identify those special features which are associated with the ectoparasitic mode of life.

4. REFERENCES

For details of the external and internal anatomy, see :

LANDOIS, L. (1868–69). " Anatomie der Bettwanze (*Cimex lectularius*) mit Berüch‹ sichtigung verwandter Hemipterengeschlechter." *Zeitschrift für wissenschaftliche Zoologie*, Vol. 18, p. 206; and Vol. 19, p. 206.
MURRAY, C. H. (1914). " Notes on the anatomy of the bed-bug (*Acanthia*) *lectularia* L." *Parasitology*, Vol. 7, p. 278.
PATTON, W. S., and EVANS, A. M. (1929). " Insects, ticks, mites and venomous animals of medical and veterinary importance." London.

4.26. Order **Anoplura** (**Siphunculata**)

Characteristics : Dorso-ventrally flattened Exopterygota which are ectoparasitic on mammals; head with eyes reduced or absent, and with mouth-parts retractible into the head and modified for piercing and sucking; thorax wingless and with segments fused; and abdomen without cerci but with gonapophyses.

The sucking lice all feed on the blood of mammals, and attach their eggs to the hair fibres. Close host-parasite relationships have been demonstrated, these being determined mainly by the composition of the blood. They are highly important animals because of the many diseases which they are known to transmit.

Genus **Pediculus**

1. GENERAL ACCOUNT

a. The only species of this genus is *P. humanus* L., which is cosmopolitan. It is a common blood-sucking parasite of man, and it has also been found on some monkeys and apes. Two subspecies are recognised : *P. humanus capitis* de G., the head louse, and *P. humanus corporis* de G., the body louse. The first lives in, and lays its eggs on, the head hair, while the second is found more commonly in underclothing, laying its eggs either in the clothing or attached to body-hairs. The eggs hatch in about a week, and the nymphs undergo three ecdyses before reaching the adult stage in about a month. The species is of great importance, since it transmits more human diseases than any other insect. These include typhus, trench fever, and relapsing fever.

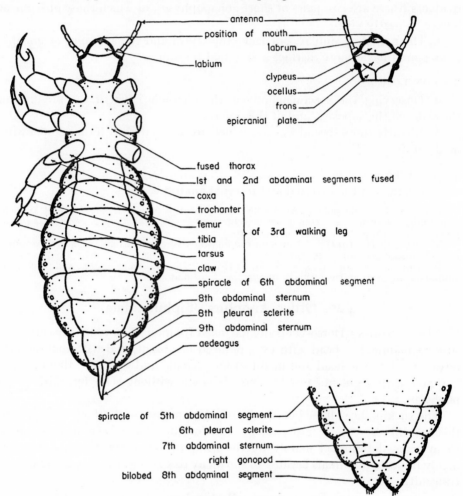

antenna
position of mouth
labrum
labium
clypeus
ocellus
frons
epicranial plate
fused thorax
1st and 2nd abdominal segments fused
coxa
trochanter
femur
tibia
tarsus
claw
} of 3rd walking leg
spiracle of 6th abdominal segment
8th abdominal sternum
8th pleural sclerite
9th abdominal sternum
aedeagus

spiracle of 5th abdominal segment
6th pleural sclerite
7th abdominal sternum
right gonopod
bilobed 8th abdominal segment

FIG.103.—*Pediculus.* A ventral view of a male, a dorsal view of the head, and a ventral view of the posterior end of the abdomen of a female.

2. EXTERNAL ANATOMY

a. The dorso-ventrally flattened **body** is divided into a small pointed head, a thorax bearing the legs, and a clearly segmented abdomen.

b. The **head** is covered dorsally by two epicranial plates, on which are based the two lateral ocelli. Anterior to this is a single plate, the frons, on which are based the antennae. Anterior again is the more strongly chitinised clypeus, and in front of this is the small labrum, which forms the upper edge of the terminal mouth. Ventrally the head is less strongly chitinised, and the lower edge of the mouth is formed by a plate, which may represent the labium. The mouth-parts are minute and highly modified (they are needle-like structures used for piercing and sucking, but when not in use they are retracted within the head ; there is no general agreement about their homologies, but it is thought that the mandibles may be absent).

c. In the **thorax** the 3 segments are indistinguishably fused, and there are no wings. The legs are all similar, each having the usual 5 joints. There is only one tarsal joint, and this bears a strong movable claw which works against a process of the tibia to form a chela-like structure (by which a firm grip of the hair can be maintained). There is a single pair of lateral spiracles between the bases of the 1st and 2nd pairs of legs.

d. The **abdomen** has 9 segments, of which the first two are fused together and the 9th is small. The terga, sterna, and pleural sclerites are clearly defined, the last being pierced by a pair of spiracular openings on each of segments 2 and 7. In the **male** the posterior end of the abdomen turns upwards so that the anus and genital opening are dorsally directed. A grooved and pointed aedeagus may be seen protruding from beneath the posterior edge of the 8th sternum. In the **female** the abdomen is wider, and its posterior end does not turn upwards. The 8th segment is bilobed, and ventrally, by the bases of these lobes, are the two gonopods (which are probably the gonapophyses of the reduced 9th segment ; they grasp the hair while the egg is being attached to it).

3. CONCLUSION

a. Observing the specimen, review the characteristics of the phylum, of the class, of the subclass, and of the order.

b. Distinguish those modifications which *Pediculus* has in common with *Cimex*.

4. REFERENCE

SIKORA, H. (1916). " Beiträge zur Anatomie, Physiologie und Biologie der Kleiderlaus (*Pediculus vestimenti* Nitzsch)." *Archiv für Schiffs- und Tropenhygiene*, Vol. 20, p. 3.

4.30. Subclass **Endopterygota (Holometabola)**

Characteristics : Insecta which develop wings internally, which pass through specialised larval and pupal stages, and which therefore undergo a complete metamorphosis.

4.31. Order **Trichoptera**

Characteristics : Endopterygota with mandibles vestigial or absent, but with well-developed maxillae and labium ; thorax with two pairs of membranous hairy wings which, when at rest, are held roof-like over the back ; larva aquatic, sometimes campodeiform and free-living, but commonly eruciform and living in artificial tubes gripped by the hooked caudal appendages ; pupa exarate and also aquatic.

Caddis flies are common, but usually nocturnal, in the vicinity of all kinds of fresh water. Some of their larvae inhabit swiftly running streams, others live in stagnant ponds and in lakes, while some are found in wet, mossy banks. A few have even colonised brackish or salt water. Many species are herbivorous, some are carnivorous, and a few, living in swift streams, spin open webs to snare the small organisms on which they feed. The trichopterans are closely related to the members of the suborder Homoneura of the Lepidoptera.

Genus **Phryganea**

I. GENERAL ACCOUNT

a. This genus, which contains the largest caddis flies, is widespread in the northern hemisphere, and closely related genera occur in the southern hemisphere. It is associated with the quiet waters of ditches, ponds, and lakes, where the female lays its eggs in gelatinous rings or ropes round the submerged stems of water plants. The larvae build their tubes of pieces of plant material neatly arranged in a spiral. They eat both vegetable and animal matter, and when fully grown they pupate inside their tubes, which are closed at both ends with a silken net through which the water can flow. After a few weeks, the pupa cuts the net with its mandibles, swims to the water surface, and splits along its back to release the imago. This happens in spring, and the life cycle takes a year.

2. EXTERNAL ANATOMY

a. In the **imago** the head, thorax, and abdomen are easily distinguished. Notice also the characteristic roof-like resting position of the wings.

b. Anteriorly on the **head** are the long, many-jointed antennae. Posterior to their bases are the prominent compound eyes, between which, dorsally, are 3 large ocelli. The clypeus protects the front of the head, and ventral to it is the narrow labrum. Of the feeble mouth-parts, the mandibles are vestigial, the reduced maxillae each possesses a free lobe, ormala, and a large palp, and the reduced labium carries two palps.

c. In the **thorax** the 1st segment is short and ring-like, with the pronotum, prosternum, and pleural sclerites reduced. In contrast, the mesothorax is large, is encased in stronger sclerites, and carries the 1st pair of wings. The metathorax is similar, but shorter, and carries the smaller hindwings. The legs are long, with powerful coxae and 5-jointed tarsi. Each of the coxae of the last two pairs of legs is subdivided to form a lateral meron.

d. The **abdomen** consists of 10 segments, but the 1st sternum is lacking

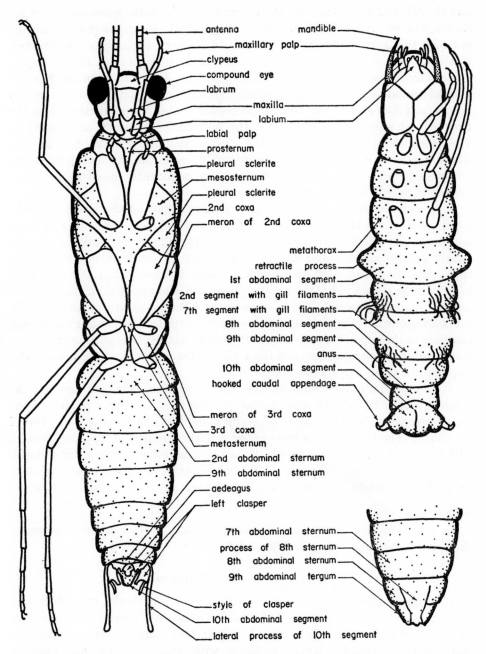

antenna
mandible
maxillary palp
clypeus
compound eye
labrum
maxilla
labium
labial palp
prosternum
pleural sclerite
mesosternum
pleural sclerite
2nd coxa
meron of 2nd coxa

metathorax
retractile process
1st abdominal segment
2nd segment with gill filaments
7th segment with gill filaments
8th abdominal segment
9th abdominal segment
anus
10th abdominal segment
hooked caudal appendage

meron of 3rd coxa
3rd coxa
metasternum
2nd abdominal sternum
9th abdominal sternum
aedeagus
left clasper

7th abdominal sternum
process of 8th sternum
8th abdominal sternum
9th abdominal tergum

style of clasper
10th abdominal segment
lateral process of 10th segment

FIG. 104.—*Phryganea*.   A ventral view of a male (left), of a larva (right), and of the posterior end of the abdomen of a female (lower right).

U

and the 9th and 10th segments are reduced. In the **male** segments 2 to 8 are simple, but the reduced 9th segment bears a single aedeagus (formed by the union of two gonapophyses), and a pair of claspers, each with a bifurcated, toothed, basal coxite and a slender distal style (the form of these claspers varies greatly in different species and genera). The 10th segment has the form of a small process (which also varies greatly between different species and genera, and may bear short terminal processes), and to it apparently belong the two long, slender, lateral processes (the homologies of which are doubtful). The abdomen of the **female** is simple and lacks gonapophyses, but the 8th sternum bears a curious backward-directed process, the 9th and 10th sterna are missing, and the 9th and 10th terga are apparently fused to form the bilobed plate which overhangs the anus.

e. Notice the spiral structure and vegetable nature of the protective tube which encloses the **larva**. Both ends of the tube are open, the wider end being anterior. Extract the larva and notice that the chitinised head bears ocelli, clearly defined clypeus and labrum, very short antennae, strong mandibles, simple maxillae with short palps, and a simple labium with a short terminal lobe. In the thorax only the pro- and meso-nota, their related pleural sclerites, and the legs are chitinised. The 10 segments of the abdomen are unchitinised, the 1st bearing one dorsal and two lateral retractile papillae (for holding the animal centrally in the tube), the 2nd to the 8th bearing filamentous gills (over which a water current is maintained), and the 10th bearing two hooked appendages (for gripping the tube) and the slit-like anus.

f. In a **pupa** removed from its case notice the feeble chitinisation and the combination of larval and adult features. The head is similar to that of the imago except for the presence of powerful mandibles (for cutting a way out of the tube). The thorax bears free appendages, the 2nd pair of legs being fringed with bristles (to form an oar by which the pupa can swim to the water surface). The abdomen still bears the larval gills, but genitalia are also present and there are specialised hooks dorsally (which help the pupa to wriggle from its tube).

3. CONCLUSION

a. Observing the specimens, review the characteristics of the phylum, of the class, of the subclass, and of the order.

4.32. Order **Lepidoptera**

Characteristics : Endopterygota in which the head lacks mandibles and bears a sucking proboscis formed of modified maxillae ; thorax with two pairs of membranous wings, which, like the whole body, are closely covered with tiny, flattened scales ; larva eruciform with well-developed mandibles, 3 pairs of true legs on the thorax, and up to 5 pairs of prolegs on the abdomen ; pupa obtect.

The butterflies, with antennae clubbed, and the moths, with antennae tapering, form a well-known, homogeneous, and easily recognised order. The adults all have similar habits, feeding by day or by night on nectar or fruit-juices. The larvae are nearly all herbivorous, feeding on leaves, wood, or grain. However, a few feed on woollen materials, and others are predaceous, some living in the nests of ants or bees and feeding on the larvae.

Genus **Pieris** (cabbage butterfly)

I. GENERAL ACCOUNT

a. The genus *Pieris* is common and cosmopolitan, having been taken by man into previously uncolonised parts of the southern hemisphere. Larger species, such as *P. brassica* L., should be examined if available, but the most widespread species is probably *P. rapae* L., which is on the wing throughout the summer. The eggs are laid on cruciferous plants, and particularly on the cabbage, into the compact heart of which the larvae eat their way. When fully grown after four ecdyses, they wander away in search of a sheltered place to pupate. This they do after supporting themselves posteriorly on a small silken pad, and spinning round the thorax a slender silken girdle. The winter is spent in the pupal stage, and there may be two generations during the summer.

2 EXTERNAL ANATOMY

a. The head, thorax, and abdomen of the **imago** are clearly separable, and they are covered by thousands of fine scales, many of which are hair-like. Where these scales obscure details of the anatomy they should be scraped away.

b. Through a strong lens or binocular microscope examine the **head**. Dorsally it is covered by the epicranium, lateral to which are the two large compound eyes, and on the anterior edge of which are based the many-jointed antennae. Anterior to the epicranium is the fronto-clypeus (formed by the fusion of frons and clypeus), and in front of this is the small labrum. On the tip of the labrum is the tiny triangular epipharynx, which overlies the base of the long coiled proboscis. The proboscis is formed of the greatly elongated galeae of the maxillae, which are grooved internally, and hooked together along their lengths (to form a tube up which nectar is sucked). The other joints of the maxillae, including the palp, are greatly reduced. Mandibles are absent, but the labium is visible as a small plate ventral to the head, and it carries prominent 3-jointed palps. The head is hollowed ventrally to accommodate the coiled proboscis, the sides of the cavity being formed by the genal plates, which also extend upwards between the compound eyes and the fronto-clypeus.

c. In the **thorax** the 1st segment is reduced to a narrow collar, but the mesothorax, which bears the 1st and larger pair of wings, is particularly well

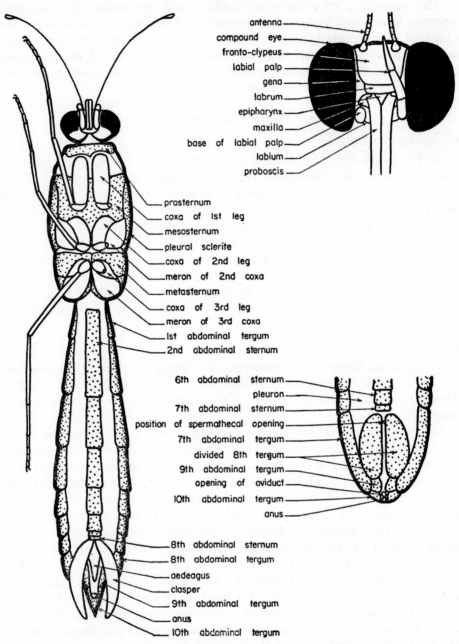

FIG. 105.—*Pieris.* Ventral views of a male and of the posterior end of the abdomen of a female, and an anterior view of the head from which the right labial palp has been removed.

developed, with a prominent mesonotum and mesosternum. The meta-thorax, which bears the hindwings, is smaller, and the metasternum is tiny. Notice how, even when extended, the forewings overlap the hindwings (so that they beat and act as one pair). Through a microscope examine the form of the scales which cover the wings. The legs have long coxae (which move little, but help to protect the ventral surface). Each of the coxae of the two hinder pairs of legs is subdivided to form a lateral meron. The trochanter, femur, tibia, and 5-jointed tarsus are slender, and there are two terminal claws. The thorax bears two pairs of spiracles.

d. The **abdomen** consists of 10 segments, of which the 1st to the 7th tergum and the 2nd to the 7th sternum are easily distinguished. The 1st sternum is represented only by a thin membrane. A pair of spiracles is present on each of the first 7 segments (the 8th, present in the larva, aborts in the adult). In the **male** the 9th segment, which is partly withdrawn inside the 8th, bears the two large claspers and a median aedeagus (formed of fused gonapophyses). Dorsal to the aedeagus is the anus, above which the terga of segments 9 and 10 form a pointed process (the 9th and 10th sterna are lacking).

e. In the **abdomen of the female** the 7th tergum is especially large, and the 8th to the 10th sterna are not developed. The 8th tergum is divided into two hinged plates which meet in the mid-ventral line, and which lie ventral to the 7th tergum. The 9th tergum is also developed into two large ventral plates, each bearing two bristle-covered processes, which lie hidden beneath the 8th tergum (the function of these processes is apparently unknown). However, the two plates of the 9th tergum maintain a slender connexion dorsally, as do also the two parts of the 10th tergum. A spermathecal opening (into which spermatozoa are introduced) is mid-ventral between the anterior ends of the 8th and 9th tergal plates, while the opening of the oviduct is mid-ventral between the 10th tergal plates and is immediately anterior to the anus.

f. In the **larva** distinguish the small head, the 3 segments of the thorax, and the 10 segments of the abdomen. In the head notice the dorsal epicranial plates, each with lateral groups of ocelli; the frons, clypeus, and labrum anteriorly; the 3-jointed antennae and powerful mandibles; and the short maxillae and the labium, each of which have a tiny palp. On the thorax are the 3 pairs of squat, 5-jointed legs, the tarsus of each bearing a single claw, while on the prothorax is a pair of spiracles. Of the 10 abdominal segments, the first 8 bear pairs of spiracles, and the 3rd to the 6th and the 10th each carries a pair of fleshy prolegs with flattened bases surrounded by rings of chitinous crochets.

g. The **pupa** more closely resembles the adult. Since the limbs are fused to the body, it is obtect, but the limb outlines can be clearly distinguished. Of the 10 abdominal segments, only the posterior are movable, and the last ends in a small process, the cremaster (by which the pupa is attached to the silken supporting pad).

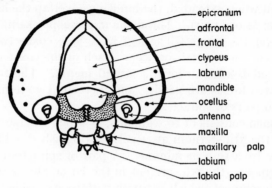

epicranium
adfrontal
frontal
clypeus
labrum
mandible
ocellus
antenna
maxilla
maxillary palp
labium
labial palp

FIG. 106.—*Pieris*.   An anterior view of the head of the larva.

3. CONCLUSION

a. Observing the specimens, review the characteristics of the phylum, of the class, of the subclass, and of the order.

b. Compare the structure of *Pieris* with that of *Phryganea*.

4.33.   Order **Coleoptera**

Characteristics : Endopterygota in which the head bears biting mouth-parts ; thorax with a large movable prothorax, with the anterior wings modified as horny elytra, and with the posterior wings large and membranous, or reduced, or absent ; larva campodeiform, eruciform, or apodous ; pupa exarate.

The beetles form the largest order of the arthropods, and perhaps also of the animal kingdom, and they include species which are terrestrial, aerial, aquatic, and even littoral.   The order is relatively modern, and has specialised in the development of a solid integument of strong, close-fitting sclerites.   The larvae also have diverse habits, but most commonly they feed on rotting organic matter of all kinds.

Genus **Melolontha** (cockchafer)

(Alternatives, differing only in detail, are *Phyllophaga* or *Lachnosterna*, which are the May and June beetles of North America, and such other members of the family Scarabaeidae as *Cetonia*, the rosechafer, *Scarabaeus*, the scarab, and *Geotrupes*, the dor beetle.)

I. GENERAL ACCOUNT

a. The species *Melolontha vulgaris* L. is a widespread and common pest in Europe (while *Phyllophaga* is an equally common pest in America).   The adults appear above ground in May and June, and feed by night, particularly on the leaves of the oak.   The eggs are laid in groups of 15 to 20 some 6 inches beneath the ground, and they hatch in about three weeks.   The larvae burrow to feed on the roots of such plants as grass and corn, and they grow for from two to four years, according to the temperature.   In the winter they dig deeper for protection.   On the average they pupate in their third summer in oval cells constructed about 2 feet below the suface.   The adults emerge from the pupae in October, but they remain in the ground until the following spring.

2.   EXTERNAL ANATOMY

a. Examine the compact and sturdy body of the **imago**, which is divided into a head, a thorax, and an abdomen, and is protected dorsally by the horny elytra.

b. The **head** is flexed ventrally, and on its sides are the large, compound eyes.   Dorsally it is particularly strongly chitinised, so that no sutures are visible, but anteriorly the clypeus and smaller labrum are distinct.   Ventrally, behind the eyes, the genae are also distinct, and are separated by the gula. The first head appendages are the antennae (segment 2), the distal joints of which are modified to form a series of overlapping plates, which are larger in the male than in the female.   The mandibles are well developed, with serrated biting edges.   Each maxilla has a basal cardo, and a stipes, which bears externally a 4-jointed palp and internally a strongly chitinised, mandible-like lobe, the lacinia.   The labium, anterior to the gula, consists of a basal mentum and a distal ligula, which carries the two 3-jointed labial palps (and with which the palpigers are fused).

c. In the **thorax** the 1st segment is distinct and movable.   It consists of the strongly chitinised pronotum, pleural sclerites, and prosternum, which are firmly fused together.   Notice how the coxae of the 1st walking legs fit closely into deep grooves.   The meso- and meta-thoracic segments are fused together, the former bearing the horny elytra and the latter the membranous wings. Detach the elytra and wings to see the subdivisions of the small mesonotum and of the large metanotum into a central scutellum and two lateral scuta. In the metanotum each scutum is subdivided into two plates.   In both segments there is also a small prescutum in front of the scutellum, but it is hidden beneath the tergum in front.   In the metanotum there is also a posterior transverse plate, the postnotum, which curves forwards near the centre line to disappear beneath the scutellum.   Notice laterally the several pleural sclerites, and ventrally the pro- and meso-sterna and the large metasternal plates. There is a pair of spiracles between the pro- and meso-thorax, and another on the metathorax.   The legs have the usual series of joints with 5-jointed tarsi.

d. In the **abdomen** 7 sterna and 8 terga are visible (although there is some disagreement, it is generally considered that 10 abdominal segments are typical of the Coleoptera, but they are not easily demonstrated in the imago).   The

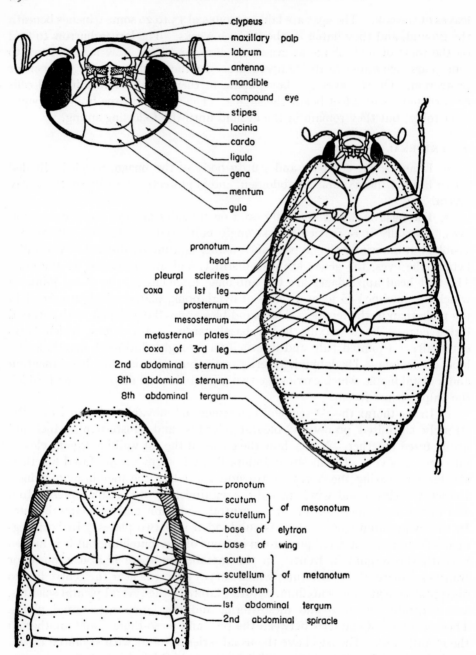

clypeus
maxillary palp
labrum
antenna
mandible
compound eye
stipes
lacinia
cardo
ligula
gena
mentum
gula

pronotum
head
pleural sclerites
coxa of 1st leg
prosternum
mesosternum
metasternal plates
coxa of 3rd leg
2nd abdominal sternum
8th abdominal sternum
8th abdominal tergum

pronotum
scutum
scutellum } of mesonotum
base of elytron
base of wing
scutum
scutellum } of metanotum
postnotum
1st abdominal tergum
2nd abdominal spiracle

FIG. 107.—*Melolontha*.   Ventral views of the head and of the body, and a dorsal view of the thorax and anterior abdominal region.

sternum of the 1st segment is lacking, and that of the 2nd is divided by the backgrowth of the coxae of the 3rd walking legs.   There is a pair of spiracles laterally on each of the first 8 segments.   The posterior abdominal segments are reduced, and are withdrawn within the anterior segments to form a cavity (into which the reproductive system opens).   In the **male** the chitinous aedeagus (formed of the partly fused gonapophyses of segment 9) is hidden within this cavity, and can be dissected out by the removal of the 7th and 8th sterna. In the **female** it is the retracted segments alone which form a tubular ovipositor.

e. The **larva** has a small head, a thorax of 3 segments with 3 pairs of walking legs, and a long, limbless abdomen.   The head lacks eyes and has unusually large mandibles ; the thorax is weakly chitinised, but the legs are stout and hairy, and each has an unjointed tarses ending in a single claw ; and the abdomen has 10 segments, the first 8 of which bear prominent spiracles.

f. The **pupa** has the wings and limbs free, and is therefore exarate.   In it can be seen the beginnings of the adult form, but the hindwings are lacking and in the abdomen the 10 segments are easily visible.

3.   CONCLUSION

a. Observing the specimens, review the characteristics of the phylum, of the class, of the subclass, and of the order.

4.34.   Order **Hymenoptera**

Characteristics : Endopterygota in which the head bears mouth-parts modified for biting and often also for sucking ; thorax with two pairs of membranous wings interlocked by hooklets ; abdomen with the 1st segment fused to the metathorax, commonly with a narrow waist, and always in the female with a specialised ovipositor formed of 3 pairs of gonapophyses ; larva usually apodous but sometimes eruciform ; pupa exarate.

This large and diverse order contains the bees, wasps, sawflies, ichneumon flies, and ants, and includes the most highly specialised social insects and the most highly developed insect parasites.   Parthenogenesis is common, and associated with parasitism is polyembryony.

Genus **Apis** (hive or honey bee)

I.   GENERAL ACCOUNT

a. The best-known species is *A. mellifica* L., which has been cultivated for its honey and introduced into every part of the world.   A colony contains between 50,000 and 100,000 individuals.   One of these is a functional female, or queen, which lays the eggs, some are the males, or drones, but most are sterile females, or workers.   These last build the nest, gather nectar, fruit juices, and pollen for food, and care for the larvae.   The central feature of the nest is the honeycomb, a vertically hanging sheet formed of a double layer of hexagonal cells placed back to back. The comb is made of wax secreted from the abdominal sterna of young workers. The cells vary in size, being small for the production of workers, larger for the drones, and largest for the queens, and into each the queen lays an egg. Many cells are also made for the storage of honey. Apparently, unfertilised eggs produce the drones, and fertilised eggs the queens and workers. Eggs hatch in about 3 days, and the larvae are fed on a pharyngeal secretion of the workers. The future queens are given this secretion throughout their development, but the drones and workers receive it only for 4 days, after which they are given honey and partly digested pollen. When fully grown they are sealed within their cells, and they pupate. The adult queen may live for several years, but when overcrowding occurs she is driven out, together with a swarm of workers and drones, to start a new hive. A newly hatched queen then takes her place after a short nuptial flight. At the most, the drones live only until the autumn, when they are driven out by the workers to die. In the summer workers live for about five weeks, but those which emerge in the autumn survive in a torpid state until the spring, when they again become active.

2. EXTERNAL ANATOMY

a. Examine first a **worker** (sterile female), noticing the usual subdivisions of the body, the head, thorax, and abdomen.

b. Detach the **head**, which is roughly triangular and is flattened from front to back. Dorso-laterally are the large, compound eyes, dorsally between them are 3 ocelli, and anteriorly are the antennae. The sclerites are obscure, but the top of the head is called the epicranial region, between the ocelli and the antennal bases is the frontal region, and beneath the eyes is the genal region. The clypeus and labrum are distinct, and ventral to the latter is the soft, triangular epipharynx. Behind the labrum are the powerful mandibles, and behind them is the proboscis composed of the maxillae and the labium.

c. Detach the **proboscis** at its base, which is in a deep groove beneath the head. Each maxilla consists of a slender basal cardo and a stouter stipes, which carries externally a tiny palp and internally a long, blade-like galea. The labium consists of a small triangular submentum, braced to the maxillae by a transverse bar, the lorum, and a stout mentum. Externally on the mentum are two palpigers, each with a labial palp, while internally are the short paraglossae and the long glossa, or tongue (actually formed of two glossae fused), on the tip of which is a small lobe, the labellum (nectar and honey flow up a ventral groove in the glossa, and so pass to the mouth via the space between the galeae).

d. The **thoracic region** contains not only pro-, meso-, and meta-thoracic segments, but also the 1st abdominal segment, the propodeum. The pro-

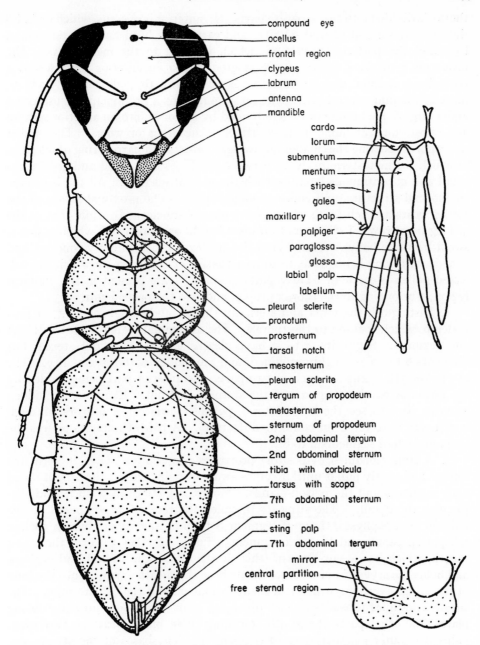

compound eye
ocellus
frontal region
clypeus
labrum
antenna
mandible

cardo
lorum
submentum
mentum
stipes
galea
maxillary palp
palpiger
paraglossa
glossa
labial palp
labellum
pleural sclerite
pronotum
prosternum
tarsal notch
mesosternum
pleural sclerite
tergum of propodeum
metasternum
sternum of propodeum
2nd abdominal tergum
2nd abdominal sternum
tibia with corbicula
tarsus with scopa
7th abdominal sternum
sting
sting palp
7th abdominal tergum
mirror
central partition
free sternal region

FIG. 108.—*Apis*. An anterior view of the head and a ventral view of the body of a worker, and, on the right, details of the mouth-parts and of an abdominal sternum.

thorax is divided into two separate parts : an anterior propectus, which includes the prosternum and pleural sclerites and carries the head and the 1st pair of legs, and the posterior pronotum, which is fused to the mesothorax. The pronotum is divided by a transverse groove into an anterior scutum and a posterior scutellum, and its outer edges pass down the sides of the body to meet in the mid-ventral line. The mesothorax has a prominent mesosternum and a large domed mesonotum subdivided by a groove into an anterior scutum and a posterior scutellum. To it are attached the larger forewings. The smaller metathorax, bearing the smaller hindwings, consists of a narrow ring of sclerites, of which the metasternum, lying between the bases of the 2nd and 3rd legs, is small and is continuous laterally with the pleural sclerites. All the legs have the normal structure, and end in 5-jointed tarsi. The proximal tarsus of the 1st leg bears a notch (with which the antennae are cleaned), while that of the 3rd leg bears rows of stiff hairs forming a brush, or scopa (with which pollen is swept from the body). The tibia of the 3rd leg is broad, slightly concave, and fringed with long hairs, so as to form a basket, or corbicula (in which the collected pollen is carried). Three pairs of spiracles are present in the thoracic region, 2 belonging to the thorax proper, and 1 to the propodeum.

e. Distinguish the terga and sterna of the 1st abdominal segment, or propodeum, which is fused to the thorax. The **abdominal region** begins with the 2nd segment. Segments 2 to 7 have clearly visible terga and sterna, but segments 8 to 10 are highly modified, and are hidden within segment 7. The 4th to the 7th sterna are each in two parts, the anterior part being hidden by the posterior overlapping part of the sternum in front. Examine the hidden anterior part to see the large, lateral, polished surfaces, or mirrors (through which wax is secreted for comb manufacture). A pair of spiracles pierces the terga of each of segments 2 to 8.

f. A **sting** (modified ovipositor) protrudes posteriorly. Grip it with fine forceps and gently pull it until it comes away, bringing with it the 8th, 9th, and 10th segments and the poison-glands. Mount the sting on a slide and distinguish the details. The sting itself, called the terebra, is composed of two pairs of gonapophyses, those of segment 8 forming the stylets (which enclose the poison canal) and those of segment 9 fusing together to form the stylet sheath, which has a saw-like tip (this sheath makes the wound and encloses and holds the stylets in position). At its base the sheath expands into the bulb of the sting, overlying which is a membranous part of the 9th sternum. The sheath continues forwards as two diverging arms which join into the oblong plates (the other parts of the 9th sternum); these plates bear the two sting-palps (the outer gonapophyses of segment 9). The bases of the stylets also diverge to join into the fulcral plates (the 8th sternum ; the 8th tergum is obscure). The other large plates, the quadrate plates, are formed from the 9th tergum. Notice the large poison sac, into which open two thread-like acid glands and an unpaired alkaline gland (the injected poison is a mixture of the two secretions). The 10th segment is largely membranous, lies dorsal to the sting, and carries the terminal anus.

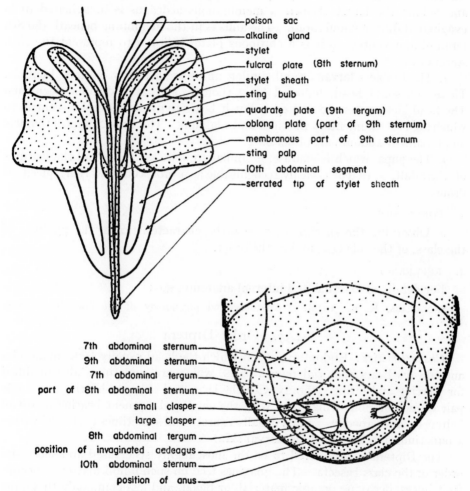

poison   sac
alkaline   gland
stylet
fulcral   plate   (8th   sternum)
stylet   sheath
sting   bulb
quadrate   plate   (9th   tergum)
oblong   plate   (part   of   9th   sternum)
membranous   part   of   9th   sternum
sting   palp
10th   abdominal   segment
serrated   tip   of   stylet   sheath

7th   abdominal   sternum
9th   abdominal   sternum
7th   abdominal   tergum
part   of   8th   abdominal   sternum
small   clasper
large   clasper
8th   abdominal   tergum
position   of   invaginated   aedeagus
10th   abdominal   sternum
position   of   anus

FIG. 109.—*Apis.* Details of the sting of a worker, and a ventral view of the posterior end of the abdomen of a drone.

g. Examine a female, or **queen**, noticing its larger size but general similarity with the structure of the worker. Here also the ovipositor is modified as a sting, and the posterior abdominal segments are like those of the worker.

h. Examine a male, or **drone**. It is larger than the worker, and is different in several details. The head bears much larger eyes, which touch each other dorsally. There is no sting, and therefore segments 8 and 9 are not so specialised.   The 8th tergum is visible, but the 8th sternum is almost completely hidden within the 7th.   The 9th and 10th terga are membranous, but the 9th sternum is well developed, and bears two pairs of claspers laterally (these are derived from the original single pair of appendages of segment 9).   Between and behind the larger claspers a membranous aedeagus is invaginated (it is evaginated during copulation).   The anus is in the membrane beneath the 8th tergum, and ventral to it is a chitinous plate (believed to represent the 10th sternum).

i. The limbless **larvae** are all similar, and have a poorly chitinised cuticle. There is a small head, followed by 3 thoracic and 10 abdominal segments. The head lacks antennae and eyes, but it bears toothed mandibles, ventral to which are two rudimentary maxillae and a labium.   There are 2 pairs of thoracic and 8 pairs of abdominal spiracles.

j. The **pupa**, which is exarate, is similar to, and has almost all the features of, the adult, so that it is easily recognisable as a prospective worker, queen, or drone.

3.   CONCLUSION

a. Observing the specimens, review the characteristics of the phylum, of the class, of the subclass, and of the order.

4.   REFERENCE

For details of external and internal anatomy, see :

SNODGRASS, R. E. (1925).   "Anatomy and physiology of the honeybee."   New York.

4.35.   Order **Diptera**

Characteristics : Endopterygota in which the head usually lacks mandibles and always bears suctorial mouth-parts, which are sometimes also modified for piercing and biting ; thorax with the large 2nd segment bearing the single pair of membranous wings, and with the small 3rd segment bearing a pair of halteres ; larva apodous ; pupa usually exarate and sometimes protected within a puparium, the hardened last larval skin.

The Diptera is considered to be the most highly specialised and successful order of the class Insecta.   The imagines feed on such liquid matter as nectar, fruit-juices, decaying organic material, or blood, and less commonly they prey upon other insects.   Many of the blood-sucking forms are of medical or veterinary importance, since they are the carriers of a variety of virulent diseases. The larvae feed on plants, organic débris, or carrion, and some are parasitic.

Genus **Culex** (mosquito)

I.   GENERAL ACCOUNT

a. The mosquitoes of this genus, and of closely related genera of the family Culicidae, such as *Anopheles*, have a world-wide distribution.   They are abundant in the tropics at all times, and in temperate and arctic regions during the summer. The normal food of both sexes is nectar and other plant juices, and only the female has mouth-parts modified for obtaining additional meals of mammalian blood. The eggs are usually laid at night, and they float in raft-like groups of about 50 on the surface of stagnant water. The larvae hatch into the water through the lower ends of the eggs, and they feed on microscopic organic débris and on algae, which are passed to the mouth by the beating of bunches of thoracic bristles. When at rest they hang head downwards from the surface film through which they breathe air. The pupae can swim actively, and when at rest they also float at the water surface to obtain air. In summer the whole life-cycle may be passed within three weeks if the temperature is high enough, but it may also take as long as two months. The winter is passed either in the larval form or in hibernation in the adult form.

2. EXTERNAL ANATOMY

a. In a permanent preparation of an **imago** distinguish through a micro-scope the head, thorax, and abdomen.

b. The **head** is highly mobile on a slender neck, its most prominent features being the black compound eyes, which are so large that they almost touch each other. Anterior to these are the antennae, each with two large basal joints, the narrow scape and the globular torus (which contains Johnston's organ, a sensory structure of unknown function), and many smaller distal joints, each bearing a ring of setae, which are longer and more numerous in the male. The clypeus extends forwards from between the eyes, and articulating with it is a long labrum-epipharynx.

c. The labrum-epipharynx and the **mouth-parts** have the form of a proboscis with associated palps. The proboscis sheath (up the cavity of which the liquid food is sucked) consists dorsally of the long, pointed, ventrally grooved labrum-epipharynx, and ventrally of the equally long, but dorsally grooved, labium, which ends in a pair of labella (reduced labial palps which are tactile). In the female the tube so formed contains two long mandibles, which are extremely fine, needle-like structures with saw edges to their tips, and two similar but stouter galeae (highly modified distal joints of the maxillae), also with saw edges to their tips (the mandibles and galeae work together when piercing the epidermis of the prey). Also within the sheath is a long, pointed hypopharynx with a fine longitudinal groove (along which saliva flows to prevent coagulation of the blood). The only other mouth-parts are the maxillary palps. In the male (which does not suck blood) the labrum-epipharynx and labium are similar, but the mandibles and galeae are short and the functionless hypopharynx is fused to the labium.

d. In the **thorax** the 1st segment is small, the 2nd large, and the 3rd of medium size. The wings belong to the mesothorax, and on the metathorax are the halteres, each with a swollen base, or scabellum, a narrow pedicel, and a distal knob, or capitellum (the function of the halteres is still doubtful, but if

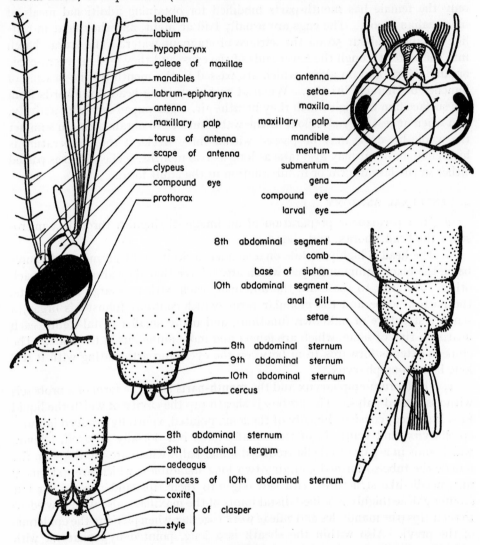

labellum
labium
hypopharynx
galeae of maxillae
mandibles
labrum-epipharynx
antenna
maxillary palp
torus of antenna
scape of antenna
clypeus
compound eye
prothorax

antenna
setae
maxilla
maxillary palp
mandible
mentum
submentum
gena
compound eye
larval eye

8th abdominal segment
comb
base of siphon
10th abdominal segment
anal gill
setae

8th abdominal sternum
9th abdominal sternum
10th abdominal sternum
cercus

8th abdominal sternum
9th abdominal tergum
aedeagus
process of 10th abdominal sternum
coxite ⎤
claw ⎬ of clasper
style ⎦

FIG. 110.—*Culex.* The head of a female seen from the right side (upper left), a ventral view of the posterior end of the abdomen of a female (middle left), and a ventral view of the posterior end of the abdomen of a male showing the results of torsion (lower left). A ventral view of the head of a larva (upper right), and a dorsal view of the posterior end of the abdomen of a larva (lower right).

they are removed flight becomes difficult or impossible). The legs are long and slender, but otherwise they are normal and have 5-jointed tarsi. There are the usual 2 pairs of thoracic spiracles.

e. The **abdomen** consists of 10 segments, of which the 1st is vestigial (and fused to the metathorax), the 2nd to the 8th are clearly visible, each with a pair of spiracles, and the 9th and 10th are partly telescoped into the 8th. In the **female** the 10th segment bears a pair of cerci and a smaller ventral projection, the post-genital plate (which is part of the 10th sternum). In the **male** the 9th and 10th segments are complex (they undergo torsion through 180°, during the first hours after emergence from the pupa ; thus the terga and anus become ventral, and the sterna and claspers dorsal). The 9th segment has the form of a ring with the ventral tergum bilobed, and it carries the large claspers, each with a basal coxite, a distal style, and a slender apical claw. The 10th segment has a prominent, bilobed, dorsal sternum, the processes of which extend posteriorly and have curved toothed tips. The aedeagus is also prominent (and is formed of the fused gonapophyses of segment 9).

f. The **larva** is elongated with a distinct head, thorax, and abdomen, but without legs. The head is broad and dorso-ventrally flattened, and it bears crescentic compound eyes (the developing eyes of the imago), behind which are the smaller accessory larval eyes. The eyes are in the epicranial plates, between which is the broad dorsal frons. Anterior to the frons is a short, broad clypeus, and in front of this is the triangular labrum. Lateral to the clypeus are two plates closely set with setae (these are the feeding brushes, which sieve the water for food particles). On the ventral side distinguish the lateral genae, between which is the submentum and the tiny, dark, toothed mentum (which is all that remains of the labium). Anterior to the genae are the antennae and the maxillae, the latter being set with feeding bristles internally and with tiny palps externally. Dorsal to the maxillae are the mandibles. The segments of the thorax are fused, but each bears a pair of lateral bristle tufts (which assist in feeding). Of the 10 abdominal segments, the first 7 are similar. The 8th segment bears laterally two rows of short spines, the combs, and dorsally a long respiratory process, the siphon tube (up which pass 2 large tracheae, on the apex of which are the 2 spiracles, and through which air is obtained ; the siphon tube is not present in *Anopheles*). The anterior wall of the siphon tube is formed of the 8th tergum and the posterior wall of the 9th tergum, so that the last segment, which is ventrally flexed, is actually the 10th. Through it opens the anus, round which are based the anal gills (containing fine trachioles) and a fringe of bristles (used for clinging to the surface film).

g. The comma-like **pupa** has a swollen head and thorax, and a long, ventrally flexed abdomen (by the movements of which it swims). Distinguish the dividing fold between the head and thorax. On the thorax are the two respiratory trumpets (through which air passages lead to anterior thoracic spiracles). Through the cuticle notice the compound eyes, the larval eyes posterior to them, the wings, and the developing limbs. The first 8 abdominal segments (actually numbers 2 to 9, since the 1st is vestigial) are distinct and movable,

X

and the last of them bears a pair of broad swimming plates, each with a stiffening midrib. Posteriorly is a small process (the 10th segment).

3. CONCLUSION

a. Observing the specimens, review the characteristics of the phylum, of the class, of the subclass, and of the order.

4. REFERENCE

For details of the external and internal anatomy of this and of other genera, see :

MARSHALL, J. F. (1938). " The British mosquitoes." London.

Genus **Calliphora** (blow fly or blue bottle)

(A similar alternative is the smaller *Musca*, the house fly.)

1. GENERAL ACCOUNT

a. The genus *Calliphora* is cosmopolitan, and the adults are commonly found around human habitations whenever the temperature rises above 12° C. The males rarely enter houses and feed exclusively on nectar, but the females, besides feeding on nectar, are strongly attracted to carcases and meat, from which they suck the juices and on which they lay their eggs. Each female lays about 1000 eggs, which begin to be deposited, in groups of from 2 to 100, some three weeks or a month after emergence from the pupa. The male, on the other hand, is fully developed sexually a few hours after emergence. The larvae, as soon as they hatch, burrow into the carrion, and feed and grow for about two weeks, the actual time depending on the temperature. They then leave the meat and burrow into the ground, where they rest for several days before contracting and turning black. This blackened protective cuticle is called the puparium, and within it lies the pupa. After about two weeks in summer, or several months in winter, the imago emerges. Emergence is effected by the distension of a frontal sac on the head which forces the cap off the puparium. The fly then escapes, the frontal sac is withdrawn, and the cuticle hardens.

2. EXTERNAL ANATOMY

a. Examine the **imago** and distinguish the head, which is mobile on a slender neck, the thorax, and the abdomen.

b. The **head** is short and broad, with two large, lateral, compound eyes, between which, dorsally, are 3 ocelli situated on the fused epicranial plates. Cut off the head and examine its frontal region. Ventral to the eyes are the genae, and between the genae is a depression, at the dorsal end of which are based the 3-jointed antennae. Arching above the antennal bases is the ptilinal, or frontal, suture (through which the ptilinum, or frontal sac, was evaginated and distended to break open the puparium). Ventrally is a mem-

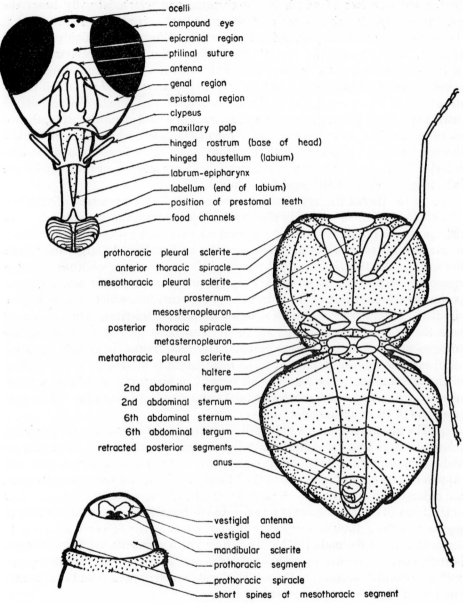

ocelli
compound eye
epicranial region
ptilinal suture
antenna
genal region
epistomal region
clypeus
maxillary palp
hinged rostrum (base of head)
hinged haustellum (labium)
labrum-epipharynx
labellum (end of labium)
position of prestomal teeth
food channels

prothoracic pleural sclerite
anterior thoracic spiracle
mesothoracic pleural sclerite
prosternum
mesosternopleuron
posterior thoracic spiracle
metasternopleuron
metathoracic pleural sclerite
haltere
2nd abdominal tergum
2nd abdominal sternum
6th abdominal sternum
6th abdominal tergum
retracted posterior segments
anus

vestigial antenna
vestigial head
mandibular sclerite
prothoracic segment
prothoracic spiracle
short spines of mesothoracic segment

FIG. 111.—*Calliphora*. An anterior view of the head, a ventral view of the thorax and abdomen, and a ventral view of the larval head.

branous ridge called the epistome, and posterior to this, beneath the head, the proboscis is hinged.

c. The **proboscis** has a basal section, the rostrum (which is part of the head), on the anterior face of which is the clypeus, and which laterally bears the maxillary palps (all that remain of the maxillae). Hinged to the rostrum is the middle region of the proboscis, the haustellum (formed of a highly modified labium). Over the anterior face of this is hinged the labrum-epipharynx, and in its posterior face is a sclerite called the theca. The labrum-epipharynx covers a deep oral groove in which lies the hypopharynx (and up which passes the absorbed liquid food). Distally are two folds, the labella (formed of the distal parts of the labium), containing a series of fine food channels (strengthened by rings of chitin, and therefore called pseudotracheae), which open externally through tiny pores (through which the liquid food and the finest of food particles enter). In the groove between the two labella are a series of prestomal teeth (which can be everted and used for rasping).

d. In the **thorax** the 1st segment is represented only by a ring of sclerites, which can be seen surrounding the gap left by the removal of the head. The ring includes 2 pronotal sclerites, 4 pleural sclerites, and 1 prosternum, to which is attached the 1st pair of legs. The mesothorax is extremely large, and carries the wings. All the visible dorsal region of the thorax is mesonotum. This is crossed by an anterior suture separating the prescutum from the scutum, and a posterior suture separating the scutum from the scutellum which is almost semi-circular. Laterally is a complex series of pleural sclerites, while ventrally both the meso- and meta-sterna are fused to adjacent pleural sclerites, and are consequently known as pleuro-sterna. The metathorax is greatly reduced, and bears the halteres laterally. The metanotum is hidden by the scutellum of the mesonotum. The legs are all normal in structure, and have 5 tarsal joints, the distal of which carry two hooks and a pad-like pulvillus. There are two pairs of thoracic spiracles.

e. The **abdomen** contains only 5 distinct terga and sterna, the former being relatively large and extending ventrally to compress the latter. Actually 10 abdominal segments have been recognised. The 1st is aborted, the 2nd (apparent 1st) is short, the 3rd to the 6th are obvious, and the 7th to the 10th are reduced and telescoped. A pair of spiracles is present on the ventral edges of the terga of each of segments 2 to 6. In the **female** the retracted 7th to 10th segments form a tubular ovipositor, and there is a pair of cerci attached to segment 10. In the **male** the hidden 9th and 10th segments are fused, the 9th bearing claspers, between which is an aedeagus (all these features can be seen only by careful dissection, or by boiling the abdomen in potash and then gently pulling out the telescoped segments).

f. The **larva** is apodous, pointed anteriorly, and covered by thin soft chitin. The head is vestigial, and is the tiny papilla which protrudes from the ring of the prothorax. Through a microscope it can be seen to bear two lobes (considered to be remnants of the antennae), and ventrally from the mouth there project two hooked mandibular sclerites (which tear the food and pull it into the mouth).   The 3 thoracic and the first 8 visible abdominal segments (the true 1st abdominal segment is missing) are all similar, each bearing numerous short spines anteriorly (to assist locomotion).   Note the lateral prothoracic spiracles and the two large posterior spiracles on the dorsal side of the flattened posterior end of the 8th (true 9th) abdominal segment.   The 9th segment (true 10th), through which the anus opens, appears as a posterior, ventral, bifurcated appendage of the 8th.

g. Examine a puparium, which shows the larval segmentation, and has the postero-dorsal end clearly marked by the two large, posterior, larval spiracles. Carefully dissect away the puparium to expose the **pupa**, noticing at the same time the larval mandibular sclerites lying extruded within the case in the region of the mouth.   The appendages of the pupa are free, and through the thin cuticle many of the features of the imago can be distinguished.

3. CONCLUSION

a. Observing the specimens, review the characteristics of the phylum, of the class, of the subclass, and of the order.

b. Compare and contrast the structure of *Calliphora* with that of *Culex*.

4. REFERENCES

For the external and internal anatomy of *Musca* and *Calliphora*, see :

HEWITT, C. G. (1914).   " The house-fly *Musca domestica* Linn.   Its structure, habits, development, relation to disease and control."   Cambridge.
     LOWNE, B. T. (1890–92). " The anatomy, physiology, morphology, and development of the blow-fly (*Calliphora erythrocephala*)."   London.

4.36.   Order **Aphaniptera** (**Siphonaptera**)

Characteristics : Small bilaterally compressed Endopterygota which are parasitic on birds and mammals ; head with or without eyes, and with mouthparts modified for piercing and sucking ; thorax without wings ; larva eruciform and apodous ; pupa exarate.

The fleas form a compact group, which is believed to have been derived from winged ancestors, since apparent traces of wings have been found on the mesothorax of some pupae.   They do not usually remain closely attached to any one host, but wander a great deal.   Consequently many species are important carriers of diseases, including plague in man.   The larvae are never parasitic, but feed on organic detritus.

Genus **Pulex**

(Other members of the Pulicidae which are similar and can be used as alternatives are *Ctenocephalus*, species of which infect cats and dogs, *Ceratophyllus*, species of which infect rats and hens, and *Xenopsylla* which is the tropical carrier of plague.)

1. GENERAL ACCOUNT

a. The common parasite of man is *P. irritans* L., which is cosmopolitan, and which is also known to infect the fox and the badger.   The adults pass part of their lives on the bodies of their hosts from which they suck blood, and part on the ground where they copulate and lay their eggs.   They can move rapidly by jumping, each leap having a maximum height of about 8 inches and a length of about 13 inches.   The larvae are caterpillar-like, but are eyeless and legless.   Moving actively by means of segmental groups of bristles, they seek out deposits of organic detritus, such as any waste food, etc., which may be lodging between floorboards or under dirty carpets.   After feeding for about 14 days, they pupate inside a silken cocoon which is concealed by adhering dust. When the adults emerge, they remain within the cocoon for some time, the stimulus for their emergence being the vibrations set up by the presence of their hosts.   The whole life cycle usually takes a little more than a month.

2.   EXTERNAL ANATOMY

a. Through a microscope examine a permanent preparation of a cleared specimen (see method of clearing on p. 334).   Notice the bilateral compression of the **body,** and distinguish the head, the thorax to which are attached the long legs, and the abdomen.

b. The **head** is a strongly built, chitinous capsule with a posterior flange overlapping the pronotum.   There are no sutures, so that the head sclerites cannot be distinguished.   On either side there is an ocellus, and immediately posterior to it is the antenna, based in a depression.   Each antenna is short, and consists of a proximal scape, an intermediate pedicel, and a distal clava of 9 joints (the antennae are larger in the male, and are apparently used for gripping the female during copulation).   Linking the antennal bases, a deep interantennal groove crosses the top of the head.

c. The **mouth-parts** are based antero-ventrally, and there are no mandibles. A tiny labrum hangs from the anterior edge of the clypeal region, and bears a long, stylet-like epipharynx.   The maxillae each have a large triangular lobe, the stipe (which is probably the galea, and is apparently not used during feeding), a long stylet (which is the lacinia modified for piercing), and a 4-jointed palp.   There is also a small hypopharynx, and a tube-like labium with a pair of 3-jointed palps (which are grooved internally, and so together form a sheath for enclosing the maxillary stylets and the epipharynx ; during feeding these palps are spread aside, the labium touches the host's skin, and the blood is drawn up through the tube formed by the two maxillary stylets and the epipharynx).

d. The 3 segments of the **thorax** are distinct (but since they have little individual freedom, the thorax forms a strong unit).   The prothorax is the smallest and carries the shortest legs, while the metathorax is the largest and

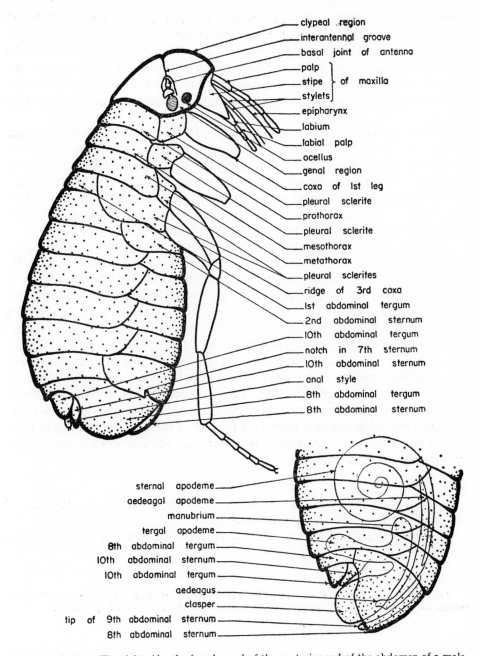

clypeal region
interantennal groove
basal joint of antenna
palp
stipe } of maxilla
stylets
epipharynx
labium
labial palp
ocellus
genal region
coxa of 1st leg
pleural sclerite
prothorax
pleural sclerite
mesothorax
metathorax
pleural sclerites
ridge of 3rd coxa
1st abdominal tergum
2nd abdominal sternum
10th abdominal tergum
notch in 7th sternum
10th abdominal sternum
anal style
8th abdominal tergum
8th abdominal sternum

sternal apodeme
aedeagal apodeme
manubrium
tergal apodeme
8th abdominal tergum
10th abdominal sternum
10th abdominal tergum
aedeagus
clasper
tip of 9th abdominal sternum
8th abdominal sternum

FIG. 112.—*Pulex.* The right side of a female, and of the posterior end of the abdomen of a male.

carries the longest legs. The pro-, meso-, and meta-nota are distinct, but each sternum is fused with the adjacent pleural sclerites to form a pleuro-sternum. Other pleural sclerites are also present. The legs are highly developed (for jumping) and have stout coxae, large femora and tibiae, and tarsi which are long, 5-jointed, and bear double terminal claws. In each of the metathoracic coxae there is an internal strengthening ridge of chitin (which gives the false appearance of a meron).

e. The **abdomen** contains 10 segments. The 1st possesses only a tergum, but the 2nd to the 7th are complete with overlapping terga and sterna. In the **female** the 7th sternum has a pair of posterior notches (which are perhaps engaged by the male's claspers) ; the 8th tergum is subdivided into two large plates which enclose a ventral genital chamber and obscure the small sternum ; the 9th segment is almost completely vestigial ; and the 10th is small, dorsally directed, perforated by the anus, and flanked by short anal stylets.

f. In the **abdomen of the male** the 8th segment has a reduced tergum and a large sternum ; the 9th segment is small and is mostly hidden by the 8th sternum, but it bears the large claspers, and its sternum also projects posteriorly ; the 10th segment is similar to that of the female. The male genitalia are highly complex (and their method of functioning is not understood). Externally are the plate-like claspers, each with a movable appendage, and the aedeagus (formed of fused gonapophyses of segment 9), which is enclosed by the claspers. Internally, in cleared specimens, there is also visible a complicated series of chitinous structures. These are the aedeagal apodeme, extending forwards from the base of the aedeagus, the slender sternal apodeme, coiling forwards from beneath it, the manubrium, extending forwards in front of the clasper, and the tergal apodeme (which is a forward projection of the 9th tergum ; the function of all these structures is unknown, but they are presumed to be of some importance during copulation).

3. CONCLUSION

a. Observing the specimen, review the characteristics of the phylum, of the class, of the subclass, and of the order.

b. Review those modifications of structure which are associated with the mode of life.

4. REFERENCE

SNODGRASS, R. E. (1946). " The skeletal anatomy of fleas (Siphonaptera)." *Miscellaneous Collections of the Smithsonian Institution, Washington*, Vol. 104, no. 18.

CHAPTER XIX

PHYLUM **ARTHROPODA** (*continued*)

5.00. Class **Arachnida**

Characteristics : Aquatic and terrestrial Arthropoda which respire either by gill-books or by lung-books, with or without tracheae ; with an anterior region, the prosoma, formed of 7 segments with the first 2 preoral, the 1st disappearing, the 2nd with chelicerae, the 3rd usually with pedipalps, and the others with walking legs ; with a posterior region, the opisthosoma, formed of not more than 13 segments and a telson ; excretion by coxal glands, and often also by Malpighian tubules ; sexes separate and development direct.

While the Crustacea, Myriapoda, and Insecta have much in common and together form a natural group, the Arachnida is an entirely isolated branch of the arthropodean stock. The method of subdivision of the body, the absence of antennae and mandibles, and the form of the anterior limbs are unique features. Evidently the arthropods split into two main groups at a very early stage in their development. Some of the earliest known arachnids are the aquatic Palaeozoic eurypterids, many of which reached a length of more than 6 feet and are the largest arthropods known. Today only a few arachnids are primitively aquatic, the great majority being terrestrial and the rest secondarily aquatic. They are typically predaceous and carnivorous, and many of them are parasitic.

5.10. Subclass **Delobranchiata**

Characteristics : Primitively aquatic Arachnida which respire by gill-books ; with the largest limbs on the last prosomatic segment ; and with the 1st opisthosomatic segment represented by the reduced pregenital segment.

This subclass contains two ancient orders : the extinct Eurypterida, which flourished in the Palaeozoic, and the Xiphosura, which persists to the present day.

5.11. Order **Xiphosura**

Characteristics : Delobranchiata with the prosoma covered by a broad horseshoe-shaped carapace ; and with the opisthosoma formed of at least 8 segments, of which the 1st bear chilaria and the 2nd a genital operculum.

The members of this order, known since the early Palaeozoic, are almost all extinct.   Only five species of the genus *Limulus*, known since the Triassic, remain alive today.

Genus **Limulus** (horseshoe crab or king crab)

1. GENERAL ACCOUNT

a. Four species of *Limulus* occur along the east coast of Asia, and the only other species is that from the east coast of North America.   The animals are found at depths of from 2 to 6 fathoms on sandy or muddy bottoms in which they lie partly buried.   They plough the sand in search of their food, which consists mainly of polychaet worms and pelecypod molluscs.   These are caught by the chelicerae and torn up or crushed between the gnathobases of the walking legs.   By beating their gill-books they are also capable of a clumsy, upside-down, swimming action.   From May to mid-July they migrate towards the shore, a male clinging to the back of each female.   There, in the shallowest water, the eggs are laid and fertilised in a series of shallow holes dug in the sand by the female.   The young, known as trilobite larvae, already resemble the adults when they hatch.

2. EXTERNAL ANATOMY

a. The **body** is divisible into a broad, horseshoe-shaped prosoma, a smaller opisthosoma, and a long caudal spine, or telson.   Ventrally, the small mouth opens between the bases of the walking legs just posterior to a prominent ridge, the camerostome.   The anus opens ventrally at the base of the caudal spine.

b. The **prosoma** is covered by a large carapace (formed of fused terga), which bears two postero-lateral projections and is joined to the opisthosoma by a broad hinge.   Dorsally on the carapace are 7 spines.   The anterior of these is median, is flanked by two small eyes, and forms the anterior end of a median ridge.   The two antero-lateral spines are each flanked by a large eye, and form the anterior ends of two lateral ridges.   Between the median and lateral ridges are two longitudinal grooves.   The sterna of the prosomatic segments form a membranous sheet visible between the bases of the legs.

c. The **prosomatic appendages** are based around the mouth.   The 1st appendages are the small, chelate, 3-jointed chelicerae (they belong to segment 2, segment 1 having disappeared).   The 2nd appendages (segment 3) are walking legs, but are sometimes called pedipalps.   They are chelate in all young animals and in adult females, but in adult males each ends in a curved claw (used for clinging to the back of the female while riding into shallow water to spawn).   Each consists of 6 joints ; the coxa, which is particularly large and projects towards the mouth as a spiny gnatho-base, the trochanter, femur, tibia, and 2 tarsi.   The appendages of segments 4 to 6 are also chelate walking legs with a similar structure, but the 6th appendage (segment 7), which is the

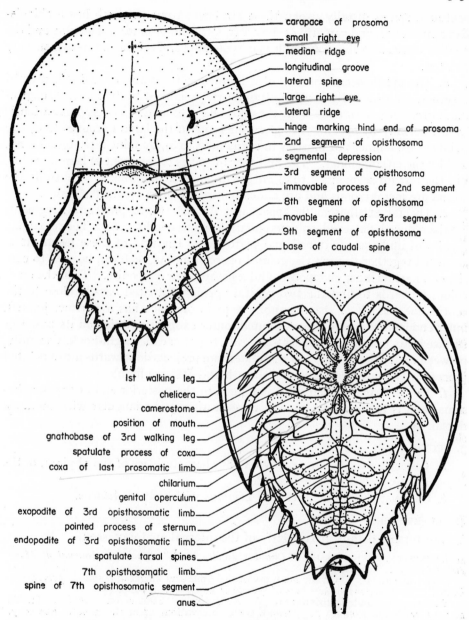

carapace of prosoma
small right eye
median ridge
longitudinal groove
lateral spine
large right eye
lateral ridge
hinge marking hind end of prosoma
2nd segment of opisthosoma
segmental depression
3rd segment of opisthosoma
immovable process of 2nd segment
8th segment of opisthosoma
movable spine of 3rd segment
9th segment of opisthosoma
base of caudal spine

1st walking leg
chelicera
camerostome
position of mouth
gnathobase of 3rd walking leg
spatulate process of coxa
coxa of last prosomatic limb
chilarium
genital operculum
exopodite of 3rd opisthosomatic limb
pointed process of sternum
endopodite of 3rd opisthosomatic limb
spatulate tarsal spines
7th opisthosomatic limb
spine of 7th opisthosomatic segment
anus

FIG. 113.—*Limulus*. Dorsal and ventral views of a female.

largest, is 7-jointed and non-chelate. The coxa of the 6th appendage is especially large, and to its outer edge is attached a spatulate spine (used for cleaning the opisthosomatic appendages). The proximal tarsus bears 4 spatulate spines distally (when these are opened out the limb has a skipole-like appearance, and can grip or dig away soft sand or mud).   The tibia and the median tarsus bear single movable spines distally, and the distal tarsus is sharply pointed.

d. The **opisthosoma** consists of 9 segments, the terga of which are fused together.   Mid-dorsally is a longitudinal ridge flanked by two lateral longitudinal grooves (continuous with those of the prosoma).   The segmentation is shown dorsally by 6 pairs of depressions lying in the lateral grooves (they are points of attachment of muscles in segments 3 to 8), by faint inter-tergal lines, and by the lateral spines.   The first pair of spines (of segment 2) is immovable, but the rest (of segments 3 to 8) are set in notches and hinged.   Ventrally the sterna are membranous and are almost entirely hidden by the flat limbs.

e. The 1st **opisthosomatic appendages** (of the 1st, or pregenital, segment) are the reduced, flattened, spinous chilaria (function unknown).   The remaining 6 pairs of limbs are flattened and plate-like.   The first of these (segment 2) are fused together to form the genital operculum, but each can be seen to consist of a narrow inner endopodite and a broad outer exopodite.   Turn the operculum forwards to find the two genital openings situated basally close to the centre line.   Each of the remaining 5 pairs of limbs has a narrow, jointed, inner endopodite, and a broad, jointed, outer exopodite, which on its posterior surface bears from 150 to 200 leaf-like gills, together called a gill-book. Centrally, between each pair of endopodites, the sternum projects downwards into a pointed process.   The last two segments, the 8th and 9th, are limbless.

f. The post-anal **caudal spine** is hinged to the posterior end of the opisthosoma (and is freely movable).   In cross section it is triangular with the apex dorsal.

3.   CONCLUSION

a. Observing the specimen, review the characteristics of the phylum, of the class, of the subclass, and of the order.

b. Contrast the segmentation of *Limulus* with that of *Astacus*.

4.   REFERENCES

For further details, particularly of the internal anatomy, see :

LANKESTER, E. R. (1881).   " *Limulus* an arachnid."   *Quarterly Journal of Microscopical Science*, Vol. 21, p. 504.
    OWEN, R. (1873).   " On the anatomy of the American kingcrab (*Limulus polyphemus*, Latr.)."   *Transactions of the Linnean Society of London*, Vol. 28, p. 459.
    PATTEN, W., and REDENBAUGH, W. A. (1899).   " Studies on *Limulus*.   II. The nervous system of *Limulus polyphemus*, with observations upon the general anatomy." *Journal of Morphology*, Vol. 16, p. 91.

5.20.   Subclass **Embolobranchiata**

Characteristics : Terrestrial Arachnida breathing by lung-books with or without tracheae, or by tracheae alone ; with the largest limbs not on the last prosomatic segment; and with the 1st, or pregenital, opisthosomatic segment either indistinguishable in the adult or forming a pedicel between the two body regions.

5.21. Order **Scorpionida**

Characteristics : Embolobranchiata in which the prosoma bears 3-jointed chelate chelicerae and large chelate pedipalps; the opisthosoma composed of 13 segments (12 in the adult) and a telson, and divisible into meso- and metasomatic regions; the 2nd (adult 1st) mesosomatic segment with a genital operculum, the 3rd with pectines, the 4th to the 7th with lung-books, and the 8th limbless; the metasomatic segments long, narrow, and limbless, and carrying a terminal telson containing a sting; ovoviviparous.

Scorpions are widespread in warmer countries. They are absent from New Zealand and Patagonia in the south, and from all land above the 45th parallel of latitude in the north. In the past they are known to have existed since the Silurian, the earliest known genus being marine.

Genus **Centrurus**

(Other genera, such as *Buthus* or *Scorpio*, are similar and can be used as alternatives.)

1. GENERAL ACCOUNT

a. Centrurus is a common genus in the Americas, and ranges as far north as Texas and Florida. Like other scorpions, they are generally nocturnal, and they feed particularly on insects and spiders. These they usually catch with the pedipalps, but if too large they can be subdued with the sting, which reaches forwards above and in front of the head. The prey is crushed by the gnathobases, and only its juices are taken as food. The sting is also used in defence. After a courtship ceremony, fertilisation is internal, and the female then kills and eats the male. The eggs are retained and hatch within the female, and the young after birth are carried for some time on their mother's back.

2. EXTERNAL ANATOMY

a. The **body** is clearly divisible into an anterior prosoma covered by an unsegmented carapace, and a posterior opisthosoma, which is segmented and ends in a telson modified as a sting. The opisthosoma is subdivisible into a broad anterior mesosoma and a long, narrow, tail-like metasoma.

b. The **prosoma** is short and cylindrical; its dorsal carapace has an anterior overhanging lip, on the outer edges of which are groups of small eyes, and a median longitudinal groove, in the middle of which is a small projection flanked by two larger eyes. The carapace is separated by two bands of soft, flexible chitin, the pleural membranes (which may be folded from sight), from the small, hard sternum situated between the bases of the last pair of walking legs (and which belongs to the last prosomatic segment).

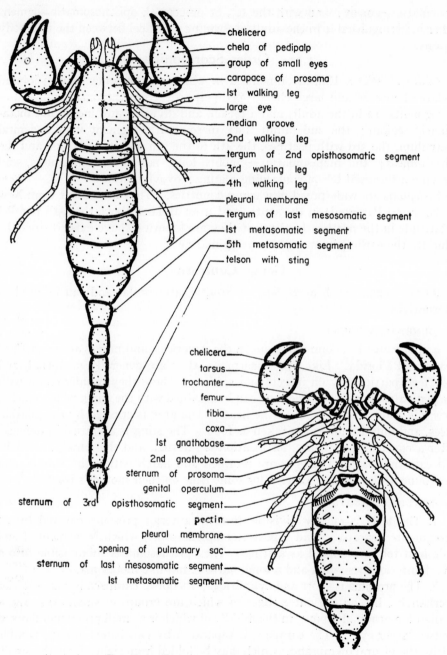

chelicera
chela of pedipalp
group of small eyes
carapace of prosoma
1st walking leg
large eye
median groove
2nd walking leg
tergum of 2nd opisthosomatic segment
3rd walking leg
4th walking leg
pleural membrane
tergum of last mesosomatic segment
1st metasomatic segment
5th metasomatic segment
telson with sting

chelicera
tarsus
trochanter
femur
tibia
coxa
1st gnathobase
2nd gnathobase
sternum of prosoma
genital operculum
sternum of 3rd opisthosomatic segment
pectin
pleural membrane
opening of pulmonary sac
sternum of last mesosomatic segment
1st metasomatic segment

Fig. 114.—*Centrurus.* Dorsal and ventral views.

c. The 1st **prosomatic appendages** are the chelicerae (of segment 2 ; the 1st, or precheliceral, segment is distinguishable only in the embryo). These protrude anteriorly, and consist of only 3 joints, of which the last two form a chela. The 2nd limbs (segment 3) are the large chelate pedipalps (used for offence), the 6 joints of which are the coxa, trochanter, femur, tibia, and 2 tarsi. On these limbs are numbers of sensory hairs. The 3rd to the 6th limbs (segments 4 to 7) are 7-jointed walking legs. Their coxae form the main ventral protection of the prosoma, and the last of their 3 tarsi each bears two claws. The coxae of the first two pairs of walking legs project inwards and forwards as gnatho-bases (which crush the food).

d. The segmentation of the **mesosoma** is obvious (except that the 1st, or pregenital, segment is distinguishable only in the embryo). The 7 segments present in the adult are seen dorsally as 7 terga, but only the last 6 of them possess sterna. Between the rows of terga and sterna are the pleural membranes.

e. The 2nd (1st adult) mesosomatic segment carries the 1st **mesosomatic appendages**, which are reduced to form a genital operculum projecting backwards over the two genital apertures. To the 3rd segment belong the 2nd tergum and the 1st sternum, and its limbs are modified as pectines (tactile organs). Segments 4 to 7 have their limbs sunk into pits, or pulmonary sacs, in the sterna. The openings of these pits are diagonally placed slits (and within each the limb has been modified into about 150 flat vascular leaves, the lung-book). The last mesosomatic segment is limbless.

f. The 5 limbless segments of the **metasoma** are hard rings formed by a close fusion of tergum with sternum. Behind the last segment the anus opens ventrally. Posterior to this is the telson, which is bulbous and drawn out into a fine curved point (within the bulb are two poison-glands which open by two tiny pores on the sides of the point). The telson also bears numbers of short sensory hairs.

3. CONCLUSION

a. Observing the specimen, review the characteristics of the phylum, of the class, of the subclass, and of the order.

b. Compare the external anatomy of *Centrurus* with that of *Limulus*.

4. REFERENCES

LANKESTER, E. R. (1881). "*Limulus* an arachnid." *Quarterly Journal of Microscopical Science*, Vol. 21, p. 504.

LANKESTER, E. R., BENHAM, W. B. S., and BECK, E. J. (1883). "On the muscular and endoskeletal systems of *Limulus* and *Scorpio* ; with some notes on the anatomy and generic characters of scorpions." *Transactions of the Zoological Society of London*, Vol. 11, p. 311.

5.22.   Order **Araneida**

Characteristics : Embolobranchiata in which the prosoma bears 2-jointed non-chelate chelicerae, and non-chelate pedipalps with large gnathobases ;

the soft opisthosoma usually without signs of segmentation, and attached to the prosoma by a slender waist ; respiration by two pairs of lung-books, by one pair of lung-books and tracheae, or by tracheae alone ; and with silk glands opening through spinnerets postero-ventrally.

Since they are the most numerous, the true spiders can be considered the most successful modern order of the Arachnida. Their fossil record goes back to the Carboniferous. Probably their best-known feature is the thread-spinning habit. In many genera this thread is used only for lining the burrow or nest, for spinning a cocoon for the eggs, or for wrapping the captured prey, but in some it is also used for the construction of various kinds of webs for snaring the prey.

Genus **Eurypelma**

(Any of the large spiders of the family Aviculariidae (Mygaliidae), such as *Avicularia* (*Mygale*) itself, are similar alternatives. In addition, the smaller spiders of the family Argiopidae, such as the common *Epeira* (*Araneus*), can be used if necessary, and the most important ways in which their structure differs from that of the Aviculariidae are indicated below.)

I. GENERAL ACCOUNT

a. The family Aviculariidae, containing the largest of the spiders, has a wide distribution in tropical and subtropical countries. It includes the trap-door spiders and the so-called bird-eating spiders.

b. *Eurypelma* is common in tropical and subtropical America, where it is also known as the tarantula. By day it lies hidden in holes which are usually natural cavities in the ground or in the trunks of trees, and which are lined by a close silken web. It does not make a snaring web, but in the evening it emerges to hunt its food, which consists of insects of all kinds. These are pierced by the chelicerae, poisoned, and then digested within their own exoskeletons by enzymes passed in through the holes made by the chelicerae. Finally, the liquefied tissues are sucked up. *Eurypelma* is four or five years old when it becomes sexually mature. It can then endure long fasts, although, like all spiders, it needs much water to drink. The eggs are laid in silken cocoons, about 1000 eggs in each, and the young hatch in about six weeks.

2. EXTERNAL ANATOMY

a. The **body** is clearly divided into a prosoma, to which the legs are attached, and an opisthosoma, which is superficially limbless. The two are joined by a narrow waist, the pedicel, and both body and limbs are thickly covered in chitinous hairs (which are probably all tactile).

b. The **prosoma** is covered dorsally by a carapace (formed of fused terga). Anteriorly in the mid-dorsal line are 8 eyes mounted on a small tubercle (in *Epeira* there are 8 eyes but no tubercle), and the region of the carapace in front

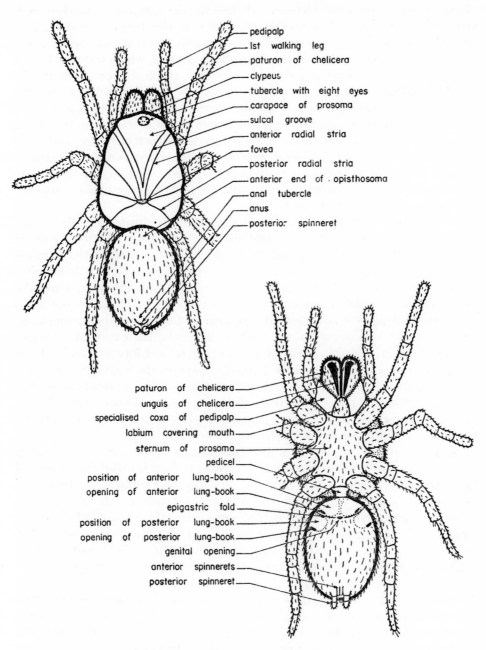

pedipalp
1st walking leg
paturon of chelicera
clypeus
tubercle with eight eyes
carapace of prosoma
sulcal groove
anterior radial stria
fovea
posterior radial stria
anterior end of . opisthosoma
anal tubercle
anus
posterior spinneret

paturon of chelicera
unguis of chelicera
specialised coxa of pedipalp
labium covering mouth
sternum of prosoma
pedicel
position of anterior lung-book
opening of anterior lung-book
epigastric fold
position of posterior lung-book
opening of posterior lung-book
genital opening
anterior spinnerets
posterior spinneret

FIG. 115—*Eurypelma*.   Dorsal and ventral views.

Y

of this is often called the clypeus. Posteriorly the carapace is marked by a series of depressions. The central depression is the fovea, and from it 8 grooves, the radial striae, pass outwards towards the intervals between the 5 pairs of large limbs. In addition, two sulcal grooves, which together form a **V**, lie close in front of the anterior pair of striae (all these depressions are the counterparts of internal ridges which are the points of attachment for the muscles of the limbs and of the sucking stomach). The prosoma is covered ventrally by a sternum, immediately anterior to which is another sternal plate, the so-called labium. The latter is hinged along its posterior edge, and hides both the tiny mouth and the rostral plate which forms the upper lip. The region anterior to the sulcal grooves dorsally and to the posterior edge of the labium ventrally is sometimes called the head, and the rest of the prosoma, composed of 4 segments, is then the thorax.

c. The 1st prosomatic segment is distinguishable only in the embryo, and the remaining 6 segments bear the **prosomatic appendages**. The first 2 pairs of appendages belong to the so-called head, and the last 4 pairs to the so-called thorax. The 1st appendages, the chelicerae, each consists of a large basal joint, the paturon (which contains a poison gland), and a fang-like distal joint, the unguis (through which the poison gland duct opens). The 3rd segment, to which also belongs the so-called labium, bears 6-jointed pedipalps which are closely covered by sensory hairs. Their basal joints, the coxae, are strongly developed (for gripping the prey ; in *Epeira* they project forwards and inwards as gnathobases which are also called maxillae), and in the male the distal tarsi are modified as intromittent organs (which transfer the spermatozoa to the female). Segments 4 to 7 bear the walking legs, each of which consists of a coxa, trochanter, femur, tibia, and 3 tarsi (in *Epeira* the distal tarsus bears two large claws which hook on to the strands of the web).

d. There are 12 segments in the **opisthosoma**. The 1st, or pregenital, segment forms the limbless pedicel, the tergum of which is called the lorum and the sternum the plagula. The 2nd, or genital, segment contains the 1st pair of lung-books (modified limbs), and is pierced mid-ventrally by an inconspicuous genital opening partly hidden by a transverse ridge, the epigastric fold (in the female *Epeira* the genital opening is on the end of a conspicuous ovipositor, the epigyne). The 3rd segment contains a 2nd pair of lung-books (but in *Epeira* it is limbless and bears instead a single spiracle which opens into a tracheal system). The position of the 4th segment is indicated by its limbs, the anterior and smaller pair of spinnerets (mobile structures through which open the ducts of the silk glands), and that of the 5th segment by the large 3-jointed posterior spinnerets (in *Epeira* the 5th segment bears four small spinnerets). The remaining 7 opisthosomatic segments are limbless, and are fused together to form the small anal tubercle, through the end of which opens the anus.

3. CONCLUSION

a. Observing the specimen, review the characteristics of the phylum, of the class, of the subclass, and of the order.

b. Compare the structure of *Eurypelma* with that of *Centrurus*.

4. REFERENCES

For the structure and habits of spiders, see:

BERLAND, L. (1932). " Les Arachnides." Paris.
COMSTOCK, J. H. (1913). " The spider book." New York.
LANKESTER, E. R. (1905). " The structure and classification of the Arachnida."
Quarterly Journal of Microscopical Science, Vol. 48, p. 165.
SAVORY, T. H. (1928). " The biology of spiders." London.

5.23. Order **Phalangida (Opilionida)**

Characteristics : Embolobranchiata in which the prosoma bears 3-jointed chelate chelicerae, non-chelate pedipalps with gnathobases, and long, thin walking legs; the opisthosoma of not more than 11 segments (10 in the adult), all of which are limbless; with a protrusible penis or ovipositor; and with respiration by tracheae.

The harvest spiders are a well-known group of animals, which are particularly noticeable in autumn, when they reach their full size.   However, since they are not considered to be of great theoretical or economic importance, they have not been so thoroughly studied as have the other orders of the Arachnida.

Genus **Phalangium** (common harvest spider)

1. GENERAL ACCOUNT

a. This and other related genera of the family Phalangiidae are widespread and common in temperate regions. *Phalangium*, when at rest, is obscured by drab coloration, and its long legs, spreading over a large area, give warning of approaching danger.   For further protection, a leg, if seized, is readily detached, and odoriferous glands can also be brought into action.   Food, which is torn into tiny pieces and swallowed, consists of small centipedes, insects, spiders, and mites, whether alive or freshly dead.   Much water is also taken, and, in an emergency, plants are pierced for their sap.   In late summer the animals are fully grown, and the males then fight fiercely and copulation occurs.   Later, each female lays about 25 unprotected eggs into some crevice, and these survive the winter.   In warmer countries some adults may also survive the colder weather.

2. EXTERNAL ANATOMY

a. The short, globular **body** is composed of a prosoma and an opisthosoma, which are closely fused together.   To the sides of the prosoma are attached the extremely long walking legs.

b. Dorsally the **prosoma** is roughly triangular, and is covered anteriorly by a carapace (formed of fused terga) and posteriorly by a single free tergum. Antero-laterally, opposite the bases of the 1st walking legs, the carapace is pierced by the two openings of the odoriferous glands (defensive stink glands), and posteriorly in the middle it bears a prominent tubercle flanked by two simple eyes. The region of the carapace behind the eyes is the tergum of segment 6, while the free tergum belongs to segment 7. The ventral side of the prosoma is protected by the bases of the walking legs and by the sternal process (which, however, consists of the fused sterna of the 2nd and 3rd opisthosomatic segments). The anterior end of this process usually obscures the prosomatic sternum, which is a small transverse plate. In front of this is another small sternal plate, the so-called labium, which is hinged posteriorly and hides the mouth. The anterior edge of the mouth is the epistome.

c. The 1st prosomatic segment is distinguishable only in the embryo, and the remaining 6 segments bear the **prosomatic appendages**. The 1st appendage (segment 2) is the 3-jointed chelate chelicera, which projects forwards and downwards. The 2nd (segment 3) is the 6-jointed pedipalp, the coxa of which bears a movable gnathobase (for chewing the food) and the distal tarsus of which ends in a hooked claw. To the 4th segment belong the sternal labium and the 1st pair of walking legs, the coxae of which also bear movable gnathobases. Each walking leg is greatly elongated, and consists of a stout, immovable coxa (which protects the ventral and lateral sides of the prosoma), a short trochanter, and long, slender femur, tibia, and tarsus. This last is subdivided into a large number of small joints, the distal bearing a claw. The 5th segment carries the 2nd walking legs, which also possess gnathobases, while the 6th and 7th segments carry walking legs which lack gnathobases. The small sternum belongs to these last 3 segments.

d. The 10 segments of the **opisthosoma** are limbless. The 1st, or pregenital, segment disappears in the adult, so that the apparent first is the 2nd, or genital, segment. The terga of segments 2 to 10 are easily distinguished (but in some of the Phalangida the terga of segments 2 to 6 are fused to each other and sometimes also to the prosomatic carapace). The sternum of the 2nd segment is represented by the anterior end of the sternal process, together with the two antero-lateral sternal plates. Anterior to the sternal process is the single genital opening (from which the long penis of the male, or the long ovipositor of the female, can be forced by gently squeezing the body of a living specimen). The sternum of the 3rd segment is represented by the posterior end of the sternal process, together with the two postero-sternal plates. Notice the two spiracles in this region. The sterna of segments 4 to 8 are clearly visible, but that of segment 9 is rudimentary, and that of segment 10 is lacking. The anus thus lies between the 10th tergum and the 8th sternum.

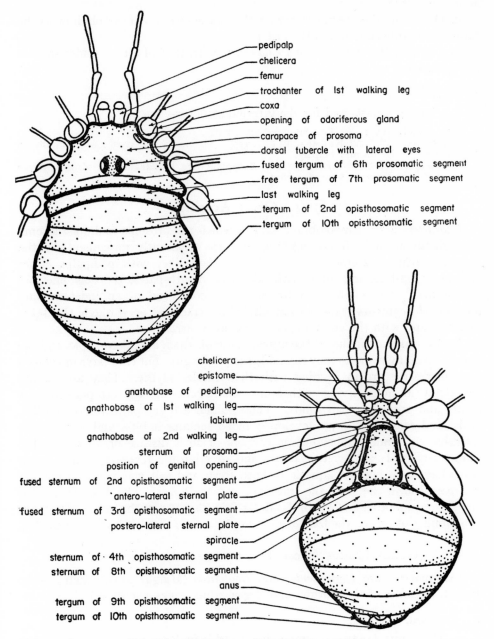

pedipalp
chelicera
femur
trochanter   of   1st   walking   leg
coxa
opening   of   odoriferous   gland
carapace   of   prosoma
dorsal   tubercle   with   lateral   eyes
fused   tergum   of   6th   prosomatic   segment
free   tergum   of   7th   prosomatic   segment
last   walking   leg
tergum   of   2nd   opisthosomatic   segment
tergum   of   10th   opisthosomatic   segment

chelicera
epistome
gnathobase   of   pedipalp
gnathobase   of   1st   walking   leg
labium
gnathobase   of   2nd   walking   leg
sternum   of   prosoma
position   of   genital   opening
fused   sternum   of   2nd   opisthosomatic   segment
antero-lateral   sternal   plate
fused   sternum   of   3rd   opisthosomatic   segment
postero-lateral   sternal   plate
spiracle
sternum   of   4th   opisthosomatic   segment
sternum   of   8th   opisthosomatic   segment
anus
tergum   of   9th   opisthosomatic   segment
tergum   of   10th   opisthosomatic   segment

FIG. 116.—*Phalangium*.   Dorsal and ventral views.

3. CONCLUSION

a. Observing the specimen, review the characteristics of the phylum, of the class, of the subclass, and of the order.

b. Contrast the structure of *Phalangium* with that of a true spider such as *Eurypelma*.

4. REFERENCES

For further details and for the internal structure, see :

BERLAND, L. (1932). " Les Arachnides." Paris.
KÜKENTHAL, W., and KRUMBACH, T. (1935). Volume 3 and part 2 of " Handbuch der Zoologie." Berlin and Leipzig.
RÖSSLER, R. (1882). " Beiträge zur Anatomie der Phalangiden." *Zeitschrift für wissenschaftliche Zoologie*, Vol. 36, p. 671.

5.24. Order **Acarina**

Characteristics : Embolobranchiata in which the prosoma and opisthosoma are indistinguishably fused together, and are apparently unsegmented ; the prosoma with chelicerae either chelate or fang-like, with pedipalps either chelate or leg-like, and often with accessory mouth-parts, the epistome and hypostome ; the opisthosoma limbless and composed of an indeterminate number of segments ; respiration either by tracheae or through the body surface ; and with the genital opening antero-ventral.

In this order are included the mites, many of which are microscopic, and the ticks. In many respects they resemble the phalangids, but they have developed a simpler structure in keeping with their modes of life. They are mainly terrestrial animals living either as scavengers or as ectoparasites of plants and animals of all kinds. Those which are ectoparasites of reptiles, birds, and mammals have developed blood-sucking habits, and are of considerable economic importance as carriers of such disease organisms as the spirochaets of Texas fever in cattle and of relapsing fever in man. A few mites have also become aquatic in both fresh and salt water, and a few are endoparasitic in the skin, the tracheae, and the lungs. The order is divided into several suborders, of which the Metastigmata contains the ticks. There are two families of ticks : the hard-bodied Ixodidae and the soft-bodied Argasidae.

Genus **Ixodes** (sheep tick or castor bean tick)

(Alternatives are *Dermacentor* and *Boophilus* (*Margaropus*), which possess eyes on the sides of the scutum, and *Argas*, which lacks a scutum.)

1. GENERAL ACCOUNT

a. The genus *Ixodes* is cosmopolitan, and it includes more than 50 species, of which *I. ricinus* L. is the best known. This is a common parasite of the sheep, and is also of frequent occurrence on such other mammals as hedgehogs, rabbits, and dogs. Given the chance, it readily feeds on man. The female, when fully gorged with blood, drops to the ground to lay about 1000 eggs, which hatch into 6-legged larvae. These crawl up plant-stems and wait until they are brushed off by some passing mammal. After feeding, they fall to the

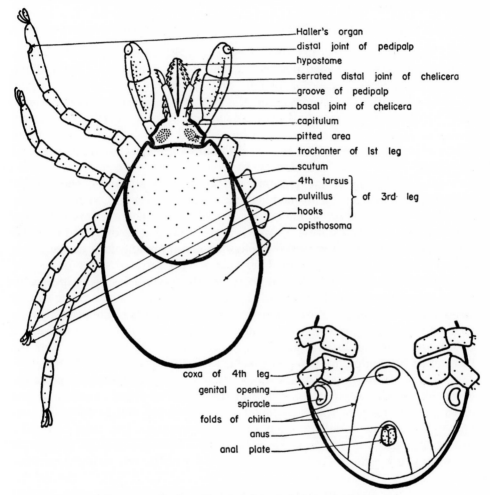

Haller's organ
distal joint of pedipalp
hypostome
serrated distal joint of chelicera
groove of pedipalp
basal joint of chelicera
capitulum
pitted area
trochanter of 1st leg
scutum
4th tarsus
pulvillus   } of 3rd leg
hooks
opisthosoma

coxa of 4th leg
genital opening
spiracle
folds of chitin
anus
anal plate

FIG. 117.—*Ixodes.* Dorsal and ventral views of a female.

ground, cast their skins, and emerge as 8-legged nymphs. These also ascend plant-stems to be brushed off by some passing host, and again they engorge and fall to the ground to cast their skins and emerge as adults. For the last time they then creep to the plant-tops and wait to be brushed off. The female immediately inserts its mouth-parts into the host, but it does not feed until it has been fertilised. The male, on becoming attached to a host, wanders in search of a female, and copulation occurs.   The fertilised female then feeds, swells greatly, and falls to the ground, where it creeps into some crevice and remains inert until the eggs develop.   These, as they are laid, are covered by a sticky secretion and transferred to the dorsal side of the tick, which then shrivels and dies.

2.   EXTERNAL ANATOMY

a. The dorso-ventrally flattened **body** is divisible into a movable head, or capitulum, bearing the mouth-parts, an anterior region bearing the walking legs, and a limbless posterior region.   The capitulum and anterior region together constitute the prosoma, and the posterior region is the opisthosoma. In the male both prosoma and opisthosoma are covered dorsally by a hard, chitinous shield, or scutum (formed of fused terga).   In the female the scutum covers only the prosoma, and the exoskeleton of the opisthosoma is soft and extensible.

b. The **capitulum of the prosoma** is formed of 3 segments, the 1st indistinguishable, the 2nd with modified chelicerae, and the 3rd with pedipalps. Anteriorly is the rostrum, formed of a ventral hypostome (a forward extension of the sternum of the capitulum), which is grooved up its centre, and laterally carries large numbers of recurved hooks (for maintaining a grip in the host's skin).   Above it are the 2-jointed chelicerae with serrated outer edges (for cutting into the skin), and lateral to it are the 4-jointed sensory pedipalps (when the hypostome and chelicerae are driven into the host, a sucking tube is formed between them).   Notice that the two middle joints of the pedipalps are grooved internally (together they form a sheath for the hypostome and chelicerae), and that the distal joint is tiny.   Dorsally on the capitulum, near the bases of the pedipalps, are two pitted areas (which are presumed to be sensory).

c. The other appendages mark the position of the **remainder of the prosoma**, which in the male is completely, and in the female is partly, covered by the scutum.   The 1st pair of legs (segment 4) are 7-jointed, the distal tarsus containing a cup-shaped Haller's organ (a sensory structure) and bearing distally two hooked claws and a sucker-like pulvillus.   The other 3 pairs of legs (of segments 5 to 7 ; those of segment 7 are missing in the larva) are similar, except that they lack a Haller's organ and possess an extra tarsal joint.   Behind the last pair of legs is a pair of prominent lateral spiracles, and on the ventral surface is the single genital opening (neither spiracles nor genital opening is present in the larva).

d. The **opisthosoma** is limbless, and shows no signs of segmentation (it is uncertain how many segments are incorporated in it).   The anus is centrally placed on the ventral surface, and is flanked by two small anal plates.   Across the ventral surface there are also regular folds in the chitin (which disappear when the body becomes distended with food).

3. CONCLUSION

a. Observing the specimen, review the characteristics of the phylum, of the class, of the subclass, and of the order.

b. Compare the external anatomy of *Ixodes* with that of *Phalangium*.

4. REFERENCES

For further details of the external and internal anatomy of this and other common ticks, see :

ROBINSON, L. E., and DAVIDSON, J. (1914). " The anatomy of *Argas persicus* (Oken 1818)." *Parasitology*, Vol. 6, p. 20.

SAMSON, K. (1909). " Zur Anatomie und Biologie von *Ixodes ricinus* L." *Zeitschrift für wissenschaftliche Zoologie*, Vol. 93, p. 185.

WILLIAMS, S. R. (1905). " Anatomy of *Boophilus annulatus* Say." *Proceedings of the Boston Society of Natural History*, Vol. 32, p. 313.

5.30. Subclass **Pycnogonida**

Characteristics : Aberrant marine Arachnida with no special respiratory structures ; with the prosoma partly segmented and lacking a carapace ; with the chelicerae chelate, non-chelate, rudimentary, or lacking ; with the pedipalps present or absent ; with the 1st pair of legs modified as ovigerous limbs, or absent ; with the 2nd, 3rd, and 4th pairs of legs 8-jointed and very long ; with the 1st, or pregenital, opisthosomatic segment well developed and bearing a 5th pair of legs, and with the other opisthosomatic segments fused and greatly reduced.

The relationships of this highly modified group of arthropods are obscure, but the pycnogonids are generally considered to be arachnids, and are commonly called sea spiders.

Genus **Nymphon**

(Alternatives are *Pallene*, which lacks pedipalps, and *Phoxichilidium* and *Pycnogonum*, which lack chelicerae and pedipalps in both sexes and ovigerous legs in the females.)

1. GENERAL ACCOUNT

a. Species of *Nymphon* occur all over the world, and are found from the extreme low-tide mark to depths of at least 150 fathoms. They live among colonies of hydrozoan coelenterates, on which they feed by chewing the polyps within the hollow of the proboscis. Apparently they swallow only the extracted juices and the smallest of food particles. The eggs are fertilised as they are laid, and are immediately picked up by the male. They hatch as 6-legged protonymphon larvae, which continue to be carried by the male until they metamorphose.

2. EXTERNAL ANATOMY

a. The extremely reduced **body** is separable into three regions : a proboscis, a central region to which the limbs are attached, and a posterior abdominal process.   The mouth is anterior on the proboscis, and the anus is posterior on the abdominal process.

  b. To indicate a similarity with other arachnids, the first 7 segments are considered to constitute a **prosoma**.   As usual, the 1st segment is indistinguishable in the adult (it is not represented by the proboscis, which is an anterior prolongation of the 2nd segment, its cavity being stomodaeum).   Segments 2 to 5 are fused together, and are distinguishable only by their limbs, but

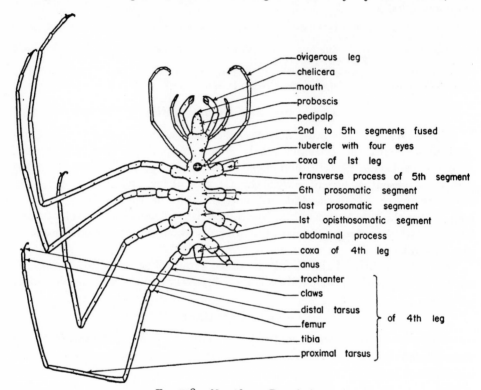

—ovigerous leg
— chelicera
—mouth
—proboscis
—pedipalp
—2nd to 5th segments fused
—tubercle with four eyes
—coxa of 1st leg
—transverse process of 5th segment
—6th prosomatic segment
—last prosomatic segment
—1st opisthosomatic segment
—abdominal process
—coxa of 4th leg
—anus
—trochanter
— claws
—distal tarsus ⎤
—femur   ⎬ of 4th leg
—tibia   ⎟
—proximal tarsus ⎦

Fig. 118.—*Nymphon.*   Dorsal view.

segments 6 and 7 are free.   Mounted dorsally on the fused segments is a tubercle with four eyes.

  c. The 1st **prosomatic appendages** (segment 2) are the 3-jointed chelate chelicerae, while the 2nd (segment 3) are the 5-jointed pedipalps (probably sensory structures).   The 4th segment bears the ovigerous legs, each consisting of 10 joints and a claw (and to which in the males, and very occasionally in the females, the egg masses are cemented).   Each of the long 8-jointed walking legs (of segments 5 to 7) is based on a lateral projection, or transverse process.   To the joints the usual names of coxa, trochanter, femur, tibia, and 4 tarsi can be applied, and on the end of the distal tarsus are one large and two smaller claws.

d. The 1st segment of the **opisthosoma** (the pregenital segment of other arachnids) is well developed, and carries the last walking legs, which are similar to the walking legs of the prosoma. The 2nd (the genital segment of other arachnids) and subsequent segments are reduced and fused together to form the abdominal process (the gonads extend forwards into the prosoma, and, like the alimentary canal, penetrate into all the walking legs ; the genital openings of the male are on the trochanters of the last 3 pairs of walking legs, while those of the female are on the trochanters of all the walking legs).

3. CONCLUSION

a. Observing the specimen, review the characteristics of the phylum, of the class, and of the subclass.

b. Compare the segmentation of *Nymphon* with that of a more typical arachnid such as *Centrurus*.

4. REFERENCES

For further details and for the internal anatomy, see :

DOHRN, A. (1881). " Die Pantopoden des Golfes von Neapel." *Fauna und Flora des Golfes von Neapel*, Vol. 3.
KÜKENTHAL, W., and KRUMBACH, T. (1932). Volume 3 and part 2 of " Handbuch der Zoologie." Berlin and Leipzig.
WIRÉN, E. (1918). " Zur Morphologie und Phylogenie der Pantopoden." *Zoologiska Bidrag från Uppsala*, Vol. 6, p. 41.

APPENDIX TO THE ARTHROPODA

1. CULTURE METHODS

a. Crustacea. Several methods are known for maintaining small fresh-water crustaceans such as *Daphnia*. One is to develop a constant supply of some unicellular green alga for food. Such a constant supply usually appears in any large aquarium which contains a few fish or aquatic reptiles, and which is kept in a light window. About once a week some of the soupy green water from this aquarium can be ladled into the tank containing the *Daphnia*. A thick suspension of yeast can also be used instead of the alga, the suspension being added until the water is slightly cloudy, and more being given when the crustaceans have cleared it. Another method, which is also very suitable for *Cyclops*, is to mix an ounce of dried sheep manure in each gallon of water, and to allow it to stand for a few days until a culture of protozoans develops. The crustaceans can then be added. Thereafter, whenever it appears neces-sary, a few lettuce leaves, or some meat or small dead animals, can be thrown in and allowed to rot. Great care must of course be taken lest so much is added that the water becomes foul, and in any case after a few months it is advisable to sieve out the crustaceans and transfer them to a new culture solution.

Larger crustaceans, like *Gammarus* and *Asellus*, will live and breed indefinitely in well-established aquaria containing a quantity of mud and rotting leaves taken from the bottom of a pond, and they can also be kept with smaller crustaceans in a culture made with sheep manure.

Land isopods, such as *Oniscus*, can best be maintained at about 20° C. in boxes containing soil rich in humus which is kept constantly damp. Stones and pieces of rotten wood will form a shelter beneath which the animals can congregate. For food they take the humus of the soil, and a slice of raw potato can also be added.

Crayfishes, such as *Astacus*, are easily kept in aquaria, and should be given a pile of stones beneath which they can hide. They will eat small pieces of any raw fish or meat, but such food must not be allowed to lie about uneaten, or the water will become fouled. Marine crabs and crayfishes can be kept in a similar manner, and fed on small pieces of raw fish or meat.

b. Myriapoda. These animals can be maintained in well-covered jars or aquaria in which the air is kept at maximum humidity. They should be given soil and rotting leaves which are kept constantly damp, but not wet, and they should be kept away from strong light. Centipedes, such as *Lithobius*, will eat small earthworms, maggots, and soft-bodied insects. Millepedes, such as *Iulus*, will feed on the decaying leaves.

c. Insecta. The methods of culturing insects are almost as many and varied as are the insects themselves, and only a few of the more important ones can be quoted here. *Blatta*, and other cockroaches, can be reared at temperatures of not less than 20° C. They should be provided with dark corners in which to retreat, and fed on such materials as bread, flour paste, sliced potato, lettuce, mashed banana, and milk. A constant supply of drinking-water is also necessary, and is best provided in a dish filled with absorbent cotton wool to prevent drowning.

The nymphs of *Ephemera* can be reared in a well-established aquarium with a layer of pond mud and decaying leaves at the bottom. Those of *Libellula*, and other dragon flies, must be kept individually to prevent cannibalism. When small they will feed on *Daphnia* (see p. 331), when larger they require small worms, such as *Enchytraeus* (see p. 206) or mosquito larvae (see below), and when almost fully grown they will readily take tadpoles and pieces of earthworms. The larvae of *Phryganea*, and similar caddis flies, also thrive in balanced aquaria, where they feed on the water weeds and on any smaller animals that may be present.

The larvae of the Lepidoptera are easily reared on their food plants, and require no special comment.

The larvae of mosquitoes, such as *Culex*, will appear in a few weeks in any aquarium left standing out of doors during the warmer months of the year, and if some mud and rotting leaves are present at the bottom of the tank, they will find sufficient food and develop fully without any special attention. If the aquarium is kept out of doors, successive batches of eggs will be laid in it, so that a constant supply of larvae can be assured.

The larvae of the blow-fly *Calliphora* are also readily obtained by putting a piece of raw meat in a shallow dish or saucer, and exposing it in an open window during the warmer weather. When it is seen that eggs have been laid, the dish can be placed on damp soil in a box or glass tank, and kept at room temperature. The box should be covered with a glass sheet to contain any smell, and to prevent water loss. When the larvae are fully grown they will crawl from the dish and pupate in the soil.

d. Other Arthropoda. For the culture methods of a large number of other arthropods, including arachnids, see :

NEEDHAM, J. G. *et al.* (1937). "Culture methods for invertebrate animals." Ithaca, New York.

2. METHODS OF FIXATION AND STORAGE

a. Onychophora. These animals should be chloroformed, dipped quickly in 90% alcohol as a wetting agent for the skin, and fixed in 5% formalin. An alternative method is to drown them in water to which a few drops of ammonia have been added. Later they can be preserved in fresh 5% formalin or transferred to 70% alcohol.

b. Crustacea. These are most conveniently killed by immersion in 5% formalin, which for marine forms should be made up with sea water, or by adding formalin up to a strength of 5% to the water in which they are confined. However, larger crustaceans, such as crayfishes or crabs, are usually killed by a short immersion in hot (not boiling) water, or, alternatively, in the case of marine species, by immersion in fresh water. Immediately movement has ceased the animals should be removed from the water, and either dissected immediately or preserved.

Barnacles, like *Lepas*, are exceptional in requiring narcotisation. This can be done by any of the common methods such as the addition to the water of crystals of menthol or of magnesium sulphate (Epsom salts). When, after some hours, the animals become insensitive, they can be killed by the addition of formalin up to a strength of 5%.

Land isopods, such as *Oniscus*, are best killed by dropping directly into 70% alcohol.

Whatever the method of killing, crustaceans should never be preserved in formalin which, unless carefully neutralised, slowly weakens and destroys the exoskeleton. Storage should be either in 70% alcohol or, better, in a 20% solution of glycerine in 70% alcohol which preserves the flexibility of the joints.

c. Myriapoda, Insecta, and Arachnida. Any of these animals should be killed by dropping directly into 70% alcohol with or without the previous use of chloroform. *Blatta,* when required for immediate dissection, should merely be chloroformed.

Storage of these animals should always be in a 20% solution of glycerine in 70% alcohol.

3. PREPARATION OF CLEARED SPECIMENS

a. For the removal of the soft tissues of the body, the standard technique is to boil in an aqueous solution of caustic potash. This leaves only the chitinous plates of the exoskeleton which are then easily studied. The strength of solution and the time of treatment vary according to the size and solidity of the specimen. Large insects should be boiled in a 5% solution, and smaller ones in a 2% solution. The smallest and most delicate should not be boiled, but should either be gently warmed in an oven or left for a day or two in a cold 2% solution. The treatment must be stopped immediately all the soft tissues have disappeared, and the specimen should then be thoroughly washed in water. After this it can either be stored in 20% glycerine in 70% alcohol, or dehydrated and mounted in Canada balsam.

4. STAINING METHODS

a. Arthopods which are naturally transparent, or which become so after clearance in caustic potash, can be stained in any chitin stain. Recommended for this purpose is carbol fuchsin (see method of preparation on p. 453) to which the specimens may be transferred direct from water. The time of staining varies with the type and size of specimen, but will probably be between a few minutes and half an hour. After staining, dehydrate by transference through the alcohols, and if necessary remove any excess stain by differentiation in 95% alcohol. Finally clear in xylol, and mount in Canada balsam.

5. SECTIONING METHOD

a. The arthropod exoskeleton is commonly so tough as to present considerable difficulties in the preparation of sections. A new method whereby even whole beetles can be satisfactorily sectioned is as follows. Fix for about 12 hours in a saturated solution of picric acid in a mixture composed of 85% dioxan, 10% formaldehyde, and 5% formic acid. Wash in several changes of dioxan until all excess picric acid is removed. Dehydrate in three 3-hour changes of 2-ethoxy-ethanol, impregnate for 12 hours with 2% celloidin in 2-ethoxy-ethanol, and clear in three 4-hour changes of benzene. The celloidin impregnation prevents subsequent imbibition pressure from disrupting the tissues. Embed in wax, trim the block to expose the tissue on one side, and solvate for 12 hours in pure ethane diol containing 5% tergitol (material can be stored in this bath). After this treatment normal sections and ribbons can be produced, and normal staining methods can be used.

CHAPTER XX

PHYLUM **MOLLUSCA**

Characteristics : Animals which are typically bilaterally symmetrical and which usually appear unsegmented; with a head, a ventral muscular foot, and a dorsal visceral hump; typically with one pair of gills, or ctenidia; with the coelom usually reduced but never absent; with a well-developed blood system, and a heart usually consisting of a ventricle and two auricles which are always enclosed in a coelomic pericardium; and with a nervous system usually containing pairs of cerebral, pleural, pedal, and visceral ganglia.

This is a sharply defined and very successful phylum, which is typically marine, but which, via a colonisation of the land, has also invaded fresh water. Until recently the relationships of the molluscs with the other invertebrate phyla have remained obscure. However, in 1952 the metamerically segmented *Neopilina galatheae* Lemche was dredged from the abyss off the west coast of Mexico. This mollusc possesses an extensive coelom and 8 or more body segments. There are 8 pairs of pedal retractor muscles (3 pairs are in the head region), 5 pairs of ctenidia with 5 pairs of retractor muscles, 2 pairs of auricles, and 6 pairs of nephridia of which two pairs are also joined by coelomoducts from the 2 pairs of gonads. Sexes are separate and fertilisation is evidently external. The nervous system resembles that of the polyplacophorans.

The nearest known relatives of *Neopilina* are Cambro-Silurian fossils, and evidently the stock is very ancient. It has been proposed that these molluscs should be accommodated in a new class, the Monoplacophora, and that they must be regarded as indicating a link between the early molluscs and the early annelids. Certainly they suggest that the Mollusca must have been derived from the old metamerically segmented coelomate stock.

1.00.   Class **Amphineura**

Characteristics : Mollusca with the body elongated and bilaterally symmetrical; head poorly developed and lacking both tentacles and eyes, but with a radula usually present; foot either large and flat, or reduced, or absent; mantle secreting calcareous spicules; no definite ganglia in the nervous system; sexes either separate or combined, and usually with a pelagic larva.

The members of this class, which are all marine, were, until the discovery of

Neopilina, regarded as being the most primitive of living molluscs. They live in or close to the littoral zone, where they feed mainly on encrusting algae and hydroids.

1.01.   Order **Polyplacophora**

Characteristics : Amphineura with the foot large and flat; the mantle secreting 8 shell plates; each lateral mantle groove containing a row of ctenidia; and sexes separate.

This order is an ancient group, and fossils are known from the Ordovician. It is sharply separated from the only other order, the hermaphroditic Aplacophora, the members of which are often worm-like with the shell, foot, and radula reduced or absent.

Genus **Ischnochiton**

I.   GENERAL ACCOUNT

a. This genus contains some of the largest species of the Polyplacophora, and it is especially common along the west coast of North America.   The animals move sluggishly near the low-tide mark, remain under rocks by day, and emerge at night to feed on small encrusting algae.   The sexes are separate, and the breeding season is in May and June, when the spermatozoa and ova are released into the quiet rock-pools at low tide.   The larvae hatch within a week, swim freely for an hour or two, and then settle and metamorphose into the adult form.

2.   EXTERNAL ANATOMY

a. The **body** is divided into a small, obscure head, a large, flat foot, and a dorsal mantle which forms a roof-like covering.   In the dorsal side of the mantle are embedded 8 calcareous plates showing growth rings.   Notice how each plate overlaps the one posterior to it (in life this articulation allows the animal to roll into a ball).   In the mantle edge surrounding these plates are thousands of pointed calcareous spicules (inserted in ectodermal pits).

b. Examine the cavity, or **mantle groove**, between the foot and the mantle edge.   Anteriorly in this groove is the head, which lacks tentacles and eyes, laterally are rows of gills, called ctenidia, and posteriorly is the anus on a papilla (in stiff, preserved specimens it may be necessary to cut away a strip of the mantle edge to uncover these structures).

c. Remove a **ctenidium** and examine its structure through a lens.   At the cut end, notice the two blood-vessels (the inner afferent and the outer efferent) and the shape of the central axis which supports the numerous gill-plates.

z

3. INTERNAL ANATOMY

a. Remove the 8 **shell-plates**, starting with the head-plate. Their firm attachment to the underlying tissues is helped by flanges which project down into the muscle layers. There are small flanges on the outer edges of all the plates, and a large flange anteriorly on all except the first.

b. With great care remove the muscle-bands and the thin skin covering the body organs. The kidney tubules, gonoducts, and dorsal blood vessel are closely attached to the underside of this skin. Next cut away the muscle of the right mantle edge to uncover the ctenidia and the efferent branchial blood vessel.

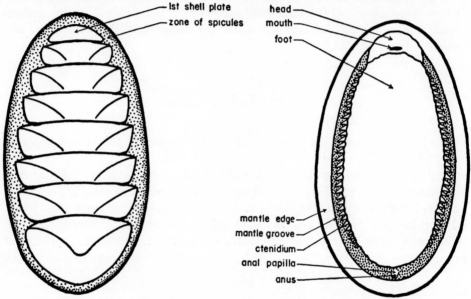

FIG. 119.—*Ischnochiton.* Dorsal and ventral views of the external features.

The dorsal part of the **blood system** consists of a large posterior heart lying in an extensive pericardium (the cavity of which is coelom). The two lateral auricles receive blood mainly from the efferent branchial vessels, and they pass it to the median ventricle, which drives it forwards through the dorsal blood-vessel to the head.

c. Mid-dorsally is the large, unpaired **gonad** (either ovary or testis), the posterior end of which lies beneath the pericardium. Distinguish the thin-walled gonoducts which open laterally into the mantle groove. Lateral to the reproductive system notice the masses of fine branching tubules which are the lateral regions of the kidneys.

d. Remove the heart, gonad, and gonoducts to uncover the **alimentary canal** and the dorsal digestive glands. Anteriorly, identify the pharynx and the salivary glands in front of it. Beneath the pharynx is a buccal mass, from which muscle-strands pass backwards and upwards. A short oesophagus leads from the pharynx into the anterior end of the capacious stomach. To uncover

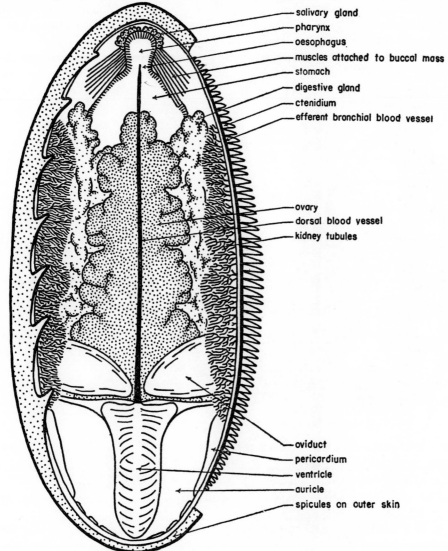

salivary gland
pharynx
oesophagus
muscles attached to buccal mass
stomach
digestive gland
ctenidium
efferent bronchial blood vessel

ovary
dorsal blood vessel
kidney tubules

oviduct
pericardium
ventricle
auricle
spicules on outer skin

FIG. 120.—*Ischnochiton.* The dorsal body organs exposed by the removal of the shell plates and of the dorsal body wall.

the remainder of the alimentary canal, carefully pick away the digestive glands. In them are embedded the posterior end of the stomach, a long, coiled intestine (typical of a herbivore), and a short rectum leading to the posterior anus. Cut through the oesophagus and the rectum and lift out the whole alimentary canal. Notice the ventral digestive glands, and if the intestine is sufficiently flexible, straighten it out to demonstrate its length.

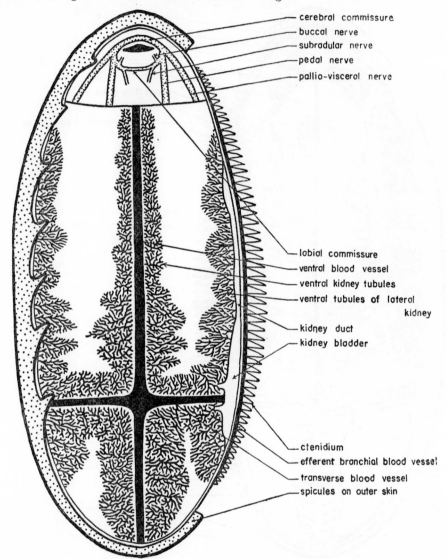

FIG. 121.—*Ischnochiton.* The ventral body organs in the base of the perivisceral haemocoel. Anteriorly, the dissection has been carried deeper to expose that part of the nervous system which surrounds the mouth.

e. Notice that the visceral mass, now nearly all removed, lay in a perivisceral cavity (which is probably haemocoel). Crossing the base of this cavity are thin muscle-strands, through which can be seen the **ventral part of the blood**

system. There is a large, longitudinal, ventral vessel (which collects blood from the head and body) and two transverse vessels, one on each side (which pass blood to the longitudinal afferent branchial vessels running beneath the efferent branchial vessels).

f. Also beneath the muscle-strands, and surrounding all these blood-vessels, are the branching **kidney tubules**. The lateral tubules open into two lateral kidney ducts, each of which is swollen posteriorly to form a bladder (from which a small ureter arises to open into the mantle groove). On each side the ventral tubules open into two separate kidney ducts, which they also obscure. These ducts open directly into the bladder.

g. Carefully remove the buccal mass and radula sac, and dissect away the muscle layers around the mouth to expose the anterior part of the **nervous system**. There are no ganglia (the ganglion cells being evenly distributed along the length of the nerve-cords), but the circumbuccal nerve-ring is large. Joining into the ring on each side are the stout pallio-visceral and pedal nerves, which run the length of the body. That part of the ring posterior to the mouth is the labial commissure, and from it arise, anteriorly, the buccal nerves and, posteriorly, the subradular nerves.

h. Finally, cut open the buccal mass to see the position of the **radula** in its diverticulum, the radula sac. Dissect out the radula, mount it on a slide, and through a microscope examine the shape and pattern on its teeth (a clearer picture is obtained if it is dehydrated and mounted unstained in Canada balsam).

3. CONCLUSION

a. Observing the specimen and the drawings made, review the characteristics of the phylum, of the class, and of the order.

b. Also review those features which are associated with the sluggish herbivorous mode of life.

4. REFERENCES

For details of the anatomy of closely related genera, see:

PLATE, L. H. (1898). "Die Anatomie und Phylogenie der Chitonen." *Zoologische Jahrbucher*, supplement 4, p. 1.
PLATE, L. H. (1902). "Die Anatomie und Phylogenie der Chitonen." *Zoologische Jahrbucher*, supplement 5, pp. 15 and 281.

2.00. Class **Gastropoda**

Characteristics : Mollusca with the body bilaterally asymmetrical; head well developed and bearing tentacles, eyes, and a radula; foot large and flat; visceral hump frequently coiled, always undergoing counter-clockwise torsion through 180°, and often subsequently undergoing some degree of detorsion; typically with the mantle secreting a single shell; the nervous system with cerebral, pleural, pedal, and visceral ganglia; sexes either separate or combined, and with or without a pelagic larva.

Although typically and mainly marine, the members of this class, via a successful colonisation of the land, have also invaded fresh water.

2.01.   Order **Prosobranchia (Streptoneura)**

Characteristics : Gastropoda which undergo torsion, but not detorsion, and which consequently have the ctenidia anterior to the heart, the mantle cavity opening anteriorly, and the visceral nerve-loop twisted into a figure of 8; shell usually well developed; sexes separate.

The majority of the gastropods belong to this order, which is almost exclusively marine.

Genus **Haliotis** (abalone, ormer, or paua)

I.   GENERAL ACCOUNT

a. The genus has a world-wide distribution in temperate and tropical seas, and individuals often occur in great numbers from the low-tide mark to depths of more than 20 fathoms.   They are found only in places where there is little or no sand, and they are particularly common on granite rocks.   They feed nocturnally on small encrusting seaweeds, and especially on red algae.   The sexes are separate, and in temperate seas breeding apparently continues throughout the warmer months.   The gametes are shed in clouds through the pores of the shell, fertilisation is external, and the larvae are pelagic.

2.   EXTERNAL ANATOMY

a. Notice the shell covering the visceral hump, and distinguish the head and foot.   The exposed parts of the **body** are heavily pigmented either green, brown, or black.   Break the attachment of the visceral hump to the shell, and twist the animal free.

b. In the **shell**, notice the flat coil with the apex posterior and on the right; the line of perforations along the left side (only the anterior ones are open, to allow water to escape from the mantle cavity); the thin outer horny layer, or periostracum; the thick, white, calcareous layer, or prismatic layer (seen where the dark periostracum has been worn from the older parts of the shell); and the inner pearly calcareous layer, or nacreous layer, with the marks of attachment of the shell muscles.

c. In the **head**, notice the mouth on a ventrally directed protuberance; the short anterior tentacles (tactile); the long median tentacles (tactile); and the stumpy posterior tentacles with the eyes at their tips.

d. The **foot** is a large muscular disc (for powerful attachment to the rock).

It is cleft anteriorly and pointed posteriorly, and dorsally on the posterior end is the pedal gland (the function of which is doubtful). A raised collar, the epipodium, encircles the foot dorsally and bears numerous epipodial tentacles (tactile).

e. In the **visceral hump**, notice the coiled apex, the free edge of the mantle (the dorsal side of this edge secretes the shell), the mantle cleft (opposite the

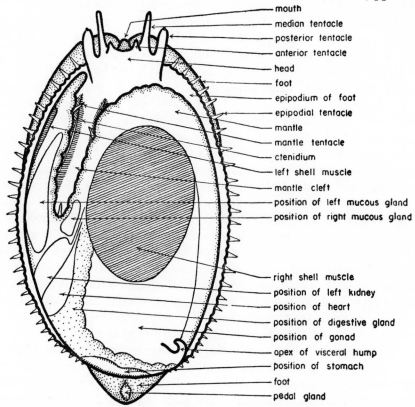

mouth
median tentacle
posterior tentacle
anterior tentacle
head
foot
epipodium of foot
epipodial tentacle
mantle
mantle tentacle
ctenidium
left shell muscle
mantle cleft
position of left mucous gland
position of right mucous gland

right shell muscle
position of left kidney
position of heart
position of digestive gland
position of gonad
apex of visceral hump
position of stomach
foot
pedal gland

Fig. 122.—*Haliotis.* A dorsal view, after the removal of the shell, to show the form of the body and the positions of the organs within the visceral hump.

line of perforations in the shell), and the mantle tentacles (usually three) on the edges of the cleft. Also visible are the positions of the large right shell muscle and the small left shell muscle, the digestive gland and stomach, the heart, and the left kidney.

f. In the **mantle cavity**, seen through the mantle cleft, identify the two ctenidia, and the two small yellow osphradia which are ventral to the anterior ends of the ctenidia (and which taste the incoming water); the rectum ending in the anus; the two kidney openings ventral to the base of the rectum; and, beneath the left edge of the mantle cleft, the large left mucous gland (the

secretion of which traps and carries away irritating sand grains, etc.). Open
the posterior end of the mantle cavity by cutting to the left of the left mucous
gland, and by separating the mantle from the rectum. Notice the small right
mucous gland, which is usually partly separated from the left gland by the
rectum, and the afferent branchial blood-vessels passing to the ctenidia.

3. INTERNAL ANATOMY

a. Although the **blood system** is seen to best advantage in specimens which
have their vessels injected with coloured latex at the time of killing, the vessels
described below can be seen without difficulty in uninjected specimens. Remove the thin skin (mantle) covering the visceral hump lateral and posterior to
the right shell muscle. This exposes the heart in its pericardium (coelom),
and the closely associated left and right kidneys. The heart consists of a
central ventricle, through which passes the rectum, and two latero-ventral
auricles, the left of which is slightly smaller than the right. Blood leaves the
ventricle partly by a small anterior aorta (to the mantle), but mainly by a large
posterior aorta which divides into two main branches, the cephalic aorta (to
the anterior end of the body) and the visceral aorta (to the organs of the
visceral hump). Capillaries and veins are lacking, and their place is taken by a
system of large lacunae (which are without walls and form a haemocoelic perivisceral cavity). Blood returning towards the heart from these lacunae passes
first into the right kidney; next through well-defined efferent renal vessels
which join together and then split apart again as the two afferent branchial
vessels supplying the ctenidia; and finally through the two efferent branchial
vessels which lead to the two auricles. Peculiarly, the small left kidney
receives only oxygenated blood from the efferent branchial vessels, and this it
passes back via the single efferent renal vessel to the ctenidia.

b. The **excretory and reproductive systems** are closely associated. The
two kidneys are hollow, sac-like structures with spongy walls. There are no
kidney ducts, but the kidney cavities open directly through small pores into the
posterior end of the mantle cavity. The large unpaired gonad (either ovary or
testis) has no gonoduct, but where it adjoins the right kidney, just posterior
to the right shell muscle, there is an opening in the kidney wall through which
ova or spermatozoa can escape via the kidney cavity. Pick away the tissue of
the right kidney near its junction with the gonad to reveal the large kidney
cavity.

c. The dissection of the **alimentary canal** is made difficult by the thinness of
the walls (the muscle layers are poorly developed and the food is kept moving by
cilia). Remove any remaining skin from the visceral hump; dissect away the
left and right kidneys and the gonad to expose the digestive glands, in which
are embedded the crop, the stomach, and part of the intestine; cut open the
ventricle to expose the rectum, which passes through it; cut away most of the

ctenidia, leaving in place only the anterior half-inch of each; skin the floor of the mantle cavity and the back of the head, taking great care not to damage the visceral nerves and ganglia, which lie immediately beneath the skin and which can be seen through it; and finally cut away any parts of the right shell muscle which obscure the alimentary canal. Carefully separate the loops of the alimentary canal, and pick away the digestive glands to expose the crop and stomach. Distinguish the buccal mass, and without disturbing the encircling nerve-ring, cut it open to find the antero-dorsal pair ot immovable horny plates (against which the ventral radula chews the food), the ventral muscular odonto-

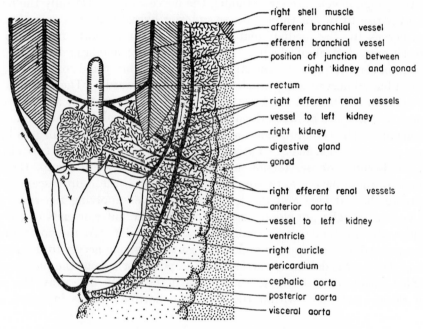

right shell muscle
afferent branchial vessel
efferent branchial vessel
position of junction between
right kidney and gonad
rectum
right efferent renal vessels
vessel to left kidney
right kidney
digestive gland
gonad
right efferent renal vessels
anterior aorta
vessel to left kidney
ventricle
right auricle
pericardium
cephalic aorta
posterior aorta
visceral aorta

FIG. 123.—*Haliotis*. The blood system in the region of the heart.

phore with the radula lying across it, and the dorsal and ventral pairs of valves that mark the posterior end of the buccal cavity. Distinguish also the pair of salivary glands lateral to the buccal mass; the long, tapering radula sac which opens into the postero-ventral end of the buccal cavity; the long oesophagus, wide at its anterior end (due to the pouching of the walls) but narrowing towards its posterior end; the capacious crop extending to the posterior end of the visceral hump; the stomach passing forwards on the left side and, close to its junction with the crop, receiving the ducts from the digestive glands; the spiral caecum of the stomach overlying the posterior end of the crop; the ventral longitudinal typhlosole within the stomach, and the valves separating the stomach cavity from the crop posteriorly and from the intestine anteriorly;

the long looped intestine lying dorsal to the oesophagus; and the rectum passing through the ventricle and ending at the anus. Finally, notice that the visceral mass lies free in a cavity, the perivisceral haemocoel.

d. To expose the anterior end of the **nervous system**, remove the salivary glands and the roof of the buccal mass posterior to the nerve-ring; remove the oesophagus and the anterior loop of the intestine, leaving in place the radula sac and taking care not to break the visceral nerves; and finally carefully dissect away the floor of the buccal mass to uncover the base of the nerve-ring and the buccal nerves. Notice the comparative absence of ganglia (due to the fact that the ganglion cells are spread along the nerve cords). Dorsally the nerve-ring gives rise to two or three pairs of anterior buccal nerves, a pair of tentacular nerves (to the median tentacles), and a pair of optic nerves (to the posterior tentacles), all of which are directed forwards; and laterally it gives rise to a pair of cerebro-pleural connectives, a pair of cerebro-pedal connectives, and a pair of buccal nerves, all of which are directed backwards. The buccal nerves pass beneath the floor of the buccal mass to join, by means of a buccal commissure, in the space between the anterior ends of the radula sheath and of the oesophagus. The cerebro-pleural and cerebro-pedal connectives all join in the pleuro-pedal ganglion mass. Laterally from this mass arise the two visceral nerves. Because of the torsion undergone by the visceral hump, the loop formed by these nerves is twisted into a figure of 8, the right visceral nerve supplying the left side and the left visceral nerve supplying the right side. The visceral ganglia are closely associated with the anterior ends of the two ctenidia, and are therefore also called branchial ganglia. At the posterior end of the visceral nerve-loop is an abdominal ganglion giving nerves to the visceral mass. The two pedal nerves arise from the posterior side of the pleuro-pedal ganglion mass, and to expose these it is necessary to cut away the right shell muscle to reach, within the foot, the narrow tunnels in which they lie.

4. CONCLUSION

a. Observing the specimen and the drawings made, review the characteristics of the phylum, of the class, and of the order.

b. Also review those features which are primitive, and those which are specialised in association with the herbivorous mode of life.

5. REFERENCE

CROFTS, D. R. (1929). " *Haliotis.*" *Memoirs of the Liverpool Marine Biological Committee*, Vol. 29.

Genus **Buccinum** (common whelk)

(The description given below applies equally to the genus *Busycon* which is also known as *Fulgur.*)

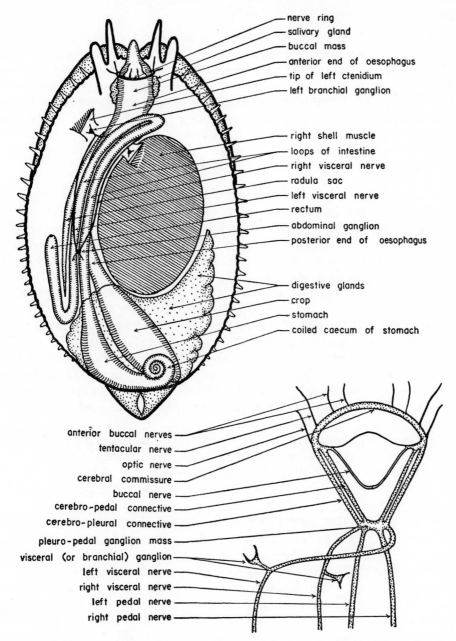

nerve ring
salivary gland
buccal mass
anterior end of oesophagus
tip of left ctenidium
left branchial ganglion

right shell muscle
loops of intestine
right visceral nerve
radula sac
left visceral nerve
rectum
abdominal ganglion
posterior end of oesophagus

digestive glands
crop
stomach
coiled caecum of stomach

anterior buccal nerves
tentacular nerve
optic nerve
cerebral commissure
buccal nerve
cerebro-pedal connective
cerebro-pleural connective
pleuro-pedal ganglion mass
visceral (or branchial) ganglion
left visceral nerve
right visceral nerve
left pedal nerve
right pedal nerve

FIG. 124.—*Haliotis.*   A dorsal view of the alimentary canal after the removal of the respiratory, excretory, and reproductive organs.   The anterior region of the nervous system.

I. GENERAL ACCOUNT

a. Species of the genus *Buccinum* are common in the arctic, antarctic, and temperate regions, and their range extends from the low-tide mark to depths of about 100 fathoms. They are carnivorous, and eat any living or freshly dead animals, particularly pelecypod molluscs and decapod crustaceans. Breeding occurs in spring, fertilisation is internal, and the embryos feed on each other while developing inside chitinous capsules. These capsules are secreted round the eggs by the pedal groove.

2. EXTERNAL ANATOMY

a. In a fresh specimen (see method of killing on p. 410) the shell must first be removed by breaking it open with bone forceps, but in preserved specimens this should already have been done to allow the penetration of the preservative. While removing the calcareous **shell** notice its structure. The wide opening leads into a coiled tube which, becoming progressively narrower, ends blindly at the apex. The opening is drawn out into a shell siphon in which the mantle siphon, a prolongation of the mantle edge, normally lies. Each coil of the shell is termed a whorl, the narrow apical whorls form the spire (the oldest part of the shell), and the line of contact between the whorls is the suture. The whole structure is built round a central column, the columella.

b. The body of the animal is clearly divisible into a head, a foot, and a coiled visceral hump. On the **head** notice the two tentacles (capable of great extension) bearing, laterally and towards their bases, two small black eyes; and the mouth situated at the end of a proboscis (which is also capable of great extension).

c. On the muscular **foot**, find the transverse pedal gland (for secreting the egg cases) situated immediately below the lip of the blunt anterior end; and the disc of calcified chitin, called the operculum (for closing the opening of the shell when the animal retracts), situated above the pointed posterior end.

d. On the coiled **visceral hump**, notice the anterior opening of the mantle cavity; the thickened edge of the mantle (for shell secretion); and, on the left side, the prolongation of the mantle edge to form a siphon (capable of even greater extension than the tentacles, and through which water enters the mantle cavity). Through the transparent mantle it can be seen that the apex of the coil is formed of a posterior, or right, digestive gland, on which lie the unpaired gonad (either ovary or testis) and the gonoduct (straight in the female, but highly convoluted in the male). The anterior, or left, digestive gland is at the base of the visceral hump, and the unpaired kidney and the heart are to the left of the base. Part of the looped stomach and intestine are also visible at the surface.

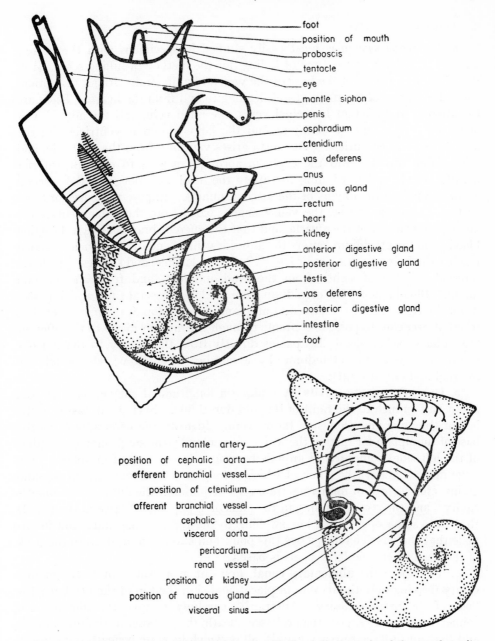

foot
position of mouth
proboscis
tentacle
eye
mantle siphon
penis
osphradium
ctenidium
vas deferens
anus
mucous gland
rectum
heart
kidney
anterior digestive gland
posterior digestive gland
testis
vas deferens
posterior digestive gland
intestine
foot

mantle artery
position of cephalic aorta
efferent branchial vessel
position of ctenidium
afferent branchial vessel
cephalic aorta
visceral aorta
pericardium
renal vessel
position of kidney
position of mucous gland
visceral sinus

FIG. 125.—*Buccinum.* A dorsal view of a male with the shell removed and the mantle cavity cut open to show the form of the body and the positions of the organs within the visceral hump. Part of the blood system as seen through the mantle.

3. INTERNAL ANATOMY

a. The **blood system** is most easily studied in specimens with the vessels injected with latex at the time of killing (for the method of killing see p. 410). Examine the left side of the base of the visceral hump, and, without dissection, trace the courses of the main vessels leading to and from the heart.   These are the afferent and efferent branchial veins, the renal vein, and the aorta.   Cut open the pericardium (coelom) to find the large muscular ventricle and the dorsal, thin-walled auricle.   The aorta arises ventrally from the ventricle, and immediately divides into the cephalic aorta (branching to give an anterior mantle artery, and continuing to supply the head and foot) and the visceral aorta (supplying the organs of the visceral hump).   Expose the bases of these aortae.   Notice next that the vein bringing blood from the kidney enters the anterior dorsal end of the auricle, and that the efferent branchial vein, bringing blood from the ctenidium, enters the anterior ventral end of the auricle.   Blood reaches the kidney, via more or less well-defined lacunae and sinuses (which are internal and out of sight), from the head and foot, and from the visceral hump.   Blood reaches the ctenidium from the large visceral sinus which passes down the right side of the visceral hump and into the top of the mantle cavity, where it branches to pass its contents through the mucous gland to the afferent branchial vessel.   Blood also passes directly from the kidney to the mucous gland (and so to the ctenidium) by a number of small vessels (which are internal and out of sight).

b. Open the **mantle cavity** by making a longitudinal cut through its roof about half an inch to the right of the mid-dorsal line.   Such a cut passes to the left of the anus and alongside the rectum.   Identify the osphradium (at the base of the siphon for tasting the water as it enters) ; the single ctenidium (that of the left side) composed of an axis bearing only one row of gill-plates ; the large mucous gland (the slime of which entangles and removes irritating sand grains, etc.) formed of numerous transverse wrinkles of the lining of the mantle cavity ; and the rectum ending in the anus on a papilla.   Notice in the female that the vagina opens on a low swelling to the right of the anus, and in the male that the vas deferens passes this point and extends almost on to the back of the head where the large penis is based.

c. To expose the **alimentary canal**, first cut away the roof of the mantle cavity (leaving only the rectum in place), and skin the top of the head and the floor of the mantle cavity.   Anteriorly, carefully remove the muscles and connective tissue to expose the proboscis sheath, the proboscis retractor muscles, and the pair of large salivary glands, all of which lie close beneath the surface. Behind and to the side of these structures, continue the dissection more deeply to expose the nerves which emerge from beneath the salivary glands, the cephalic aorta (the base of which was previously uncovered), and the long oesophagus.

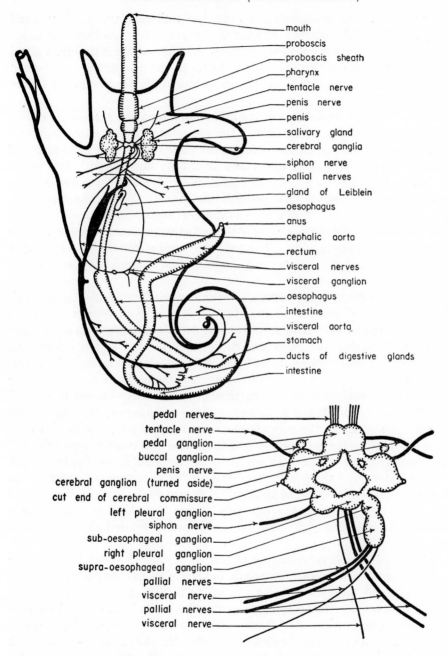

mouth
proboscis
proboscis sheath
pharynx
tentacle nerve
penis nerve
penis
salivary gland
cerebral ganglia
siphon nerve
pallial nerves
gland of Leiblein
oesophagus
anus
cephalic aorta
rectum
visceral nerves
visceral ganglion
oesophagus
intestine
visceral aorta
stomach
ducts of digestive glands
intestine

pedal nerves
tentacle nerve
pedal ganglion
buccal ganglion
penis nerve
cerebral ganglion (turned aside)
cut end of cerebral commissure
left pleural ganglion
siphon nerve
sub-oesophageal ganglion
right pleural ganglion
supra-oesophageal ganglion
pallial nerves
visceral nerve
pallial nerves
visceral nerve

FIG. 126.—*Buccinum.* A dorsal view of a dissection of the alimentary canal with the digestive glands removed. Below is the ring of ganglia and the main nerves (the cerebral commissure has been cut and the cerebral ganglia turned aside).

Cut the proboscis retractor muscles, separate the proboscis from its sheath, and gently pull it forwards to reveal the anterior part of the oesophagus encircled by a ring of ganglia, the ducts of the salivary glands, and the thin-walled gland of Leiblein (function unknown), which is dorsal to the oesophagus just behind the ring of ganglia. Split open the proboscis longitudinally to find the radula enclosed in a radula sheath.

d. Dissect out the **remainder of the alimentary canal** by tracing its course inside the visceral hump. To do this, carefully pick away the obscuring parts of the digestive glands and of the gonad, at the same time noticing the course of the visceral aorta (the base of which was previously uncovered). This vessel passes latero-ventrally to the anterior digestive gland, and then penetrates the posterior digestive gland to pass beneath the gonad. Notice that the oesophagus suddenly increases in diameter as it enters the visceral hump, and that it then passes back to the posterior V-shaped stomach, into which open the ducts of the digestive glands. The intestine passes forwards, following a twisting course, until it joins the wide rectum, which opens anteriorly at the anus on a papilla.

e. To uncover the **nervous system**, remove the salivary glands, cut through the oesophagus just anterior to the ring of ganglia, and dissect away the proboscis and its sheath. Notice how the cephalic aorta branches posteriorly to the ring of ganglia, the main branch crossing the top of the oesophagus from left to right and turning down beneath it. Remove the cephalic aorta. The ring of ganglia, and the bases of the nerves coming from it, are partially obscured by a gelatinous connective tissue, which must be gently cleared away. Identify the cerebral ganglia on top of the oesophagus; the large nerves passing to the tentacles; the nerve to the siphon on the left; the nerve to the penis on the right (in the male only); and the pallial and visceral nerves twisted so that those from the right cross dorsal to the oesophagus to supply the left side, while those from the left pass ventral to the oesophagus to supply the right side. Follow the course of the visceral nerves to the base of the visceral hump, where the nerve of the left side passes dorsal to the oesophagus to join with that of the right side in the dorsally situated pair of visceral ganglia.

f. The details of the anterior **ring of ganglia** are obscured by the sheathing connective tissue. The easiest way to demonstrate them is to cut the cerebral commissure, which links the cerebral ganglia, turn aside these two ganglia, and with great care remove the oesophagus so that the ventral ganglia of the nerve-ring can be seen from the inside. The pedal ganglia are anterior, and give rise to bunches of pedal nerves which extend forwards. In the male, the right pedal ganglion also gives rise to the large penis nerve. The tentacle nerves arise from the cerebral ganglia. The small buccal ganglia are attached anteriorly to the cerebral ganglia (the fine buccal commissure linking the buccal ganglia will have been broken). The pedal, cerebral, and buccal ganglia are symmetrical, but the posteriorly situated pleural ganglia are not. Each pleural ganglion has a specialised posterior region called the oesophageal ganglion. On the left there is the suboesophageal ganglion, which forms a link between the pleural ganglia, and which bears the two pallial nerves and the visceral nerve which cross to the right side. On the right there is the supraoesophageal ganglion, which is free and directed backwards, and which bears the two pallial nerves and the visceral nerve which supply the left side.

4. CONCLUSION

a. Observing the specimen and the drawings made, review the characteristics of the phylum, of the class, and of the order.

b. Compare the advanced asymmetrical condition of *Buccinum* with the more primitive symmetrical condition of *Haliotis*.

5. REFERENCE

DAKIN, W. J. (1912). "*Buccinum.*" *Memoirs of the Liverpool Marine Biological Committee*, Vol. 20.

2.02. Order **Opisthobranchia**

Characteristics : Gastropoda which undergo detorsion, and which consequently have the ctenidia posterior to the heart, the mantle cavity opening laterally or posteriorly, and the visceral nerve-loop not twisted into a figure of 8; with the ctenidia and mantle cavity sometimes absent, when respiration is through the body surface which often develops secondary gills; shell usually reduced or absent; hermaphrodite.

The members of this order are considered to have descended from prosobranchiate gastropods, and, like them, they are marine.

Genus **Aplysia** (sea hare)

1. GENERAL ACCOUNT

a. Species of this genus occur from the Arctic to the Antarctic, and from the low-tide mark to depths of about 40 fathoms. They are often very numerous where the water is uncontaminated and food plentiful. When young they feed mainly on red algae, but when older they take both brown and green algae. They are able to change their appearance to red, brown, or olive-green, according to the colour of the weed on which they find themselves. In spring they migrate to the intertidal zone, where cross-fertilisation occurs and the eggs are laid. These hatch into free-swimming, pelagic, veliger larvae.

A A

2. EXTERNAL ANATOMY

a. Anteriorly, distinguish the **head** and neck (the latter is capable of considerable extension). The head bears the mouth; an anterior pair of short tentacles with grooved outer edges and broad, flattened bases (tactile organs); a posterior pair of longer tentacles called rhinophores, also with grooved outer edges but with the grooves closed proximally (olfactory organs); a pair of small black eyes anterior and lateral to the bases of the rhinophores; and a small penis lateral to the base of the right anterior tentacle. Passing back along the right side of the neck from the base of the penis, an open spermatic groove (ciliated) extends to the common genital opening on the visceral hump.

b. The muscular **foot**, blunt in front and pointed behind, is elongated, narrow, and partly grooved (for climbing seaweed stalks). Laterally, it bears a pair of large fleshy outgrowths, the parapodia, which project upwards and inwards to enclose the visceral hump (they can be used as fins to enable the animal to swim).

c. Turn aside the parapodia to expose the **visceral** hump, over which the mantle secretes a thin chitinous shell. However, since the mantle edges turn up and over this shell, it is almost entirely enclosed, and is only in contact with the outside through a small pore, the shell aperture. Notice, on the right side, the opening into the mantle cavity.

d. Turn to the left the flap covering the **mantle cavity**. Notice the outline of the purple gland (for secreting a protective screen of purple dye) inside the edge of this flap; the single large foliose ctenidium attached posteriorly where the afferent (ventral) and efferent (dorsal) branchial blood-vessels are visible; the small opening of the kidney duct close to the posterior point of attachment of the ctenidium; the line of the common hermaphrodite duct ending in the common genital opening; and the outline of the opaline gland (for secreting a nauseating fluid as a defence mechanism) to the right of the genital duct. In a fresh specimen the single osphradium (for tasting the water passing to the ctenidium) is visible as a yellowish patch anterior to the point of attachment of the ctenidium.

e. Inserting scissors into the shell aperture, cut away the mantle edges, and remove the **shell**, which is horny (there is little or no calcareous impregnation), transparent, and flattened (coiling occurs in the larva but is later lost). New growth takes place anteriorly, and growth-rings are visible. Posteriorly, the shell is pointed and curves ventrally, this region being called the umbo, and there is a concavity on the right, called the anal incision.

3. INTERNAL ANATOMY

a. Make a cut through the body-wall between the common hermaphrodite duct and the opaline gland, taking care not to dig deeply, since the visceral

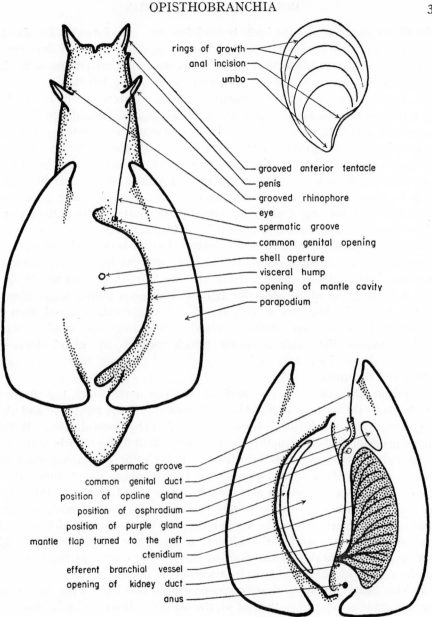

rings of growth
anal incision
umbo

grooved anterior tentacle
penis
grooved rhinophore
eye
spermatic groove
common genital opening
shell aperture
visceral hump
opening of mantle cavity
parapodium

spermatic groove
common genital duct
position of opaline gland
position of osphradium
position of purple gland
mantle flap turned to the left
ctenidium
efferent branchial vessel
opening of kidney duct
anus

FIG. 127.—*Aplysia*. A dorsal view of the external features, and, on the right, the shell and the mantle cavity which has been opened by turning the mantle flap to the left.

nerves and ganglia lie immediately beneath. Continue the cut obliquely forwards so that it reaches and passes along the mid-dorsal line between the bases of the tentacles. Also continue the cut backwards along the base of the right parapodium, across the body behind the anus, and forwards for about an inch along the base of the left parapodium.   Pin down the right flap, cut the strands of connective tissue that hold the organs of the visceral mass in place, roll the whole mass on to the left side, and pin down the left flap.

b. Trace the course of the **alimentary canal**.   Anteriorly, in front of the nerve-ring, is the muscular buccal mass.   Make a longitudinal dorsal incision through the top of this mass, and inside notice the anterior plate against which the broad radula can grind.   The radula itself is set posteriorly on a muscular cushion, the odontophore.   The narrow oesophagus, surrounded by the ring of ganglia, swells into a capacious, thin-walled crop on the lateral walls of which is a pair of narrow salivary glands.   The ducts of these glands pass forward through the ring of ganglia to open into the posterior end of the pharynx. Behind the crop, and separated from it by a deep constriction, are the anterior and posterior gizzards, with muscular walls.   Cut open these chambers to find the teeth, which, although normally fixed to the inner lining, may, after preservation, become loose in the cavity.   In the anterior gizzard the teeth are large and blunt, but in the posterior gizzard, which has thinner walls, they are smaller, more slender, and more pointed.   The alimentary canal then disappears into the massive digestive gland.   Pick away the whole digestive gland to expose the small stomach, which receives the gland ducts, the posteriorly directed caecum, and the long coiled intestine which ends in the rectum and the anus.

c. Locate the visceral nerves and the anterior aorta which together come from beneath the anterior end of the crop, pass round the right side and above the gizzards, and end dorsal to the anterior end of the visceral mass.   Without damaging either of these structures, separate the floor of the mantle cavity from the underlying visceral mass by cutting through the common genital duct where it reaches the common genital aperture, through the rectum where it reaches the anus, and through any binding connective tissue.   As this separation proceeds, locate the heart (to which the anterior aorta leads), and avoid cutting those vessels (from the ctenidium and the kidney) which enter the thin-walled auricle.   Notice the **kidney**, a triangular organ with the apex posterior, which remains in the floor of the mantle cavity to the left of the ctenidium, and which is best seen by transmitted light.

d. The **heart** lies in a spacious pericardium (coelom) with the smaller ventricle anterior to, and to the left of, the auricle.   Blood (with haemocyanin in solution) enters the right end of the auricle from the efferent branchial and efferent renal vessels, having reached the ctenidium and the kidney through a system of large sinuses and lacunae, which take the place of both capillaries and veins and which form the large perivisceral cavity (haemocoel).   Remove a section of mesentery from the perivisceral cavity, and notice that it is full of holes (fenestrated) to permit the passage of the blood.   At the left anterior end of the ventricle find the short aorta, which splits immediately into an anterior aorta (supplying the head, neck, parapodia, and anterior region of the

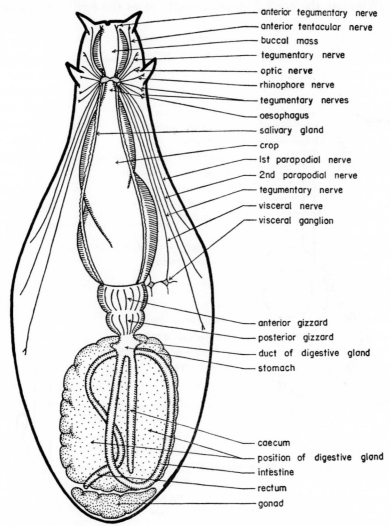

anterior tegumentary nerve
anterior tentacular nerve
buccal mass
tegumentary nerve
optic nerve
rhinophore nerve
tegumentary nerves
oesophagus
salivary gland
crop
1st parapodial nerve
2nd parapodial nerve
tegumentary nerve
visceral nerve
visceral ganglion

anterior gizzard
posterior gizzard
duct of digestive gland
stomach

caecum
position of digestive gland
intestine
rectum
gonad

FIG. 128.—*Aplysia.*   A dorsal view of a dissection of the alimentary canal.

visceral mass) and a visceral aorta (supplying the intestine and digestive gland, but broken when this gland was removed).

e. Trace the course of the hermaphrodite **reproductive system.**   The large gonad (an ovo-testis, shedding ripe spermatozoa and unripe eggs to prevent self fertilisation) is the most posterior organ in the visceral mass, and from its anterior surface there arises the posterior hermaphrodite duct.   This prominent and highly coiled duct passes forwards, and after looping over a small caecum, the spermatheca (which stores spermatozoa received from another individual), enters the genital mass to swell out as the fertilisation chamber.

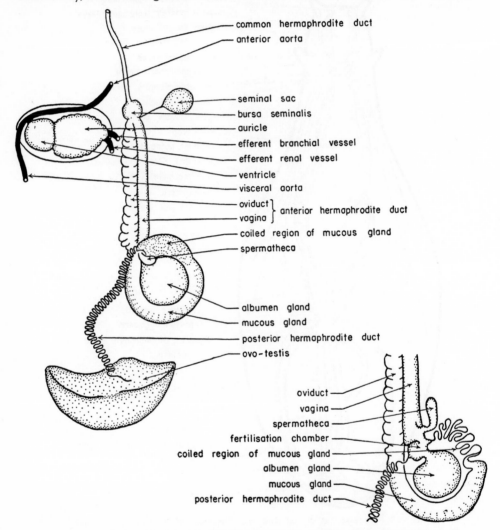

FIG. 129.—*Aplysia.*   The heart and the hermaphrodite reproductive system, and, on the right, the organs of the genital mass separated to show their relationships.

Also within the genital mass are the globular albumen gland (applying an albumen coat to each egg) and the banana-shaped mucous gland (forming the mucilage which holds the egg mass together).   Dissect apart these various organs to find their interrelationships (see Fig. 129).   From the genital mass there passes forwards the large anterior hermaphrodite duct, which is divided into three parallel grooves: the straight vagina on the left (up which spermatozoa are introduced during copulation), the sacculated oviduct on the right (down which the eggs pass), and the tiny and invisible sperm duct (down which the spermatozoa pass). At the anterior end of this triple duct is the swollen bursa seminalis, into which opens a narrow duct from the spherical

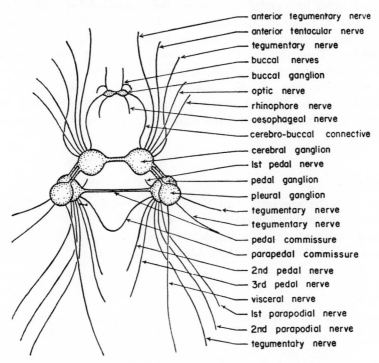

anterior tegumentary nerve
anterior tentacular nerve
tegumentary nerve
buccal nerves
buccal ganglion
optic nerve
rhinophore nerve
oesophageal nerve
cerebro-buccal connective
cerebral ganglion
Ist pedal nerve
pedal ganglion
pleural ganglion
tegumentary nerve
tegumentary nerve
pedal commissure
parapedal commissure
2nd pedal nerve
3rd pedal nerve
visceral nerve
Ist parapodial nerve
2nd parapodial nerve
tegumentary nerve

FIG. 130.—*Aplysia*. The nerve ring and the main nerves.

seminal sac (whose function is to absorb the seminal fluid and cellular detritus introduced with the spermatozoa during copulation). The bursa seminalis marks the beginning of the common hermaphrodite duct, a simple tubular structure which extends forwards to the common genital opening from which the sperm groove (ciliated) runs to the penis.

f. To expose the anterior end of the **nervous system**, cut through the anterior end of the oesophagus and the posterior end of the crop, withdraw the oesophagus from the ring of ganglia, and remove it and the crop together with the salivary glands. Distinguish the dorsal pair of cerebral ganglia which gives rise to a pair of cerebro-buccal connectives, two pairs of tegumentary nerves (to the body-wall), a pair of anterior tentacular nerves, a pair of optic nerves, and a pair of rhinophore nerves; the entero-ventral pair of pedal ganglia which gives rise to three pairs of pedal nerves, two pairs of parapodial nerves, and a pair of tegumentary nerves; and the postero-ventral pair of pleural ganglia which gives rise to two pairs of tegumentary nerves and a pair of visceral nerves. The cerebral ganglia are linked to the pedal and pleural ganglia by cerebro-pedal and cerebro-pleural connectives respectively, the cerebral ganglia are linked to each other by a cerebral commissure, and the pedal ganglia are linked to each other by a pedal commissure and a parapedal commissure. The pleural ganglia are not joined together. The cerebro-buccal connectives, arising from the cerebral ganglia, pass beneath the buccal mass to join the buccal ganglia. Turn the buccal mass forwards to find these ganglia, the buccal commissures which link them, and the buccal and oesophageal nerves to which they give rise. Finally, follow the course of the visceral nerves backwards to find the dorsally situated pair of visceral ganglia, the visceral commissure which links them, and the numerous branches to the organs of the visceral mass.

4. CONCLUSION

a. Observing the specimen and the drawings made, review the characteristics of the phylum, of the class, and of the order.

b. Also review those features and defence mechanisms which are associated with the sluggish herbivorous mode of life.

5. REFERENCE

EALES, N. B. (1921). *"Aplysia."* *Memoirs of the Liverpool Marine Biological Committee*, Vol. 24.

Genus **Clione** (sea butterfly)

I. GENERAL ACCOUNT

a. This and other related genera, all commonly known as sea butterflies, were once considered to constitute a separate class, the Pteropoda. They have a cosmopolitan distribution in the plankton.

b. Especially well known is *Clione limacina* (Phipps), which occurs in huge swarms in the surface waters of the Arctic Ocean, and which extends as far south as the English Channel and the waters off New York. It feeds predaceously on other smaller planktonic animals, and, like so many of them, it is almost completely transparent. It is hermaphrodite, but cross-fertilisation is probably the general rule. There does not appear to be any definite breeding season.

2. EXTERNAL ANATOMY

a. The **head** is distinct, and bears, as its most prominent feature, 3 pairs of white buccal cones, which may either be considerably extended, or retracted and covered by the two cephalic hoods (these cones are sensory, and they also secrete a sticky substance for gripping the prey). The mouth is anterior within the circle of the buccal cones. Based on the cephalic hoods is an anterior pair of tentacles (tactile), while dorsally on the back of the head is a posterior pair of shorter tentacles bearing eyes (in preserved specimens these posterior tentacles are usually invaginated and seen only as small pits).

b. The **foot** is represented ventrally by a small median lobe and two larger lateral lobes, and laterally by the pair of large parapodia (which are used for swimming).

c. The uncoiled **visceral hump** is situated between and posterior to the parapodia, and it lacks any trace of a shell. The anus opens ventral to the posterior edge of the right parapodium, and the genital opening is beneath the front edge of the right parapodium. Notice the absence of both a mantle cavity and a ctenidium (respiration takes place through the whole body surface).

3. INTERNAL ANATOMY

a. If the specimen is small it can be stained and mounted on a microscope slide (see method on p. 411). If it is as large as an inch or more in length it can be opened by a longitudinal dorsal incision through the skin. **Within the head** distinguish the buccal mass, which is large and trilobed (the ventral lobe contains the radula, and the lateral lobe contains numerous hooked jaws); the long, thin-walled oesophagus, starting anterior and dorsal to the buccal mass and ending within the digestive gland; the pair of cerebral ganglia, with their most prominent nerves leading to the buccal cones, the anterior tentacles, the skin, and the eyes; the thread-like salivary glands passing beneath the cerebral ganglia to enter the buccal cavity; and the transverse septum, which separates the cavity (probably haemocoel) of the head from that of the visceral hump.

b. **Within the visceral hump** the body organs are concentrated between the parapodia (so that the tail is lightened and does not upset the balance; the animal swims, as a moth flies, in a horizontal position). Notice the large, yellowish digestive gland which entirely encloses the stomach; the short intestine emerging from the posterior end of the digestive gland and passing obliquely forwards to open on the right side; the pinkish gonad (ovo-testis) posterior to the digestive gland; and the transverse septum which separates the cavity of this region from that of the tail. The heart (an auricle and a ventricle in a pericardium) and the kidney are not easily distinguished.

    c. Open the animal again by a longitudinal ventral incision. The herma-

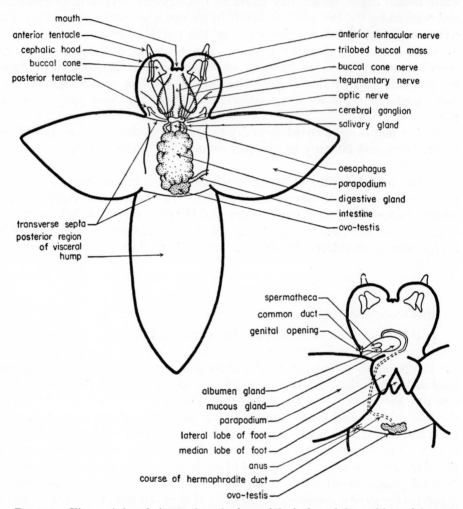

FIG. 131.—*Clione.* A dorsal view to show the form of the body and the positions of the main body organs. On the right is a ventral view of the anterior region to show the form of the foot and the position of the reproductive system.

phrodite duct passes up the right side, and the **genital mass** to which it leads is in the base of the head. This mass is composed of an albumen gland, a mucous gland, and a spermatheca, and it opens on the right side through a short common hermaphrodite duct.

    d. **Within the parapodia,** notice the crossing patterns of the muscle strands.

4. CONCLUSION

a. Observing the specimen, review the characteristics of the phylum, of the class, and of the order.

b. Also review those special features which are associated with the pelagic mode of life, and the many ways in which the animal resembles *Aplysia*.

5. REFERENCES

For further details regarding the structure of this and other pelagic opistho-branchiates, see :

PELSENEER, P. (1885). " The cephalic appendages of the Gymnosomatous Pteropoda, and especially of *Clione*." *Quarterly Journal of Microscopical Science*, Vol. 25, p. 491.

PELSENEER, P. (1888). " Report on the Pteropoda collected by H.M.S. Challenger during the years 1873–1876. Part III. Anatomy." *Report of the Scientific Results of the Voyage of H.M.S. Challenger. Zoology.* Vol. 23.

2.03. Order **Pulmonata**

Characteristics : Gastropoda which lack ctenidia, and which have the mantle cavity developed as a lung with a small external opening and a highly vascular dorsal wall ; which undergo torsion, but in which the nervous system is symmetrical due to the great shortening of the visceral nerves and the consequent withdrawal of the visceral ganglia into the sub-oesophageal region ; with only one kidney and one auricle ; and hermaphrodite.

Having descended from marine forms, the members of this order are specialised for terrestrial life. However, many genera such as the common *Lymnaea* and *Planorbis* have invaded fresh water, and a few have even returned to live in salt marshes or between tide-marks. Almost all the pulmonates breathe air, but a few species, for instance of *Lymnaea*, live in deep lakes and have the lung full of water.

Genus **Helix** (common or edible snail)

1. GENERAL ACCOUNT

a. The various species of *Helix* are terrestrial animals which usually remain hidden by day. They feed, mainly by night or after rain, on such living vegetable matter as leaves or fruit, from which fragments are torn and swallowed by means of the radula. In winter they hibernate by burrowing into the soil, withdrawing into the shell, and closing the shell aperture with a mucous secretion hardened with calcium phosphate. Copulation and egg-laying occur at any time when the snails are not hibernating. The eggs are large, are laid in the ground under the cover of leaves, etc., and hatch directly into tiny snails.

2. EXTERNAL ANATOMY

a. In a freshly killed or preserved snail (for the method of killing and preserving see p. 411) examine the **shell** with its spiral structure and prominent

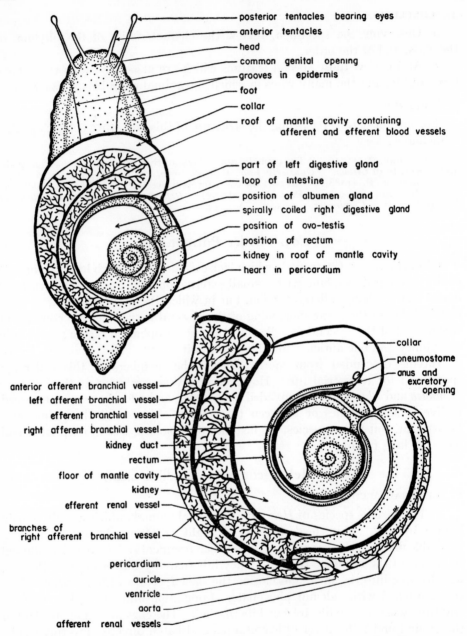

posterior tentacles bearing eyes
anterior tentacles
head
common genital opening
grooves in epidermis
foot
collar
roof of mantle cavity containing
    afferent and efferent blood vessels

part of left digestive gland
loop of intestine
position of albumen gland
spirally coiled right digestive gland
position of ovo-testis
position of rectum
kidney in roof of mantle cavity
heart in pericardium

collar
pneumostome
anus and
    excretory
    opening

anterior afferent branchial vessel
left afferent branchial vessel
efferent branchial vessel
right afferent branchial vessel
kidney duct
rectum
floor of mantle cavity
kidney
efferent renal vessel

branches of
    right afferent branchial vessel

pericardium
auricle
ventricle
aorta
afferent renal vessels

FIG. 132.—*Helix*.   A dorsal view with the shell removed to show the visceral hump and the positions of the organs within it, and, below, the mantle cavity exposed by cutting open and turning aside its roof (the direction of blood flow is shown by arrows).

lines of growth. The large anterior opening, with its flanged lip, faces ventrally and to the right, while the posterior apex of the spiral points dorsally and to the right. Cut open the shell with bone forceps, and extract the animal. While doing this, notice that the shell is built round a central hollow axis, the columella; that the coils are tightly fused together along the suture; and that the shell wall is composed of three layers, the outer periostracum (horny and pigmented), the middle layer (calcareous and porcelain-like), and the inner layer (calcareous and pearly).

b. The body is divided into a head and foot, which are not clearly separable, and a coiled visceral hump. The **head** bears the ventral mouth, which has three prominent lips, two lateral and one ventral; the small anterior tentacles (tactile, and capable of invagination); the larger posterior tentacles (also capable of invagination), each bearing an eye; and the common genital aperture behind and above the right lateral lip. Two grooves run back from the sides of the head to the base of the visceral hump, that on the left starting just posterior to the lateral lip, and that on the right starting from the common genital aperture.

c. The elongated **foot** is blunt anteriorly and pointed posteriorly, and its pedal gland (for secreting the lubricating mucus which helps locomotion) opens above the front of the foot and below the inferior lip of the head.

d. The **visceral hump**, coiling up from the dorsal side of the foot, makes about four and a half turns, and through the thin mantle covering it some of the internal organs can be seen. The first half-turn of the spiral contains the first half of the mantle cavity, the roof of which is thickened anteriorly as the collar (for secreting the shell), but elsewhere is very thin and vascular (for respiration). Find the small external opening, or pneumostome, of this lung-like region of the mantle cavity. The second half-turn of the spiral contains the second half of the mantle cavity. This is almost filled by the large kidney, close to the morphologically anterior end of which lies the heart. Along the inner margin of the whole mantle cavity run the rectum and the kidney duct. The remainder of the coiled visceral hump contains the dark brown lobes of the digestive gland, on the surface of which there are visible a loop of the intestine, the lighter brown or whitish albumen gland of the reproductive system, and the ovo-testis.

3. INTERNAL ANATOMY

a. Open the mantle cavity by cutting through its roof transversely just behind the collar, and longitudinally along the side of the rectum. Pin aside the roof of the cavity, together with the kidney and the heart. Trace the course of the **blood system**. The most prominent vessel, the efferent branchial vein taking blood to the heart, runs along the middle of the roof. Cut open the pericardium to expose the large, thin-walled auricle and the smaller muscular ventricle.   Locate the aorta leading from the posterior end of the ventricle, and notice that it splits almost immediately into a visceral aorta (which passes along the ventral surface of the digestive gland to supply the whole visceral hump) and a cephalic aorta (which disappears beneath the surface to supply the head and foot).   From these aortae the blood enters a system of irregular lacunae (which take the place of capillaries and veins, and form a perivisceral cavity), and then, returning towards the heart, it enters the afferent branchial vessel.   This is a looped vessel running along the left side of the mantle cavity, across the top just posterior to the collar, and back along the right side.   Blood from the head and foot enters the left arm of the vessel, while blood from the visceral hump enters the right arm.   The numerous branches of the afferent branchial vessel break into capillaries in the roof of the mantle cavity.   In addition, that part of the right arm of the vessel which lies alongside the kidney gives rise to a number of afferent renal vessels.   Blood from the kidney passes into the base of the efferent branchial vessel via the large efferent renal vessel.

b. The **excretory system** is simple.   The single kidney, already located in the roof of the mantle cavity, is drained by a single kidney duct.   This duct passes along the outer edge of the kidney, and then crosses to and runs along the inner edge, where it lies above the rectum.   Trace it forwards to the anterior end of the mantle cavity.   Cut up from the pneumostome through the mantle collar to find the elongated, slit-like opening of the kidney duct in the right edge of the pneumostome close to the anus.

c. In dissecting the **alimentary canal**, first separate the rectum and turn it to one side.   Make a longitudinal incision through the floor of the mantle cavity, and continue it forwards along the mid-dorsal line to the front of the head. Turn aside the flaps and notice the well-developed perivisceral cavity (haemo-coel) composed of blood lacunae.   Remove the skin (mantle) covering the spiral visceral hump.   Without injuring the nervous system or the complicated reproductive system, identify the muscular buccal mass, posterior to which is the nerve-ring ; the narrow oesophagus passing through the nerve-ring together with the prominent retractor muscle of the radula ; the thin-walled crop extending into the base of the visceral hump ; the pair of salivary glands closely applied to the sides of the crop, and their two ducts passing forwards through the nerve-ring to open into the top of the buccal mass ; the thin-walled stomach, which is wider than the crop and which coils into the second turn of the spiral visceral hump to receive, from opposite sides, the ducts of the lobed left digestive gland and of the smaller coiled right digestive gland ; and the intestine, which lies within the left digestive gland and which follows an S-shaped course to join the long rectum previously located.

d. Separate the **reproductive system** from the alimentary canal.   Locate the ovo-testis (which is protandrous to prevent self-fertilisation) in the inner

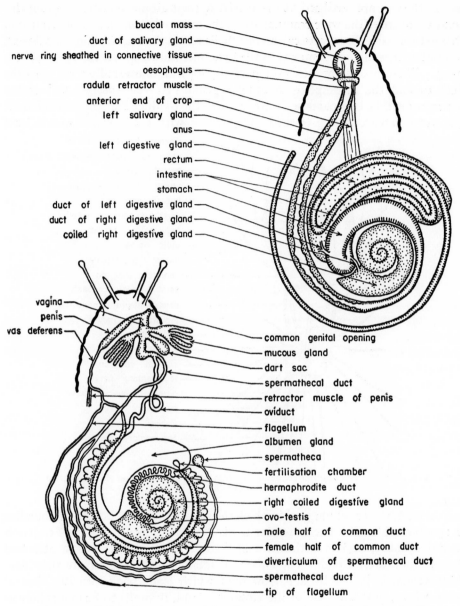

buccal mass
duct of salivary gland
nerve ring sheathed in connective tissue
oesophagus
radula retractor muscle
anterior end of crop
left salivary gland
anus
left digestive gland
rectum
intestine
stomach
duct of left digestive gland
duct of right digestive gland
coiled right digestive gland

vagina
penis
vas deferens

common genital opening
mucous gland
dart sac
spermathecal duct
retractor muscle of penis
oviduct
flagellum
albumen gland
spermatheca
fertilisation chamber
hermaphrodite duct
right coiled digestive gland
ovo-testis
male half of common duct
female half of common duct
diverticulum of spermathecal duct
spermathecal duct
tip of flagellum

FIG. 133.—*Helix.* Dorsal views of the alimentary canal and of the hermaphrodite reproductive system.

surface of the right coiled digestive gland. From it the convoluted hermaphrodite duct runs forwards to the base of the albumen gland (which adds a
layer of albumen to each egg), in which is embedded the fertilisation chamber

(where the ova are fertilised before receiving their albumen coats). From this
point there arises the wide common duct, the outer edge of which is a sacculated
channel (whose walls secrete calcareous shells round the eggs as they pass down),
while the inner edge is a smooth-walled channel (down which the spermatozoa
pass). These two regions are only partially separated internally ; slit open the
duct to find the incomplete dividing septum. At the anterior end of the
common duct its two parts separate to form the oviduct and the vas deferens.
The vas deferens, coiling towards its junction with the penis, is joined by a

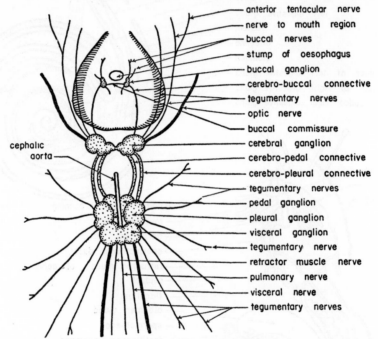

FIG. 134.—*Helix*. The anterior region of the nervous system showing the concentration of
the ganglia.

narrow duct, the flagellum (inside which the spermatozoa are bound into bundles
or spermatophores). The muscular penis is protrusible through the common
genital opening, and is withdrawn again by the retractor muscle attached
close to its posterior end. The twisted oviduct, which is relatively short and
thick-walled, is joined by a narrow duct which leads back into the visceral
hump where, near the base of the albumen gland, it swells to form a spherical
spermatheca (in which the spermatozoa received from another snail are stored).
Attached to the spermathecal duct there is often found a long, narrow diverticulum. The oviduct opens into a short, thick-walled vagina, into which there
also open a pair of tufted mucous glands (which secrete a lubricating mucous)
and a highly muscular dart sac (which secretes a calcareous spicule and,

previous to copulation, stabs it into the side of another snail, apparently as a method of stimulation). The anterior end of the vagina joins the anterior end of the penis to open at the common genital aperture.

e. To expose the anterior part of the **nervous system**, cut through the oesophagus, the salivary gland ducts, and the radula retractor muscle immediately behind the nerve-ring, and turn the crop to one side. Then pull the stumps of the oesophagus and the salivary gland ducts through the nerve-ring and turn them forward. The ganglia and nerves forming the ring are enclosed in an envelope of dense connective tissue, which must be dissected away. Identify the cerebral ganglia. From them there pass forwards the pair of cerebro-buccal connectives which lead to the buccal ganglia situated lateral to the bases of the salivary gland ducts ; the two pairs of tegumentary nerves to the body-wall ; the pair of anterior tentacular nerves which also give a branch to the mouth region ; and the pair of posterior tentacular, or optic, nerves which run alongside the retractor muscles of the posterior tentacles. Posteriorly from the cerebral ganglia, the cerebro-pedal and cerebro-pleural connectives run respectively to the pedal and pleural ganglia. These ganglia, together with the visceral ganglia, form a ring through the centre of which passes the cephalic aorta. From the visceral ganglia there arise laterally a pair of mantle nerves, and posteriorly, bound together in a common connective tissue sheath, the genital nerve on the left and the median mantle nerve on the right. Pull aside the genital and median mantle nerves to find the numerous pedal nerves passing back beneath them from the pedal ganglia.

f. Open the **buccal mass** to find the antero-dorsal horny jaw (against which the radula chews the food) ; the ventral horny radula projecting from the postero-ventral radula sac (which secretes the radula) ; and the ventral muscular mass, the odontophore (for moving the radula which lies along it). Dissect out the radula, and examine it under a lens or microscope to see the rows of small, backward-pointing teeth.

4. CONCLUSION

a. Observing the specimen and the drawings made, review the characteristics of the phylum, of the class, and of the order.

b. Also review those features which are associated with the terrestrial mode of life.

Genus **Limax** (slug)

(*Ariolimax* can be used as an alternative. Its anatomy is essentially similar to that of *Limax*, and it can be dissected in the manner described below. However, it is less suitable, since the structure of the mantle cavity is considerably obscured by the large kidney, and the alimentary canal is complicated by the tight spiral twisting of the intestine and digestive gland around the crop.)

B B

I. GENERAL ACCOUNT

a. The genus *Limax* is widely distributed throughout the world, and, like
Helix, it is common on cultivated land and in gardens.   It is a herbivore which

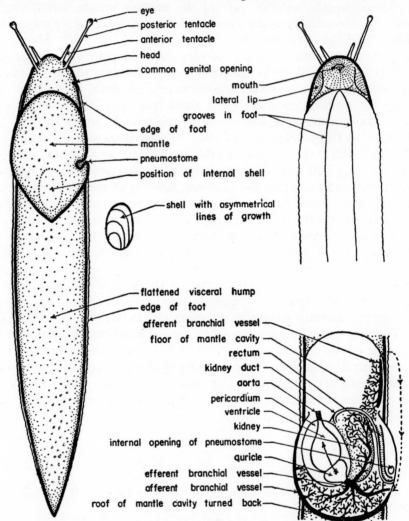

FIG. 135.—*Limax*.   A dorsal view of the body (left), a ventral view of the anterior end (upper
right), and the details of the mantle cavity as seen after the roof has been hinged back.

emerges to feed in the evening and after rain, and which hides by day in dark,
damp places.   It hibernates during the winter, and is at least two years old
before reaching sexual maturity.   Reproduction takes place from spring to
autumn, the large eggs are laid in some damp, sheltered place, and the young
slugs resemble the adults.

2. EXTERNAL ANATOMY

a. Examine the elongated body (for a method of killing and preserving, see p. 411), and notice the absence of any external shell or of any raised visceral hump. The **head** bears an antero-ventral mouth; a pair of lateral lips; a pair of retractile anterior tentacles (tactile); a pair of longer, retractile, posterior tentacles, each with a small black eye at its tip; and a common genital opening behind and above the posterior end of the right lateral lip.

b. The long **foot** is blunt anteriorly and pointed posteriorly. It has two shallow parallel grooves running along its ventral surface, and another groove, the pedal gland (which secretes the lubricating slime), is situated transversely above the front of the foot and below the base of the head.

c. The **visceral hump** is flattened and elongated, extending along the top of the foot from just behind the head to the end of the pointed tail. The mantle, much reduced, forms a shield-like structure rounded in front and pointed behind. It has an overhanging edge, especially in front (so that the head can be withdrawn beneath it for protection), and a rudimentary shell is embedded in its posterior end (as a protection for the underlying heart).

d. Cut open the mantle and extract the **shell** from the sac in which it lies. Notice that the shell is partly horny and partly calcareous, and that it is asymmetrical as shown by the lines of growth.

3. INTERNAL ANATOMY

a. Cut away the overhanging edge of the mantle. To open the **mantle cavity**, partly detach the mantle by cutting along its right edge beneath the pneumostome, across the front, and along its left edge. Leaving its posterior margin intact as a hinge, pull the mantle back. Identify the pericardium on the left, the large kidney to the right of the pericardium, and on the extreme right, near the internal opening of the pneumostome, the kidney duct and the rectum.

b. Open the pericardium to uncover the single auricle and ventricle inside, and examine the **blood system of the mantle cavity**. The afferent branchial vessel encircles the anterior edge of the lung-like cavity, and gives branches to its roof and to part of its floor. Blood enters the auricle from the roof of the mantle cavity and from the kidney, and it leaves the ventricle through the aorta.

c. Leaving only the ventricle in place, cut across the back of the mantle and remove it together with the attached organs. Open the animal by a longitudinal mid-dorsal incision from the top of the head to the tip of the tail, and pin aside the flaps. Notice the extensive perivisceral cavity (haemocoel) formed of the large blood lacunae. Trace the course of the **alimentary canal**. Into the top of the muscular buccal mass are inserted the anterior ends of the oesophagus and the salivary gland ducts. The narrow oesophagus passes back through the nerve-ring to open into the thin-walled crop. This crop, which is wide and very capacious, runs straight back and disappears from view inside the visceral mass. The left salivary gland lies on top of the anterior end of the crop, while the right gland is ventral, and so out of sight. Gently turn aside the intestine and digestive gland to expose the full length of the crop and,

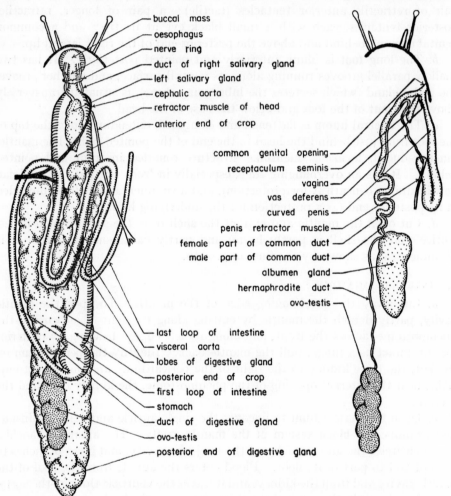

buccal mass
oesophagus
nerve ring
duct of right salivary gland
left salivary gland
cephalic aorta
retractor muscle of head
anterior end of crop

common genital opening
receptaculum seminis
vagina
vas deferens
curved penis
penis retractor muscle
female part of common duct
male part of common duct
albumen gland
hermaphrodite duct
ovo-testis

last loop of intestine
visceral aorta
lobes of digestive gland
posterior end of crop
first loop of intestine
stomach
duct of digestive gland
ovo-testis
posterior end of digestive gland

FIG. 136.—*Limax*. Dissections of the alimentary canal and of the hermaphrodite reproductive system.

at its posterior end, the globular stomach, which receives a duct from the digestive gland. The long intestine emerges from the stomach to run forwards up the left side. It then makes two further loops towards the posterior end before merging into the rectum, which was previously seen to end close to the pneumostome. The intestine in its last loop is narrow, and is usually empty.

Between the coils of the intestine and along the sides of the crop the lobes of the large digestive gland fill all the crevices.

d. Trace the **course of the aorta** arising from the posterior end of the ventricle. Passing through the first anterior loop of the intestine, it divides into a cephalic aorta and a visceral aorta. The cephalic aorta passes forwards, crossing the crop from left to right, and turns down beneath the oesophagus to supply the head. The visceral aorta turns backwards, and, passing between the digestive gland and the crop, supplies all the posterior organs of the visceral mass. Inside the flaps of the body-wall, pinned aside, notice the two large posterior veins, which carry blood forwards from the muscles of the body-wall to the kidney and the mantle cavity.

e. Find the large ovo-testis, posterior and dorsal to the visceral mass, and, dissecting forwards from it, separate the **reproductive system** from the digestive system. From the ovo-testis there emerges the narrow hermaphrodite duct, which is not convoluted, and which passes forwards between the crop and the digestive gland close to the visceral aorta. It enters the anterior end of the large albumen gland (which secretes the egg albumen), and at the same point there arises the wide and twisted common duct. This common duct is incompletely divided longitudinally into two canals, the larger of which is the female duct (down which the eggs pass and where the egg-shells are secreted) and the smaller the male duct (down which the spermatozoa pass). Close to their anterior ends these two ducts separate. The separate female duct is termed the vagina; it is broad, and it passes almost straight to the common genital opening. The separate male duct is termed the vas deferens; it is narrow, and it loops back to enter the posterior end of the penis. The penis (which can be everted through the common genital opening) is broad and muscular, and is bent into a J-shape. A retractor muscle is attached to its posterior end, and anteriorly it ends at the common genital opening. Situated between the bases of the vagina and the penis is a blindly ending sac, the receptaculum seminis (which stores the spermatozoa received from another individual).

f. Cut through the oesophagus and the salivary gland ducts immediately behind the nerve-ring, and turn aside the alimentary canal and the digestive gland. Pull the stumps of the oesophagus and the salivary gland ducts forwards through the nerve-ring. Remove the dorsal head retractor muscles, the ventral (right) salivary gland, and any other tissue tending to obscure the anterior part of the **nervous system**. Carefully dissect away the dense connective tissue which sheaths the ganglia, and remove the diaphanous epithelium which covers the large nerves passing back along the base of the body cavity. Distinguish the pair of dorsal lobed cerebral ganglia which give rise to a pair of cerebro-buccal connectives leading to the buccal ganglia dorsal to the buccal mass; two pairs of large tegumentary nerves (to the mouth and body wall), the outer of which gives branches to the anterior tentacles ; and a pair of very prominent optic nerves (to the posterior tentacles). The buccal ganglia are linked by a buccal commissure, and each gives rise to several buccal nerves (to the buccal mass). The ventral part of the nerve-ring is formed of the pedal, pleural, and visceral pairs of ganglia, and through the centre of this ganglion mass the cephalic aorta passes. Laterally the pedal and pleural ganglia are linked to the cerebral ganglia by the cerebro-pedal and cerebro-pleural connectives respectively. The numerous pairs of nerves arising from the viscero-pleuro-pedal ganglion mass mostly supply the foot and the body-wall, and the

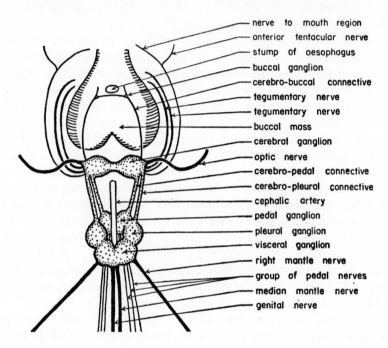

nerve to mouth region
anterior tentacular nerve
stump of oesophagus
buccal ganglion
cerebro-buccal connective
tegumentary nerve
tegumentary nerve
buccal mass
cerebral ganglion
optic nerve
cerebro-pedal connective
cerebro-pleural connective
cephalic artery
pedal ganglion
pleural ganglion
visceral ganglion
right mantle nerve
group of pedal nerves
median mantle nerve
genital nerve

FIG. 137.—*Limax*. The anterior nerve ring as seen after the removal of the oesophagus.

most prominent of them is the pair of large tegumentary nerves which arises from the visceral ganglia to pass back along the whole length of the body cavity. Between these two large nerves there also emerge from the visceral ganglia a median or pulmonary nerve which runs to the mantle cavity ; a left or retractor muscle nerve which innervates the retractor muscles of the head ; and a right or visceral nerve which leads via a ventral unpaired gastric ganglion to the organs of the visceral mass.

g. Open the **buccal mass** to find the radula, postero-ventral and situated on a muscular odontophore, and the antero-dorsal horny plate against which the radula grinds.

4.   CONCLUSION

a. Observing the specimen and the drawings made, review the characteristics of the phylum, of the class, and of the order.

b. Distinguish those peculiar features which are associated with the flatten-
ing of the visceral hump, and contrast the structure of *Limax* with that of
Helix.

5.   REFERENCE

SIMPSON, G. B. (1901).   " Anatomy and physiology of *Polygyra albolabris* and *Limax
maximus."   Bulletin of the New York State Museum,* Vol. 8, p. 237.

3.00.   Class **Pelecypoda (Lamellibranchia)**

Characteristics : Mollusca with the body typically bilaterally symmetrical
and bilaterally compressed ; head poorly developed and bearing labial palps,
but lacking eyes, tentacles, and a radula ; foot usually pointed and wedge-
shaped ; mantle bilobed and enclosing the whole body ; two shells, secreted by
the two mantle lobes, linked dorsally by a ligament and medially by adductor
muscles ; ctenidia usually greatly enlarged as a sieve for obtaining minute
food particles ; sexes usually separate, and usually with pelagic larvae.

The pelecypod molluscs are specialised for a sedentary mode of life, and for
the capture of food by a filter mechanism.   A few, for protection, have
developed the habit of boring into wood or rock, or of swimming rapidly, but
the feeding habits have not been affected by these peculiarities.

3.01.   Order **Protobranchia**

Characteristics : Pelecypoda in which the ctenidia are unspecialised and
retain their primitive function of respiration ; labial palps enlarged as a feeding
mechanism ; foot bilobed anteriorly ; and two adductor muscles.

In view of the structure of the ctenidia, this is considered to be the most
primitive order of the Pelecypoda.

Genus **Yoldia**

(The smaller *Nucula* is a less satisfactory alternative.)

I.   GENERAL ACCOUNT

a. Yoldia occurs in both the Atlantic and the Pacific, but is not present
round the British coasts.   The various species are found most commonly in
mud between the low-tide mark and a depth of about 5 fathoms, but they
have been dredged from below 100 fathoms.   The animal grips the mud by
opening the flaps of the peculiarly shaped and very sensitive foot, and in this
way it can move and burrow rapidly.   It is also described as sometimes leaving
the bottom and leaping through the water.   The food consists of small animals,

such as foraminiferans, ostracods, and small molluscs which are extracted from the mud by the labial palps. Breeding takes place during the warmer months, fertilisation is external, and the eggs develop into ciliated pelagic larvae.

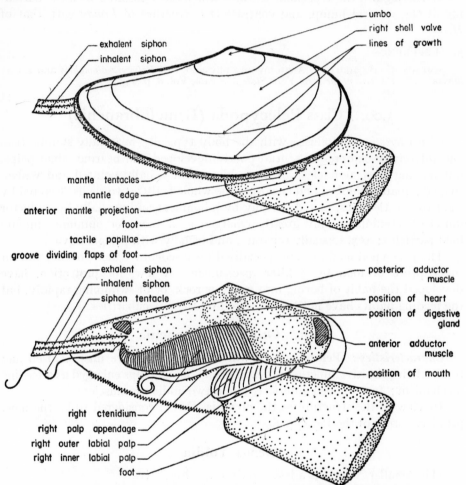

umbo
right shell valve
lines of growth

exhalent siphon
inhalent siphon

mantle tentacles
mantle edge
anterior mantle projection
foot
tactile papillae
groove dividing flaps of foot

exhalent siphon
inhalent siphon
siphon tentacle

posterior adductor muscle
position of heart
position of digestive gland
anterior adductor muscle
position of mouth

right ctenidium
right palp appendage
right outer labial palp
right inner labial palp
foot

FIG. 138.—*Yoldia*. The external features as seen from the right side, and the organs of the mantle cavity as seen after the removal of the right mantle lobe.

2.   EXTERNAL ANATOMY

a. In specimens killed in an extended condition (for the method see p. 390) notice the visible parts of the **body**. These are the two shells, the large foot directed forwards, the edge of the mantle, and the two siphons directed backwards (in life these siphons are highly extensible and project from the mud).

b. Examine the characteristic shape of the **foot**. It is large and muscular, and is deeply grooved anteriorly.   The two flaps formed by this groove can be opened out, and their free margins have a fringe of papillae (tactile).

c. The **bivalve shell** is from yellowish-brown to olive-green in colour, and it shows prominent lines of growth (in fresh specimens these details may be obliterated by the black stain of the mud).   Notice that the shell-valves hinge together dorsally, and that they are rounded anteriorly but pointed posteriorly. The oldest part of the shell by the hinge is termed the umbo, and on it the outer coloured horny layer, the periostracum, is usually worn away to reveal the white, chalky prismatic layer beneath.

3.   INTERNAL ANATOMY

a. Remove the right **shell valve** by separating it from the mantle, cutting the anterior and posterior adductor muscles where they join the shell, and pulling the valve back until the hinge is broken.   Inside the shell notice the pearly lining or nacreous layer ; the two roughened areas for the attachment of the adductor muscles ; and, in the hinge, the black ligament flanked by large numbers of fine teeth (which interlock with the corresponding teeth of the other valve).

b. Each **mantle lobe** has a broad, thickened edge (for shell secretion).   The two lobes are modified to form the two posterior siphons, the ventral of which is inhalent (and conveys fresh water into the mantle cavity) and the dorsal exhalent (and conveys fouled water from the mantle cavity) ; the long, fila-mentous siphon tentacle attached to one side of the base of the siphons (this tentacle is tactile, and it projects from the mud alongside the siphons) ; the pair of anterior mantle projections (tactile and possibly of use in cleaning the foot) ; and the numerous small mantle tentacles (tactile).

c. Leaving in place the siphons, cut away the free edge of the right mantle to expose the organs of the **mantle cavity.**   Identify the inner and outer labial palps (the surfaces of which are grooved and ciliated for the separation of food particles) ; the grooved palp appendage attached to the posterior end of the outer palp (the palp appendages are extended into the mud, and the cilia within the groove drive mud and food particles to the palps) ; the small mouth at the anterior ends of the labial palps above the base of the foot ; the right ctenidium with its posterior extremity joined to the septum which separates the inhalent and exhalent siphons (so that the water taken in must pass up-wards through the ctenidium) ; the anterior and posterior adductor muscles ; and, within the visceral mass, the positions of the digestive gland and of the heart.

d. Carefully detach the thin mantle epithelium covering the visceral mass, and dissect away the right labial palps.   Distinguish the greenish right digestive gland ; the right **gonad** (yellow in the male and dark brown in the female), which, according to its degree of development, may ramify forwards and downwards from the region of the heart ; and the mass of white, moss-like **kidney** tubules which also extend forwards and downwards from the region of the heart. The ducts of the gonad and the kidney are not easily distinguished, but they have a common opening into the posterior end of the mantle cavity so that their contents may escape through the exhalent siphon.

e. Inside the **pericardium** notice the thin-walled right auricle with the efferent branchial vessel leading into it. Both auricles open into a median ventricle, through which passes the intestine, and from the ventricle there emerge an anterior aorta, running forwards along the left side of the intestine, and a posterior aorta, running backwards along the ventral side of the intestine.

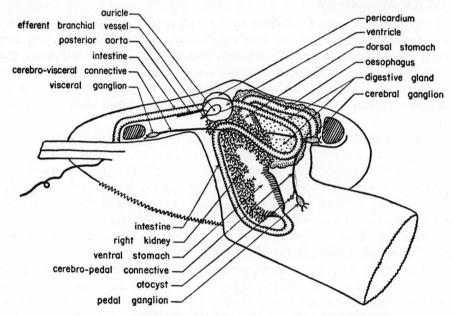

FIG. 139.—*Yoldia*.   A general dissection seen from the right side.

f. To uncover the **alimentary canal**, remove the right gill and carefully pick away the right digestive gland and gonad.   This operation exposes a loop of the intestine, the large foot retractor muscles, and, passing across the muscles, a large nerve, the cerebro-visceral connective. Without damaging this connective, carefully cut away the foot retractor muscles.   Find the dorsal end of the stomach, which can be identified by its position just anterior to the pericardium and by its striated wall. Uncover the rest of the stomach, which extends into the foot, by cutting away as much as is necessary of the tissue of the foot. Notice the white kidney tissue encrusting the posterior wall of the stomach. Trace the course of the alimentary canal. The mouth, ventral to the anterior adductor muscle, opens into the long oesophagus, which leads to the dorsal end of the capacious stomach. The stomach, receiving the ducts of the digestive glands, extends ventrally into the foot, and is constricted into two chambers. The intestine runs in a dorsal direction behind the stomach, turns forwards beneath the pericardium, and finally loops back to pass through the ventricle and to open at the anus behind the posterior adductor muscle.

g. In the **nervous system** the large cerebral ganglia lie close above the mouth, and they are linked by a broad cerebral commissure which passes anteriorly to the oesophagus. They are joined to the visceral and pedal ganglia by the cerebro-visceral and cerebro-pedal connectives respectively. The right cerebro-visceral connective has already been located. Follow its course posteriorly to find the right visceral ganglion anterior and ventral to the posterior adductor muscle. Uncover the right pedal ganglion, which is as large as the cerebral ganglion, by gently removing the muscle strands of the foot from the region anterior to the ventral end of the stomach, and then trace the course of the right cerebro-pedal connective. Notice that, just dorsal to the pedal ganglion, the cerebro-pedal connective branches to innervate an otocyst (a balance organ consisting of a closed sac containing a single otolith).

4. CONCLUSION

a. Observing the specimen, review the characteristics of the phylum, of the class, and of the order.

b. Distinguish those special features which are associated with a life spent partially buried in soft mud.

5. REFERENCE

DREW, G. A. (1899). " The anatomy, habits, and embryology of *Yoldia limutula, Say."* *Memoirs from the Biological Laboratory of the Johns Hopkins University,* Vol. 3, no. 3.

3.02. Order **Filibranchia**

Characteristics : Pelecypoda in which the ctenidia are greatly enlarged for use as a feeding mechanism, and in which the junctions between the gill filaments are either absent or weakly formed of interlocking groups of cilia ; foot small ; byssal glands well developed ; one or two adductor muscles.

Genus **Mytilus** (sea mussel)

1. GENERAL ACCOUNT

a. This is a cosmopolitan and exceptionally common genus which is found particularly between tide-marks, but which also occurs in smaller number to depths of 2 or 3 fathoms. It is tolerant of wide variations in salinity. The individuals are usually found in tightly packed masses attached by their byssus threads to rocks or wooden structures, but, although they usually remain sedentary, they can move slowly by the secretion of new byssus threads and the breaking of old ones. Food consists of organic detritus, protozoans, and diatoms which are filtered from the sea-water.   The time of breeding varies with the locality, but it is some time between mid-winter and early autumn. Fertilisation is external, and there is a free swimming larva.

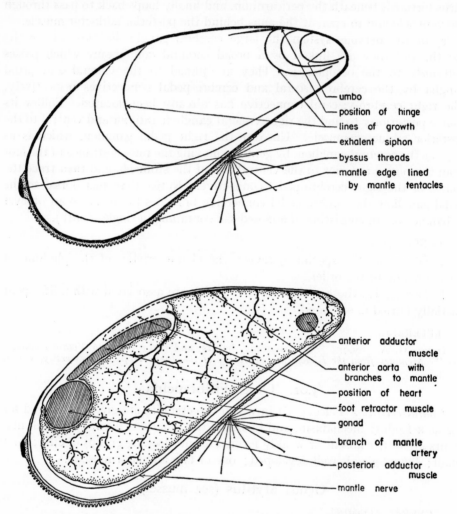

umbo
position of hinge
lines of growth
exhalent siphon
byssus threads
mantle edge lined
by mantle tentacles

anterior adductor
muscle
anterior aorta with
branches to mantle
position of heart
foot retractor muscle
gonad
branch of mantle
artery
posterior adductor
muscle
mantle nerve

FIG. 140.—*Mytilus*.   The external features as seen from the right side, and the right mantle lobe exposed by the removal of the right shell valve.

2.   EXTERNAL ANATOMY

a. The animal may be killed and preserved in a relaxed condition (method on p. 410), but if possible it is better to dissect it alive.   Notice that, instead of the foot, a bunch of strong **byssus threads** (used for anchoring) protrudes from between the two shell-valves.   Postero-ventrally can be seen the papillated edge of the **mantle**, and postero-dorsally is the exhalent siphon (also part of the mantle edge).

b. Examine the structure of the **shell-valves**. The umbo, the oldest part of the shell, is anterior and dorsal (instead of mid-dorsal as in a normal pelecypod), the hinge is above and behind the umbo, and there are curving lines of growth.

3. INTERNAL ANATOMY

a. Remove the right **shell-valve** by separating the mantle from the shell, cutting the two adductor muscles and the foot retractor muscles where they join the shell, and bending back the valve until the hinge is broken. Notice that the hinge is composed only of a broad ligament, and that the shell has an outer dark horny periostracum, a middle calcareous prismatic layer (usually visible at the umbo where the periostracum is worn away), and an inner calcareous nacreous layer. Break the shell to see the relative thicknesses of these three layers.

b. The two **mantle folds** are joined together along the entire dorsal side. Postero-dorsally they separate to form the exhalent siphon (through which water leaves the mantle cavity), but they are united again posteriorly by the branchial membrane which forms the ventral side of the exhalent siphon. Postero-ventrally and ventrally they are separate (and through this large aperture water enters the mantle cavity). The mantle edge is composed of a thin outer fold (which secretes the nacreous and prismatic layers, and which is normally ensheathed by the edge of the periostracum); a moderately thin middle fold (which on its outer edge secretes the periostracum, and on its inner edge is ciliated); and a relatively thick inner fold, the edge of which is convoluted and bears short mantle tentacles (it is ciliated, and is very sensitive to touch and to sudden changes in light intensity). Each mantle fold is greatly thickened by the gonad which extends into it. Identify the right gonad (when mature the testis is cream coloured and the ovary reddish); the anterior and posterior adductor muscles; the foot retractor muscles (their contraction shortens the foot and so tightens the byssus threads); the branching course of the mantle artery crossing the surface of the gonad; the position of the heart; and the prominent posterior mantle nerve running close to the mantle edge.

c. Cut away the free hanging part of the right mantle fold to expose the mantle cavity, in which the most prominent structure is the long, curtain-like **ctenidium** (the feeding mechanism). The axis of the ctenidium is fused along the dorsal wall of the mantle cavity; two rows of gill filaments hang from this axis and form two gill lamellae; on reaching the ventral edge of the gill, each filament turns up (the outer one outwards and the inner one inwards) to end dorsally close to the axis. With a seeker find the upturned ends of the lamellae, and demonstrate that each filament is only lightly attached to its neighbours. Notice that the effect of this gill structure is the separation of upper and lower chambers of the mantle cavity. Water enters the ventral chamber, passes through the ctenidium, and leaves the dorsal chamber via the exhalent siphon. Notice, on both sides of the base of the ctenidium, the long transversely folded areas of skin known as the plicate membranes (these are more highly vascular than the gills and are the respiratory structures).

d. In the lower chamber of the **mantle cavity** identify the inner and outer right labial palps; between these palps the deep ciliated groove leading to the wide, slit-like mouth; the small brown foot deeply grooved posteriorly to form a byssal gland (for secreting the byssal threads); the byssal cavity (also a byssal gland) which is the inner point of attachment of the byssal threads; and the keel-like base of the visceral mass posterior to the byssal cavity. Cut away the right ctenidium to expose fully the upper chamber of the mantle cavity. In it identify the right urino-genital papilla, on which open, side by side, the right kidney duct and the right gonoduct; the anus on the posterior surface of the posterior adductor muscle; and, showing through the skin, the two cerebral ganglia, posterior and ventral to the outer edges of the mouth, and the right visceral ganglion, antero-ventral to the posterior adductor muscle at a point inside the line of attachment of the right ctenidium. Also visible, for some distance posterior to the right cerebral ganglion and anterior to the right visceral ganglion, is part of the right cerebro-visceral connective. In a freshly killed specimen the dark brown kidney can be seen on both sides of the base of the ctenidium from the region of the labial palps to that of the posterior adductor muscle, but in a preserved specimen the brown colour tends to fade.

e. Remove the thin skin covering the dorsal side of the visceral mass, and pick away the gonad tissue. This exposes, anteriorly, the green digestive gland; medially, the heart flanked by the brown Keber's organ; and posteriorly, the intestine crossing the dorsal side of the posterior adductor muscle. The brown kidney tissue is also exposed running lateral to the whole visceral mass.

f. Examine the structure of the **heart** inside the pericardium (the only coelomic space in the body). The elongated ventricle is pierced along its full length by the intestine, and lateral to it are the two elongated auricles. Blood enters the auricles laterally from a number of small sinuses which are thin-walled and obscured by the organs of Keber, and leaves the ventricle anteriorly through the anterior aorta, which swells into an aortic bulb as it leaves the pericardium. The anterior aorta gives rise to a pair of mantle arteries (seen before the mantle was removed), and continues forwards to give further branches to the two mantle lobes and to the viscera.

g. The right half of the **excretory system** consists of the elongated kidney at the base of the ctenidium. This is linked by a narrow strip of kidney tissue to the right Keber's organ, or " pericardial gland ", which lies lateral to the heart. There is an internal opening into the pericardium (not easily seen), and an external opening on the urino-genital papilla.

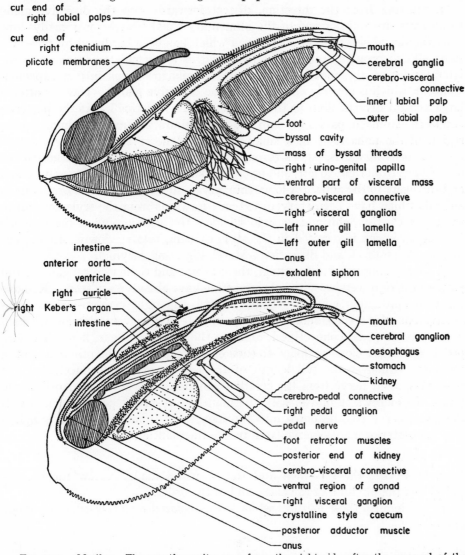

cut end of
right labial palps

cut end of
right ctenidium

plicate membranes

mouth
cerebral ganglia
cerebro-visceral
connective
inner labial palp
outer labial palp

foot
byssal cavity
mass of byssal threads
right urino-genital papilla
ventral part of visceral mass
cerebro-visceral connective
right visceral ganglion
left inner gill lamella
left outer gill lamella
anus
exhalent siphon

intestine
anterior aorta
ventricle
right auricle
right Keber's organ
intestine

mouth
cerebral ganglion
oesophagus
stomach
kidney
cerebro-pedal connective
right pedal ganglion
pedal nerve
foot retractor muscles
posterior end of kidney
cerebro-visceral connective
ventral region of gonad
right visceral ganglion
crystalline style caecum
posterior adductor muscle
anus

FIG. 141.—*Mytilus*. The mantle cavity seen from the right side after the removal of the right mantle lobe, the right ctenidium, and the right labial palps (above). A general dissection seen from the right side (below).

h. In the right half of the **reproductive system**, notice that the right gonad (the sexes are separate) extended from the mantle fold down both sides of the foot retractor muscles and among the organs of the visceral mass. The ventral regions of the right and left gonads entirely fill the ventral keel-like part of the visceral mass.   The right gonoduct opens alongside the kidney duct on the urino-genital papilla.

i. Starting from the intestine, dissect forwards into the digestive gland to uncover the anterior end of the **alimentary canal** (this is most easily done from the dorsal side, and in a specimen which has been hardened by preservation).   Food brought from the ctenidia passes along ciliated tracks into the lateral sides of the mouth.   The short oesophagus opens into a capacious stomach, which is entirely embedded in the digestive gland.   There is often a large ventral diverticulum to the stomach.   The intestine leaves the posterior end of the stomach, passes beneath the pericardium, and extends almost to the region of the anus to form a small blind sac, the crystalline style caecum. It then turns forwards, passes through the digestive gland, loops beneath the oesophagus from right to left, and passes back again through the digestive gland and the heart to the anus.   A long, thin, crystalline style (reduced or absent in animals which have been starved) extends forwards from the style caecum to rub against a thin, chitinous gastric shield at the anterior end of the stomach (this style, which is secreted in the style caecum, rotates slowly, stirring the food in the stomach and liberating a starch digesting enzyme).

j. Of the simple **nervous system**, the cerebral and right visceral ganglia and parts of the right cerebro-visceral connective have already been seen.   Remove the thin epithelium covering them.   Follow the right cerebro-visceral connective back from the cerebral ganglion until it gives a ventral branch, which is the cerebro-pedal connective leading to the right pedal ganglion.   The two pedal ganglia are closely applied to each other deep within the proximal end of the foot.   Uncover the full length of the cerebro-visceral connective.   The most prominent nerve from the cerebral ganglion is the anterior mantle nerve (most of which was removed with the mantle) ; from the pedal ganglion it is the pedal nerve passing down into the foot ; and from the visceral ganglion it is the posterior mantle nerve (seen before the mantle was removed).

4.   CONCLUSION

a. Observing the specimen and the drawings made, review the characteristics of the phylum, of the class, and of the order.

b. Distinguish those features which are associated with the sedentary mode of life.

5.   REFERENCE

WHITE, K. M. (1937).   " *Mytilus.*"   *Memoirs of the Liverpool Marine Biological Committee,* Vol. 31.

Genus **Pecten** (scallop)

1.   GENERAL ACCOUNT

a. Species of *Pecten* are found all over the world.   The animals live gregariously on the sea bottom, especially in depths of about 20 fathoms.

Most of their time is spent lying quietly on the right shell-valve while they sieve from the water the particles of detritus, diatoms, and other tiny organisms which serve as food. However, they are in no way fixed, and they can swim in a rapid, if spasmodic, manner by a quick opening and closing of the shell-valves. Breeding takes place throughout the year, but it is at a maximum in summer. The genus is peculiar in that some species are hermaphrodite while in others the sexes are separate. Fertilisation is external, and there is a free swimming veliger larva.

2. EXTERNAL ANATOMY

a. Distinguish the **orientation** of a specimen by the fact that the shell-valves are unequal, the right being more convex than the left (which in some species is quite flat).

b. The right **shell-valve** is worn clean and white (since the animal normally rested on it). The flatter left valve is usually darker in colour, and often has encrusting plants and animals growing on it. Associated with the swimming habit, the valves are thin and ribbed (for lightness combined with strength), and are joined together by a hinge, which is greatly elongated (and so strengthened) by the development of flanges which are called auriculae. Notice how the anterior and posterior auriculae differ in shape. When the valves are closed they lock tightly together except immediately anterior and posterior to the auriculae, where they do not even meet (through the two holes formed in this way water is ejected during feeding and swimming; during swimming the hinge is to the rear). Distinguish the prominent lines of growth.

c. The highly sensitive **mantle edge** may also be visible externally. It is pigmented and lined by rows of tentacles and eyes, but its detailed structure is seen better after the shell has been removed.

3. INTERNAL ANATOMY

a. Remove the convex right shell-valve by separating it from the mantle, cutting the large adductor muscle where it joins the shell, and pulling back the valve until the hinge is broken. Complete the examination of the right **shell-valve**. The ribs seen externally coincide with grooves internally; the hinge is greatly strengthened by a thick black ligament; the calcareous prismatic layer forms the substance of the shell (the outer horny periostracum is usually worn completely away); and there is a thin inner nacreous layer.

b. The mantle is divided into two lobes. In its central region each **mantle lobe** is thin and transparent, so that through it there are visible the visceral mass; the heart; part of the mantle nerve which, coming from the visceral ganglion, branches to supply the mantle edge; and the two parts of the single adductor muscle (the larger part is of striped muscle fibres, and is used during the spasmodic swimming, while the smaller part is of smooth muscle fibres, and

C C

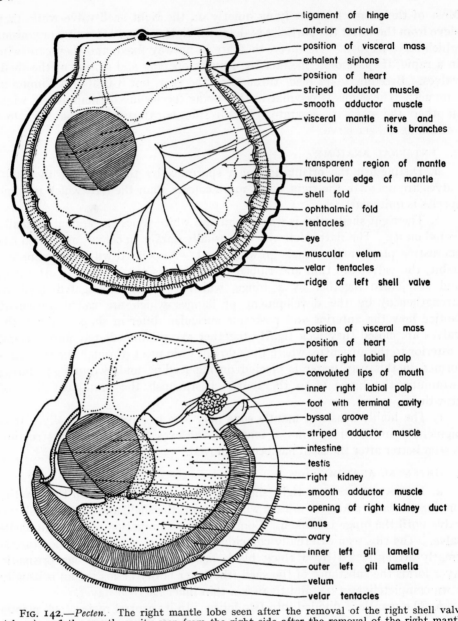

ligament of hinge
anterior auricula
position of visceral mass
exhalent siphons
position of heart
striped adductor muscle
smooth adductor muscle
visceral mantle nerve and
                    its branches

transparent region of mantle
muscular edge of mantle
shell fold
ophthalmic fold
tentacles
eye
muscular velum
velar tentacles
ridge of left shell valve

position of visceral mass
position of heart
outer right labial palp
convoluted lips of mouth
inner right labial palp
foot with terminal cavity
byssal groove
striped adductor muscle
intestine
testis
right kidney
smooth adductor muscle
opening of right kidney duct
anus
ovary
inner left gill lamella
outer left gill lamella
velum
velar tentacles

FIG. 142.—*Pecten.* The right mantle lobe seen after the removal of the right shell valve (above), and the mantle cavity seen from the right side after the removal of the right mantle lobe and the right ctenidium (below).

is capable of a sustained contraction). The mantle edge is thickened, and projecting inwards from it is the muscular velum, bearing velar tentacles. The velum is not continued across the two shell-holes adjacent to the auriculae, and the two mantle apertures thus formed may be termed exhalent siphons. Along the mantle edge there are also two other much smaller folds : the outer or ophthalmic fold (which bears both eyes and tentacles) and the inner or shell fold (which secretes the shell). The muscles of the mantle edge (used during swimming to open and close the valve-like velum) lie within the velum and extend for some distance inside the shell fold.

c. Cut away the free part of the right mantle fold and examine the large right **ctenidium** (which is used for both respiration and feeding). Two gill lamellae hang from the gill axis, which is attached along its length beneath the adductor muscle. The gill filaments (ciliated) composing the lamellae are easily separable from their neighbours, and on reaching the free edge of the ctenidium they turn up again to end near the gill axis. At the anterior end of the ctenidium find the outer and inner right labial palps (ciliated and enclosing between them the food-groove for conveying food from the gill to the mouth).

d. Without damaging the gill axis, cut away the lamellae of the right gill to expose the inner part of the **mantle cavity**. Identify the highly convoluted lips (ciliated) at the anterior end of the labial palps ; the wide, slit-like mouth partly hidden by the lips ; the small foot (probably used for cleaning the palps and the ctenidia) ; the terminal cavity of the foot (function doubtful) ; the byssal groove along the ventral surface of the foot (in some species anchoring byssus threads are secreted only in the young, while in others the threads are produced and used throughout life) ; the large ventral extension of the visceral mass containing the gonads (a testis dorsally and an ovary ventrally) ; the right kidney on the anterior surface of the adductor muscle ; the opening of the kidney duct at the ventral end of the kidney ; the end of the intestine crossing the posterior surface of the adductor muscle ; and the anus, which is free on a papilla.

e. Remove the thin skin covering the heart. This operation opens the pericardium (coelom) and uncovers the ventricle and the two auricles. Dissect out as much as possible of the **blood system**. Blood enters the right auricle laterally from the right efferent branchial vessel (which runs from the ctenidium along the gill axis) and from the right mantle vein (most of which was removed with the mantle). The ctenidium received its blood from the kidney. Blood leaves the ventricle (which is pierced by the intestine) either through the anterior or the posterior aorta. The anterior aorta runs dorsal to the intestine and disappears into the digestive gland to supply the alimentary canal, the foot, and the gonads. The posterior aorta arises from the postero-ventral end of the ventricle, and runs back ventrally and to the right of the intestine. It gives rise to the posterior mantle artery (most of which was removed with the mantle), the adductor artery (which enters the adductor muscles just anterior to the cleft separating its two parts), and the rectal artery (which runs alongside the posterior end of the intestine).

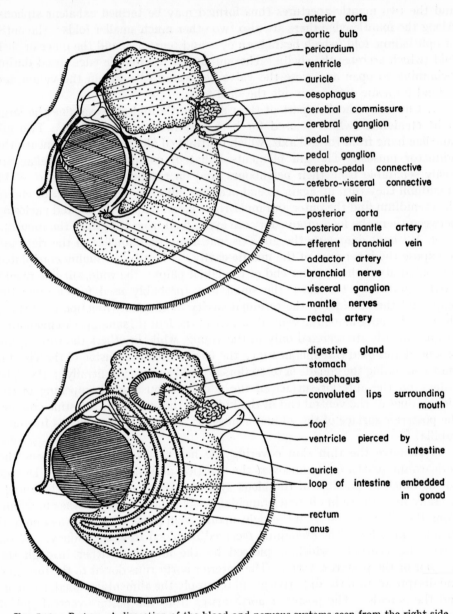

anterior aorta
aortic bulb
pericardium
ventricle
auricle
oesophagus
cerebral commissure
cerebral ganglion
pedal nerve
pedal ganglion
cerebro-pedal connective
cerebro-visceral connective
mantle vein
posterior aorta
posterior mantle artery
efferent branchial vein
adductor artery
branchial nerve
visceral ganglion
mantle nerves
rectal artery

digestive gland
stomach
oesophagus
convoluted lips surrounding mouth
foot
ventricle pierced by intestine
auricle
loop of intestine embedded in gonad
rectum
anus

Fig. 143.—*Pecten*. A dissection of the blood and nervous systems seen from the right side (above), and a dissection of the alimentary canal seen from the right side (below).

f. Most of the **excretory system** of the right side has already been seen. The large kidney opens ventrally into the mantle cavity and dorsally into the pericardium. Excretion is also carried on by the Keber's organs, which are reduced and lie within the walls of the auricles so as to give them a brownish colour.

g. The **reproductive system** is peculiar in that some species are hermaphrodite. In an hermaphrodite *Pecten* the testis (which ripens first) is dorsal to the ovary. There are no gonoducts. The spermatozoa escape into the dorsal ends of the kidneys, and so pass out through the renal openings, and the ova later follow the same path.

h. To dissect the **nervous system**, first cut away the right labial palps, and remove any skin still covering the dorsal part of the visceral mass together with that covering the gonads. Pick away the gonad tissue in the region above and behind the base of the foot to uncover the right cerebral and pedal ganglia, which lie close together linked by a short cerebro-pedal connective. The cerebral ganglia are bilobed (possibly the posterior lobe is a remnant of the pleural ganglion), and are joined together by a long cerebral commissure which loops over the oesophagus. Find the pedal nerve which passes into the foot from the pedal ganglion. From the cerebral ganglion a prominent cerebro-visceral connective passes ventrally through the gonad tissue to reach the large visceral ganglion, which is closely applied to the ventral surface of the adductor muscle. The right and left visceral ganglia lie so close together that they appear as one bilobed ganglion. Each gives rise to a branchial nerve (which passes upwards into the ctenidial axis) and several mantle nerves (which pass outwards across the ventral surface of the adductor muscle to reach the mantle).

i. Finally dissect out the **alimentary canal**. The oesophagus and stomach are embedded in the digestive gland, which must be carefully picked away. The stomach is roughly oval, but has an irregularly folded wall. Into it open the ducts of the digestive glands. From the base of the stomach the intestine descends through the gonad tissue. This first part of the intestine secretes and contains the crystalline style, which protrudes upwards into the stomach (the style is kept in rotation by large cilia lining the intestine, and, as it wears away in the stomach, it releases a digestive enzyme). The second part of the intestine loops upwards through the gonad and the digestive gland, while the third and last part turns ventrally again to pierce the heart and cross the posterior surface of the adductor muscle. Its terminal portion, which opens at the anus, may be called the rectum.

4. CONCLUSION

a. Observing the specimen and the drawings made, review the characteristics of the phylum, of the class, and of the order.

b. Distinguish those features which are associated with the sedentary mode of feeding, and those which are associated with the active swimming habit.

5. REFERENCE

DAKIN, W. J. (1909). "*Pecten.*" *Memoirs of the Liverpool Marine Biological Committee*, Vol. 17.

3.03. Order **Eulamellibranchia**

Characteristics : Pelecypoda in which the ctenidia are greatly enlarged for use as a feeding mechanism, and in which the junctions between the gill filaments are permanent and vascular ; foot well developed ; byssal glands small or absent ; one or two adductor muscles.

Genus **Anodonta** (fresh-water mussel or clam)

(Several other eulamellibranchs are commonly used as alternatives. These are *Unio*, another fresh-water mussel, *Mya*, a marine clam, *Ostrea*, the oyster, and *Cardium*, the cockle. *Unio* is essentially similar to *Anodonta*, and the others are sufficiently similar to be dissected according to the following instructions. Details of the anatomy of *Ostrea* and *Cardium* can also be obtained from the references given on p. 396.)

1. GENERAL ACCOUNT

a. Fresh-water mussels of the family Unionidae, to which *Anodonta* belongs, are found in streams, rivers, and lakes all over the world. *Anodonta* itself is also widespread. It is an extremely slow-moving animal, and most species live almost completely buried in the muddy bottoms of lakes and sluggish rivers. Tiny particles of organic detritus and microscopic animal and plant organisms are sieved from the water for food. The breeding season is during summer, fertilization is internal, and the eggs are retained in the gills of the female. There they develop into peculiar glochidia larvae which, for dispersal, attach themselves to passing fish and live for a time as parasites in the skin.

2. EXTERNAL ANATOMY

a. In a living specimen (for culture methods see p. 410), or in a specimen killed in a relaxed condition (for the method see p. 411.), identify the two shell-valves, the large, wedge-shaped foot, and the mantle edge which posterodorsally is specialised as inhalent and exhalent siphons (through which water enters and leaves the mantle cavity).

b. Examine one of the **shell-valves** and distinguish the umbo antero-dorsally ; the long dorsal hinge ; the rings of growth ; the dark outer horny layer, the periostracum ; and at the umbo, where the periostracum is usually worn away, the white calcareous prismatic layer.

3. INTERNAL ANATOMY

a. Remove the right **shell-valve** by separating it from the mantle, cutting the anterior and posterior groups of muscles where they join the shell, and pulling the valve back until the hinge breaks. Inside the shell-valve notice the long black hinge ligament, and the thin, pearly nacreous layer with roughened areas where the anterior and posterior groups of muscles were attached.

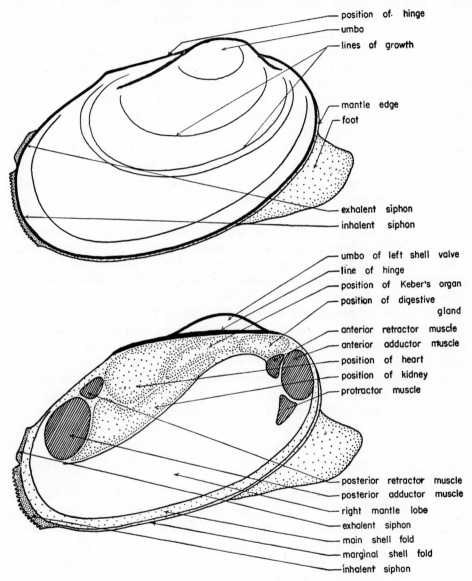

— position of hinge
— umbo
— lines of growth

— mantle edge
— foot

— exhalent siphon
— inhalent siphon

— umbo of left shell valve
— line of hinge
— position of Keber's organ
— position of digestive gland
— anterior retractor muscle
— anterior adductor muscle
— position of heart
— position of kidney
— protractor muscle

— posterior retractor muscle
— posterior adductor muscle
— right mantle lobe
— exhalent siphon
— main shell fold
— marginal shell fold
— inhalent siphon

FIG. 144.—*Anodonta.* The external features seen from the right side (above), and the details of the mantle seen after the removal of the right shell valve (below).

b. Examine the structure of the right **mantle lobe.** It is fused to the left mantle lobe along the whole dorsal side, while anteriorly, ventrally, and posteriorly it is free. Its large central area is so thin as to be semi-transparent, and it is especially thin where it crosses the ends of the muscles. Through it can be seen the anterior adductor muscle (for pulling the shells together), close behind which is the protractor muscle (for extending the foot) and the anterior retractor muscle (for withdrawing the foot) ; the posterior adductor muscle (also for pulling the shells together), and in front of it the posterior retractor muscle (also for withdrawing the foot) ; the dorsal pericardium ; anterior to the pericardium, the brown Keber's organ ; and posterior and ventral to the peri-cardium, the brown kidney. The free edge of the mantle is thickened to form a shell fold, and a shallow groove separates the margin of this fold (which secretes the periostracum) from the main part (which secretes the prismatic layer ; the whole surface of the mantle secretes the nacreous layer). Posteriorly the mantle edge is modified to form the darkly pigmented siphons. The edges of the ventral inhalent siphon are covered with papillae (for tasting the incoming water), while the edges of the dorsal exhalent siphon are smooth.

c. Leaving the edges of the siphons in place, cut away the free hanging part of the right mantle lobe. Examine the right **ctenidium**. It is composed of filaments fused to form an inner and an outer lamella. The filaments are so completely fused that they cannot be separated, but by looking through one of the gill lamellae at a light, they can be seen lying parallel to each other. The filaments originate from the right and left sides of the ctenidial axis, which is fused along most of its length to the dorsal side of the mantle cavity. They descend to the free edges of the lamellae, and then turn upwards again, the filaments forming the outer lamella turning outwards and those forming the inner lamella turning inwards. On reaching the dorsal side of the mantle cavity once more, the ends of the outer filaments fuse to the mantle, while those of the inner filaments lie close alongside the foot anteriorly and fuse with those of the left side posteriorly. This arrangement almost completely separates the lower part of the mantle cavity from an upper, or epibranchial, chamber, which can be seen through the exhalent siphon. Water enters the ventral siphon, passes upwards through the ctenidium, and emerges from the exhalent siphon.

d. The **feeding mechanism** depends on the sieving of the water during its passage through the gill lamellae. The particles are then passed (by gill cilia) to the labial palps (which are also ciliated). Notice how the deep food-groove between the inner and outer labial palps leads to the transverse slit-like mouth situated above and in front of the foot. The lips of the mouth are forward continuations of the labial palps.

e. Without injuring the ctenidial axis, cut away the right inner and outer gill lamellae. Notice the hollow nature of each lamella, and how its inner and outer walls are held together by the strands of tissue which cross the internal space. The cavity of each lamella opens into an elongated epibranchial chamber, and the two **epibranchial chambers** lie side by side.   Posteriorly they communicate with each other and with the epibranchial chambers of the other

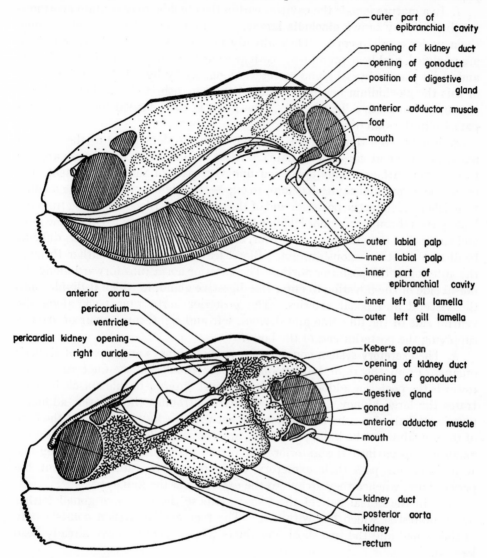

outer part of
epibranchial cavity

opening of kidney duct

opening of gonoduct

position of digestive
gland

anterior adductor muscle

foot

mouth

outer labial palp

inner labial palp

inner part of
epibranchial cavity

inner left gill lamella

outer left gill lamella

anterior aorta

pericardium

ventricle

pericardial kidney opening

right auricle

Keber's organ

opening of kidney duct

opening of gonoduct

digestive gland

gonad

anterior adductor muscle

mouth

kidney duct

posterior aorta

kidney

rectum

FIG. 145.—*Anodonta*. The mantle cavity seen from the right side after the removal of the right ctenidium (above), and a general dissection showing the heart and the excretory and reproductive systems (below).

side.   In the right inner chamber, opposite the middle of the base of the foot, find the small, slit-like openings of the right kidney duct and the right gono-duct, the latter anterior and internal to the former.   Just inside the exhalent siphon, dorsal to the posterior adductor muscle, notice the anus on a small papilla.

f. In a mature female the cavities within the ctenidia may contain enormous numbers of tiny brown **glochidia larvae**. Extract some of these and examine them under a microscope. They already possess two shell-valves, but these are modified, and bear prominent teeth at their free edges. The foot is absent, and in its place a byssal gland secretes a long, sticky byssal thread (by means of this the glochidium becomes attached to some fish, and the shell teeth are also used to obtain a better grip ; the larva is then carried for a time as a parasite in the skin of the fish).

g. Remove the thin skin (mantle) covering the dorsal side of the visceral mass, taking great care not to damage those organs which are closely applied to its inner surface. This operation uncovers part of the **blood system**, and opens the pericardial cavity (coelom) to expose the right auricle and the median ventricle pierced by the posterior end of the intestine. Blood returning from the body passes through irregular lacunae to the kidneys, whence it enters the gills, and so reaches the auricles. However, even in injected specimens it is difficult to dissect out the venous system. Blood leaves the ventricle either through the anterior or the posterior aorta. The anterior aorta runs forward along the dorsal side of the intestine to enter the digestive gland, in which it divides into the visceral and pedal arteries. The posterior aorta runs back along the ventral side of the intestine and divides, left and right, into a pair of arteries supplying the posterior end of the body.

h. The **excretory system** consists of a pair of kidneys and a pair of Keber's organs. From the right kidney opening the broad kidney duct runs back towards the posterior adductor muscle, and just anterior to this muscle it penetrates the large kidney. The kidney partly surrounds the anterior adductor muscle, and also has a forward extension between the kidney duct and the base of the ctenidium. The kidney is hollow, and the cavity (coelom) of this forward extension opens into the anterior end of the pericardium. The kidney-like Keber's organs pass their excretory products into the anterior end of the pericardium, whence they escape to the exterior via the kidneys.

i. Skin the dorsal half of the foot to expose the extensive gonad (either ovary or testis) which lies within it. The **reproductive system** consists only of this gonad and the two short gonoducts whose openings have already been located.

j. Dissect out the **nervous system** as follows. Turn aside the right labial palps to uncover the right side of the mouth. Gently remove the skin from this area to expose the small right cerebral ganglion, which is orange in colour, and which lies close to the surface against the antero-ventral side of the protractor muscle. Next find the two visceral ganglia, which lie so close together as to appear as one ganglion, and which can easily be seen through the skin covering the ventral side of the posterior adductor muscle.   The pedal ganglia are located close together in the anterior end of the base of the gonad close to the base of the

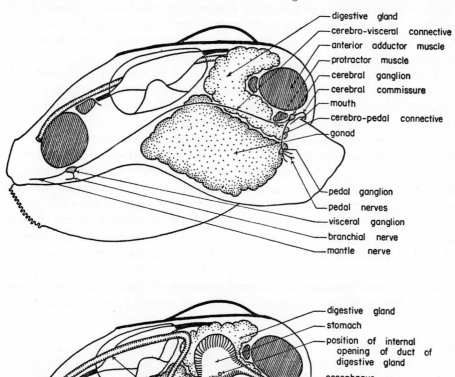

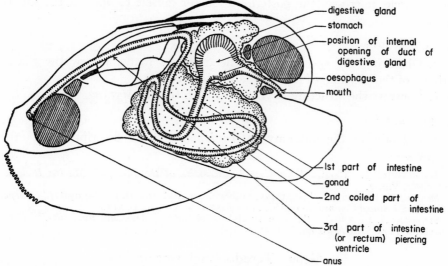

FIG. 146.—*Anodonta*.   The nervous system seen from the right side (above), and the alimentary canal seen from the right side (below).

digestive glands.   Having found the different ganglia, dissect out the long right cerebro-visceral connective which runs back past the digestive gland and along the inner surface of the kidney; the cerebro-pedal connective which follows an almost straight line between the two ganglia ; the cerebral commissure which, passing anterior to the oesophagus, links the two cerebral ganglia ; the numerous pedal nerves passing from the pedal ganglion into the muscles of the foot ; and from each visceral ganglion, the large lateral nerve to the ctenidium, and the large posterior mantle nerve which gives branches to the mantle, the siphons, and the posterior adductor muscle.

k. Finally expose the **alimentary canal** by carefully picking away the digestive gland and the gonad, and by opening the ventricle. The oesophagus passes dorsally between the protractor muscle and the anterior adductor muscle. The large globular stomach is entirely hidden by the digestive glands. Cut open the stomach to find the internal openings (latero-ventral) of the ducts of the left and right digestive glands. The first part of the intestine, leaving the postero-ventral end of the stomach, has thickened walls and encloses a crystalline style which projects forwards and upwards into the stomach (this style, secreted by the intestine walls and kept rotating by means of large cilia, is worn away in the stomach to release a carbohydrate digesting enzyme ; it is not present if the animal has been starved). The second part of the intestine, which has thinner walls, loops within the gonad, and then passes dorsally to the anterior end of the pericardium. The third part of the intestine, which is wider, and is often called the rectum, is almost straight, and passing through the ventricle, it crosses the posterior adductor muscle to open at the slit-like anus.

4. CONCLUSION

a. Observing the specimen and the drawings made, review the characteristics of the phylum, of the class, and of the order.

b. Contrast the structure of *Anodonta* with that of *Mytilus*.

5. REFERENCES

For details of the anatomy of *Anodonta*, and for descriptions of other genera, see :

JOHNSTONE, J. (1899). " *Cardium.*" *Memoirs of the Liverpool Marine Biological Committee*, Vol. 2.

MOORE, H. F. (1903). " Anatomy, embryology, and growth of the oyster." *Report of the United States Commission of Fish and Fisheries*, Vol. 29, p. 317.

SIMPSON, G. B. (1884). " Anatomy and physiology of *Anodonta fluviatilis.*" *Report of the New York State Museum*, Vol. 35, p. 169.

Genus **Teredo** (ship worm)

1. GENERAL ACCOUNT

a. The distribution of this highly specialised, wood-boring eulamellibranchiate is world-wide, perhaps because it was carried everywhere in the days of wooden ships. It burrows into, and lives inside, any wood which is immersed in sea-water, and while doing this it swallows and partly digests the wood, particularly the cellulose. However, the main food supply consists of microscopic living organisms taken in through the siphon which projects from the entrance to the burrow, and caught in the usual manner by the ctenidia. Breeding takes place throughout the warmer months. In some species fertilisation is external, but in others, including the well-known *T. navalis* L., it is internal. In the latter case early development takes place in the gills, but in both cases free-swimming veliger larvae are formed.

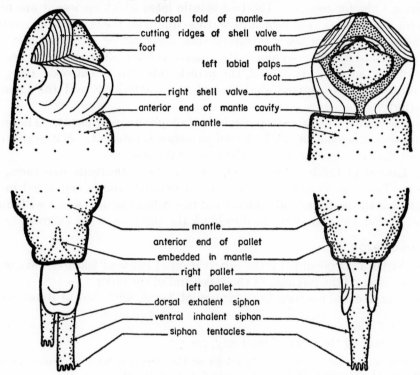

FIG. 147.—*Teredo*. The external features of the anterior and posterior ends seen from the right side (left), and from the ventral side (right).

2.   EXTERNAL ANATOMY

  a. Distinguish the **orientation** of the body. At the anterior end are the shell-valves, at the posterior end are the siphons, and on the dorsal side the shell-valves are partly embedded in the mantle.

  b. The main part of each **shell-valve** is normal in structure and shows rings of growth, but anteriorly there are sharp cutting edges flanked by file-like cutting ridges (the valves are moved by the adductor muscles, and act like jaws to grind the wood and enlarge the burrow).

  c. Ventrally the shell-valves enclose an almost square opening, through which can be seen the **foot** (this is reduced and acts as a second lower lip).

Anterior to the foot is the slit-like mouth, and posterior to it is the slit-like opening into the mantle cavity.   Insert a seeker into both these openings.

d. Identify the outer and inner pairs of **labial palps,** which are continuous with the dorsal and ventral lips of the mouth (food particles touching any part of the body, the gills, or the mantle are carried by cilia via the groove between the labial palps to the mouth).

e. The greatly elongated body lies posterior to the shell-valves and to the posterior adductor muscle.   The two **mantle lobes** which enclose it are fused together ventrally so as to form a tube (this eliminates the mantle edge, so that neither a periostracum nor a prismatic shell layer can be secreted ; however, the whole mantle surface secretes a thin nacreous layer which is used to line the walls of the burrow).   If desired, the mantle tube can be cut open along the mid-ventral line to expose the visceral mass anteriorly and the ctenidia posteriorly.

f. The mantle cavity opens posteriorly through the two **siphons.**   The larger ventral siphon is inhalent, while the dorsal siphon is exhalent.   Notice the rings of short tentacles (sensory) round the ends of the siphons.

g. Lateral to the bases of the siphons are two calcareous structures, the **pallets.**   The anterior end of each pallet is pointed, and is embedded in the mantle, but the posterior end is broad and free (when the siphons are withdrawn for protection, the pallets are used to block the entrance to the burrow).

3.   CONCLUSION

a. As far as is possible by the observation of external features, review the characteristics of the phylum, of the class, and of the order.

b. Compare and contrast the anatomy of *Teredo* with that of *Anodonta.*

4.   REFERENCE

For details of the internal anatomy, see :

LAZIER, E. L. (1920–23).   " Morphology of the digestive tract of *Teredo navalis.*" *University of California Publications in Zoology,* Vol. 22, p. 455.

4.00.   Class **Cephalopoda**

Characteristics : Mollusca with the body bilaterally symmetrical ; head highly developed with eyes and a radula ; foot probably represented by the circumoral arms and tentacles, and certainly by the exhalent siphon ; visceral hump either coiled or straight ; shell either well developed, or reduced, or absent ; ganglia well developed and highly centralised to form a brain ; sexes separate, eggs large and heavily yolked, and development direct.

The class is divided into two orders, the Dibranchia, described below, which is the more successful, and the Tetrabranchia which is the more primitive in having a well-developed calcareous shell, two pairs of ctenidia and kidneys, and simple eyes.   The dibranchiates are common in all the seas, but of the tetrabranchiates only *Nautilus* survives today.   In the past the tetra-branchiates were abundant from the early Cambrian to the late Cretaceous, and they included the prominent suborder Ammonoidea.

4.01.   Order **Dibranchia**

Characteristics : Cephalopoda with 8 or 10 arms or tentacles which, at least in the young, bear suckers ; eyes highly developed ; chromatophores present ; poison glands opening into the mouth ; shell internal, reduced, and sometimes absent ; only one pair of ctenidia and kidneys ; and with an ink-gland.

There are two suborders : the Decapoda, which, like *Loligo* and *Sepia*, have a reduced shell and 10 arms, and the Octopoda, which, like *Octopus*, have no shell and only 8 arms.   Also belonging to the Decapoda is the fossil order Belemnoidea which flourished in the Mesozoic.

Genus **Loligo** (common squid)

(The cuttlefish *Sepia*, which has a shorter and flatter body than *Loligo*, can be used as an alternative.   The method of dissection is the same, and the most important differences in detail between it and *Loligo* are mentioned in the course of the following description.)

I.   GENERAL ACCOUNT

a. The genus *Loligo* has a world-wide distribution in the warmer seas, and species occur in coastal shallows, in deeper waters, and in the abysses.   They are frequently found in groups, either swimming freely or resting on the sea bottom.   They can move swiftly, either forwards or backwards, by the com-bined actions of the fins and the funnel, and for food they catch shrimps, crabs, and small fishes.   These are grabbed by a lightning-like extension of the two tentacles, held by the eight arms, and killed by an injection of poison.   For protection, squids have great powers of rapid colour change, and when attacked they can emit a cloud of black ink, behind which to retire.   In temperate regions, according to the species, breeding takes place some time between late winter and late summer, and, again according to species, it involves a migration either into shallow water or into deep water.   Fertilisation is within the mantle cavity of the female, and the large yolky eggs, covered by a sticky secretion of the nidamental glands, are then laid and attached to some support. They hatch directly into tiny squids, there being no larval form.

2.   EXTERNAL ANATOMY

a. The **body** is obviously divisible into a head region bearing the arms and tentacles, and a pointed visceral hump with lateral fins.   However, it is generally considered that into the head region is incorporated the foot, the

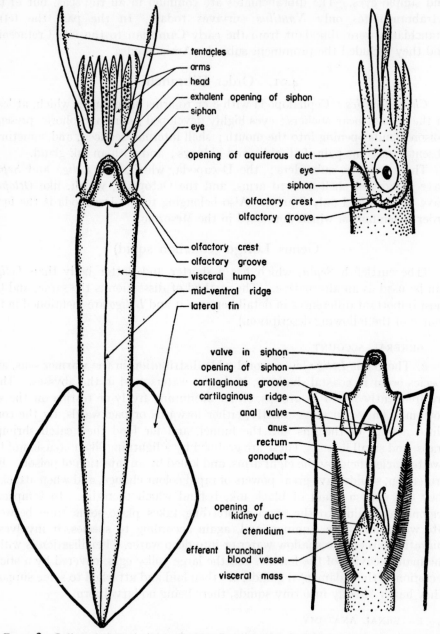

tentacles
arms
head
exhalent opening of siphon
siphon
eye

opening of aquiferous duct
eye
siphon
olfactory crest
olfactory groove

olfactory crest
olfactory groove
visceral hump
mid-ventral ridge
lateral fin

valve in siphon
opening of siphon
cartilaginous groove
cartilaginous ridge
anal valve
anus
rectum
gonoduct

opening of
kidney duct
ctenidium
efferent branchial
blood vessel
visceral mass

FIG. 148.—*Loligo*. A ventral view to show the form of the body (left), a lateral view of the head region (upper right), and the mantle cavity opened by a longitudinal ventral cut through the mantle wall.

anterior end of which is represented by the arms and tentacles and the posterior end by the siphon.

b. In the **head region** distinguish the 8 pointed arms (for holding the prey), each with two rows of stalked suckers along its inner side; the two larger tentacles (shot out to catch the prey) with stalked suckers only towards their tips; the mouth within the ring of arms; the two horny, beak-like jaws protruding from the mouth, the ventral jaw overlapping the dorsal; the roughened circular inner lip surrounding the mouth; the smoother circular outer lip surrounding the inner lip; the circular buccal fold surrounding the outer lip and bearing 7 pointed buccal lobes between the bases of the arms; the pair of exceptionally large and well-developed eyes; immediately anterior to each eye, the small aquiferous pore leading into the eye-chamber; immediately posterior to each eye, the olfactory crest (absent in *Sepia*), the concavity behind which acts as an olfactory organ (for tasting the water); and ventral to the head, separated from it by a deep groove, the tubular siphon (through which water escapes from the mantle cavity).

c. The **visceral hump** is long and pointed, and bears two lateral fins (by means of which the animal swims forwards). These fins, extensions of the mantle, are very muscular, containing longitudinal, vertical, and transverse muscle-sheets. The transverse fibres, running in parallel groups, are particularly evident on the ventral fin surface. Notice the circular opening around the back of the head which leads into the mantle cavity. Also notice that the skin, especially dorsally, contains innumerable dark spots, the chromatophores (each, situated within the dermis, consists of a pigment cell surrounded by muscle strands which cause the cell to expand or contract during the process of colour change).

3. INTERNAL ANATOMY

(Part of the dissection described below is carried out from the ventral side and part from the dorsal side. To avoid confusion, it should be constantly borne in mind that the terms left and right, and dorsal and ventral, refer strictly to the animal.)

a. Open the **mantle cavity** by a longitudinal cut made along the full length of the visceral hump just to one side of the mid-ventral line. Such a cut passes to one side of the median septum which separates the posterior part of the mantle cavity into left and right halves. Also open the funnel by a longitudinal cut. At the anterior end of the mantle cavity notice that latero-ventrally and mid-dorsally the inner side of the mantle is joined to the body of the animal by cartilaginous ridges fitting into cartilaginous grooves (water enters the cavity dorsally on both sides, and these locking devices help to keep the two inhalent currents separated from the single exhalent current which passes out through the ventral siphon). Identify the pair of large, sac-like valves lateral to the

D D

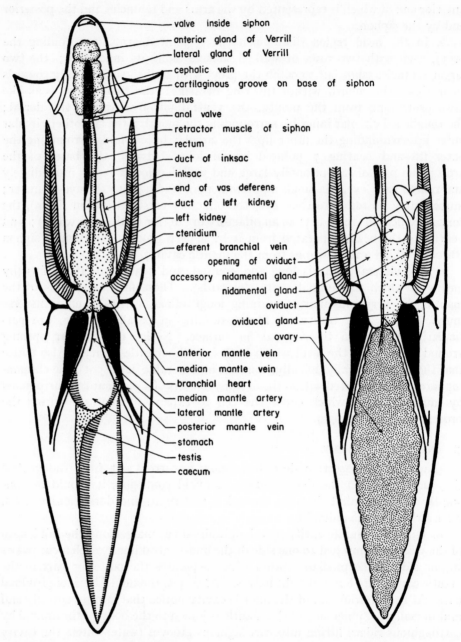

valve inside siphon
anterior gland of Verrill
lateral gland of Verrill
cephalic vein
cartilaginous groove on base of siphon
anus
anal valve
retractor muscle of siphon
rectum
duct of inksac
inksac
end of vas deferens
duct of left kidney
left kidney
ctenidium
efferent branchial vein
opening of oviduct
accessory nidamental gland
nidamental gland
oviduct
oviducal gland
ovary
anterior mantle vein
median mantle vein
branchial heart
median mantle artery
lateral mantle artery
posterior mantle vein
stomach
testis
caecum

FIG. 149.—*Loligo.* A ventral view of the visceral mass of a male, and, on the right, a ventral view of the visceral mass of a female from which the left nidamental gland has been removed to expose the left accessory nidamental gland.

siphon (for preventing the outflow of water); the single valve at the outer opening of the siphon (for preventing the inflow of water); the two ctenidia (so placed that the inhalent streams of water pass directly on to them); the rectum ending in the anus at the base of the siphon; the two anal valves (function doubtful) attached to the sides of the anus; the two openings of the kidney ducts set on papillae lateral to the base of the rectum; the reproductive opening on the end of the prominent gonoduct to the left of the base of the rectum; and the visceral mass pendent from the mid-dorsal line.

b. Breaking the median septum, pin aside the mantle flaps. Cut away the ventral side of the funnel. Remove the thin skin covering the organs of the visceral mass, and notice the **periyisceral cavity** (coelom) within it. (In *Sepia*, find the ink sac at the posterior end of the visceral mass, and, without breaking it, remove it together with its duct.)

c. In the **female**, the **reproductive system** forms the ventral side of the visceral mass. Identify the single large posterior ovary (the large yolked eggs are shed into the coelomic body cavity); the pair of large white nidamental glands (which secrete an elastic egg membrane); the oviduct on the left leading from the coelom to the mantle cavity, into which it opens through a slit with large folded lips; and, on the side of the oviduct, the large oviducal gland (which secretes the outer egg shell). Remove the nidamental glands to find, beneath their anterior ends, the pair of accessory nidamental glands which are speckled with orange. Taking care not to injure the stomach and the long, thin-walled caecum, remove the ovary and the accessory nidamental glands (in *Sepia* the ovary is dorsal to the stomach and caecum and therefore need not be removed).

d. In the male, and in the female from which the ovary and the nidamental glands have been removed, examine the organs of the **visceral mass**. Find the small ink sac dorsal to the posterior end of the rectum, and its duct passing dorsal to, and entering, the anterior end of the rectum. Gently squeeze the ink sac and notice that the black ink (composed of melanin granules) emerges from the anus (in life it is passed out via the siphon to form a cloud behind which the animal can escape). Also identify the large cephalic vein which emerges from the roof of the funnel to pass back dorsal to the ink sac; the visceral nerves, one on each side of the cephalic vein; the three glands of Verrill (function doubtful), one anterior and two lateral in the roof of the siphon; the large siphon retractor muscles lateral to the cephalic vein, and the even larger head retractor muscles dorsal to them; the pair of kidneys between which the rectum disappears posteriorly; the pair of accessory, or branchial, hearts at the bases of the ctenidia; the efferent branchial vessels leading from the ctenidia; the anterior mantle veins joined by the median mantle veins; the pair of large posterior mantle veins with the pair of small lateral mantle arteries passing along their inner borders; the single median mantle artery passing ventrally from between the posterior ends of the kidneys ; the sac-like stomach ; and the long pointed caecum which, in the male, covers the single dorsal testis.

  e. The **excretory system** consists merely of the kidneys and the short kidney ducts already located.

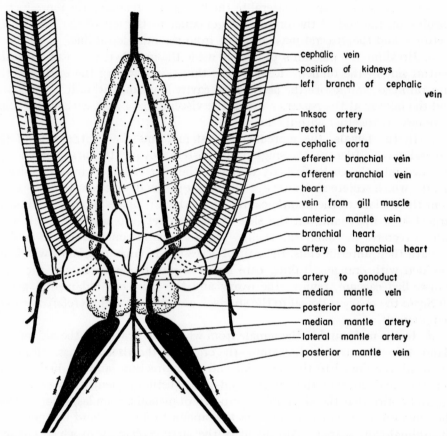

cephalic vein
position of kidneys
left branch of cephalic
                        vein

inksac artery
rectal artery
cephalic aorta
efferent branchial vein
afferent branchial vein
heart
vein from gill muscle
anterior mantle vein
branchial heart
artery to branchial heart

artery to gonoduct
median mantle vein
posterior aorta
median mantle artery
lateral mantle artery
posterior mantle vein

FIG. 150.—*Loligo.*   The blood system in the region of the true and of the branchial hearts.

  f. Trace the course of the closed and almost bilaterally symmetrical **blood system,** preferably in an injected specimen.   Separate the kidneys posteriorly, and follow forward the courses of the mantle arteries until they are seen to fuse together and enter the large median heart.   Notice that the posterior mantle veins do not enter this heart, but disappear into the posterior ends of the kidneys.   Pick away the kidney tissue to show that they enter the branchial hearts.   Similarly, the cephalic vein, splitting into two veins which penetrate the anterior kidney tissue, passes its blood into the branchial hearts.   Also entering the branchial hearts are the veins formed on each side by the union of the anterior mantle vein, the median mantle vein, and the vein from the gill muscle. From each branchial heart the blood is pumped through an afferent branchial vessel to the ctenidium. This vessel is obscured by the prominent efferent branchial vessel which takes the oxygenated blood to the median heart (owing to the valves in the branchial and median hearts, solutions used for injecting the blood system do not usually penetrate the afferent and efferent branchial vessels). Remove the pericardium from the median heart. Blood is pumped from this heart either through the cephalic aorta, which is displaced to the right and which, disappearing dorsally, supplies the head region, or through the posterior aorta, which is median and which divides to give the one median and two lateral mantle arteries. The posterior aorta, at its point of origin, also gives rise to two arteries which run forward across the ventral surface of the heart, the one to the ink sac and the other to the rectum (in *Sepia* the ink sac artery runs back to the posterior end of the visceral mass) ; a pair of arteries which supply the muscles of the branchial hearts ; and, to the left, a single artery which supplies the gonoduct. In the male, turn the stomach to one side and notice that a genital artery enters, and a genital vein leaves, the anterior end of the testis. In both sexes cut the posterior aorta and the efferent branchial vessels, and turn the heart forwards to find the base of the genital artery leaving its antero-dorsal side. Close by, the genital vein can be seen to enter the right branch of the cephalic vein running within the right kidney.

g. Remove the heart and any remaining kidney tissue, and turn aside the branchial hearts to uncover the **middle region of the alimentary canal**. Separate the rectum, together with the ink sac, from the cephalic vein. Dissect out the cephalic vein, and, while doing so, notice the large branch which enters it dorsally (from the digestive gland). From the space between the funnel retractor muscles remove the connective tissue and the thin sheet of muscle (part of the head retractor muscles) which cover the digestive gland (in the embryo there are two digestive glands, but in the adult they are fused together ; in the adult *Sepia* they remain separate). At the posterior end of this gland make a median longitudinal cut to find the narrow oesophagus and the anterior aorta, which both pass through the gland tissue. Follow the course of the oesophagus back to the right side of the visceral mass, where it joins into the large, sac-like stomach. At its left anterior end the stomach is also linked with the long, thin-walled caecum and with the short intestine which leads to the rectum. Obscuring these connections is a diverticulum of the caecum which, starting from the left, curves to the right and encircles the anterior end of the stomach and the posterior end of the oesophagus (this diverticulum is not present in *Sepia*). Find the two ducts which leave the posterior end of the digestive gland (further evidence of its double nature), and which unite just before entering the anterior end of the caecum, close to its junction with the

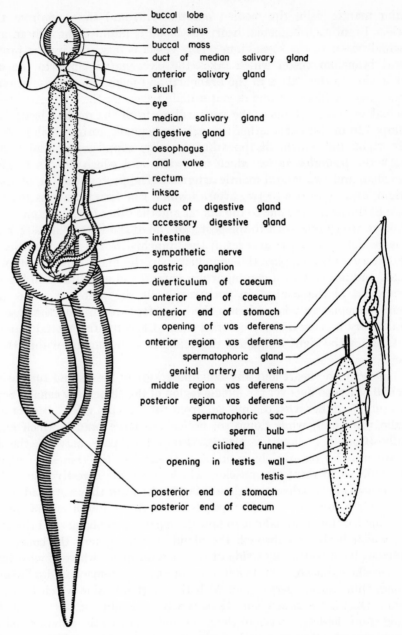

buccal lobe
buccal sinus
buccal mass
duct of median salivary gland
anterior salivary gland
skull
eye
median salivary gland
digestive gland
oesophagus
anal valve
rectum
inksac
duct of digestive gland
accessory digestive gland
intestine
sympathetic nerve
gastric ganglion
diverticulum of caecum
anterior end of caecum
anterior end of stomach
opening of vas deferens
anterior region vas deferens
spermatophoric gland
genital artery and vein
middle region vas deferens
posterior region vas deferens
spermatophoric sac
sperm bulb
ciliated funnel
opening in testis wall
testis
posterior end of stomach
posterior end of caecum

FIG. 151.—*Loligo.* Ventral views of the alimentary canal, and of the reproductive system
of a male.

stomach. Around the walls of these ducts is the accessory digestive gland (which is usually, though without adequate reason, termed the pancreas). Also notice the gastric ganglion (the centre of the sympathetic nervous system), which, located near the base of the intestine, gives numerous nerves to the stomach, the caecum, the intestine, and the oesophagus.

h. To expose the **anterior end of the alimentary canal**, cut away the remains of the siphon, together with the siphon retractor muscles, and follow forward the courses of the oesophagus and the anterior aorta by carefully removing the digestive gland. At the anterior end of the digestive gland distinguish, and leave in place, the median salivary gland (this secretes poison and not digestive enzymes), which is ventral to the oesophagus immediately posterior to the skull (in *Sepia* there are two salivary glands in this position). Detach at their bases the ventral pair of arms and the pair of tentacles; remove the muscles from the region between the eyes until the cartilage of the skull is reached (do not damage the skull); and finally dissect away the muscles and connective tissue between the skull and the mouth until the globular buccal mass is exposed. Notice that the buccal mass is enclosed in a large buccal sinus, which is the swollen anterior end of the cephalic vein. The oesophagus passes forwards through the skull, and, together with the duct of the median salivary gland, enters the posterior end of the buccal mass. Lateral to these points of junction is a pair of lateral salivary glands (also secreting poison) applied to the wall of the buccal mass.

i. In the **male reproductive system** the single testis and the anterior end of the vas deferens have already been located. However, the main part of the sperm-duct lies immediately dorsal to, and so is obscured by, the left branchial heart and the left posterior mantle vein. Separate this duct from the adjacent blood-vessels, and trace the course followed by the spermatozoa. The testis has a longitudinal, slit-like opening in its ventral surface through which the spermatozoa escape into the coelom. They are then collected by a ciliated funnel, and passed into the sperm-bulb at the posterior end of the vas deferens (in *Sepia* the sperm-bulb is absent). From the sperm-bulb the highly convoluted vas deferens runs forwards to enter the prominent spermatophoric gland (which secretes the membranes of the spermatophore around groups of spermatozoa). The fully formed spermatophores are passed back through the middle region of the vas deferens to be stored in the spermatophoric sac, and from this sac the anterior region of the vas deferens passes forwards to the genital opening. During copulation the left ventral arm (known as the hectocotylised arm) picks the spermatophores from the opening of the vas deferens and transfers them to the female. Notice that on this arm the distal suckers are replaced by long papillae.

j. Turn the specimen dorsal side uppermost. Make a shallow longitudinal incision along the middle line of the visceral hump to open the shell sac.

Extract the horny **shell** and examine its shape (in *Sepia* the shell is largely calcareous).

k. To expose the **anterior part of the nervous system**, skin the dorsal side of the head, dissect away the muscles covering the skull, and remove the dorsal part of the skull to uncover the cerebral ganglia. While doing this, take care to preserve the pair of postorbital nerves which can be seen passing through the transparent cartilage in a dorsal direction. Continue the dissection laterally

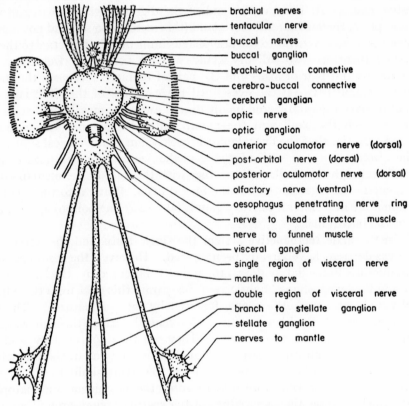

brachial   nerves
tentacular   nerve
buccal   nerves
buccal   ganglion
brachio-buccal   connective
cerebro-buccal   connective
cerebral   ganglion
optic   nerve
optic   ganglion
anterior   oculomotor   nerve   (dorsal)
post-orbital   nerve   (dorsal)
posterior   oculomotor   nerve   (dorsal)
olfactory   nerve   (ventral)
oesophagus   penetrating   nerve   ring
nerve   to   head   retractor   muscle
nerve   to   funnel   muscle
visceral   ganglia
single   region   of   visceral   nerve
mantle   nerve
double   region   of   visceral   nerve
branch   to   stellate   ganglion
stellate   ganglion
nerves   to   mantle

FIG. 152.—*Loligo.* A dorsal view of the nervous system.

to expose the large optic ganglia, noticing and removing the so-called white bodies (which probably produce leucocytes) surrounding the ganglia. Cut away the muscles posterior to the skull to reveal the anterior end of the digestive gland, the oesophagus, and the median salivary gland. Remove all these structures together with any remaining connective tissue which obscures the visceral ganglia and the nerves to which they give rise. Continue the dissection in front of the cerebral ganglia to uncover the small supra-buccal ganglion and the large brachial nerves lateral and ventral to it. Cut away one eye together with its optic ganglion, and examine the brain from both dorsal and lateral aspects. The cerebral ganglia are distinct, but the other eight ganglia composing the brain are so fused together as to be almost inseparable. These other ganglia are the pleural ganglia lateral to the oesophagus, and the brachial, pedal, and visceral ganglia ventral to the oesophagus. Notice that the cerebral ganglia do not give rise to any nerves; that the pleural ganglia give rise to the large optic nerves (leading to the optic ganglia), the anterior oculomotor nerves (to the anterior eye muscles), the postorbital nerves (to the anterior part of the head retractor muscles), and the posterior oculomotor nerves (to the posterior eye muscles); that the visceral ganglia give rise to a pair of nerves to the head retractor muscles, a pair to the muscles of the funnel, a pair of large mantle nerves, and a visceral nerve (formed of two nerves fused; it is double at its point of emergence and posteriorly it again separates into two: in *Sepia* the two visceral nerves remain separate); that the pedal ganglia give rise to numerous small nerves, of which the most important are the auditory and the inferior oculomotor nerves; and that the brachial ganglia give rise to the four pairs of brachial nerves and the pair of tentacular nerves. The supra-buccal ganglion is attached to the anterior end of the cerebral ganglia by the cerebro-buccal connectives, and to the brachial ganglia by the brachio-buccal connectives. It gives rise to a number of buccal nerves which innervate the buccal mass.

l. Turn the specimen ventral side uppermost, and, following the course of the mantle nerves, dissect out the **posterior part of the nervous system.** The mantle nerves pass outwards through the head retractor muscles and give branches to the large stellate ganglia (the motor centres of the mantle). Passing the ganglia, and receiving branches from them, they enter the mantle and branch to innervate the fins. The posterior ends of the visceral nerves were located earlier passing back on each side of the cephalic vein, and they were removed with that vein.

m. Cut transversely through one of the **eyes.** Notice the outer transparent cornea; the narrow space between the cornea and the lens (normally filled with fluid); the fleshy iris which encircles the outside of the lens, and which is modified dorsally into a small flap projecting down over the pupil; the almost spherical lens held in place by the ciliary body; the large inner cavity (also filled with fluid); and the heavily pigmented retina. Attached to the inner surface of the eyeball are the eye muscles.

n. Cut open the **buccal mass.** Distinguish the two beak-like jaws, the ventral overlapping the dorsal; the ventral radula, the posterior end of which is enclosed in a radula sac; and the tongue which is antero-ventral to the radula, and on which opens the duct from the median salivary gland.

4. CONCLUSION

a. Observing the specimen and the drawings made, review the characteristics of the phylum, of the class, and of the order.

b. Also review those peculiar features which are associated with the active swimming and predaceous mode of life.

5. REFERENCES

TOMPSETT, D. H. (1939). " *Sepia.*" *Memoirs of the Liverpool Marine Biological Committee*, Vol. 32.

WILLIAMS, L. W. (1909). " The anatomy of the common squid *Loligo pealii*, Lesneur." Leiden.

APPENDIX TO THE MOLLUSCA

I. CULTURE METHODS

a. Marine molluscs are not easily kept in the laboratory unless special facilities are available, but small specimens of all the species described above may live for at least a few days, and sometimes for several weeks, if kept in large tanks of cool sea-water.

b. The various fresh-water species of the orders Pulmonata and Eulamellibranchia are easily cultured. Pulmonate snails, such as *Lymnaea* or *Planorbis,* are usually kept in balanced aquaria, and they live and breed with little or no attention. Eulamellibranchs, such as *Anodonta*, are almost as easily kept. Several small specimens, 1 or 2 inches long, will thrive in a large aquarium, the floor of which is covered with sand to a depth of at least 3 inches. If the aquarium is kept in a window and fish are added, phytoplankton should flourish, and on them Anodonta can feed.

c. Terrestrial species of the order Pulmonata, such as *Helix*, should be kept in a glass or earthenware container with a gauze top, and fed on lettuce leaves and on whole oats rolled in calcium carbonate powder. The container, kept in a cool place where the light is dim, should hold 2 or 3 inches of soil, which must be kept damp but not wet, and several layers of dead leaves, the outer of which must remain dry to prevent an excessive growth of mould. *Limax* can be kept in the same way, but it likes even less light, it does not require calcium carbonate, and it will eat a wide variety of foods such as bread, raw potatoes, turnips, and most green vegetables.

2. METHODS OF KILLING

a. The marine molluscs should not be killed quickly but should first be narcotised (exceptions are *Loligo* and *Sepia*, which, like fish, quickly die when taken out of the water). Narcotisation may be effected by the addition of crystals of menthol or of magnesium sulphate (Epsom salts) to a small volume of sea-water in which the animals have been placed, or alternatively by the addition, drop by drop, of alcohol. In neither case should the water be stirred or the container touched, lest the animals contract. When after several hours they become insensitive, the specimens can be dissected immediately or preserved either in 5% formalin or in 70% alcohol.

b. The fresh-water and terrestrial pulmonates, and the fresh-water eulamellibranchs, are best killed by asphyxiation in stoppered bottles entirely full of water. After about twenty-four hours, when all the dissolved air has been used up, they will be found insensitive and fully extended. A more rapid, but poorer, method, which can be used for terrestrial pulmonates only, is to allow the animal to extend fully on the end of a stick and then to plunge the stick into boiling water. It is always better to dissect the freshly killed animals, but they may be preserved for later dissection in either 5% formalin or 70% alcohol.

3. METHOD OF STAINING AND MOUNTING *CLIONE*

a. Permanent mounts may be made of small specimens of *Clione* after staining in borax carmine. If the animals are preserved in 70% alcohol they can be transferred directly into the borax carmine solution, but if they are preserved in 5% formalin they should be thoroughly washed in water before being transferred via 30% and 50% alcohols (about twenty minutes in each) to 70% alcohol. After over-staining in borax carmine (for an hour or more) they should be placed in acid 70% alcohol and kept there until the excess stain is removed. They are then ready to be transferred through normal 70% alcohol, 90% alcohol, absolute alcohol, a mixture of equal parts of absolute alcohol and xylol, and xylol (about twenty minutes in each solution), and mounted in Canada balsam on a microscope slide.

b. Alternatively, if the animals are first transferred to and washed in water, they may be over-stained in some haematoxylin solution such as Delafield's or Erhlich's. As before, the excess stain must be removed in acid solution, preferably in acid 70% alcohol, after which the colour of the stain must be changed from red to blue in alkaline 70% alcohol. Finally, they may be taken from normal 70% alcohol to Canada balsam as already described.

CHAPTER XXI

PHYLUM ECHINODERMATA

Characteristics : Adults unsegmented, having a radial symmetry which affects most of the body organs and which almost obscures the bilateral larval symmetry; locomotion usually by tube feet; endoskeleton of dermal calcareous ossicles; coelom extensive and forming the perivisceral cavity, the cavity of the perihaemal sinus system, and the cavity of the peculiar water vascular system; haemocoel usually extremely reduced and forming the cavity of the slight vascular system; nervous system simple and remaining attached to the epidermis; no nephridia or other special excretory organs; sexes usually separate, and development through specialised pelagic larval stages.

The echinoderms form a compact phylum which is exclusively marine. Today they are common from the littoral zone to the greatest ocean depths, and in the past they were abundant in most ages of which fossil records remain. They are particularly interesting because, of all the invertebrates, they are considered to be most closely related to the chordates and so to the vertebrates.

1.00. Class Crinoidea

Characteristics : Echinoderms which are attached during part or all of their life by an aboral stalk composed of dermal ossicles; mouth central and anus lateral on the oral surface; usually with each of the five arms branching once at its base; with ciliated food-grooves running from the arms to the mouth; with tube feet represented by ciliated food collecting tentacles, often called podia; no spines; no madreporite; and no pedicellariae.

This class contains some of the most primitive echinoderms. Most of its members are fossil, and they are known to have been extraordinarily abundant during the Palaeozoic period. There are relatively few surviving genera, and most of these live in deep water.

1.01. Order Articulata

Characteristics : Crinoidea with the central disc covered by a flexible tegmen containing numerous small ossicles, and with open food-grooves on the oral surface.

Genus **Antedon** (feather star)

I. GENERAL ACCOUNT

a. This common genus, which must be chosen as the type, is unfortunately aberrant in several respects, and particularly in that a stalk is present only in the young stage.

b. Feather stars have a world-wide distribution from depths of about 2 fathoms down into the abysses. They normally remain inactive, clinging to

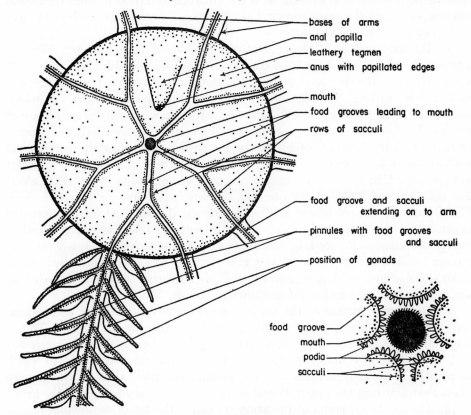

bases of arms
anal papilla
leathery tegmen
anus with papillated edges
mouth
food grooves leading to mouth
rows of sacculi

food groove and sacculi
                    extending on to arm
pinnules with food grooves
                                and sacculi
position of gonads

food   groove
mouth
podia
sacculi

FIG. I53.—*Antedon*.   The external features of the oral surface, and (below) the mouth region considerably enlarged.

rocks etc. by means of their cirri, and extending their arms widely to collect the microscopic plants and animals which serve as food. These particles are passed along ciliated grooves to the mouth. *Antedon* can also swim well, five arms beating back while the alternate five arms are making the slower recovery movement. In temperate regions breeding is in spring and early summer, fertilisation is external, and the eggs are attached in clusters to the pinnules. There they remain until the larvae develop ciliated bands and break free.   After swimming, but not feeding, for from twelve to forty-eight hours, these barrel-shaped larvae settle to form stalked pentacrinoid larvae, which are found attached to hard objects such as stones or shells.   After about six months the stalk is absorbed and the adult shape assumed.

2. EXTERNAL ANATOMY

a. Examine the central disc-like **body** (for method of killing see p. **442**) and distinguish the oral surface, with the small central mouth, from the aboral surface, on which the arms and cirri are inserted.   Notice that each of the five arms branches once at its base.

b. The **oral surface** of the central disc is covered by a leathery skin, the tegmen, in which are embedded tiny calcareous plates.   Identify the small, round mouth ; the five food-grooves (ciliated) which radiate from the mouth and, before reaching the edge of the disc, divide to form ten grooves, which pass on to the ten arms ; and the anus on a prominent papilla between two of the radii.   Through a lens or binocular microscope, notice that the tegmen is perforated by numbers of minute pores (which open into the perivisceral coelom, but which are in effect the external apertures of the water vascular system since that system also opens into the perivisceral coelom) ; that along the sides of each food-groove are single or multiple rows of yellowish dots, the sacculi (these, colourless in life, are closed dermal vesicles of unknown function) ; that projecting inwards from the edges of the food-grooves, and so partly covering them, are large numbers of podia (which are ciliated for food capture and are equivalent to the tube feet of other echinoderms ; those nearest the mouth are largest and are possibly sensory) ; and that the edges of the anus bear small papillae (of unknown function).

c. The **aboral surface** of the central disc is partly covered by the tegmen and partly by a central skeletal plate called the centro-dorsal ossicle.   To the edges of this ossicle are attached a varying number of cirri (for gripping rocks, etc.).   Each cirrus is made up of a column of skeletal plates, the distal of which is pointed and partly hooked to form a claw.   Remove some of the cirri to show that abutting the centro-dorsal plate are the five basal plates of the arms.

d. The five basal **plates of the arms** are called the 1st primibrachial plates, and external to them are the five triangular 2nd primibrachial plates.   To each 2nd primibrachial plate are joined two brachial plates, each being the first of the series of brachial plates which form the jointed skeleton of an arm.   The 1st and 2nd brachial plates are distinct, but the 3rd and 4th are partially fused.   Similar partial fusions are formed between certain definite joints along the length of each arm (and they appear to act as autotomy joints).   The 1st pinnule is attached to the 2nd brachial plate, the 2nd pinnule to the 4th plate, and the 3rd pinnule to the 5th plate.   Each pinnule is supported by a row of jointed skeletal plates, the pinnularies.

e. Detach one of the largest **pinnules** and examine its structure under a strong lens or a microscope.   The skeletal plates, extending along one border,

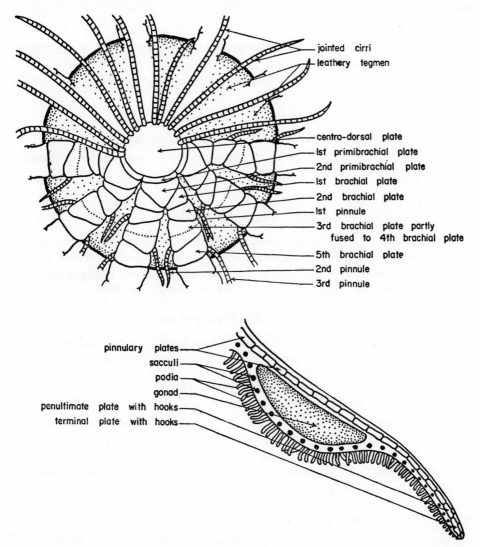

FIG. 154.—*Antedon.*   The external features of the aboral surface (in the lower half of the figure the cirri have been removed to expose the bases of the arms, while in the upper half the details of the arms have been omitted to clarify the structure and arrangement of the cirri). Below is one of the pinnules considerably enlarged.

become smaller towards the tip, and the two distal plates bear a number of small hooks.   Along the opposite border runs the food-groove which is fringed on both sides by podia.   Near the bases of the podia are the sacculi.   Proximally, the pinnule is swollen to contain a gonad which is either a testis or an ovary (there are no gonoducts and the gametes escape by a rupture of the pinnule wall).

3. CONCLUSION

a. As far as is possible from the external features alone, review the characteristics of the phylum, of the class, and of the order.

b. Also distinguish those features which are associated with the relatively sedentary mode of life.

4. REFERENCES

For further details, particularly of the internal anatomy, see :

CHADWICK, H. C. (1907). "*Antedon.*" *Memoirs of the Liverpool Marine Biological Committee*, Vol. 15.
MORTENSEN, T. (1927). "Handbook of the echinoderms of the British Isles." London.

2.00. Class Asteroidea

Characteristics : Free-living star-shaped echinoderms in which the arms are not sharply marked off from the central disc ; anus and madreporite aboral ; ambulacral grooves open and containing rows of tube feet ending in suckers ; pedicellariae present ; alimentary canal extending into the arms.

2.01. Order Forcipulata

Characteristics : Asteroidea in which the pedicellariae are stalked, and in which the calcareous ossicles have prominent protruding spines.

Genus Asterias (starfish)

I. GENERAL ACCOUNT

a. This cosmopolitan genus is common from between tide-marks to depths of below 200 fathoms. Normally sluggish, it feeds largely on pelecypod molluscs whose shell-valves are slowly forced open by the steady pull of the tube feet, but other animals are also eaten, especially if they are in a dying condition. If, as is usual, the prey is too large to be taken into the stomach, this organ is everted through the mouth and wrapped round the food so that digestion takes place externally. When injured, the starfish has considerable powers of regeneration. The breeding season is in spring, fertilisation is external, and the bipinnaria larvae swim in the plankton for several weeks while feeding on diatoms, etc. The starfish is sexually mature after one year.

2. EXTERNAL ANATOMY

a. Examine the **body** of a specimen killed in an extended condition (for the method see p. 442), and distinguish the oral surface, with the ambulacral grooves and tube feet, from the aboral surface, with the pink spiny skin.

b. On the **oral surface** the central mouth is conspicuous, and so are the five ambulacral grooves leading to it. Each groove is packed, in an apparently

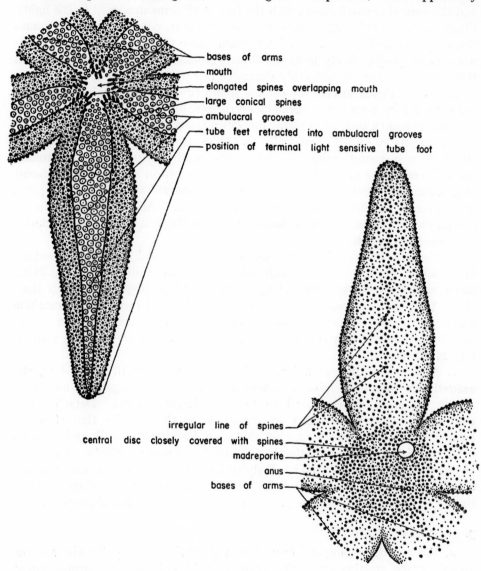

bases of arms
mouth
elongated spines overlapping mouth
large conical spines
ambulacral grooves
tube feet retracted into ambulacral grooves
position of terminal light sensitive tube foot

irregular line of spines
central disc closely covered with spines
madreporite
anus
bases of arms

FIG. 155.—*Asterias.* The external features of the oral and aboral surfaces.

haphazard manner, with large numbers of tube feet, or podia, each ending in a sucker (these tube feet have great powers of expansion and contraction, and they are the organs of attachment and of locomotion). On the end of each

E E

arm the single terminal tube foot (which is often difficult to find in preserved specimens) lacks a sucker and has an orange-coloured tip (it is light sensitive, and the animal normally rests with the tips of all arms upturned to the light). Flanking the ambulacral grooves are rows of blunt, conical calcareous spines (these are specialised dermal ossicles which, since their epidermal covering is worn away, project freely from the skin). Notice at the edges of the mouth that these spines are considerably elongated (for pushing in the food).

c. On the **aboral surface** the conical spines projecting through the skin are smaller but very numerous, especially on the central disc. There is a tendency for them to form a somewhat zigzag line down the centre of each arm, and other lines along its edges. Eccentrically on the central disc, the most prominent structure is a round, calcareous plate, the madreporite, which is situated opposite one of the interradii. Its surface is grooved in a manner reminiscent of a brain coral, and along the bases of these grooves are rows of tiny pores (the external openings of the water vascular system). Also eccentrically on the central disc is the inconspicuous anus situated in the next interradius clockwise from the madreporite.

d. Using a strong lens or binocular microscope and keeping the animal under water, examine the pink body-wall between the white spines. In living and in well-preserved specimens, large numbers of tiny, finger-like evaginations of the body-wall are easily visible. These are the semi-transparent **branchiae** which give a velvet appearance to the skin (their cavities are extensions of the perivisceral coelom, they contain coelomic fluid, and they are probably respiratory in function).

e. Also surrounding each large spine is a ring of small white dots, the **pedicellariae** (modified spines). These are particularly large and numerous among the large spines lateral to the ambulacral grooves. Detach some, and, mounting them in water on a microscope slide, notice that they are formed of three calcareous ossicles, the basal forming the stalk and the two distal working against each other like the blades of forceps (the function of the aboral pedicellariae is to keep the body surface free from detritus and from the many larvae which would otherwise settle on and encrust the starfish, while that of the oral pedicellariae is probably to clean the ambulacral grooves).

3. INTERNAL ANATOMY

a. Without disturbing or injuring the madreporite, remove the skin from the aboral surface, starting by cutting along both sides of one of the arms. Great care is necessary in detaching the skin, particularly from the central disc, since the alimentary canal and its diverticula are closely attached to the inner surface by mesenteries. Notice the extensive **perivisceral coelom**, and the long, thin strand of the aboral muscle running along the length of each arm above the diverticula of the alimentary canal.

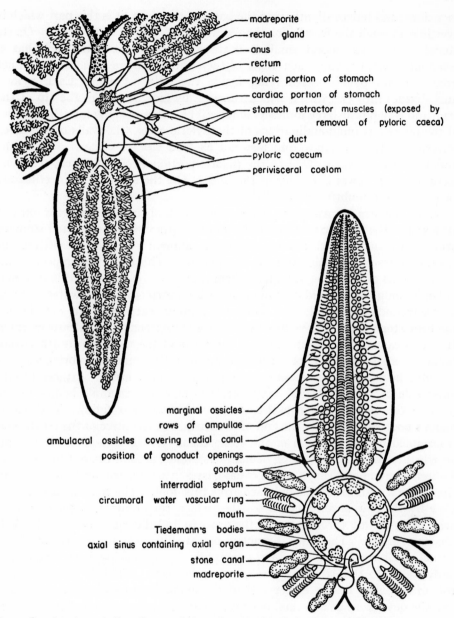

madreporite
rectal gland
anus
rectum
pyloric portion of stomach
cardiac portion of stomach
stomach retractor muscles (exposed by
        removal of pyloric caeca)
pyloric duct
pyloric caecum
perivisceral coelom

marginal ossicles
rows of ampullae
ambulacral ossicles covering radial canal
position of gonoduct openings
gonads
interradial septum
circumoral water vascular ring
mouth
Tiedemann's bodies
axial sinus containing axial organ
stone canal
madreporite

FIG. 156.—*Asterias*. A dissection, made from the aboral surface, of the alimentary canal (above),
        and of the water vascular and reproductive systems (below).

b. Distinguish the parts of the **alimentary canal**.   The mouth opens through
an extremely short oesophagus (out of sight) into the large stomach, which is
divided into cardiac and pyloric portions.   The cardiac portion is globular and

capacious, and bulges slightly into the bases of the arms (it is this part which is eversible through the mouth for the external digestion of large prey). On its aboral side is the much smaller, flattened, pyloric portion, which has a pentagonal shape. Into each angle of the pentagon there opens a large duct from the two pyloric caeca lying inside the adjacent arm. Each pyloric duct divides into two ducts, which run side by side almost to the tip of the arm, and which bear large numbers of lateral branches opening into the cavities of the numerous blind-ending sacs of the pyloric caeca (the walls of the caeca secrete digestive enzymes, and also act as food storage organs). From the middle of the aboral surface of the pyloric portion of the stomach, the short rectum passes upwards to end in the anus. On the sides of the rectum are two glands (of doubtful function).

c. In one arm cut away the pyloric caeca to find the two retractor muscles attached to the cardiac portion of the stomach (they pull the everted stomach back into place). Next remove the whole alimentary canal by cutting the stomach retractor muscles and the oesophagus. This operation exposes some of the vessels of the **water vascular system** (the coelomic cavity of this system is full of an albuminous fluid containing amoeboid corpuscles). A water vascular ring surrounds the mouth, and its cavity communicates with the exterior via the bent stone canal, the walls of which are strengthened by calcareous rings. It is this canal which opens through the pores of the madreporite (the whole canal system is lined by cilia which beat inwards, thus tending to bring water in through the madreporite which sieves out any solid particles). Attached to the inner side of the circumoral vessel are the nine Tiedemann's bodies (which produce the amoeboid corpuscles of the water vascular fluid). Two Tiede-mann's bodies lie opposite the end of each arm, but the place of the tenth body is occupied by the junction of the stone canal. (Polian vesicles, such as are attached to the circumoral ring of many asteroids, are not present in *Asterias*.) From the circumoral ring a radial canal passes into each arm and extends to its tip, where it ends inside the light sensitive tube foot. The canal is hidden from view by the row of ambulacral ossicles, which runs down the centre of each arm. Cut cleanly through one of the arms to find the canal as a small hole in the cut surface. The canal branches repeatedly along its length, and each branch swells into a small bladder, or ampulla, before turning down through the body-wall into the cavity of one of the tube feet. A tightly packed, zigzag row of ampullae lies on either side of the ambulacral ossicles, between them and the outer zone of marginal ossicles. Through a lens examine the relations between the radial canal, the ampullae, and the tube feet as seen in the cut end of the detached arm.

d. The peculiar **haemal system** and the perihaemal spaces (coelom) which surround it are not easily traced in a dissection. However, their most prominent parts, the axial organ (sometimes called the heart although its true function is doubtful), contained in the axial sinus (perihaemal coelom), can be seen attached to the outer side of the stone canal.

e. The **reproductive organs**, either ovaries or testes, occur in pairs in the proximal ends of the arms. They lie in the perivisceral coelom unsupported by mesenteries, but each is attached to the body-wall by a very short gonoduct. This gonoduct (ciliated) opens laterally through a small pore almost at the point of junction of the arms.

f. The **nervous system** is largely in the form of a network of tiny fibres underlying the ectoderm and endoderm all over the body, but concentrations of these fibres do occur in places. Thus a radial nerve runs down each arm, and may be seen through a lens as a thin yellow or brown line passing along the middle of an ambulacral groove from which the tube feet have been removed (it can sometimes be seen more clearly by holding up the arm, from which the alimentary canal has been dissected, and looking through it at a light). It is usually possible to trace the course of this nerve inwards until it joins into the circumoral nerve-ring.

4. CONCLUSION

a. Observing the specimen and the drawings made, review the characteristics of the phylum, of the class, and of the order.

5. REFERENCES

CHADWICK, H. C. (1923). "*Asterias.*" *Memoirs of the Liverpool Marine Biological Committee*, Vol. 25.

MORTENSEN, T. (1927). "Handbook of the echinoderms of the British Isles." London.

3.00. Class **Ophiuroidea**

Characteristics : Free-living, star-shaped echinoderms in which the arms are sharply marked off from the central disc; madreporite on the oral surface; no anus; ambulacral grooves covered by ossicles; tube feet without suckers; no pedicellariae; alimentary canal confined to the central disc.

More species of ophiuroids are known than of any other echinoderm class, and they also occur in very great numbers. They are all active animals and move comparatively quickly, not by means of the tube feet, but by the walking actions of the arms. Some species multiply asexually by a division of the central disc.

3.01. Order **Ophiurae**

Characteristics : Ophiuroidea in which the five unbranched arms can bend laterally but not towards the mouth.

Genus **Ophioderma** (brittle star)

(The following description applies generally to such other brittle stars as *Ophiura*, *Ophiocoma*, and *Ophiothrix*, which, however, differ in such details as the relative sizes of the skeletal plates covering the central disc and of the spines on the marginal plates of the arms.)

I. GENERAL ACCOUNT

a. Ophioderma is found commonly along the shores of the Mediterranean and North Atlantic, and related genera are cosmopolitan. Brittle stars occur on the sea-shore and in shallow seas, and they have also been dredged from great depths. They are active animals, and crawl on the sea-bottom by the co-ordinated movements of the arms, but since these arms can only bend laterally, the whole oral surface remains in contact with the substratum. Food consists of a variety of animals such as worms, crustaceans, molluscs, and other echinoderms which are small enough to be swallowed, and of organic detritus, which is trapped in mucus secreted by the tube feet and carried into the stomach by ciliary currents. Breeding generally takes place in spring and summer, fertilisation is external, and each egg develops into a pelagic ophio-pluteus larva which feeds on other smaller pelagic organisms. Some species of the genus *Amphiura* are hermaphrodite, and retain the eggs in the genital bursae.

2. EXTERNAL ANATOMY

a. In a specimen killed in an extended condition (for the method see p. 442) examine the general shape of the **body**, and distinguish the oral surface, with the mouth in the centre of the disc, from the aboral surface.

b. On the **oral surface** of the central disc the star-shaped mouth is prominent, and opposite its five corners the five arms arise. The skin covering the disc is leathery in the sections between the arms, and in it are embedded large numbers of small, closely packed, calcareous ossicles. In one of the five sections the madreporite opens, but its tiny pores are usually obscured by pigmentation. Between the sides of the arms and the sections of the central disc are ten deep grooves, the genital bursae, into which the gonoducts open (possibly the bursae also subserve respiration and excretion, and their inner lining is ciliated). Lateral and internal to the bases of the arms are five prominent buccal plates (dermal ossicles), and lateral and internal to them are ten angular plates. The internal borders of the angular plates bear spines and form the edges of the mouth.

c. The **aboral surface** of the central disc is entirely covered by the leathery skin, and is set with great numbers of tiny calcareous ossicles. Notice the absence of an anus.

d. The **arms** are snake-like, and externally they are sheathed by four rows of calcareous dermal plates, one row being ventral (this covers the ambulacral groove), one dorsal, and two lateral (the epidermis covering these plates is rudimentary). Each lateral plate bears about ten spines (which help to grip the substratum). From tiny pores set in the sutures between the ventral and lateral plates, the short tube feet (sensory organs) emerge, one pair to each segment of the arm.   At the base of each arm, from between the innermost ventral and lateral plates, the large oral tube feet emerge.   There are twenty of these, ten being superficial and ten hidden beneath them, and they project inwards over the entrance to the mouth (for tasting and pushing in the food).   At the tip of each arm is a single tiny tube foot (also thought to be a tasting organ) which is pale coloured and which pierces the single terminal plate.   Forming the core to each arm is a row of large vertebral ossicles.   Cut cleanly through one of the arms near its base to find one of these large white ossicles on the cut surface.

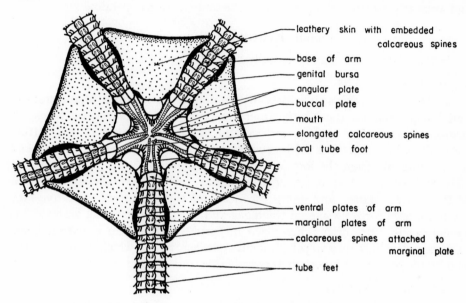

leathery skin with embedded calcareous spines
base of arm
genital bursa
angular plate
buccal plate
mouth
elongated calcareous spines
oral tube foot

ventral plates of arm
marginal plates of arm
calcareous spines attached to marginal plate
tube feet

FIG. 157.—*Ophioderma*.   The external features of the oral surface.

3.   CONCLUSION

   a. As far as is possible from the external features alone, review the characteristics of the phylum, of the class, and of the order.

   b. Compare the habits and external structure of *Ophioderma* with those of *Asterias*.

4.   REFERENCES

   For further details, particularly of the internal anatomy, see :

CUÉNOT, L. (1888).   " Études anatomiques et morphologiques sur les Ophiures." *Archives de Zoologie Expérimentale et Générale*, Vol. 6, p. 33.
   DELAGE, Y., and HÉROUARD, E. (1903).   Volume 3 of " Traité de zoologie concrète. Les échinodermes." Paris.
   LUDWIG, H. (1878).   " Beiträge zur Anatomie der Ophiuren." *Zeitschrift für wissenschaftliche Zoologie*, Vol. 31, p. 346.

4.00. Class **Echinoidea**

Characteristics : Free-living globular or discoidal echinoderms with no arms ; anus and madreporite aboral ; ambulacral grooves covered by ossicles ; tube feet ending in suckers ; large numbers of movable spines ; and well developed pedicellariae.

4.01. Order **Endocyclica**

Characteristics : Echinoidea with the body nearly spherical ; with the mouth and anus at opposite poles ; and with the ambulacra not petaloid.

Genus **Echinus** (sea urchin)

(*Strongylocentrotus* is an essentially similar alternative.)

I. GENERAL ACCOUNT

a. The genus *Echinus* is widely distributed in the Atlantic, Mediterranean, and Pacific, but off the North American coasts it is replaced by *Strongylocentrotus.* These sea urchins are usually common on a rocky sea-bottom, especially where there is a thick growth of *Fucus* and *Laminaria.* They occur most commonly from the low-tide mark to a depth of about 20 fathoms, but they are also found at much greater depths. They move slowly by means of the ventral spines, and climb by means of the tube feet. The five large teeth are used for browsing on the algae and on small encrusting animals such as polyzoans. Breeding takes place in spring, fertilisation is external, and each egg develops into a pelagic echinopluteus larva, which feeds on other planktonic organisms before metamorphosing and settling to the bottom.

2. EXTERNAL ANATOMY

a. Two specimens should be examined, the one preserved whole in alcohol (for the method see p. 442) and the other dried and scraped clean (for the method see p. 443). Orientate the body by distinguishing the oral surface, which is relatively flat, from the aboral surface, which is domed.

b. Examine the whole specimen first. On the **oral surface** the mouth is central, and from it protrude the five teeth of the internal jaw apparatus. The circular lip surrounding the mouth is rough but flexible, and round it is a broad, soft membrane, the peristome. Inside the peristome are embedded ten small calcareous ossicles, the buccal plates, and on its surface is a ring of ten large buccal tube feet (sensory organs probably used for tasting), each of which pierces, and so marks the position of, one of the buccal plates. At the outer edge of the peristome, in line with the ten tube feet, are ten branching gills (these are contractile and strongly ciliated ; their cavities open into the coelomic cavity of the jaw apparatus into which oxygen, dissolved in the coelomic fluid, is passed).

c. At the outer edge of the peristome the solid **shell** begins (it is covered externally by a ciliated epidermis), and over its surface pass five ambulacra, each seen as a double row of tube feet extending upwards towards the aboral

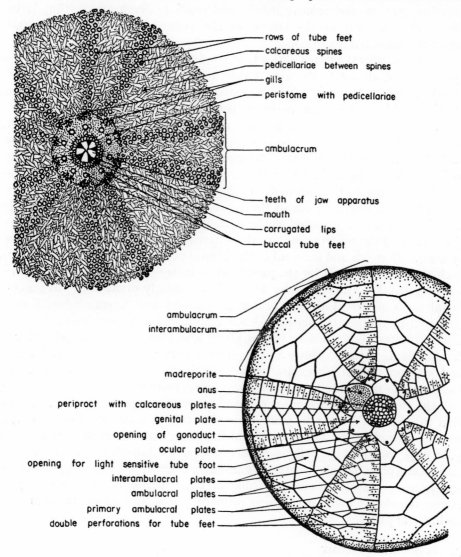

rows of tube feet
calcareous spines
pedicellariae between spines
gills
peristome with pedicellariae

ambulacrum

teeth of jaw apparatus
mouth
corrugated lips
buccal tube feet

ambulacrum
interambulacrum

madreporite
anus
periproct with calcareous plates
genital plate
opening of gonoduct
ocular plate
opening for light sensitive tube foot
interambulacral plates
ambulacral plates
primary ambulacral plates
double perforations for tube feet

FIG. 158.—*Echinus*. The external features of the oral surface (above), and of the aboral surface of a dried cleaned specimen (below).

pole.   The shell surface is closely covered with long and short spines (specialised dermal ossicles from which the covering epidermis has been worn), which, being set on ball-and-socket joints, are movable.   Between the bases of the spines and over the peristome are large numbers of small pedicellariae (specialised spines), each composed of a stalk joined to the body by a ball-and-socket joint and surmounted by a head formed of three blades (these blades, closing together, pick up and remove débris, and crush to death any settling larvae etc.). Detach some of the largest of the pedicellariae and examine their structure through a microscope.

d. On the **aboral surface** notice that the five ambulacra and the covering of spines extend almost to the aboral pole, near which the large madreporite is clearly visible. Also notice that a small area of the surface round the aboral pole is flexible. This is the periproct through which opens the anus.

e. Complete the examination of the aboral surface using the dried specimen. The central periproct is seen to be composed of numbers of tiny **dermal plates** embedded in a flexible membrane through which the anus opens asymmetrically. It is surrounded by a rigid ring of five pentagonal ossicles, the genital plates, so called because on the outer edge of each is a large pore through which opens one of the gonoducts. Four of the genital plates are of equal size, while the fifth is larger and is modified as the madreporite (the numerous tiny pores on the surface of the madreporite are the external openings of the water vascular system). Between and external to the genital plates are the five ocular plates, each of which is pierced for the passage of a single terminal tube foot (which is light sensitive). The remainder of the shell is clearly divided into five ambulacral areas (external to the ocular plates) and five interambulacral areas (external to the genital plates). Each ambulacral and each interambulacral area is composed of a double row of plates which interlock with each other to form a zigzag suture. However, the sutures between the rows of ambulacral and interambulacral plates are always relatively straight. Both the ambulacral and the interambulacral plates bear bosses (with which spines articulated), and the ambulacral plates are perforated for the passage of tube feet. Notice that the perforations are in pairs (since the stalk of each tube foot is split, it requires two pores for its passage), and that each ambulacral plate bears three pairs of perforations (actually each tube foot passes through a separate primary ambulacral plate, but these primaries are fused in trios ; the fine sutures between the primary plates are easily visible in large, well-cleaned specimens ; in *Strongylocentrotus* more than three primary plates have fused to form each ambulacral plate).

3. INTERNAL ANATOMY

a. With the aboral side of the animal uppermost, cut through the shell round the equator. Leaving the madreporite and the periproct in place, and avoiding damaging those internal organs which are closely applied to the inside of the shell, break away the upper part of the shell piece by piece. Notice the very spacious perivisceral coelom, in which the most conspicuous organs are

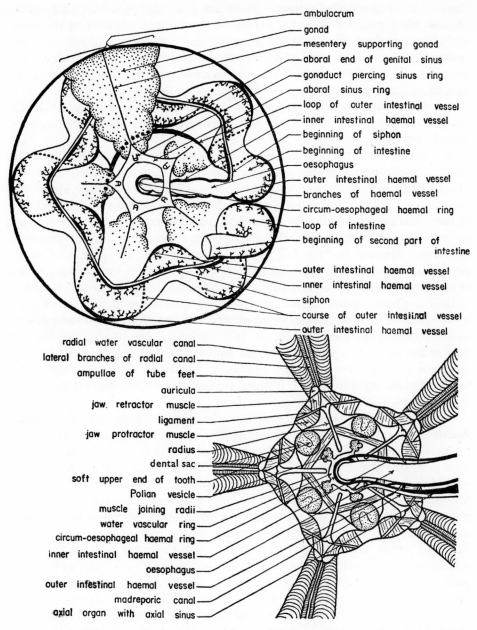

ambulacrum
gonad
mesentery supporting gonad
aboral end of genital sinus
gonaduct piercing sinus ring
aboral sinus ring
loop of outer intestinal vessel
inner intestinal haemal vessel
beginning of siphon
beginning of intestine
oesophagus
outer intestinal haemal vessel
branches of haemal vessel
circum-oesophageal haemal ring
loop of intestine
beginning of second part of intestine

outer intestinal haemal vessel
inner intestinal haemal vessel
siphon
course of outer intestinal vessel
outer intestinal haemal vessel

radial water vascular canal
lateral branches of radial canal
ampullae of tube feet
auricula
jaw retractor muscle
ligament
jaw protractor muscle
radius
dental sac
soft upper end of tooth
Polian vesicle
muscle joining radii
water vascular ring
circum-oesophageal haemal ring
inner intestinal haemal vessel
oesophagus
outer intestinal haemal vessel
madreporic canal
axial organ with axial sinus

FIG. 159.—*Echinus.* A general dissection, seen from the aboral side, with four of the gonads largely removed and with the second, or upper, part of the intestine cut away to expose the first, or lower, part. Below is the jaw apparatus seen from the aboral side.

those of the **reproductive system**.   There are five large gonads, either ovaries
(yellow when mature) or testes (white when mature), situated in the interambulacral regions and held in place by mesenteries.   A short gonoduct
emerges from the aboral end of each gonad to pierce the aboral sinus ring and
open through a genital plate.   The aboral sinus ring (part of the perihaemal
system, the cavity of which is coelom and the function doubtful) gives a branch,
the genital sinus, to each gonad, and this branch ends blindly inside the
oral end of the gonad.   The anus and the madreporite protrude through the
aboral sinus ring.

   b. Remove the aboral sinus ring and the gonads to uncover the **alimentary
canal**.   Notice centrally the jaw apparatus, from the top of which the oesophagus emerges.   The oesophagus passes upwards half-way to the aboral side
before turning down and suddenly expanding as the intestine.   The first part
of the intestine, undulating up (in each ambulacral region) and down (in each
interambulacral region), encircles the coelomic cavity in an anti-clockwise
direction.   Having made a full circuit, it loops back on itself, the second
part of the intestine following the same undulating course, and weaving in and
out above the folds of the first part of the intestine.   On reaching the vicinity
of the oesophagus again, the intestine narrows to form the rectum, which turns
up to the anus.   Thin threads of mesentery attach both parts of the intestine
to the inside of the shell.   From the junction of the oesophagus and the first
part of the intestine a narrow tube, the siphon, separates itself, and runs close
alongside the inner border of the intestine.   It joins again into the end of the
first part of the intestine (and it is suggested that its function is to act as a bypass
for the excess water taken in with the food).

   c. Also alongside the intestine wall run the inner and outer intestinal **haemal
vessels** (these are part of the haemal system, have haemocoelic cavities, and
probably perform some of the functions of a blood system).   The inner vessel
runs alongside the siphon, while the outer vessel undulates along the opposite
wall of the intestine.   These two vessels, which are particularly obvious on the
first part of the intestine, are linked by large numbers of small branches.   The
undulating outer vessel also gives rise to a prominent loop vessel which passes
inwards towards, and closely skirts one side of, the base of the jaw apparatus.
This loop swells, and receives two branches from the outer vessel before again
joining into it.   Trace the course of the two intestinal vessels as far as the oesophagus, and notice that they turn along its walls on opposite sides to join into a
circumoesophageal haemal ring which lies on top of the jaw apparatus.   Just
before entering the haemal ring, the outer vessel joins with the base of the axial
organ (of doubtful function) which ascends alongside the madreporic canal of
the water vascular system.

   d. The **perihaemal system** of coelomic sinuses is reduced and discontinuous.
The aboral sinus ring and its five branches have already been seen, but there is

no similar oral ring (unless the coelomic cavity of the jaw apparatus can be considered as such a ring greatly enlarged). The axial sinus, around which the axial organ has grown, ends blindly at its oral end, while at its aboral end it opens into the coelom of the madreporic canal. There are five radial peri-haemal canals, which end blindly both orally and aborally, and which lie hidden beneath the five radial water vascular canals.

e. Leaving the jaw apparatus, the oesophagus, and the rectum in place, dissect out the intestine and its supporting mesenteries. Identify the parts of the **water vascular system**. The water vascular ring lies on top of the jaw apparatus beneath the haemal ring, and attached to it, opposite each inter-ambulacrum, is a small sacculated Polian vesicle (which holds the reserve liquid of the water vascular system). Alongside the axial organ the madreporic canal rises from the water vascular ring to the madreporite (water enters the system through the sieve-like madreporite and down the madreporic canal, which is homologous with the stone canal of *Asterias*, but lacks calcareous plates in the wall). Out of sight ventrally, opposite the five ambulacra, five radial canals leave the water vascular ring. Each radial canal, passing down-wards between the ossicles of the jaw apparatus, comes into sight beneath one of the calcareous auriculae to run in an aboral direction closely applied to the inside of the shell. Along both sides of each radial canal is a zone of ampullae, flattened, leaf-like vesicles, each communicating with one of the tube feet. Through a lens notice the large numbers of lateral branches which link the radial canal to the ampullae.

f. On top of the **jaw apparatus** (also known as Aristotle's lantern) identify the five narrow ossicles known as the radii, each of which is joined by two ligaments to the base of the shell and by muscles to the neighbouring radii. A thin peritoneum covers the whole jaw apparatus, thus separating its coelomic cavity from the perivisceral cavity. Opposite each interambulacrum, the peritoneum bulges upwards to form a thin-walled vesicle called a dental sac (this may be considered as an internal gill; the external gills pass oxygen into the coelom of the muscular jaw apparatus where it is most needed, and the internal gills pass some of it into the perivisceral coelom). Inside each dental sac is the curved upward extremity of one of the teeth. Identify the retractor muscles attached to the auriculae (these pull in the teeth and so open the mouth), and the protractor muscles extending from between the auriculae to the upper edge of the jaw apparatus (these push out the teeth and so close the mouth).

g. Detach the jaw apparatus by cutting through the muscles, the ligaments, and the peritoneum, and also through the lip round the edge of the mouth. Notice that the radial water vascular canals, leaving the base of the jaw apparatus, cross the inner surface of the peristome, each giving two branches without ampullae to the buccal tube feet. Clear away the obscuring peritoneum from part of the top and from one side of the jaw apparatus. Identify the **ossicles of the jaw apparatus**. The teeth themselves are long and narrow, their oral ends being extremely hard, while their middle and aboral parts are soft (these soft regions are newly secreted). Each tooth is partly enclosed by a large ossicle, the alveolus, which externally is V-shaped, and which is strongly linked to the neighbouring alveoli by muscles (each arm of the V is really a separate ossicle, but the two are fused solidly together). Across the upper ends of each alveolus is a strong, bow-shaped ossicle known as the epiphysis (to this the upper ends of the protractor muscles are attached). On top of the jaw apparatus the five radii, noticed earlier, overlie five broader radial ossicles, the rotulae.

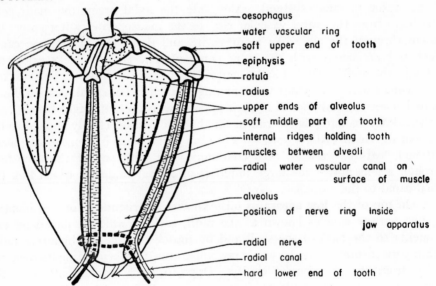

oesophagus
water vascular ring
soft upper end of tooth
epiphysis
rotula
radius
upper ends of alveolus
soft middle part of tooth
internal ridges holding tooth
muscles between alveoli
radial water vascular canal on surface of muscle
alveolus
position of nerve ring inside jaw apparatus
radial nerve
radial canal
hard lower end of tooth

FIG. 160.—*Echinus*. The jaw apparatus seen from one side.

h. On that side of the jaw apparatus still covered by peritoneum, examine the surface of the muscle between two of the alveoli to find, passing downwards, the transparent **radial water vascular canal**. Carefully dissect away the overlying radius and rotula to expose that part of the canal which crosses the upper surface of the muscle to join into the water vascular ring.

i. The main part of the nervous system consists of a circumoesophageal nerve-ring, which lies close to the mouth inside the jaw apparatus, and five radial nerves, which pass outwards between the bases of the alveoli to follow the lines of the five ambulacra. Dissect away the muscle connecting two of the alveoli and remove such other tissue as may be necessary to follow the course of one of these radial nerves inwards to its junction with the nerve ring. Each nerve leaves the jaw apparatus immediately beneath a radial water vascular canal, and remaining in this relationship with the canal, it extends almost to the aboral pole.   Strip away one of the radial canals to find the nerve underneath.   Although it is not possible to distinguish it in a dissection, a solid haemal strand, arising from the circumoesophageal haemal ring, passes along the surface of each radial nerve between it and the radial canal.

j. Complete the examination of the jaw apparatus by separating its component ossicles.   On the **alveoli** notice the large inward-directed flanges (for muscle attachment), and the two similar but smaller flanges between which the teeth are held.   Also notice the long flange, the carina, along the inner surface of each tooth.

4. CONCLUSION

a. Observing the specimens and the drawing made, review the characteristics of the phylum, of the class, and of the order.

b. Compare and contrast the structure of *Echinus* with that of *Asterias*.

5. REFERENCES

BRONN, H. G. (1904).   Volume 2, part 3, and book 4 of " Klassen und Ordnungen des Thier-Reichs.   Echinodermen (Stachelhäuter).   Die Seeigel."   Leipzig.
DELAGE, Y., and HÉROUARD, E. (1903).   Volume 3 of " Traité de zoologie concrète. Les échinodermes."   Paris.
MORTENSEN, T. (1927).   " Handbook of the echinoderms of the British Isles." London.

4.02.   Order **Clypeastroida**

Characteristics : Echinoidea with the body usually flattened to a disc shape ; with the mouth mid-ventral, but with the anus displaced laterally ;   and with petaloid ambulacra.

Genus **Echinarachnius** (sand dollar)

1. GENERAL ACCOUNT

a. Sand dollars are common off the east and west coasts of North America and in the southern Pacific, and they occur from the low-tide mark to depths of more than 800 fathoms.   They live where there is sand, and lie either on the surface or partly buried.   Locomotion and burrowing are mainly accomplished by means of the movements in co-ordinated waves of the short spines which cover the body.   For food the animals select sand grains covered with unicellular animals or plants, especially diatoms, and pass them into the mouth by means of the tube feet.   Little appears to have been recorded about their breeding habits.

2. EXTERNAL ANATOMY

a. Examine simultaneously a specimen preserved whole (for the method see p. 442) and another dried and with the spines removed (for the method see p. 443). Notice the flattened shape of the **body,** and distinguish the oral surface, with its central mouth, from the aboral surface.

b. Except within the ambulacral grooves, the **oral surface** is closely covered by tiny calcareous spines (the modified ossicles used for locomotion).   Around the mouth the spines are larger, and they project inwards to cover the opening (they help to push in the food).   From the mouth five ambulacral grooves containing tube feet radiate outwards, each dividing irregularly, and so widening out until it touches its neighbours.   Thus round the edge of the disc there is a complete ring of tube feet.   The ambulacral and interambulacral plates which

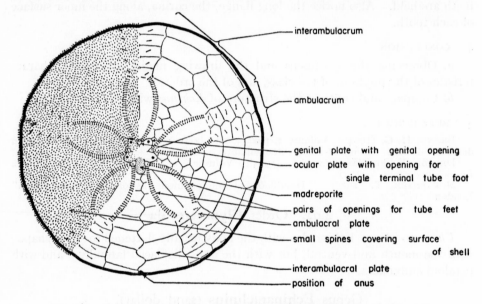

interambulacrum

ambulacrum

genital plate with genital opening
ocular plate with opening for
                    single terminal tube foot
madreporite
pairs of openings for tube feet
ambulacral plate
small spines covering surface
                                      of shell
interambulacral plate
position of anus

FIG. 161.—*Echinarachnius.*   The aboral surface with the spines partly removed.

form the oral surface of the shell are so tightly fused together that they cannot easily be distinguished.

c. The **aboral surface** is entirely covered by the tiny spines.   The five ambulacra are peculiar in that their aboral ends are arranged like the petals of a flower (petaloid ambulacra).   Each ambulacrum may be traced as a double row of tube feet from the outer end of the ' petal ' to the edge of the disc, where it merges into the fringe of tube feet previously seen.   The arrangement is particularly clear in a dried, cleaned specimen, in which the ambulacral and interambulacral plates are also visible.   At the aboral end of each ambulacrum is a small pore through which the single terminal tube foot (which is light sensitive) emerges.   Each of these pores passes through a small ocular plate. Between the ocular plates are the four large genital plates and the even larger madreporite.   The four genital plates each contain a single pore (through which opens a gonoduct), while the madreporite is pierced by large numbers of tiny pores (the external openings of the water vascular system).

d. The **anus**, which is situated on the edge of the disc between two rows of interambulacral plates, is in the same interambulacrum as the madreporite.

3. CONCLUSION

a. As far as is possible from the external features alone, review the characteristics of the phylum, of the class, and of the order.

b. Also review the main points of similarity and of difference between *Echinarachnius* and *Echinus*.

4.03. Order **Spatangoida**

Characteristics : Echinoidea with the body partially flattened, heart-shaped, and clearly bilaterally symmetrical ; with both mouth and anus eccentric ; with petaloid ambulacra ; and with no jaw apparatus.

Genus **Echinocardium** (heart urchin)

(The urchin *Spatangus* is a similar alternative.)

1. GENERAL ACCOUNT

a. The distribution of *Echinocardium* is world-wide, and the individuals tend to live gregariously. They burrow into the sand by the movements, in co-ordinated waves, of their curved, flattened, and backward-pointing spines. They normally lie about 4 to 6 inches deep in a small chamber, the walls of which are strengthened by a slime secreted by the epidermis. A chimney leads from this chamber to the surface, and through this the tube feet can be extended to obtain food. It is also presumed that, perhaps by night, the animals emerge to search for their food, which consists of tiny organisms and organic particles picked up by the tube feet. The eggs, which are laid in spring and perhaps again in summer, develop into free-swimming, pelagic, echinopluteus larvae.

2. EXTERNAL ANATOMY

a. Examine simultaneously a specimen preserved whole in alcohol (method on p. 442) and another dried and with the spines removed (method on p. 443). Notice the bilateral symmetry of the **body,** and distinguish the aboral from the oral surface, on which opens the mouth, and the anterior from the posterior end, at which opens the anus and towards which the spines point.

b. On the **oral surface** notice that the mouth is displaced forwards, and that it has a projecting, scoop-like, hinder edge (this edge is formed from the single terminal plate of the hindmost interambulacrum). The flexible peristomial membrane, set with small calcareous plates, is present only as a semi-circle in front of the mouth. Of the five ambulacra radiating from the mouth, that leading forwards is the shortest, while the two passing backwards are the

F F

longest. The tube feet are large, but they extend only a short distance from the mouth (they are called oral tube feet, and their function is to transfer food particles into the mouth). The interambulacral areas are covered with long, curved spines, while the ambulacral areas bear only short, thin spines.

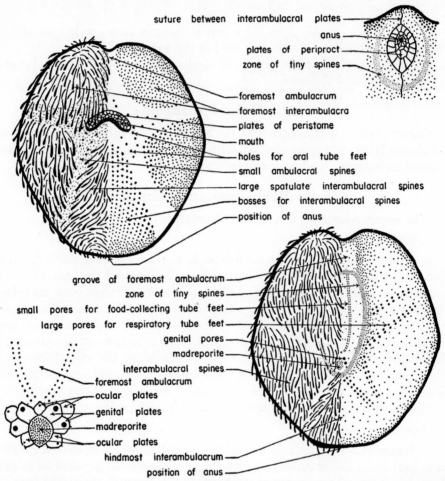

suture between interambulacral plates

anus

plates of periproct

zone of tiny spines

foremost ambulacrum
foremost interambulacra
plates of peristome
mouth
holes for oral tube feet
small ambulacral spines
large spatulate interambulacral spines
bosses for interambulacral spines
position of anus

groove of foremost ambulacrum
zone of tiny spines
small pores for food-collecting tube feet
large pores for respiratory tube feet
genital pores
madreporite
interambulacral spines
foremost ambulacrum
ocular plates
genital plates
madreporite
ocular plates
hindmost interambulacrum
position of anus

FIG. 162.—*Echinocardium.* On the left is the oral surface from half of which the spines have been removed, and (below) details of the aboral apical plates. On the right are details of the region around the anus, and (below) the aboral surface from half of which the spines have been removed.

With a lens examine the structure of one of the largest spines, and notice that its free end expands into an oar-like blade (for digging a way through the sand). The sutures separating the double row of ambulacral plates may be visible in some dried specimens, but those separating the very large interambulacral plates are obscure.

c. The details of the aboral surface of a whole specimen are hidden by the covering of large, backward-pointing spines. These spines are mainly based in the interambulacral areas, but smaller numbers of them are also based in the ambulacral areas.

d. Examine the **aboral surface** of a dried, cleaned specimen to see the irregular petaloid arrangement of the upper ends of the ambulacra. The two hindmost and the two lateral ambulacra show clearly the double rows of paired openings for the passage of large tube feet (these are the respiratory tube feet), but the foremost ambulacrum is different. It is the longest of the five, it is set in a deeper groove, and its tube feet are smaller but more numerous (they collect sand-grains with adherent food particles, and pass them via the oral tube feet to the mouth). At the hinder end of this ambulacrum, still within the groove, are the aboral apical plates pierced by the four openings of the gonoducts and the pores of the madreporite (in females of related genera the eggs are shed into the groove, and develop there beneath the roof formed by the long spines of the adjacent interambulacra). Forming an elongated and complete ring round the apical plates and most of the groove is a narrow zone on which were based large numbers of tiny spines (their function is unknown).

e. Through a lens examine the region of the **apical plates**. The four openings of the gonoducts, the pores of the madreporite, and the five tiny openings for the terminal (sensory) tube feet of the five ambulacra are easily visible, and in large and well-cleaned specimens, the sutures delimiting the genital, madreporic, and ocular plates may also be seen.

f. The anus, on the hind surface, is surrounded by a flexible membrane, the **periproct**, in which are embedded numbers of small calcareous plates. It is partly surrounded by a narrow zone of the peculiar tiny spines, and beneath it is another ring-like zone of similar spines.

3. CONCLUSION

a. As far as is possible from the external features alone, review the characteristics of the phylum, of the class, and of the order.

b. Notice the points of similarity and of difference between *Echinocardium* and *Echinus*.

5.00. Class **Holothurioidea**

Characteristics : Free-living, cucumber-shaped echinoderms with no arms; mouth and anus terminal at opposite ends; madreporite usually internal; ambulacral grooves covered by the leathery body-wall; most of the tube feet, when present, end in suckers; some tube feet, always present, are enlarged and modified as circumoral tentacles; ossicles greatly reduced and confined within the thick, muscular wall; no spines; no pedicellariae.

5.01. Order **Pedata**

Characteristics : Holothurioidea with tube feet arranged either in five long double rows, or scattered irregularly over the surface.

Genus **Cucumaria** (sea cucumber)

(*Thyone* and *Holothuria*, which both differ slightly in detail, may be dissected according to the following directions.)

1. GENERAL ACCOUNT

a. Cucumaria is a cosmopolitan genus, and is found from the low-tide mark to depths of about 200 fathoms.   Some species are also abyssal.   Moving sluggishly, partly by the action of the tube feet and partly by waves of contraction in the muscular body-wall, it feeds on minute organisms of all kinds which are caught in the sticky slime covering the branched tentacles.   From time to time each tentacle is pushed into the mouth so that the captured food can be sucked from it.   *Holothuria* feeds in a different manner by using the tentacles to push sand, containing food particles, into the mouth.   As a defence mechanism, some or most of the viscera can be thrown out through the cloacal opening or through a rupture in the body-wall.   The animal then escapes, and in two or three weeks the lost viscera are regenerated.   In temperate regions the eggs are laid in late winter and early spring, and they develop into free-swimming pelagic larvae.   These larvae are barrel-shaped, and are not auriculariae like those produced, for instance, by *Holothuria*.

2. EXTERNAL ANATOMY

a. Orientate the **body** of a specimen preserved in a relaxed condition (method on p. 443).   The oral end is surrounded by a ring of bushy tentacles, and the side on which the animal normally lies is less darkly pigmented.

b. At the **oral end** notice the large size of the mouth, round which is a circular lip and a darkly pigmented peristomial membrane.   The ten tentacles (which are enlarged tube feet, highly modified as tactile and food-collecting organs) ring the edge of the peristome, and there are two of them to each ambulacrum.   Each tentacle has a thick base which divides abruptly into innumerable tiny branches.

c. Along the trunk of the body run the five **ambulacra**, each visible as an irregular double row of tube feet ending in suckers (sometimes the tube feet may be found completely retracted when their positions are marked by pores in the skin).   Three adjacent ambulacra, which are more plentifully supplied with tube feet than the other two and which are also closer together, are referred to as the trivium (and on them the animal crawls).   The other two ambulacra form the bivium, and the skin covering them and the bivial interambulacrum is very darkly pigmented.   Occasional scattered tube feet are to be found in the interambulacral areas, particularly in the region of the bivium (in *Thyone* the tube feet are thickly scattered over the whole body surface).

d. Apart from the mouth, there are two **external openings**. The single gonoduct opens between the bases of the two tentacles which are situated opposite the bivial interambulacrum, while the anus is at the apex of the aboral end.

3. INTERNAL ANATOMY

a. Rest the specimen in its natural position on the trivium (in *Thyone* the two short tentacles belong to the middle ambulacrum of the trivium). Regarding the mouth as anterior, the anus as posterior, and the bivial interambulacrum as dorsal, cut through the thick, leathery skin along the right edge of the bivial interambulacrum from the anus to the base of the tentacles. Make a similar cut along the upper margin of the right trivial ambulacrum, join the two cuts by transverse incisions, and carefully detach the section of body-wall. Enlarge the window thus made by cutting away the bivial interambulacrum as far as the base of the mesentery which hangs from it. Carefully separate this mesentery from the body-wall, and then enlarge the window still further by cutting away the left bivial ambulacrum. Notice the extensive **perivisceral coelom**, in which the most obvious organs, twisted together, are the coils of the alimentary canal, the masses of gonad tubules, and the two large branching respiratory trees.

b. Without breaking the various diaphanous mesenteries which are attached to the coils of the alimentary canal, examine the **reproductive system**. The single gonad, either ovary or testis, is suspended from the dorsal mesentery, which was attached along the centre line of the bivial interambulacrum. It is composed of large numbers of narrow tubules arranged in two mop-like bunches, one on each side of the mesentery. The free ends of the tubules penetrate into almost all corners of the posterior end of the perivisceral coelom. From between the bases of the gonad tufts, the single gonoduct passes in an oral direction within the mesentery. Whether it is an oviduct or a vas deferens, it is a simple tube which opens externally between the two tentacles situated opposite the bivial interambulacrum.

c. Trace the course of the **alimentary canal**, cutting away any obstructing gonad tubules and pulling aside the right respiratory tree. The mouth opens into a pharynx, but this is hidden inside a peripharyngeal chamber, the wall of which is strengthened by an embedded ring of ten small calcareous ossicles, five radial and five interradial (these ossicles and the peripharyngeal chamber, the cavity of which is coelom, appear to be the vestiges of a jaw apparatus similar to that of *Echinus*). From the peripharyngeal wall to the body-wall there extend five large retractor muscles, one to each radius (the contraction of these muscles causes a defensive invagination of the anterior end of the body,

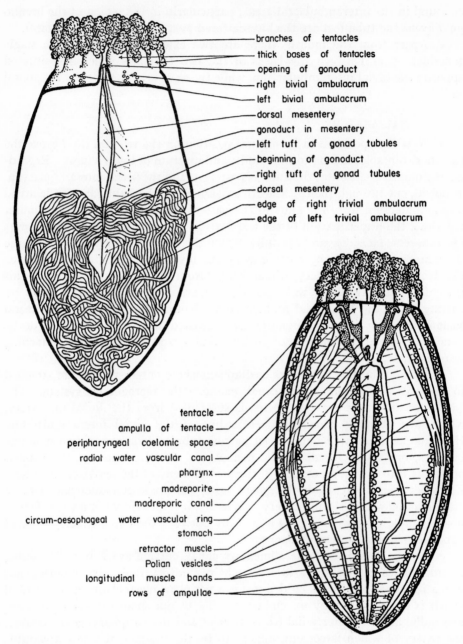

branches of tentacles
thick bases of tentacles
opening of gonoduct
right bivial ambulacrum
left bivial ambulacrum
dorsal mesentery
gonoduct in mesentery
left tuft of gonad tubules
beginning of gonoduct
right tuft of gonad tubules
dorsal mesentery
edge of right trivial ambulacrum
edge of left trivial ambulacrum

tentacle
ampulla of tentacle
peripharyngeal coelomic space
radial water vascular canal
pharynx
madreporite
madreporic canal
circum-oesophageal water vascular ring
stomach
retractor muscle
Polian vesicles
longitudinal muscle bands
rows of ampullae

FIG. 163.—*Cucumaria.* A dissection of the reproductive system. Below are the details of the water vascular system and of the inner body wall as seen after the removal of most of the viscera.

including the tentacles). The short oesophagus is also hidden from view, since it is encircled by the water vascular and haemal rings. It opens into a small, muscular-walled chamber, the stomach, which in turn leads to the long,

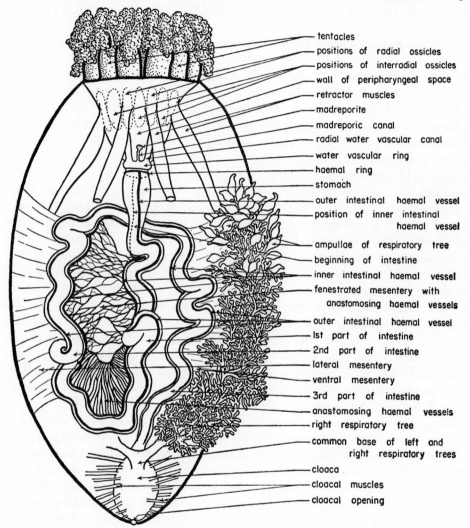

tentacles
positions of radial ossicles
positions of interradial ossicles
wall of peripharyngeal space
retractor muscles
madreporite
madreporic canal
radial water vascular canal
water vascular ring
haemal ring
stomach
outer intestinal haemal vessel
position of inner intestinal
    haemal vessel
ampullae of respiratory tree
beginning of intestine
inner intestinal haemal vessel
fenestrated mesentery with
    anastomosing haemal vessels
outer intestinal haemal vessel
1st part of intestine
2nd part of intestine
lateral mesentery
ventral mesentery
3rd part of intestine
anastomosing haemal vessels
right respiratory tree
common base of left and
    right respiratory trees
cloaca
cloacal muscles
cloacal opening

FIG. 164.—*Cucumaria*. A general dissection as seen after the removal of the reproductive system and with the left respiratory tree omitted.

narrow, and highly convoluted intestine. The first part of the intestine, passing back, is attached by the dorsal mesentery along the centre of the bivial interradius; the second part, passing forward, is attached by the lateral mesentery along the centre of the interradius above the left trivial ambulacrum; and the third part, passing back again, is attached by the ventral mesentery along the centre of the interradius between the middle and right trivial ambulacra. The end of the intestine opens into a short, wide cloaca into which the two large respiratory trees also open. The cloaca is attached to the body-wall on all sides by numerous muscle strands (their contraction dilates the cloaca).

d. The **haemal system** (of vessels which either have haemocoelic cavities or are so reduced as to be mere strands of tissue) is well developed in relation to the intestine, but not elsewhere. The narrow circumoesophageal ring is situated just behind the wider water vascular ring. Anteriorly, it gives rise to five radial haemal vessels, thin strands of tissue which pass along the pharynx, and then turn back inside the body-wall to reach almost to the cloacal opening (throughout their entire length they are hidden beneath the radial water vascular canals). There is no axial organ, but posteriorly the ring gives rise to two haemal vessels, the one passing above and the other below the stomach to reach the intestine. They are known respectively as the outer, or mesenterial, intestinal vessel and the inner, or antimesenterial, intestinal vessel (and they contain a liquid which probably serves some of the functions of blood). The outer vessel follows a simple course closely applied to the outer wall of the intestine along the line of its junction with the dorsal, lateral, and ventral mesenteries. It gives large numbers of small branches to the intestine wall, and near its anterior end it also gives a small genital branch to the gonad. The inner intestinal vessel passes along the full length of the inner surface of the intestine, also giving large numbers of small branches to the intestine wall. Between the first and second parts of the intestine is a fenestrated mesentery, and across this the first and second parts of the inner intestinal vessel are linked by large numbers of anastomosing vessels (it may be significant that this anastomosing system closely overlies the left respiratory tree). Neither the outer nor the inner intestinal vessels extend on to the cloaca. (In *Holothuria* the inner intestinal vessel and the anastomosing vessels follow a somewhat different course ; for details consult references on p. 442.)

e. Cut through the anterior and posterior ends of the intestine and through the lateral and ventral mesenteries. Lift out the intestine complete. If difficulty has been encountered in following out the branches of the intestinal haemal vessels, pin out the intestine under water, and, on a dark background, gently open out the convolutions and stretch taut the fenestrated mesentery. All the vessels should then be clearly visible.

f. The **perihaemal system** and the **nervous system** each consists of a circum-oral ring close beneath the peristomial membrane, and of radial sinuses and nerves along the inner surface of the body-wall. There is no axial sinus, and neither system can easily be seen in a dissection.

g. The two **respiratory trees** are the right and left branches of a diverticulum of the anterior end of the cloaca, and each consists of a main trunk which branches repeatedly. The branches end in narrow tubules, which are often swollen into thin-walled ampullae (in *Holothuria* some of the branches are considerably modified, and produce a sticky secretion which, extruded through the cloacal opening, entangles attackers). Cut open the cloaca to find the single opening into the common base of the two trees (sea-water is pumped in and out of the trees by the action of the cloacal muscles, and oxygen diffuses into the coelomic fluid; probably the trees also act as excretory organs, and certainly they are hydrostatic organs so that, when the tentacles are suddenly withdrawn, water is expelled to make room for them).

h. Dissect away the cloaca together with the respiratory trees, and identify the various parts of the **water vascular system**. The water vascular ring is large and encircles the oesophagus. Posteriorly and laterally it gives rise to two greatly elongated Polian vesicles (reservoirs of the water vascular fluid). Mid-dorsally, opposite the centre of the bivial interambulacrum, it gives rise to the small madreporic canal which leads to the tiny madreporite (since the madreporite opens into the coelom, it is coelomic fluid that is passed into the water vascular system). Radially it gives rise to the five water vascular canals which lead forwards through, and along the inner surface of, the wall of the peripharyngeal space. At their bases these radial canals are wide and easily visible through the thin wall, but they quickly become narrower, and pass from sight beneath the calcareous radial ossicles within the wall. Cut into the peripharyngeal space to find the radial canals extending beneath the ossicles, and also to see the large ampullae of the tentacles, each of which receives a small branch from the adjacent canal. After approaching the region of the mouth, the radial canals turn back inside the body-wall, and, running beneath the five radially situated, longitudinal, muscle bands, give lateral branches to the ampullae of the tube feet. Cut transversely through the body-wall in the region of a longitudinal muscle band to find on the cut surface the small hole which marks the position of the radial canal.

i. Examine the structure of the **body-wall**. Beneath the epidermis is a thick layer of connective tissue, and internal to that is a prominent circular muscle layer. Only in the five radii are longitudinal muscles strongly developed, and it is to these that the five retractor muscles are joined. The dark pigment is in the outermost layer of the connective tissue, and small peculiarly shaped ossicles also abound in this region. Make a preparation of these ossicles on a slide (for the method see p. 443), and, through a microscope, examine their shapes.

4. CONCLUSION

a. Observing the specimen and the drawings made, review the characteristics of the phylum, of the class, and of the order.

b. Compare and contrast the structures of *Cucumaria* and *Echinus*.

5. REFERENCES

BRONN, H. G. (1904). Volume 2, part 3, and book 1 of " Klassen und Ordnungen des Thier-Reichs. Echinodermen (Stachelhäuter). Die Seewalzen." Leipzig

DELAGE, Y., and HÉROUARD, E. (1903). Volume 3 of " Traité de zoologie concrète. Les échinodermes." Paris.

APPENDIX TO THE ECHINODERMATA

1. CULTURE METHODS

a. Since *Antedon, Echinarachnius, Echinocardium,* and *Cucumaria* are all specialised feeders requiring large numbers of small, even microscopic, food particles, they are not easily kept alive in marine aquaria for more than a few weeks unless unusual facilities are available.

b. However, *Ophioderma,* and particularly *Asterias* and *Echinus,* are fairly easily kept. *Ophioderma* may live as a scavenger in a large aquarium which contains other carnivorous animals, or, by itself, it may be fed on finely chopped fish or shell-fish. *Asterias* prefers living food, particularly marine bivalves such as *Mytilus,* but when sufficiently hungry it will eat dead shell-fish chopped up and given raw. *Echinus* and other similar endocyclic echinoids are the most easily kept, since they will readily eat dead food such as small pieces of raw fish, shellfish, or even lean beef. The water must be kept cool (certainly below 15° C. and preferably below 10° C.), and it should also be well aerated by mechanical means. Two meals a week are usually adequate, and any unfinished food must be removed to prevent fouling of the water.

2. METHODS OF KILLING

a. *Antedon* may be killed quickly in an extended condition by immersion in fresh water, after which it is best preserved in 70% alcohol.

b. The same method may also be used for *Asterias, Ophioderma,* and the various Echinoidea, but in order that the tube feet shall be fully extended, it is usually better to employ some method of narcotisation. Such methods are the addition of crystals of magnesium sulphate (Epsom salts), or crystals of menthol, or drops of 70% alcohol, to the small volume of sea-water in which the animals are confined. *Asterias* should be placed upside down during narcotisation so that the tube feet can extend easily. When, after some hours, during which the animals are left undisturbed, the tube feet or the arms no longer respond to a touch, the specimens may be preserved either in 70% alcohol or in 5% formalin. In the case of an *Echinus* required for dissection, a small hole should be punched in one side of the shell, or a small cut made through the peristomial membrane, to let in the preservative. For general preservation, 70% alcohol is the better preservative for echinoderms, since 5% formalin, unless neutralised, tends to weaken, and finally dissolve, the calcareous ossicles. However, in the case of an *Asterias* or an *Echinus* required for dissection, this weakening may prove to be an advantage.

c. The killing of *Cucumaria* and other holothurians in an extended condition is a slightly more difficult matter. The animals should first be thoroughly narcotised by one of the methods described above. Then each in turn should be gripped with blunt forceps just behind the tentacles, to prevent any possible retraction while the tentacles are plunged for a few minutes into 5% formalin. Next, with a hypodermic syringe, inject 70% alcohol into the cloacal opening and also through the body-wall into the perivisceral coelom. Finally the whole animal may be preserved in 70% alcohol. Alternatively, 5% formalin may be injected and the animals preserved in that fluid, but in this case, unless the formalin is neutralised, the calcareous ossicles may ultimately dissolve entirely away.

3. METHOD OF DRYING AND CLEANING AN ECHINOID

a. Kill the specimen by immersion in fresh water (for about half an hour), and then transfer to a 1 in 1000 solution of mercuric chloride (corrosive sublimate) for about twelve hours. After this the animal may be dried, and the spines, the pedicellariae, and the thin skin rubbed off to expose the plates.

b. Alternatively, after killing in fresh water, the peristomial membrane may be cut out, the viscera extracted through the hole, and the shell dried empty.

4. METHOD OF PREPARING HOLOTHURIAN OSSICLES

a. Cut away a tentacle, or a small piece of the body-wall, and boil it in test tube containing a 20% aqueous solution of potassium hydroxide (caustic potash) until all the tissue has dissolved away. Let the tube stand until tiny particles are seen to settle to the bottom. Then pour off the solution and add clean water. Allow the particles to settle once more, and again change the water. With a fine pipette transfer some of the particles, which are the tiny ossicles, to a glass slide and examine their shape through a microscope.

b. A permanent preparation may be made by replacing the water in the tube with two changes of 90% alcohol, with absolute alcohol, and then with xylol. Finally, pipette some of the particles into a drop of Canada balsam on a slide, and add a cover-glass.

CHAPTER XXII

PHYLUM CHORDATA

Characteristics : Typically bilaterally symmetrical animals, which, at least in some stage of development, possess a notochord and a dorsal tubular nerve-cord, and which usually also possess gill slits perforating the pharynx wall.

The chordates form an extensive and diverse phylum, and in type they range from the sessile and degenerate ascidians through the pelagic Larvacea to *Amphioxus* and the vertebrates. All the non-vertebrate chordates are marine.

1.00. Class Hemichorda

Characteristics : Chordates in which the body is clearly divided into a preoral proboscis, a collar, and a trunk, all of which contain large coelomic cavities; notochord short and confined to the preoral region; nerve-cord usually in contact with the epidermis; and no endostyle.

There are two orders : the Enteropneusta described below, and the curious Pterobranchia. The latter contains the genera *Cephalodiscus* and *Rhabdopleura*, which both live in deep water in tubular houses secreted by the proboscis. They commonly reproduce by asexual budding, and in *Rhabdopleura* this results in colony formation. It is interesting to note that the Graptolites, which are some of the earliest known fossils, are now considered to belong to the Pterobranchia.

1.01. Order Enteropneusta

Characteristics : Worm-like Hemichorda with a relatively large proboscis, a simple collar, and a trunk with large numbers of gill-slits and a terminal anus; sexes separate, development usually through a pelagic tornaria larva, and no asexual budding.

Genus Dolichoglossus

(*Balanoglossus* can be used as an alternative, and the minor points of difference are mentioned in the following account.)

I. GENERAL ACCOUNT

a. Dolichoglossus and other related genera are widely distributed in shallow seas and up to the low-tide mark. Using the proboscis, they dig U-shaped burrows in the sand or mud, and strengthen the walls with mucus secreted by the epidermis. For food, the sand or mud is swallowed and its organic content digested. The waste from the anus is ejected from the burrow to form a casting. In temperate regions breeding occurs in spring and summer, fertilisation is external, and each egg develops into a characteristic pelagic tornaria larva, which later metamorphoses and settles to the bottom.

2. EXTERNAL ANATOMY

a. The animal (which can be killed by the methods given for polychaets on p. 206) has a **body** clearly divided into an anterior proboscis, a short collar region, and a long trunk.

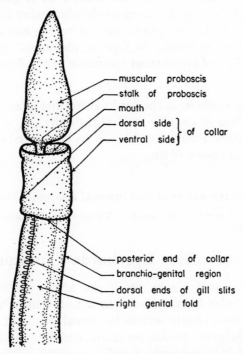

muscular proboscis
stalk of proboscis
mouth
dorsal side ⎱
                ⎰ of collar
ventral side

posterior end of collar
branchio-genital region
dorsal ends of gill slits
right genital fold

FIG. 165.—*Dolichoglossus.* The anterior end seen from the right side.

b. The **proboscis** is muscular, has a tall cone shape, and is joined posteriorly by a thin stalk to the collar region. It is preoral, and the large, permanently open mouth is immediately ventral to the point of junction of the proboscis stalk. On the left of the proboscis base, close to or on the stalk, is a tiny proboscis pore (in some species of *Balanoglossus* there is also a pore on the right ; through these pores water passes in and out of the proboscis coelom during the distension and contraction which accompanies burrowing).

c. The **collar region** is featureless. Its anterior margin overlaps the base of the proboscis, and its posterior margin overlaps the anterior end of the trunk (the collar region also swells and shrinks during burrowing, water being passed in and out of the two collar coelomic cavities through two pores which open into the 1st pair of gill slits on the trunk).

d. The **trunk** can be subdivided into an anterior branchio-genital region with a longitudinally folded dorsal surface, and a posterior abdominal region which is almost cylindrical. In the branchio-genital region are numbers of paired gill slits opening dorso-laterally (there are about 50 pairs in the adult). Their openings are partly obscured by upturned flaps of the body-wall which contain the gonads and which are called genital folds. These folds extend for a short distance beyond the posterior ends of the rows of gill-slits (and posterior to them in *Balanoglossus* hepatic caeca of the alimentary canal cause swellings on the body-wall). A shallow groove runs along the mid-dorsal line between the two rows of gill-slits and along the tapering abdominal region to the terminal anus (it marks the line of attachment internally of the dorsal nerve cord).

3. CONCLUSION

a. As far as is possible from the external features alone, review the characteristics of the phylum, of the class, and of the order.

b. Distinguish those features which can be considered as special modifications to the burrowing mode of life.

4. REFERENCE

For an account of the external and internal anatomy, see:

DELAGE, Y., and HÉROUARD, E. (1898). Volume 8 of " Traité de zoologie concrète. Les procordés." Paris.

2.00. Class **Urochorda** (Tunicata)

Characteristics : Chordates in which the adults are usually sessile with a more or less globular body enclosed in a test, and in which the chordate characteristics are most clearly seen in the larval stage ; at metamorphosis the notochord is lost, the nerve-cord degenerates, and the gill-slits multiply to form a feeding mechanism ; endostyle usually present ; coelom always absent ; sexes separate or combined, and asexual budding common.

The peculiarities of the members of this class are the outcome of a sedentary habit, and those genera which today are free swimming have obviously been derived from sedentary ancestors.

2.10. Subclass **Larvacea**

Characteristics : Free-swimming paedomorphic forms resembling the larvae of other urochordates in that they are composed of a body and a tail in which the notochord and nerve-cord are well developed ; but differing from them in the possession of gonads, of a large replaceable test which is not composed of tunicin, of a tail which is ventrally attached, and of two gill-slits which open directly to the exterior.

These paedomorphic urochordates, also known as appendicularians, are all small and pelagic. They possess some theoretical importance, since they indicate the way in which the cephalochordates and vertebrates may also have arisen by paedogenesis.

2.11. Order **Endostylophora**

Characteristics : Larvacea in which the pharynx contains a ventral endostyle.

Genus **Oikopleura**

1. GENERAL ACCOUNT

a. This genus is widely distributed in the surface waters of the open oceans. Each individual secretes a relatively large test (about the size of a cherry), called a house, but is only lightly attached inside it. By a constant beating of the tail, water is drawn in through an anterior window which is covered by a fine lattice to prevent the entrance of all but the tiniest particles. These tiny particles, minute planktonic animals and plants, form the food, and are extracted from the water by an internal filtering device which is also part of the house. As water enters the window, the pressure rises to force open a valve in the posterior wall of the house. The jet of water escaping through this valve drives the whole house forwards. In the wall near the head is a small trap-door through which, in a moment of danger or when the lattice becomes clogged, a few unusually strong strokes of the tail enable a quick escape. A new house is then rapidly secreted by a special oikoplastic region of the epidermis. Reproduction is continuous, the animals breeding as protandrous hermaphrodites as soon as they reach full size. Fertilisation is external, and development is direct.

2. EXTERNAL ANATOMY

a. The shape of the animal, with its sharply defined body and tail regions, is roughly that of a tadpole. The **body region** narrows anteriorly to the terminal mouth, while posteriorly it is considerably enlarged in a dorso-ventral direction. The ventral side is marked by the point of insertion of the tail.

b. The long, flat **tail** is narrow at its point of origin, but immediately broadens out. Due to it having moved from a terminal to a mid-ventral position, and at the same time having undergone torsion through an angle of 90°, it is not flattened from side to side but from front to back.

3. INTERNAL ANATOMY

a. The internal features are most easily seen in a permanent stained preparation (see method on p. 470). There is no coelom, and in the body region the spaces between the various organs are **haemocoelic lacunae** which contain blood.

b. In the narrower anterior part of the body region lies the **alimentary canal**. The terminal mouth, permanently open, leads into a large pharynx, from which there are three exits, two being the latero-ventral gill openings, and the other the postero-dorsal opening into the oesophagus.   Inside the pharynx distinguish

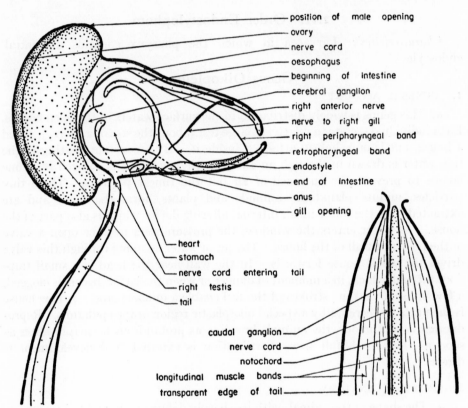

position of male opening
ovary
nerve cord
oesophagus
beginning of intestine
cerebral ganglion
right anterior nerve
nerve to right gill
right peripharyngeal band
retropharyngeal band
endostyle
end of intestine
anus
gill opening

heart
stomach
nerve cord entering tail
right testis
tail

caudal ganglion
nerve cord
notochord
longitudinal muscle bands
transparent edge of tail

FIG. 166.—*Oikopleura.*   The body and tail seen from the right side, and the anterior end of the tail seen from the posterior side.

the short endostyle antero-ventrally (this is a thick-walled ciliated groove which secretes mucus) ; the retropharyngeal ciliated band which leads upwards and backwards from the posterior end of the endostyle to the ventral side of the oesophagus ; the two peripharyngeal ciliated bands which lead left and right from the anterior end of the endostyle, and which, turning backwards, do not come together again until they enter the dorsal side of the oesophagus ; and the two simple tubes which are the latero-ventral gill slits and which open directly to the exterior (these gill slits contain long cilia which draw a constant stream of water into the mouth ; food particles from the filtering device, which enter with the water, become enclosed in the strands of mucus which pass from the endostyle to the oesophagus along both the retropharyngeal and peripharyngeal ciliated bands). The oesophagus (strongly ciliated) loops back to enter the left posterior side of the capacious stomach. From the right posterior side of the stomach, the intestine emerges to loop forwards and open at the mid-ventral anus.

c. The hermaphrodite **reproductive system** is very prominent, and occupies almost the whole of the body region posterior to the junction of the tail. Left and right there are two kidney-shaped testes, and sandwiched between them is the single kidney-shaped ovary (the spermatozoa, which mature first, escape via a temporary pore opening through the skin at the dorsal end of the testes ; the eggs are released by a rupture of the body wall which probably results in the death of the animal).

d. Ventral to the stomach distinguish the transparent **heart** (which maintains a circulation through the lacunae).

e. In the **nervous system** distinguish the compact cerebral ganglion lying dorsal to the pharynx. Close to the left side of this ganglion the single sense-organ, an otocyst, may be visible. Five large nerves emerge from the ganglion, two passing forward round the mouth, two passing postero-laterally to the gill-slits, and one, the nerve-cord itself, running dorsal to the pharynx, downwards in front of the gonads, and into the tail. In the tail the nerve-cord passes along the left (original dorsal) side of the notochord. Near its anterior end is a prominent caudal ganglion, and smaller ganglia also occur along its length.

f. Examine the form of the **notochord**, and notice that it does not penetrate into the body region. Lateral to the notochord and nerve-cord are longitudinal muscle-bands, two on each side, and lateral to them the tail is thin and transparent.

4. CONCLUSION

a. Observing the specimen, review the characteristics of the phylum, of the class, of the subclass, and of the order.

5. REFERENCES

DELAGE, Y., and HÉROUARD, E. (1898). Volume 8 of " Traité de zoologie concrète. Les procordés." Paris.

HERDMAN, W. A. (1892). " Notes on the structure of *Oikopleura*." *Proceedings and Transactions of the Liverpool Biological Society*, Vol. 6, p. 40.

KÜKENTHAL, W., and KRUMBACH, T. (1933–35). Volume 5 and part 2 of " Handbuch der Zoologie." Berlin and Leipzig.

2.20. Subclass **Ascidiacea**

Characteristics : Urochordates in which the adults are sessile, either remaining simple or budding to form colonies ; test permanent, usually thick, and composed of tunicin ; pharynx large, and with its wall pierced by numerous

G G

gill-slits, which are subdivided to form stigmata, and which open outwards into a peripharyngeal atrial cavity; mouth and atrial opening both directed forwards.

2.21. Order **Enterogona**

Characteristics : Ascidiacea in which the gonads are situated within the loop of the intestine.

Genus **Ciona** (sea squirt)

(The instructions given below may also be used for the dissection of *Ascidia*.)

I. GENERAL ACCOUNT

a. Both *Ciona* and *Ascidia* are cosmopolitan, their wide distribution being possibly due to transportation by ships. They are both shallow-water forms, and occur from the low-tide mark to depths of about 100 fathoms. Each individual is enclosed in a thick protective test, by which it is also closely attached to a rock or some other form of support. By ciliary action water is drawn in through the mouth, and by the sieving action of the gill-slits unicellular animals and plants, and probably also organic detritus, are extracted for food. There is no definite breeding season, and the gametes are shed when the animal is fully grown. Fertilisation is external, and the floating egg develops into an *Oikopleura*-like tadpole larva which later settles and metamorphoses.

2. EXTERNAL ANATOMY

a. Examine a specimen killed in an extended condition (see method on p. 470). The animal is entirely enclosed in a semi-transparent, sac-like **test** (which is secreted by the epidermis, and is composed of a cellulose-like substance called tunicin). The basal end of the test is thickened and roughened to form a hold-fast (by which it was anchored), while the free end has two arms. The mouth opens on the longer terminal arm, and the atrial opening (through which waste and reproductive products leave) is on the smaller lateral arm.

b. Place the specimen in the position shown in Fig. 167, and, to expose the **body** of the animal, dissect away that half of the test which is then uppermost. Notice that the margin of the mouth bears 8 lobes, while the margin of the atrial opening bears only 6 ; that in the depressions between the lobes are bright-red spots of pigment (possibly light sensitive) ; and that within the thin body wall lie prominent longitudinal muscle-bands (in *Ascidia* the longitudinal muscle-fibres are not concentrated into bands) ; and that circular muscle-fibres are also present, and are most strongly developed just behind the mouth and the atrial opening to form the peribuccal and periatrial muscle-bands respectively. At the base of the sac-like body the visceral mass is visible through the body wall.

c. By reference to conditions in the larva and in other chordates it is possible to fix the **orientation of the body**. The mouth is morphologically anterior, the visceral mass posterior, and the atrium and its opening dorsal. Through the transparent body-wall identify the cerebral ganglion antero-dorsally, and the branching nerves emerging from it; the twisting line of the endostyle, which marks the ventral edge of the pharynx; the net-like pharynx wall laterally; the empty space of the atrial cavity dorsally; and the rectum

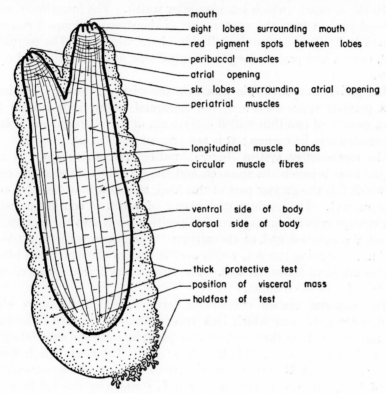

mouth
eight lobes surrounding mouth
red pigment spots between lobes
peribuccal muscles
atrial opening
six lobes surrounding atrial opening
periatrial muscles

longitudinal muscle bands
circular muscle fibres

ventral side of body
dorsal side of body

thick protective test
position of visceral mass
holdfast of test

Fig. 167.—*Ciona*. The external features seen from the right side after the removal of the right half of the test.

emerging from the dorsal side of the visceral mass to open into the atrial chamber.

3. INTERNAL ANATOMY

a. Cut through the body-wall into the atrial chamber, and, taking extreme care not to damage the pharynx, remove the body-wall from the entire right side of the specimen. The atrial cavity extends ventrally between the pharyngeal and body-walls, but these two walls are connected by numerous strands of tissue (containing blood vessels) which must all be carefully cut. Identify the parts of the **alimentary canal**. Inside the mouth is a short buccal

G G 2

cavity (the wall of which is ectoderm, and which is lined by the inturned test). The posterior limit of this cavity is marked by a circle of slender tentacles (which taste the incoming water), and posterior to them is the greatly enlarged pharynx. This is divided into a small anterior prebranchial region (without gill-slits) and a large posterior branchial region (the details of which are described below). The oesophagus, emerging from the postero-dorsal end of the pharynx, passes to the stomach (which has glandular walls). The intestine (containing a typhlosole) arises from the ventral side of the stomach, loops forwards, and then turns back again across the left side of the stomach. The rectum turns forward, enters, and passes along the ventral side of the atrium, and opens at the anus.

b. The perivisceral cavity, in which the oesophagus, stomach, and intestine lie, is a peculiar space known as the **epicardial cavity** (it is formed by the posterior growth of two thin-walled diverticula of the pharynx, and it is some-times considered to be coelom ; it is not present in *Ascidia*).

c. The **reproductive system** (hermaphrodite and protogynous) is centred within the loop between the stomach and the intestine. The single compact ovary, which fills the greater part of this loop, is hollow (and the eggs are shed into the cavity). The oviduct (the cavity of which is continuous with the ovarian cavity) runs forwards to reach a position ventral to the rectum, and to open into the anterior end of the atrium. The single testis is made up of thin, white, branching tubules, which overlie part of the ovary and often also part of the adjacent intestinal wall. The narrow vas deferens runs close along the ventral side of the oviduct.

d. The **vascular system** consists of lacunae, which are mere channels between the organs, and which lack true walls (their cavity is haemocoel). They ramify throughout the body, into the pharynx wall, and even into the test, but most of them are not visible in a dissection. The heart can, however, be seen as a transparent, U-shaped tube situated anterior to the gonads within the intestinal loop. It has no true wall, but is formed by the infolding of one side of a transparent pericardium (the cavity of which is sometimes considered to be coelom). (The blood leaves one end of the heart to pass forwards beneath the endostyle, up through the branchial bars, back along a hyper-pharyngeal space, and over the organs of the visceral mass to the other end of the heart. However, the system is extraordinary, in that the heart only makes a few beats in one direction before reversing its action and so reversing the circulation.)

e. There is no **excretory system** (but in *Ascidia* there is a ductless renal organ consisting of a mass of large cells which store nitrogenous waste, and lying within the loop formed by the end of the intestine and the beginning of the rectum).

f. Of the degenerate **nervous system**, only the cerebral ganglion and its nerves are easily visible.

g. Open the **pharynx** by making a longitudinal cut through the right side, and examine the inner details through a lens. The original gill-slits have been

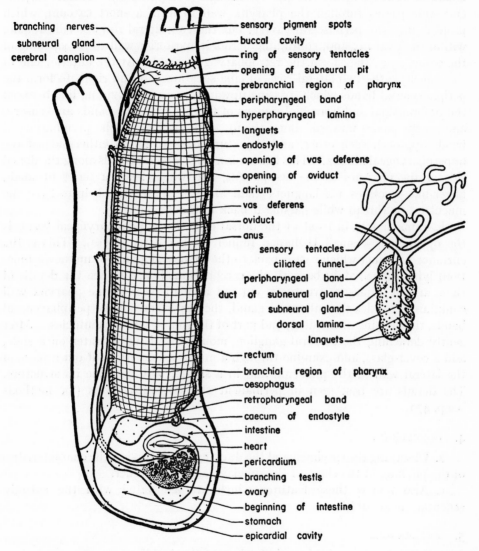

branching nerves
subneural gland
cerebral ganglion

sensory pigment spots
buccal cavity
ring of sensory tentacles
opening of subneural pit
prebranchial region of pharynx
peripharyngeal band
hyperpharyngeal lamina
languets
endostyle
opening of vas deferens
opening of oviduct
atrium
vas deferens
oviduct
anus

sensory tentacles
ciliated funnel
peripharyngeal band
duct of subneural gland
subneural gland
dorsal lamina
languets

rectum
branchial region of pharynx
oesophagus
retropharyngeal band
caecum of endostyle
intestine
heart
pericardium
branching testis
ovary
beginning of intestine
stomach
epicardial cavity

Fig. 168.—*Ciona.* A general dissection seen from the right side after the removal of the right body wall, and details of the structure of the subneural gland and part of the adjacent pharynx wall.

subdivided to form a network, the tiny holes of which are called stigmata (the cilia of the pharynx wall pass water through this sieve into the atrium). Along the ventral side of the pharynx is the narrow endostyle, which is a groove containing long cilia ventrally and short cilia laterally. The groove has thick edges (which are sensory and secrete mucus, and this mucus, by ciliary action, is passed upwards across the gills to entangle food particles). Posteriorly, the endostyle passes through the pharynx wall to form a short caecum, which projects into the perivisceral cavity, but the two lateral rows of cilia remain within the pharynx and, continuing across its posterior wall to the opening of the oesophagus, they form the retropharyngeal band. At the anterior end of the endostyle the two lateral rows of cilia separate, left and right, to form the peripharyngeal bands which, passing upwards, mark the dividing line between the prebranchial and branchial regions of the pharynx (the bands are sensory, and mucus passes upwards along them). Antero-dorsally the peripharyngeal bands approach each other, and then turn back to lie on either side of the hyperpharyngeal lamina. This lamina is a ridge which extends along the dorsal side of the pharynx to the oesophagus, and which bears a series of small, finger-like processes, the languets (these are also ciliated and help to twist the mucus into a thread while passing it back to the oesophagus).

h. Immediately in front of the dorsal ends of the peripharyngeal bands is the opening of a small U-shaped funnel (with ciliated edges). This is the entrance to a duct which passes back to the **subneural gland** (of unknown function) lying immediately beneath the cerebral ganglion. To see the details of these and of adjacent structures, cut out a small piece of the pharynx wall containing, besides the subneural gland, the upper ends of the peripharyngeal bands, the opening of the duct, and part of the ring of sensory tentacles. After gently detaching the cerebral ganglion, mount the tissue in water on a slide, add a cover-glass, and examine through a microscope. Also cut out a piece of the lateral wall of the pharynx, and in a similar way examine its structure. The details are best seen in permanent stained preparations (for methods see p. 470).

4. CONCLUSION

a. Observing the specimen and the drawings made, review the characteristics of the phylum, of the class, of the subclass, and of the order.

b. Also review those features which are associated with the entirely sedentary mode of life.

5. REFERENCES

For the structure of this and of others of the Ascidiacea, see :

DELAGE, Y., and HÉROUARD, E. (1898). Volume 8 of " Traité de zoologie concrète. Les procordés." Paris.

HERDMAN, W. A. (1899). " *Ascidia.*" *Memoirs of the Liverpool Marine Biological Committee*, Vol. 1.

KÜKENTHAL, W., and KRUMBACH, T. (1933–35). Volume 5 and part 2 of " Handbuch der Zoologie. Tunicata." Berlin and Leipzig.

2.30. Subclass **Thaliacea**

Characteristics : Pelagic Urochorda with a permanent test composed of tunicin ; with the atrium opening posteriorly ; and with relatively few gill-slits.

The members of this subclass show considerable diversity of structure, although they all live similar pelagic lives in the open oceans. One of their most striking characteristics is an alternation of sexual and asexual generations, and a consequent complexity of life-history.

2.31. Order **Pyrosomatida**

Characteristics : Thaliacea which by budding form large, thimble-shaped colonies of sexual, ascidian-like individuals ; in which the body-wall contains rings of feeble muscles only at the anterior and posterior ends ; pharynx with numerous (up to 50) pairs of gill-slits ; and no larval stage since the oozooid (asexual generation) is reduced and retained within the blastozooid (sexual generation).

The only genus of this order is *Pyrosoma*, and there are eight species. These are all found in the warmer seas, and all are noted for the exceptional brilliance of their phosphorescence.

Genus **Pyrosoma**

1. GENERAL ACCOUNT

a. The genus is widespread in the open waters of tropical and subtropical seas. The individuals of the colonies take in water through the mouth, and by the sieving action of the pharynx wall, unicellular animals and plants are extracted for food. The water then passes through the atrial opening into the large central cavity of the colony, and by escaping through a posterior opening causes the whole colony to move forwards. The individuals, or blastozooids, of the colony are protogynous hermaphrodites, and breeding continues through-out the year. The ovary of each blastozooid develops only one ovum, which is fertilised by a spermatozoon shed into the water by another older colony. The zygote is retained, and develops into an oozooid which represents the asexual generation. This oozooid develops a stolon, which buds a chain of four blastozooids. These coil in a ring round the oozooid, which then begins to degenerate, and at this stage they escape by a rupture of the atrial wall. The little group of blastozooids then sinks into deep water, and does not return to the surface until, by budding, a small but typical colony has been formed.

2. EXTERNAL ANATOMY

a. In a **colony** preserved whole (for the method see p. 470) notice the extreme transparency and the elongated thimble-shape. The open end of the colony is in the rear, and is surrounded by an inturned diaphragm.

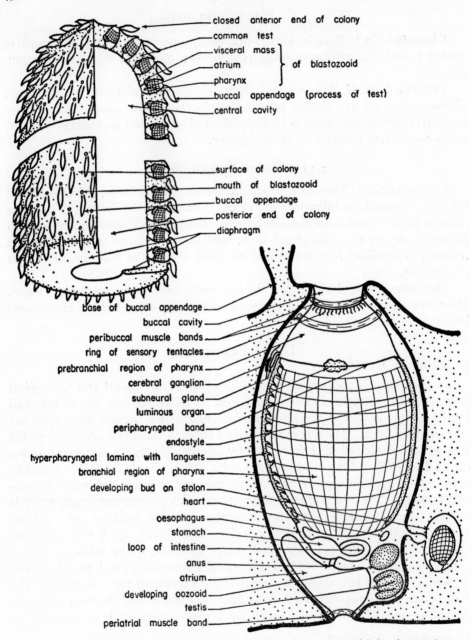

closed anterior end of colony
common test
visceral mass
atrium
pharynx
} of blastozooid
buccal appendage (process of test)
central cavity

surface of colony
mouth of blastozooid
buccal appendage
posterior end of colony
diaphragm

base of buccal appendage
buccal cavity
peribuccal muscle bands
ring of sensory tentacles
prebranchial region of pharynx
cerebral ganglion
subneural gland
luminous organ
peripharyngeal band
endostyle
hyperpharyngeal lamina with languets
branchial region of pharynx
developing bud on stolon
heart
oesophagus
stomach
loop of intestine
anus
atrium
developing oozooid
testis
periatrial muscle band

FIG. 169.—*Pyrosoma*. The anterior and posterior ends of a colony which has been cut open to show the central cavity, and details of the structure of a blastozooid.

b. Examine a colony which has been split open lengthwise. The colony wall is formed of tunicin, and in it are embedded the numerous individuals, or **blastozooids**. The mouth of each blastozooid opens outwards, but its atrial cavity opens into the large central cavity of the colony. The edge of the mouth is raised to form a papilla, which also carries a long buccal appendage. This appendage is part of the tunicin test, and it is based on the side of the mouth which is nearest the open end of the colony. Within the thickness of the colony wall notice the tiny opaque visceral masses of the blastozooids.

3. INTERNAL ANATOMY

a. In a stained permanent preparation of a slice of body-wall cut length-wise from the colony (see method of staining on p. 470) examine a blastozooid through a low-power microscope. The **body**, embedded in the common test, has a large pharynx and a smaller atrium. Distinguish the endostyle marking the morphologically ventral side (which is also that side directed towards the closed end of the colony). Confirm that the buccal appendage is on the morphologically dorsal side (which is directed towards the open end of the colony). Morphologically the mouth is anterior and the atrial opening posterior.

b. The mouth opens into the **alimentary canal** through a short buccal cavity (which is lined by ectoderm and by an inturned fold of the test). The posterior margin of this cavity is marked by a ring of short tentacles (which are sensory for tasting the incoming water). Surrounding this region are the peribuccal muscle bands (sphincters which can close the mouth). The large pharynx is divided into an anterior prebranchial region and a posterior branchial region which is pierced by the gill-slits (and is described in detail below). The oesophagus arises from the postero-dorsal side of the pharynx, and turns down to enter the small globular stomach. The intestine emerges ventrally, loops dorsally to the left of the stomach, and then turns posteriorly to open into the atrium.

c. The **atrium** can be seen as a small space which opens posteriorly into the central cavity of the colony. Surrounding this opening is the periatrial muscle band (a sphincter by which the atrium can be closed). However, there are also two large anterior extensions of the atrium which pass up the left and right sides of the pharynx, and which are not usually visible.

d. The **pharynx**, since it is flanked by the extensions of the atrial cavity, is supported only in the mid-dorsal and mid-ventral lines. It contains a ventral endostyle (ciliated and glandular), from the posterior end of which the retro-pharyngeal ciliated band passes dorsally to the opening of the oesophagus, and from the anterior end of which the two peripharyngeal ciliated bands pass left and right to the dorsal side. On these peripharyngeal bands are the two luminous organs (which produce the brilliant phosphorescence). Dorsally, the two peripharyngeal bands approach each other, and then pass back to the oesophagus on either side of the dorsal lamina, which also bears a series of languets. (Mucus secreted by the endostyle passes upwards over the ciliated gill-bars to trap the food particles, and then moves back along the sides of the hyperpharyngeal lamina to the oesophagus. The retropharyngeal and peri-pharyngeal bands also carry the mucus upwards.)

e. Dorsal to the anterior end of the hyperpharyngeal lamina is the **cerebral ganglion.** Beneath the ganglion is the subneural gland, which opens by a single duct into the prebranchial region of the pharynx.

f. The only visible part of the blood system is the small **heart,** which is situated just behind the posterior end of the endostyle (the vessels themselves are wall-less lacunae running between the organs and through the gill-bars).

g. In the hermaphrodite **reproductive system** is a single ovary containing only one ovum. If this has already been fertilised, it will be seen as a develop-ing oozooid which buds four blastozooids from a stolon and becomes extremely large before it is shed. An unfertilised ovum is connected with the atrial cavity by a short oviduct, but after fertilisation this degenerates. The single lobed testis is posterior to the ovary, and it opens into the atrial cavity through an obscure vas deferens.

h. Opposite the posterior end of the endostyle the body wall is everted to form a **stolon** (which produces new individuals and so increases the size of the colony). Examine a series of the developing buds which are attached to these stolons.

4. CONCLUSION

a. Observing the specimens, review the characteristics of the phylum, of the class, of the subclass, and of the order.

b. Compare and contrast the structure of a blastozooid of *Pyrosoma* with the structure of *Ciona.*

5. REFERENCES

DELAGE, Y., and HÉROUARD, E. (1898). Volume 8 of " Traité de zoologie concrète. Les procordés." Paris.
HUXLEY, T. H. (1860). " On the anatomy and development of *Pyrosoma.*" *Trans-actions of the Linnean Society of London,* Vol. 23, p. 193.
KÜKENTHAL, W., and KRUMBACH, T. (1933–35). Volume 5 and part 2 of " Handbuch der Zoologie." Berlin and Leipzig.

2.32. Order **Salpida**

Characteristics : Thaliacea which do not form permanent colonies ; in which the body-wall contains a series of incomplete muscle bands ; pharynx with only one pair of large gill-slits ; no larval stage ; and with the oozooid (asexual generation) well developed and free.

The order contains the two genera *Salpa* and *Cyclosalpa*, of which about twenty-five species have been described. Most of these are found in the warmer seas, but some species occur from the Arctic to the Antarctic.

Genus **Salpa**

I. GENERAL ACCOUNT

a. The sexual and asexual forms of *Salpa* are similar in structure, have a glass-like transparency, and occur in the surface waters of all oceans. Movement takes place by the contraction of muscle bands in the body-wall, which forces water out through the atrial opening; the rigidity of the test then causes a return to the normal shape, during which water enters the mouth; and the extreme reduction in the numbers of gill-slits reduces to a minimum the resistance to the flow. Some of the food particles contained in the water, particularly radiolarians and diatoms, are caught when they stick to the mucus which lines the pharynx wall. Breeding continues throughout the year. The sexual form, or blastozooid, is a protogynous hermaphrodite, the single ovary produces only one ovum, and fertilisation is internal. The young oozooid develops by feeding through a placental attachment to the atrial wall, and it finally escapes through the atrial opening. It possesses a stolon instead of gonads, and from this is budded a chain of blastozooids which break free in groups. These groups sometimes exist for long periods before the individuals composing them separate.

2. EXTERNAL ANATOMY

a. Examine the **oozooid** (which if small can be stained and mounted by the method on p. 470). Determine the orientation of the body by means of the dorsal muscle-bands, the two lateral backward-pointing projections of the test, and the prominent ventral keel of the test. The anterior mouth and posterior atrial opening are both slightly upturned. The mouth is a transverse slit (its movable dorsal and ventral lips turn in to form valves which allow water to enter but not to leave), while the atrial opening is smaller and circular (and lacks a valve).

3. INTERNAL ANATOMY

Within the body-wall notice that most of the **muscle-bands** are incomplete ventrally (the contraction of these bands drives water from the atrium, and so propels the body forwards). However, round the edges of the mouth and the atrial opening the bands are complete, and form the peribuccal and periatrial muscles respectively.

b. The mouth opens through a poorly defined buccal cavity into a large pharynx. Dorsally, just inside the mouth, is a tentacle (probably for tasting the incoming water). In the **pharynx** the ventral side is marked by the endostyle (which is ciliated and secretes adhesive mucus for food capture), while the postero-dorsal side is marked by an oblique hyperpharyngeal lamina. This lamina is attached to the dorsal wall anteriorly and to the ventral wall posteriorly, and the large spaces on either side of it are considered to represent either a single pair of enormous gill-slits or the spaces left by the complete disappearance of the lateral walls of the pharynx. From the posterior end of the endostyle a retropharyngeal ciliated band passes into the oesophagus, while from the anterior end two peripharyngeal ciliated bands pass upwards and backwards round the pharyngeal walls to come together again at the antero-dorsal end of the lamina. The lamina itself is grooved along its mid-ventral

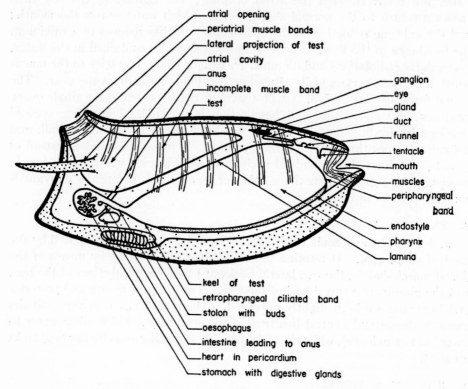

FIG. 170.—*Salpa.* An oozooid seen from the right side.

line, and the two ciliated bands continue back along its latero-ventral edges until they enter the dorsal side of the oesophagus.

c. The **atrium** is the large cavity posterior to the oblique lamina, and in effect it is continuous with the cavity of the pharynx.

d. The **visceral mass** is tightly coiled in the postero-ventral region of the body (it is the only opaque part, and is also frequently phosphorescent). The tightness of the coiling usually obscures the details, but there is an oesophagus leading back, a stomach turning ventrally, and an intestine running forwards past the left side of the oesophagus to open into the left ventral side of the atrium. On the walls of the stomach is a pair of branching digestive glands.

e. Anterior to the visceral mass is the **heart**, which is formed of the infolded walls of a pericardial vesicle (the blood-vessels are wall-less lacunae extending between the organs, beneath the endostyle, and up the centre of the lamina).

f. The large cerebral ganglion of the **nervous system** is situated in the body-wall at a point dorsal to the upper ends of the peripharyngeal ciliated bands. There are 10 main pairs of slender nerves emerging from it, and on its antero-dorsal surface is a single large, horseshoe-shaped eye.

g. The subneural gland of other urochordates is represented by a **ciliated funnel** (function unknown, but probably sensory), which has moved forwards along the mid-dorsal line and lost its association with the cerebral ganglion. However, beneath the ganglion are two neural glands, each with a separate duct leading forwards (these are apparently newly developed structures, and their function is unknown).

h. Finally examine a detached chain of **blastozooids** and an individual blastozooid. The muscle-bands are less numerous and not so strongly developed ; there are several distinct eyes ; there is no stolon ; within the visceral mass, to the left and right of the stomach, is a pair of branching testes, the ducts of which open separately into the ventral side of the atrium just posterior to the anus ; and there is a single ovary which, when young, is situated within the visceral mass, but which, while maturing, migrates upwards between the side of the atrium and the body-wall and comes to lie laterally on the right side.

4. CONCLUSION

a. Observing the specimens, review the characteristics of the phylum, of the class, of the subclass, and of the order.

b. Compare the structure of *Salpa* with that of a blastozooid of *Pyrosoma*.

5. REFERENCES

BROOKS, W. K. (1893). " The genus *Salpa*." *Memoirs of the Biological Laboratory of the Johns Hopkins University*, Vol. 2.
DELAGE, Y., and HÉROUARD, E. (1898). Volume 8 of " Traité de zoologie concrète. Les procordés." Paris.
KÜKENTHAL, W., and KRUMBACH, T. (1933–35). Volume 5 and part 2 of " Handbuch der Zoologie." Berlin and Leipzig.

2.33. Order **Doliolida**

Characteristics : Barrel-shaped Thaliacea in which the sexual form (blasto-zooid) is solitary, a tailed larval stage is present, and the asexual form (oozooid) carries a series of specialised buds (blastozooids) on a cadophore ; the body-wall containing a series of complete muscle bands ; and the pharynx with several pairs of gill-slits.

Genus **Doliolum**

I. GENERAL ACCOUNT

a. Of the three genera belonging to this order, *Doliolum* is the best known. It is found particularly commonly in tropical seas, but, carried by the Gulf

Stream, it also occurs as far north as the English Channel. It lives in the surface waters of the sea, and it has also been recorded down to depths of 100 fathoms. It is almost completely transparent, and it swims actively forwards by the contraction of the muscle-bands which drives water through the atrial opening. The rigidity of the test causes the body to swell again, and so draws more water in through the mouth. At the same time unicellular animals and plants are caught in the mucus on the pharynx walls. Reproduction is continuous, and there is marked alternation of generations. The blastozooid is a protogynous hermaphrodite, the ovary of which develops three ova in succession. Each ovum is fertilised internally, and is then shed to develop rapidly into a tailed larva, the young oozooid. This feeds, grows, and develops a stolon on which probuds are formed. The probuds detach themselves, migrate round the body by means of pseudopodia, and so reach a dorsal process, the cadophore. Here each divides several times to form the definitive buds, which fasten themselves to the cadophore in two lateral and two median rows. The buds of the lateral rows become gastrozooids which gather food, while those of the median rows become phorozooids, or nurses. Later buds move on to the dorsal processes of the phorozooids, which then detach themselves and swim freely away. These later buds develop into gonozooids (blastozooids with gonads), which themselves ultimately break free, grow considerably, and reproduce sexually. Thus, while there is only one type of oozooid, there are three types of blastozooids.

2. EXTERNAL ANATOMY

a. Examine an **oozooid** (asexual form). If it is unmounted, notice its transparency and its barrel-shape, but the structure is most easily seen in a stained preparation (see method of staining on p. 470). Orientate the body by means of the postero-dorsal process, the cadophore. The large anterior mouth and the posterior atrial opening are similar, except that the former is fringed by 10 oral lobes, while the latter is fringed by 12 atrial lobes (these lobes bear large numbers of sensory cells, possibly for tasting the water).

b. Examine the **cadophore** to find the various kinds of blastozooids which may be attached to its dorsal surface. The small stolon which produces the probuds is mid-ventral.

3. INTERNAL ANATOMY

a. Within the body-wall notice that all the muscle fibres are concentrated into 9 hoop-like **muscle bands** (by their contraction water is driven from the atrial opening and the animal moves forwards). Of these bands, the first surrounds the edge of the mouth, and the last two surround the atrial opening.

b. The large, permanently open mouth leads directly into the **pharynx**, there being no distinguishable buccal cavity. Within the pharynx distinguish the short ventral endostyle (a ciliated groove which secretes mucus); the postero-ventral opening of the oesophagus ; the retropharyngeal ciliated band leading from the posterior end of the endostyle into the left ventral side of the oesophagus (it carries food particles into the oesophagus and continues right through into the stomach) ; the two peripharyngeal ciliated bands passing upwards, left and right, from the anterior end of the endostyle to the dorsal side of the pharynx, and thence turning back along the mid-dorsal line and

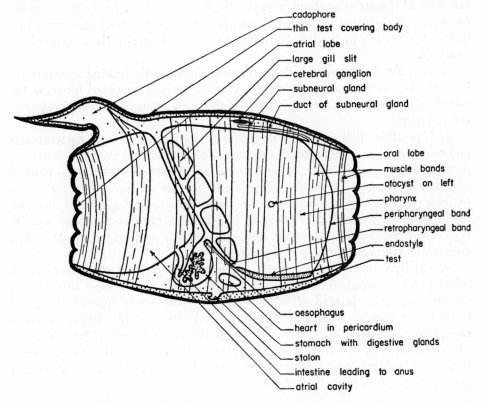

cadophore
thin test covering body
atrial lobe
large gill slit
cerebral ganglion
subneural gland
duct of subneural gland

oral lobe
muscle bands
otocyst on left
pharynx
peripharyngeal band
retropharyngeal band
endostyle
test

oesophagus
heart in pericardium
stomach with digestive glands
stolon
intestine leading to anus
atrial cavity

FIG. 171.—*Doliolum*. An oozooid seen from the right side.

down between the gill-slits to end in the dorsal side of the oesophagus (they also transport mucus and trapped food particles) ; and the few pairs of large gill-slits piercing the wall, or diaphragm, which separates the pharynx from the atrium. Distinguish the large posterior atrial cavity.

c. In the ventral **visceral mass** the organs are so tightly packed together that the course of the rest of the alimentary canal is usually obscured. However, it may be possible to see that the short oesophagus opens downwards into a small swollen stomach which is flanked by two digestive glands. From the ventral end of the stomach a short intestine turns upwards to open into the antero-ventral side of the atrial cavity.

d. Anterior to the stomach is the **heart**, which is formed by the infolding of a pericardial vesicle (as usual, the blood circulates through wall-less lacunae between the body organs, beneath the endostyle, and through the gill-bars).

e. The **nervous system** includes the cerebral ganglion situated dorsal to the pharynx, and a group of nerves which arises from it. The main nerves, which may be visible, are the pair supplying the edges of the mouth, the pair supplying the sides of the atrial opening, and the single nerve which passes down to the otocyst. This otocyst (which is a balance organ composed of an otolith in a hollow vesicle) lies in the left body-wall at a point opposite the middle of the pharynx.

f. Identify the **subneural gland** (function unknown) situated immediately beneath the cerebral ganglion. Its duct opens through a ciliated funnel in the mid-dorsal wall of the pharynx in front of the dorsal ends of the peripharyngeal ciliated bands.

g. If possible, distinguish the structure of any laterally placed **gasterozooids** and centrally placed **phorozooids** which may be attached to the cadophore. A gasterozooid has an enormous mouth and a large pharynx with several pairs of gill-slits, which, because of the reduction of the atrium, open directly to the exterior (the collected food materials are passed into the cadophore for distribution to the phorozooids and growing buds). The phorozooids have a more typical barrel-shape. If possible, also examine a free phorozooid with young gonozooids attached to the dorsal process.

h. Finally examine a fully grown **gonozooid**. Compared with the oozooid, it has 12 lobes surrounding the mouth (instead of 10) and 10 lobes surrounding the atrial opening (instead of 12). It has 8 muscle bands (instead of 9), and has a larger number of smaller gill-slits. It lacks a ventral stolon, a dorsal cadophore, and an otocyst. To the left of the visceral mass it has an ovary (which matures first, but produces only three ova, one at a time) and a large testis, and both gonoducts open close together into the atrial cavity at a point just ventral and to the left of the anus.

4. CONCLUSION

a. Observing the specimens, review the characteristics of the phylum, of the class, of the subclass, and of the order.

b. Compare the life-history and structure of *Doliolum* with those of *Salpa*.

5. REFERENCES

For further details, particularly of the structure of the gasterozooid, phorozooid, gonozooid, and larva, see :

DELAGE, Y., and HÉROUARD, E. (1898). Volume 8 of " Traité de zoologie concrète. Les procordés." Paris.

NEUMANN, G. (1906). " *Doliolum.*" *Wissenschaftliche Ergebnisse der Deutschen Tiefsee-Expedition,* Vol. 12.

ULJANIN, B. (1884). " Die Arten der Gattung *Doliolum* im Golfe von Neapel." *Fauna und Flora des Golfes von Neapel,* Vol. 10.

3.00.   Class **Cephalochorda**

Characteristics : Chordates with an elongated, fish-like shape, but without a specialised head, paired limbs, or a heart ; notochord extending along the length of the body to a point in front of the anterior end of the nerve-cord ; body flanked by myotomes ; endostyle present ; large numbers of gill-slits ; coelom well developed ; segmentally arranged excretory organs ; sexes separate, and no asexual budding.

The various members of the class are much alike, but they can be divided into two orders according to whether gonads are present on both sides of the body or on the right side alone.

3.01.   Order **Branchiostomida**

Characteristics : Cephalochorda with gonads on both sides of the body.

Genus **Amphioxus (Branchiostoma)**

I.   GENERAL ACCOUNT

a. Amphioxus and other related genera have a world-wide distribution in shallow seas, but they are of local occurrence, and live only in the purest sand or gravel. *Amphioxus* normally lives partly or completely buried in the sand, but sometimes, especially at night, it may emerge. It has a rapid, fish-like swimming action, and it can travel at high speed through sand as well as water. When at rest the semi-transparent body is usually upright, with only the mouth protruding from the sand. The food, which is strained from the water taken in through the mouth, is almost entirely vegetable, and consists of diatoms, desmids, and vegetable débris. In temperate regions breeding takes place in early summer, and the timing is often so precise that the ova and spermatozoa of a whole group of animals are shed within a period of twenty-four hours, particularly in the evening. The fertilised eggs develop into larvae which live freely and grow for about three months before developing the sand boring habits of the adult.

2.   EXTERNAL ANATOMY

a. The **body** is bilaterally compressed, pointed at both ends, and without any specialised head or limbs. Distinguish the long, tapering posterior end from the more abruptly tapering anterior end.

b. Through a lens identify the **external features**. These are the rostrum, which forms the anterior point of the body ; the two parts of the oral hood, which hang down as flaps from the sides of the anterior mouth ; the long, low dorsal fin running from head to tail ; the corresponding ventral fin, which is present only in the posterior third of the body ; the posterior caudal fin, which is formed of the expanded posterior ends of the dorsal and ventral fins ; the two

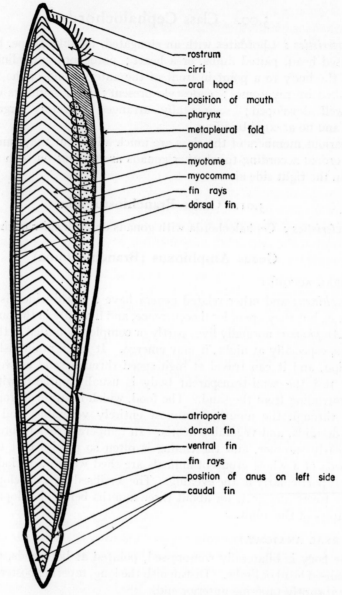

— rostrum
— cirri
— oral hood
— position of mouth
— pharynx
— metapleural fold
— gonad
— myotome
— myocomma
— fin rays
— dorsal fin

— atriopore
— dorsal fin
— ventral fin
— fin rays
— position of anus on left side
— caudal fin

FIG. 172.—*Amphioxus* (*Branchiostoma*). The external features seen from the right side.

latero-ventral metapleural folds in the anterior two-thirds of the body ; the atrial opening at the anterior end of the ventral fin ; and the less obvious anus, which opens ventrally to the left of the caudal fin.

c. The prominent ➤-shaped lines on the sides of the body are connective tissue septa, or myocommata, which divide the two lateral muscle-sheets into segments, or **myotomes** (the number of muscle segments, 60 or more in the adult, indicates the number of true body segments present). Notice that the myotomes of the left side alternate with those of the right.

3. INTERNAL ANATOMY

a. Take a specimen which has been partly macerated in nitric acid to soften the binding connective tissue (see method on p. 470). Lay it on its left side, and, before starting the dissection, identify through a lens as many as possible of the **internal features**. Notice the position of the mouth at the posterior end of the space, or vestibule, enclosed by the oral hoods; the oblique lines of the gill-slits in the pharynx wall immediately posterior to the mouth; the long row of segmentally arranged gonads dorsal to the metapleural fold; and the numerous fin-rays (not segmentally arranged) which support the dorsal and ventral fins except at the extreme anterior and posterior ends (there is a single row of fin-rays in the dorsal fin, a double row in the ventral fin, and none at all in the metapleural folds).

b. Fix the specimen down by means of two pairs of pins which cross but do not pierce it. Carefully remove the diaphanous skin from the right side (it consists of an epidermis and a thin underlying dermis). Then, using fine forceps or needles, and taking extreme care not to damage or displace any underlying organs, remove one by one the myotomes of the right side. Commence this dissection near the anterior end of the body, and start the removal of each myotome at its anterior angle (if the myotomes do not come away easily the maceration has not been carried far enough). This process, when completed along the full length of the animal, exposes all the important body-organs. Identify first the **skeletal system**, of which the most important element is the prominent, elastic, orange-coloured notochord (composed of large, vacuolated cells) extending along the length of the dorsal side. Other skeletal structures are the fin-rays already seen; the jointed bars which support the free edges of the oral hood and carry numerous fine bars, which penetrate and support the cirri; and the branchial skeleton, which consists of the gill-bars in the pharynx wall.

c. The white tubular **nerve-cord** lies along the dorsal side of the notochord. Notice its lack of ganglia. Through a binocular microscope it is possible to see large numbers of black dots (which are large, light-sensitive pigment cells) lying along the length of the nerve-cord. The largest of these dots is on the dorsal side of the anterior end of the cord, and is called the eye.

d. In the **reproductive system** there are 26 pairs of gonads arranged in two latero-ventral rows in the pharyngeal and the immediate post-pharyngeal regions. The sexes are separate, but externally the testes and ovaries look alike. Remove one or two of them, and while doing so notice that they lie in the wall of the peripharyngeal atrium and bulge into the atrial cavity (there are no gonoducts ; when the gametes are ripe they are shed into the atrial cavity by a rupture of the gonad wall and of the atrial lining ; they then escape through the atriopore, and fertilisation is external). Mount the gonads in a drop of water or dilute glycerine, tear them open, and examine their contents through a microscope. The ovary contains large eggs, but the contents of a testis are finely granular, and only if fully mature can spermatozoa with long tails be distinguished.

e. Remove all the gonads from the right side to uncover the **alimentary canal**. The mouth is a circular opening in the diaphragm, or velum, at the posterior end of the vestibule (it is surrounded by a sphincter muscle). The edges of the mouth are inturned, and they bear about a dozen sensory velar tentacles which project back into the pharynx. The pharynx is large and, except in the mid-dorsal line, is surrounded by the extensive atrial cavity. It is divided into a short prebranchial region and a long branchial region pierced by the gill-slits (which form the sieving mechanism for obtaining the food particles). Looking through the pharynx wall, identify the ventral endostyle (a deep ciliated groove with thick walls which secrete mucus). The left and right peripharyngeal ciliated bands pass upwards and backwards from the anterior end of the endostyle to the mid-dorsal line. There they approach each other and turn back to flank the hyperpharyngeal groove, which extends to the opening of the stomach (mucus passes forwards along the endostyle, upwards over the gill-bars and the peripharyngeal bands, and then, together with the trapped food-particles, it moves back along the hyperpharyngeal groove to the stomach). The stomach is the slightly dilated anterior end of the intestine, and it arises from the postero-dorsal side of the pharynx. From it there emerges laterally a blind diverticulum, the so-called hepatic caecum, which projects forwards into the atrial cavity and along the right wall of the pharynx. Posteriorly the intestine narrows to the anus, which is displaced to the left side of the ventral lobe of the caudal fin.

f. Notice the extent of the **atrial cavity** (which is lined by ectoderm). Ventrally and laterally it surrounds the pharynx and the stomach, and there is also a narrow extension which passes back along the right side of the intestine almost to the anus. The cavity opens to the exterior through the atriopore.

g. With great care dissect out the anterior part of the pharynx together with the velum and the oral hood, and open it by a cut made just to one side of the ventral endostyle. Open it, flatten it beneath a cover-glass, and examine its detailed structure through a microscope. The edges of the **oral hood** are prolonged into oral cirri (their number increases with age), and they and the inner surface of the hood are ciliated (and sensory). Posteriorly the inner lining of the hood is thickened and strongly ciliated to form the wheel organ (which creates a current into the mouth). Within the wheel organ, and just to the right of the mid-dorsal line, is a longitudinal groove called Hatschek's pit (which is probably a sense organ).

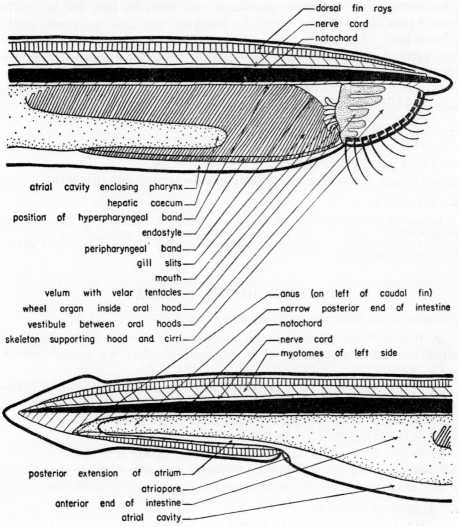

dorsal fin rays
nerve cord
notochord

atrial cavity enclosing pharynx
hepatic caecum
position of hyperpharyngeal band
endostyle
peripharyngeal band
gill slits
mouth
velum with velar tentacles
wheel organ inside oral hood
vestibule between oral hoods
skeleton supporting hood and cirri

anus (on left of caudal fin)
narrow posterior end of intestine
notochord
nerve cord
myotomes of left side

posterior extension of atrium
atriopore
anterior end of intestine
atrial cavity

FIG. 173.—*Amphioxus* (*Branchiostoma*). A general dissection seen from the right side after the removal of the myotomes and gonads.

h. Distinguish the velum and the velar tentacles, and identify the details of the **pharynx wall** (which is ciliated throughout). Notice again the endostyle, the peripharyngeal ciliated bands marking the boundary between the prebranchial and branchial regions of the pharynx, and the hyperpharyngeal groove flanked by the ciliated bands. Examine the structure of the gill-slits (there are about 180 pairs in the adult), which slope obliquely upwards and

H H

forwards. The strips of pharyngeal wall between the gill-slits are supported by gill-bars composed of a stiff, chitin-like substance. Dorsally these bars bifurcate and fuse with their neighbours, but ventrally they are free. The ventral ends of alternate gill-bars also bifurcate, and these are known as the primary bars. The other gill-bars, with simple ventral ends, are the secondary bars (since they are secondary down-growths which have split each primary gill-slit into two). Notice also the strengthening cross-bars, or synapticula, which join together the primary gill-bars by passing internal to the secondary bars (to which they also fuse in older animals).

4. CONCLUSION

a. Observing the specimen and the drawings made, review the characteristics of the phylum, of the class, and of the order.

b. Compare and contrast the structure of *Amphioxus* with that of *Oikopleura*.

5. REFERENCES

DELAGE, Y., and HÉROUARD, E. (1898). Volume 8 of " Traité de zoologie concrète. Les procordés." Paris.
WILLEY, A. (1894). " *Amphioxus* and the ancestry of the vertebrates." *Columbia University Biological Series*, Vol. 14.

APPENDIX TO THE CHORDATA

1. METHOD OF FIXATION AND PRESERVATION

a. Bottom-living chordates such as *Dolichoglossus* and *Ciona* should be narcotised, killed, and preserved by the methods given for marine annelids (see p. 206).

b. Pelagic chordates such as *Oikopleura*, *Pyrosoma*, *Salpa*, and *Doliolum* can be similarly treated, but, if necessary, narcotisation can be dispensed with, and they can be killed by quickly making up the sea-water in which they are confined to a strength of 5% formalin.

c. *Amphioxus* is most satisfactorily killed by taking it from the sea-water and plunging it directly into Bouin's fixative. It can be stored in the fixative, or after about twenty-four hours it can be transferred to 70% alcohol for storage.

2. METHOD OF STAINING

a. Whole specimens of such chordates as *Oikopleura*, *Salpa*, and *Doliolum*, as well as pieces of *Pyrosoma* colony or of *Ciona* and *Amphioxus* pharynx, can be stained by the methods given for small whole worms (see p. 207).

3. MACERATION OF *Amphioxus*

a. To macerate, and so soften, the connective tissue binding the myotomes of *Amphioxus*, soak large specimens in 20% nitric acid for from twenty-four to forty-eight hours. They should then be washed in and returned to 70% alcohol until they are required for dissection.

GENERAL REFERENCES

In addition to the special references given for each genus, the following general references contain a mine of valuable information on the classification, life histories, structure, and function of the invertebrate types, as well as on the techniques of handling and examining them.

BORRADAILE, L. A., EASTHAM, L. E. S., POTTS, F. A., and SAUNDERS, J. T. (1932). " The Invertebrata." Cambridge.

CARLETON, H. M., LEACH, E. H., and HAYNES, F. (1938). " Histological technique. ' Oxford.

GRASSÉ, Pierre-P. (editor). (1949 onwards). " Traité de Zoologie." Paris.

HARMER, S. F., and SHIPLEY, A. E. (editors). (1895–1909). Volumes 1 to 6 of " The Cambridge natural history." London.

HEGNER, R. W. (1933). " Invertebrate zoology." New York.

HYMAN, L. H. (1940 onwards). " The invertebrates." New York.

IMMS, A. D. (1925). " A general textbook of entomology." London.

LANKESTER, E. R. (editor). (1900–1909). The various volumes of " A treatise on zoology." London.

NEEDHAM, J. G. (editor). (1937). " Culture methods for invertebrate animals." New York.

PARKER, T. J., and HASWELL, W. A. (1898). Volumes 1 and 2 of " A text-book of zoology." London.

PRATT, H. S. (1935). " A manual of the common invertebrate animals exclusive of insects." Philadelphia.

SEDGWICK, A. (1898–1909). Volumes 1 to 3 of " A student's text-book of zoology." London.

SNODGRASS, R. E. (1935). " Principles of insect morphology." New York.

WARD, H. B., and WHIPPLE, G. C. (1918). " Fresh-water biology." New York.

WEBER, H. (1935). " Lehrbuch der Entomologie." Jena.

GENERAL APPENDIX

1. FIXATIVES

a. *Bouin's normal fixative.*

Saturated aqueous solution of picric acid . . .	75 c.c.
40% formaldehyde	25 c.c.
Glacial acetic acid	5 c.c.

The mixture keeps indefinitely, and is probably the best general-purpose fixative. Usually specimens are left in it for about twenty-four hours before being transferred directly to 70% alcohol, but they do not deteriorate if they are left in it for months.

b. *Bouin's alcoholic fixative (Duboscq-Brasil)*

Saturated solution of picric acid in 80% alcohol . .	75 c.c.
40% formaldehyde	25 c.c.
Glacial acetic acid	5 c.c.

The alcohol in this mixture acts as a wetting agent, and the fixative has greater penetrative power than Bouin's normal fixative. It is therefore especially valuable for animals with a water-resistant outer coat, such as those with a chitinous exoskeleton. It has the same properties, and is used in the same way as Bouin's normal fixative.

c. *Schaudinn's fluid.*

Saturated aqueous solution of mercuric chloride . .	2 parts
Absolute alcohol	1 part

The fluid is used particularly for protozoans, which are fixed in it for from ten to thirty minutes. They should then be washed in 50% alcohol, and any free mercuric chloride should be removed by immersion for about ten minutes in 70% alcohol which is tinged a light brown by the addition of a few drops of a concentrated alcoholic solution of iodine.

2. PRESERVATIVES

a. *Formaldehyde.* This is a gas which dissolves in water to the extent of 40%, and is then sold as liquid formalin. By the addition of 7 parts of water to 1 part of formalin, a 5% solution is obtained. This is the strength at which it is normally used as a preservative, but in the case of delicate marine animals the dilution should be carried out with sea-water.

Old or chilled solutions of formaldehyde often produce a white precipitate of para-formaldehyde. However, unless the process has continued for a long time, the preserving power of the remaining solution is not significantly affected.

Formalin is usually acid due to the production within it of formic acid. Using any common indicator, it can be neutralised by the addition of a few drops of a strong solution of caustic soda or of a greater quantity of magnesium carbonate, but after a time it will become acid once more. A better method is to stand the formalin over an excess of borax, which neutralises the acid as it is formed. However, because of this problem of acidity, formalin cannot be recommended for the preservation of animals with calcareous skeletons or spicules.

b. *Ethyl alcohol.* This is obtained as commercial spirit which is contaminated with water to the extent of about 4%. From this spirit the lower grades of alcohol can be made as follows.

Spirit	Amount of water	Grade of alcohol
10 vols.	$1\frac{1}{2}$ vols.	80%
10 vols.	3 vols.	70%
10 vols.	$8\frac{1}{2}$ vols.	50%
10 vols.	$20\frac{1}{2}$ vols.	30%

For preservation, 70 % is the strength normally used, but soft-bodied animals should not be dropped directly into it, or severe shrinkage will result. After narcotisation, such animals should be transferred slowly through 30 % and 50 % alcohols. Hard-bodied animals, such as insects, which are required for external examination only can be placed directly into 70 % or 90 % alcohols.

3. STAINS

a. *Alum carmine.*

Carmine	25 gms.
Glacial acetic acid	25 c.c.
Distilled water	500 c.c.

Powder the carmine, and dissolve it by boiling gently in the mixture of liquids. Then add the following solution :

Potassium alum	25 gms.
Distilled water	500 c.c.

Again boil gently, and then cool and filter. After the addition of a few thymol crystals as a preservative it will keep for at least a year.

b. *Borax carmine.*

Borax	4 gms.
Distilled water	100 c.c.

Dissolve the borax in the water and then add :

Carmine	3 gms.

Boil gently for about thirty minutes and then dilute with :

70 % alcohol	100 c.c.

Allow to stand for a few days, and filter before use. Specimens can be transferred into the stain directly from 70 % alcohol. The normal practice is to over-stain heavily, and remove the excess in a 1 % solution of hydrochloric acid in 70 % alcohol.

c. *Carbol fuchsin.*

Basic fuchsin.	1 gm.
Absolute alcohol	10 c.c.

Dissolve the basic fuchsin, and then mix with the following solution :

Phenol	5 gms.
Distilled water	100 c.c.

The mixture is ready for use immediately, it is stable, and it keeps indefinitely.

d. *Delafield's haematoxylin.*

Haematoxylin	4 gms.
Absolute alcohol	25 c.c.

Dissolve the haematoxylin, and then mix with the following solution :

Saturated aqueous solution of ammonium alum	400 c.c.

Expose the mixture to light for a few days in a flask plugged with cotton-wool, and then filter. Add :

Glycerine	100 c.c.
Methyl alcohol	100 c.c.

This final mixture should be kept in a warm place in a bottle plugged with cotton-wool, and allowed to ripen for about two months. It is then ready for use, and if it is kept in a well-stoppered bottle, it should retain its staining power for at least a year. Specimens should be transferred to water before staining.

e. *Ehrlich's haematoxylin.*

Haematoxylin	2 gms.
Absolute alcohol	100 c.c.

After dissolving the haematoxylin, add the following substances in order :

Glycerine	. 100 c.c.
Distilled water	. 100 c.c.
Glacial acetic acid	. 10 c.c.
Potassium alum	in excess.

Ripen the mixture for about two months in a bottle plugged with cotton-wool, and then store it in a closely stoppered bottle in which it should keep for about a year. Transfer the specimens to water before staining.

f. *Mayer's acid haemalum.*

Haematein	. 1 gm.
90% alcohol	. 50 c.c.

Dissolve the haematein by warming, but not boiling, in an oven or water-bath (remember that 90% alcohol is highly inflammable). Then add the following solution :

Potassium alum	. 50 gms.
Distilled water	. 100 c.c.

Filter the mixture, and then add :

Glacial acetic acid	. 20 c.c.

The stain is immediately ready for use, the specimens being first transferred to water.

g. *Leishman's stain.*

This stain is most conveniently obtained already made up as a powder, which, for use, is dissolved as follows :

Leishman's stain	. 0·15 gms.
Absolute methyl alcohol (acetone free)	. 100 c.c.

If kept in an air-tight bottle, this solution will retain its staining power for several months.

4. OTHER SOLUTIONS

a. *Chloroform water.* This is used for killing earthworms, etc., and is made simply by shaking up a few c.c. of chloroform in a large volume of water.

b. *Glycerine jelly.*

Gelatine	. 10 gms.
Distilled water	. 60 c.c.

Soak the gelatine in the water for about two hours before adding :

Glycerine	. 70 c.c.
Phenol	. 1 gm.

Heat the solution gently in a water bath, mix thoroughly, and allow to cool. When it is required for use, melt the jelly in a hot-water bath. Transfer the specimens into the hot jelly either from water or from glycerine.

c. *Lactophenol solution.*

Phenol	. 10 gms.
Lactic acid	. 10 c.c.
Glycerine	. 10 c.c.
Distilled water	. 10 c.c.

The mixture should be kept in a brown bottle or in a dark place, because exposure to light causes it to turn yellow. Nematodes, after clearance in lactophenol, can be mounted directly in glycerine jelly.

INDEX OF AUTHORS

GENERAL INDEX

Abalone. See *Haliotis*, 342
Acanthocephala, 144
Acarina, 326
Acoela, 47
Actinia, 87; culture, 116; fixation and preservation, 117
Actiniaria, 86
Actinoloba, 87
Actinophrys, 13
Actinosphaerium, 13; culture, 34; fixation, 36; staining, 37
Actinozoa, 78
Agar method of arresting movement in Protozoa, 35
Alcohol, ethyl, 472
Alcyonacea, 79
Alcyonaria, 78
Alcyonium, 79; fixation and preservation, 116; staining, 117
Allolobophora, 186; culture, 206; fixation and preservation, 207; smear of seminal vesicle contents, 207
Alum carmine, 473
Amoeba, 9; culture, 34; fixation, 36; staining, 37
Amoebina, 9
Amphineura, 336
Amphioxus, 465; fixation and preservation, 470; maceration, 470; staining, 470
Amphipoda, 239
Amphiporus, 124
Amphitrite, 183; fixation and preservation, 206
Ancylostoma, 137; fixation and preservation, 143; mounting, 143
Anemonia, 87; fixation and preservation, 117
Anisoptera. See Odonata, 276
Annelida, 174; appendix, 205; culture, 205; fixation and preservation, 206; smear of seminal vesicle contents, 207; staining, 207
Anodonta, 390; culture, 410; fixation and preservation, 411
Anomura. *See* Decapoda, 242
Anopheles, 302
Anoplura, 285
Anostraca, 212
Antedon, 413; culture, 442; fixation and preservation, 442
Anthomedusae, 94

Anthozoa, 78
Aphaniptera, 309
Apis, 297; fixation and preservation, 333
Aplysia, 353; fixation and preservation, 410
Appendix, general, 472; for special appendices, *see* under phyla.
Apterygota, 257
Apus, 216; fixation and preservation, 333
Arachnida, 313; fixation and preservation, 333
Araneida, 319
Araneus, 320; fixation and preservation, 333
Arenicola, 178; fixation and preservation, 206
Argas, 326; fixation and preservation, 333
Ariolimax, 369; fixation and preservation, 411
Armadillidium, 237; fixation and preservation, 333
Arrow worm. See *Sagitta*, 170
Arthropleona. *See* Collembola, 261
Arthropoda, 208; appendix, 331; culture, 331; fixation and preservation, 333; preparation of cleared specimens, 334; sectioning, 334; staining, 334
Articulata, 412
Ascaris, 133; fixation and preservation, 143
Ascaroidea, 130
Ascidia, 450; fixation and preservation, 470
Ascidiacea, 449
Asellus, 237; culture, 331; fixation and preservation, 333
Astacus, 243; culture, 332; fixation and preservation, 333
Asterias, 416; culture, 442; fixation and preservation, 442
Asteroidea, 416
Astrangia, 91; culture, 116; fixation and preservation, 117
Aurelia, 112; fixation and preservation, 117; staining, 117
Avicularia, 320; fixation and preservation, 333

Balanoglossus, 444; fixation and preservation, 470
Balantidium, reference to structure, 31

477

Printed in Great Britain by Richard Clay (The Chaucer Press), Ltd.,
Bungay, Suffolk